T/£15

Three Phases of Matter

Three Phases of Matter

Alan J. Walton

Senior Lecturer in Physics
The Open University

London · New York · St Louis · San Francisco · Auckland ·
Düsseldorf · Johannesburg · Kuala Lumpur · Mexico ·
Montreal · New Delhi · Panama · Paris · São Paulo ·
Singapore · Sydney · Tokyo · Toronto

Published by
McGraw-HILL Book Company (UK) Limited
MAIDENHEAD · BERKSHIRE · ENGLAND

Library of Congress Cataloging in Publication Data

Walton, Alan J.
   Three phases of matter.

   Includes index.
   1. Matter—Properties. I. Title.
QC173.3.W34   530   76-3451
ISBN 0-07-084063-6

5 4 3 2 1   7 9 8 7 6

To my parents

Contents

Preface

This text has its origins in a first-year undergraduate course entitled "The Structure and Properties of Matter" which I gave while at The University of Sussex. Then my brief was to give students (who were potential chemists, physicists, biologists, and material scientists) a "real feel" for what solids, liquids, and gases are like at the atomic level, keeping mathematics to a minimum. My aim is still to give first place to the physical picture; my audience is still, I hope, the same. I do assume, however, that the reader has a knowledge of elementary calculus and an understanding of—as opposed to a manipulative ability with—Newton's laws of motion. No prior knowledge of physical chemistry is assumed since it has been my experience that such concepts as the mole, the Avogadro constant, and relative atomic mass are often the victims of the assumption that someone else is "doing" them.

In the mid-1960s it was fashionable in certain institutions to denounce the type of macroscopic approach to solids, liquids, and gases typified by such texts as Newman and Searle's *The General Properties of Matter* and, instead, to go hell for leather at the "real physics". Students reared on this approach alone may be an even more dangerous breed than any sired on Newman and Searle! Not only may they believe that viscosities are actually measured by pulling flat plates with spring balances but they may regard the lack of data on liquids at pressures of, say, a hundred times the critical value as a mere oversight. Mercifully, the pendulum is starting to swing back in favour of a more balanced diet. So I include "corroborative details".

In keeping with current trends I have tried to show something of the actual methodology of science. If there is one view (however jaundiced it be) of the scientific method implicit in the text it is this: First describe your model in words (an analogue often helps) then quantify (it often helps to start out by considering a one-dimensional version of the problem) and check against experiment (if possible designing an experiment to show up *departures* from, rather than agreement with, the theory). This, of course, begs the question as to what constitutes a satisfactory level of agreement. I have tried to choose examples which illustrate various courses of action which are open when faced with discrepancies—ranging from the unblushing "fudge factor" to the radically new model. In two instances—van der Waals' equation and the heat capacity of solids—I have gone to some lengths to show what is involved in researching a phenomenon. Hopefully, my quasi-conversational style will prevent my views of what is necessarily subjective from being mistaken with those of the "establishment".

The dominant theme of the text is the extent to which the properties of solids, liquids, and gases—both their structure and their transport properties—are determined by the competing effects of the atoms' kinetic and potential energies. In a nutshell, a substance is in the gaseous phase when the mean atomic kinetic energy $\frac{1}{2}m\overline{u^2}$ greatly exceeds the dissociation energy of an isolated pair of atoms (ΔE), in the solid phase when $\frac{1}{2}m\overline{u^2} \ll \Delta E$ and in the liquid phase when $\frac{1}{2}m\overline{u^2} \approx \Delta E$. To bring in mention of temperature I follow Jeans' example and look at how energy is transferred at the atomic level between a gas and a solid; this shows that empirical temperature is proportional to $\frac{1}{2}m\overline{u^2}$. The perfect gas scale of temperature and the result of perfect-gas kinetic theory, $p = \frac{1}{3}mn\overline{u^2}$, gives the constant of proportionality (chapters 3 and 4). After deriving the equation of state of a perfect gas—here I must acknowledge a great debt to that singularly inspiring text *Physics for the Enquiring Mind* by Eric Rogers—the validity of each assumption implied in the derivation is questioned. Scattering of atomic beams from solid surfaces shows that the assumptions of zero dwell-time and of specular reflection are normally untrue. Free expansion shows ΔE is finite; van der Waals' equation introduces a finite ΔE and a finite atomic radius in the a and b correction terms. In discussing transport processes in gases (chapter 5) I pay particular attention to how momentum and energy are accommodated at the surface of the solid. This is anything but an academic nicety—the energy accommodation coefficient may be as low as 0·01. Chapter 6 (the approach adopted here was developed jointly with Paul Clark and Andrew Millington) arrives at the Maxwell–Boltzmann distribution function via a "bookshelf game" in which distinguishable books are sorted among modules of a bookcase; the number of "modules" along each shelf varying with the shelf-level. This procedure introduces the density of states factor *ab initio* and opens the way for a more formal discussion.

A short, fairly traditional, chapter 7 defines a thermally perfect solid as one in which $\frac{1}{2}m\overline{u^2} = 0$ and shows how different crystal structures are produced by associating a basis with a lattice. The consequences of a finite $\frac{1}{2}m\overline{u^2}$ are faced in chapter 8. Here, in discussing the coupled-oscillator model of a solid, I have tiptoed into what is normally the preserve of advanced undergraduate texts. Again though, the arguments proceed by induction: By examining what happens to a series of coupled gliders on an air-track we can guess what should happen in a one-dimensional structure. From this we can further guess how a three-dimensional structure behaves (Debye's theory becomes a simplification of the otherwise very difficult problem of evaluating $C_{V,m}$ exactly). Once we have established the energy-equivalence of a vibrational mode and a harmonic oscillator (which is assumed to be one of Planck's), phonons appear naturally (chapter 10). Having argued the phonon gas into existence the results of gas kinetic theory can be taken over (though not unthinkingly) to derive the thermal conductivity of a non-metal. The free electron gas appeared during earlier discussions of the heat capacity of metals so the way is now open to discuss thermal and electrical conduction in metals. Chapter 9 (which can with little loss to chapter 10, be read after chapter 10) examines the mechanical properties of solids—the familiar elastic moduli—and the role of structural imperfections, be they cracks, steps or the familiar dislocations, in limiting the strengths of materials.

In discussing simple liquids (chapters 11 and 12) I have adopted a cell model in which an atom is perfectly free within its cell but requires an activation energy to escape from its cell. At this stage the student should be able to draw on what he has learnt of the other two phases of matter—the cell model, of course, combines elements of a perfect gas model and a perfect solid model. Were this not the printed word I would have dispensed with Bernal's model and supplied instead a reel of film showing a molecular dynamics simulation. A series of stills (Fig. 11.19) from such a film (my thanks here to Dr John Lewis) may make good in part this deficiency.

Although the book is primarily concerned with the microscopic, a clear understanding of the conditions under which a substance exists as a solid, as a liquid, and as a gas is a prerequisite. So chapter 1 provides this macroscopic background. I have stressed the p–V–T surface. Students familiar with plotting, say, how the length of a wire varies with the load, all too often come unstuck with a p–T diagram which is peppered all over with points. Chapter 1 also includes a simple discussion of internal energy (defined operationally via an adiabatically enclosed system into which energy is fed via a paddle wheel) and of heat capacity. Chapter 2 is also scene-setting. It shows how atomic masses and sizes can be measured and points to Stern's experiments on scattering of hydrogen and helium at the surface of alkali halide crystals (which vindicates de Broglie's hypothesis) as a tale with a moral; particularly important since gas kinetic theory assumes classical mechanics. In addition, chapter 2 introduces the Mie and Lennard-Jones potential models.

Since learning is doing, a number of exercises have been built into the text. Some of these are retrospective, allowing the student to test what he has learnt; others are anticipatory to encourage the student to venture a little ahead on his own; yet others are there to provide the opportunity to make asides which might get out of perspective if made in the main text. Hopefully the reader will tackle the exercises as he meets them—at very least he should study the answers and comments before proceeding with the text. I have tried to aim the, mainly retrospective, end-of-chapter problems at the average student. The average student does not get a "first"! Indeed this student has been very much in mind while writing. Perhaps I have not avoided verbosity but as a reader I prefer an argument which is first advanced one way and then another to a single concise statement which must be read and reread for hidden depths! I also like to progress slowly towards a definition—of the "state of a system in equilibrium", for example—rather than to define each of the terms precisely and immediately to expect the student to comprehend a statement synthesized out of many such definitions!

For the most part, I have followed the recommendations of the Symbols Committee of The Royal Society as set out in *Quantities, Units, and Symbols* (1975), The Royal Society, London. Some few departures were thought desirable. The constant k seems very overworked; it is recommended for circular wave-number, thermal conductivity, rate constant of a reaction, and the Boltzmann constant (all of which occur in this text). Confusion is very likely in certain areas, as, for example, in the gas kinetic relation for thermal conductivity (where I write $\kappa = \frac{1}{2}n\bar{u}\lambda k$). Where confusion is unlikely I may use the same symbol for several quantities. My choice of dx or δx may seem somewhat erratic! Let me illustrate how I use d and δ. The familiar thermodynamic relation $dU = -p\,dV$ applying to an adiabatic system quite properly uses d. A temperature gradient might also be written dT/dx. However, once we embark on a discussion of the mechanism of thermal conduction in a gas we will wish to take $dx = \lambda$, the gaseous mean free path. Since λ is anything but an infinitesimal at low pressures it is surely better to write the gradient as $\delta T/\delta x$.

This book was written, in part, while a visitor at the Clarendon Laboratory, Oxford and at the Physics Department, Princeton University. I am naturally very grateful for the opportunities which these visits offered for writing. Thanks are also due to many colleagues and friends for much useful discussion. Let me name but four: Dr Paul Clark, Prof. Tom Carver, Dr Harry Rosenberg and Prof. Ken Smith.

1. The *p-V-T* Surface

Gold and iron are solids; alcohol and water are liquids; oxygen and nitrogen are gases. So it might seem. However as scientific statements these leave much to be desired—they contain no mention of the experimental conditions. It is true that on a mild day here on planet Earth, when the atmospheric pressure is right, water is indeed a liquid. But change the temperature and/or the pressure slightly and the liquid may turn into a solid or into a gas. Our observations of the natural world, observations gathered since early childhood, have been made within a very restricted range of temperature and pressure. At most, the temperature and pressure will have changed by some ten per cent. Small wonder then that gaseous gold or solid air are not part of *our* everyday experience. Had we been born not on Earth but on another planet our experiences as to what is a liquid, what is a solid, and what is a gas would have been quite different. An inhabitant of Venus would regard lead as a liquid. A Martian might, so to speak, have to shovel away the carbon dioxide.

Clearly, if we want to study the conditions under which a substance exists as a solid, a liquid, or a gas we must be less parochial in our choice of the experimental environment. Once this study is completed we can move on to discover what is happening at the atomic level—the goal of this book. So in this chapter we look at how the phase in which a substance is found is related to its temperature, pressure, and volume. We shall also look at the energy changes involved in altering the temperature, pressure, and volume of the substance.

1.1 A closed system

There is at least one substance which is familiar to us all as a solid, as a liquid, and as a gas—water. We get the solid form from the refrigerator; the liquid form at the turn of a tap; the gaseous form from the spout of a kettle on the boil. We all know the salient properties of the solid, liquid, and gaseous *phases* of at least this one substance. We also know that two phases may coexist in equilibrium—ice and water for example. You may even claim to have seen all three phases coexist together in equilibrium. The problems arise when we assert that our everyday experiences are experiments. If you remove an ice cube from the refrigerator it will in time melt. The solid ice cube will rest on a pool of liquid water and be surrounded by water vapour. While it is indisputable that all three phases are present, they are *not* in equilibrium; the ice will eventually all melt, the liquid will eventually all evaporate. Other objections can be made to this simple observation. You have no real idea of the total volume occupied by the substance. It poses few problems to measure the volumes occupied by the liquid and the solid. However the volume occupied by the gas is very indeterminate for as the liquid evaporates the gas diffuses away, eventually to be dispersed throughout Earth's atmosphere. An additional complication arises as the water evaporates; we are no longer dealing with a pure substance—with a single *component*—but with a mixture of gaseous water, nitrogen, oxygen, carbon dioxide, and several other components.

These three disadvantages—that of a non-equilibrium condition, of an indeterminate total volume, and of having a mixture of substances—can be overcome by using the piston and cylinder arrangement shown in Fig. 1.1. Here a fixed amount of the substance under investigation is contained within the cylinder. We shall in fact assume that there is one mole of substance present. (This term will be defined properly in chapter 2 but for the present you may take it that there is one mole—written 1 mol—of a substance present if it contains 6.02×10^{23} atoms when it is a monatomic substance like argon or 6.02×10^{23} molecules when it is a molecular substance like carbon dioxide.) The molar volume V_m occupied *in toto* by the substance (which may be present in one or more phases) is easy to find; it is of course Al where A is the cross-sectional area of the piston and l is the distance between the piston face and

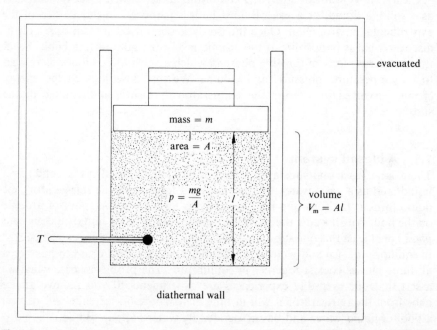

Fig. 1.1   A piston and cylinder arrangement for studying the p–V_m–T properties of a substance.

the end of the cylinder. By way of shorthand we shall use the word "system" to refer to "the substance under investigation contained within the cylinder and occupying the volume V_m".

The pressure p of the system can be changed at will by altering the "weights" on the piston. If the combined mass of weights plus piston is m then, provided there is no friction between the piston and the cylinder, $p = mg/A$, where g is the local acceleration due to gravity. (By placing the piston and cylinder in an evacuated vessel, as shown in Fig. 1.1, we eliminate the effects of atmospheric pressure. Without this evacuated surround, allowance must be made for atmospheric pressure pushing on the piston.)

The temperature T of the system (read with a thermometer—say, of the familiar mercury-in-glass type) may be set to any desired value by placing the *diathermal* wall (one that allows heat to pass) in contact with a suitable "oven" or "fridge". (These are not shown in Fig. 1.1.)

It is important always to remember that p, V_m, and T relate to the *system*. If two (or three) phases are present in equilibrium—say a liquid and a gas— the volume of each phase simply cannot equal Al! So we can only refer to the volume of the *system*. However, at equilibrium the temperature of each phase will be the same and equal to that of the system. Likewise the pressure of the liquid and gaseous phases will be the same and equal to that of the system. These strictures do not apply when a *single* phase is present; at equilibrium the pressure, temperature, *and* volume of the system are equal to the pressure, temperature, *and* volume of the substance.

1.2 The $p-V_m-T$ surface

Collecting data

We are now in a position to use the type of apparatus shown in Fig. 1.1 to make a systematic study of what happens as we change the pressure, volume, and temperature of the system.

You might think it would be possible to pull values of p, V_m, and T out of a hat and then to adjust the system of Fig. 1.1 to conform to these *ad hoc* values. Why not, for example, first set the piston position l (Fig. 1.1) so that $V_m (= Al)$ has the value drawn for it? The temperature T could then be set at the value drawn for it by placing a fridge or oven, as appropriate, in contact with the diathermal wall. Finally, why not set p at its drawn value by placing the appropriate mass m on the piston?

If you try to carry out this experiment you will discover that (unless you have been particularly lucky in the values you pulled for p, V_m, and T) it simply cannot be done! If you set V_m and T in the manner described you will find that in attempting to give p the value pulled from the hat you change V_m from its drawn value. You might instead have settled the values for p and T hoping to then adjust V_m; what you discover now is that (provided there is only

3

one phase present—be it solid, liquid, or gas) on adjusting V_m you change p. (As we shall shortly see, when two or three phases are present there is some latitude in the choice of V_m when p and T are fixed.) In a final desperate attempt at beating the system you might decide first to give p and V_m their drawn values and then to fix T. Again, unless you have been lucky in the draw, you will not succeed! Changing T in the apparatus of Fig. 1.1 will change V_m. In general, we are only free to randomly choose the values for any two of p, V_m, and T.

One way to study the behaviour of the substance is indeed to select arbitrary values for any *two* of p, V_m, and T and to measure the value of the third once the system has come to equilibrium. A less haphazard way is to fix, say, T and then to study exhaustively how V_m depends on p. We would then choose a new value for T and repeat the study. But whichever means are employed the problem arises of how to represent the wealth of data—data in the form of many triplets of (p, V_m, T) values at which the system is in equilibrium. By equilibrium we mean that pressure, volume, and temperature are stable with time. One such triplet might, for example, be $p = 5 \times 10^5$ Pa (where Pa, short for *pascal,* means newton metre^{-2}), $V_m = 7 \times 10^{-4}$ m^3 mol^{-1}, and $T = 200$ K (where K stands for kelvin).

Presenting the data

We could, of course, simply leave the data in tabular form. It is, however, much more instructive to plot it graphically using a set of p, V_m, and T axes (Fig. 1.2(a)). Each triplet of experimental values (p, V_m, T) plots as a single *point* in this space. To plot the point $(5 \times 10^5$ Pa, 7×10^{-4} m^3 mol^{-1}, 200 K) we go up the pressure axis a distance corresponding to 5×10^5 Pa, then by amount $V_m = 7 \times 10^{-4}$ m^3 mol^{-1} along a line parallel to V_m in the p–V_m plane and finally by amount $T = 200$ K along a line perpendicular to the p–V_m plane (Fig. 1.2(b)). After plotting out all the experimental points—the more there are the better—we would next draw in a surface to link them together as best we could. (This is, of course, akin to linking points together with a curve in the more usual two-dimensional graph.)

What the surface tells us

Although the precise shape of the p–V_m–T surface depends on the particular substance under investigation the general form of the surface is broadly similar for many different substances. For simple substances which expand on melting (e.g. carbon dioxide) the p–V–T surface has the form shown in Fig. 1.3. When talking in generalities it is unnecessary to refer to the *molar* volume V_m but we shall frequently do so to keep reminding ourselves that the volume of the system depends on the amount of substance present; double this and all the measured volumes will be doubled. Although drawn as a solid object in Fig. 1.3 (to give it perspective) the p–V–T surface is just that. It hangs in p–V–T space. It can

4

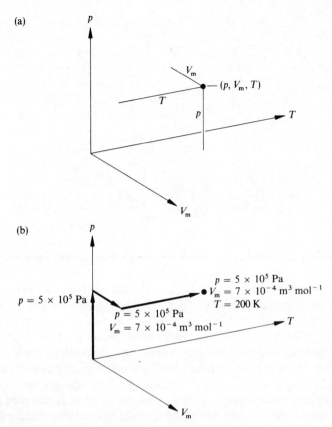

Fig. 1.2 (a) The coordinates (p, V_m, T) tell us how far the point is from the V_m-T plane, the p-T plane and the p-V_m plane. (b) How to plot a point (p, V_m, T) in practice.

hardly be emphasized enough that the (p, V_m, T) values which are measured when the system is truly in equilibrium lie *on the surface* and *only on the surface*. You should not be surprised—the surface is simply the graphical representation of equilibrium values of (p, V_m, T). If you attempt to give the system values of (p, V_m, T) other than values lying on the surface the system will not be in equilibrium; one or more of p, V_m, and T will change so as to bring the system to equilibrium. Once equilibrium is attained the value of (p, V_m, T) will lie on the surface. (In the *non*-equilibrium situation the values of the pressure and temperature will vary throughout the system—you can probably picture swirling currents in which p and T changes from one region to another—so no single point in p-V_m-T space could possibly represent the system.)

If you were to carry out such an experimental study using apparatus like that shown in Fig. 1.1 you would observe that for certain ranges of the

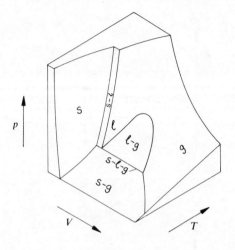

Fig. 1.3 The general form of the *p–V–T* surface of a simple substance which expands on melting.

independent variables (any two of p, V_m, and T) the substance exists wholly as a solid (s) as a liquid (l) or as a gas (g). The regions of the surface corresponding to these single phases are indicated in Fig. 1.3. In accord with our everyday experiences we see that the gaseous phase exists at high volumes and temperatures, the solid when the temperature and volume are low, and the liquid phase when the temperature and volume have intermediate values. Within other ranges of (p, V_m, T) two phases exist in equilibrium; the system consisting of solid plus liquid (s–l), solid plus gas (s–g) or liquid plus gas (l–g). At one particular pair of values of p and T and only at these particular values are all three phases (s–l–g) present in equilibrium. The line along which this occurs is called the *triple line* and such a line exists for all elements except helium.

It is worth noting that when two or three phases are present there is some latitude in the choice of V for a fixed (p, T). If, as shown in Fig. 1.4, the temperature is fixed at a value T and the pressure at p such that liquid and gas are present, the volume V the system may have any value between V_l and V_g. At a volume V_l the substance is wholly in the liquid phase; at volume V_g it is wholly in the gaseous phase. At some intermediate volume V—which, of course, measures the total volume of the *system*—both liquid and gas are present. The density of the liquid which is present throughout line *bd* (Fig. 1.4) is found by dividing the total mass of the substance by the volume V_l while the density of gas which is present throughout is the total mass divided by volume V_g. The line *ac* is called the *saturated liquid line*; line *ce* the *saturated gas line*.*

---

* Line *ce* is also called the *saturated vapour line*; the word *vapour* being used to denote a gas at temperatures lower than that at point *c*. In this text we shall normally avoid using the word vapour, preferring instead to draw attention, where appropriate, to the temperature of the gas.

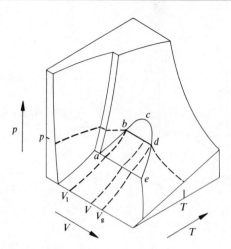

Fig. 1.4 Both the gas and the liquid phases are present when the system volume has a value V between V_l and V_g. Line ac is called the saturated liquid line. Line ce is called the saturated gas line.

Because of this latitude in the choice of V when there are two or three phases present at a fixed (p, T) we must always remember to specify V under such conditions; omit to specify V and we will not know where we are on the surface. While this caution is unnecessary when there is only a single phase present, we can avoid possible pitfalls if we choose V_m and T, or V_m and p, as the independent variables.

Exercise 1.1

As was mentioned earlier, one would be very unlikely in practice to construct the p–V–T surface of a substance by haphazardly choosing the values for two of p, V, and T and then proceed to measure the value of the third when the system is in equilibrium. It is a much simpler task to arrange to keep one of p, V, and T constant, vary another, and study the value of the third when equilibrium is attained. Figure 1.5 shows the paths followed on the p–V–T surface in three such experiments. Describe, in your own words, what happens to the substance—in particular what phases are present—as each of these paths is followed. Compare your answers with those given on p. 449 before reading on.

So far we have only considered the general form of the p–V–T surface of a substance which expands on passing from the solid to the liquid phase. For a substance which contracts on melting the p–V–T surface has the general form shown in Fig. 1.6. By studying the changes occurring along the line drawn at constant temperature T—a so-called *isotherm*—you should be able to satisfy yourself that there is indeed a reduction in volume when the substance passes

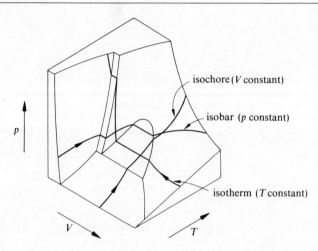

Fig. 1.5 Lines of constant pressure (isobars), constant volume (isochores) and constant temperature (isotherms) on the *p–V–T* surface.

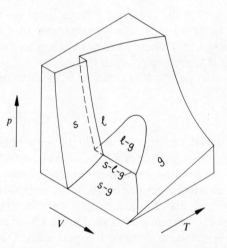

Fig. 1.6 The general form of the *p–V–T* surface for a substance which contracts on melting.

from the solid to the liquid phase. As we have already mentioned, the exact form of the $p–V_m–T$ surface depends on the substance; that for water is shown in Fig. 1.7. To give an idea of the scale of pressures encompassed in this diagram, normal atmospheric pressure is about 1.0×10^5 Pa. The roman numerals I to VII refer to the seven different forms of solid water which have been observed at extremely high pressures. As Fig. 1.7 makes plain, the volume decrease which occurs when "ice" melts is only found with type I ice. When type VII, for example, melts there is an increase in volume.

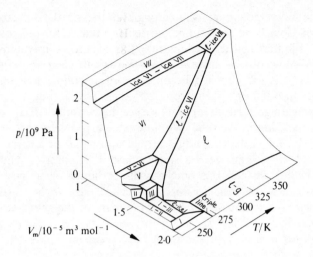

Fig. 1.7 The p–V_m–T surface of water.

The critical point

Experiments in which the volume of the system is kept constant are usually fairly difficult to perform if only because dangerously large pressures can all too easily build up as the temperature of the system is increased. However, if, as shown in Fig. 1.8, we start at point *1*, with gas and liquid present, and increase T the volume occupied by the liquid decreases, while that occupied by the gas grows. On reaching point *2* the substance is wholly gaseous. If we start instead at point *3* the volume occupied by the gas decreases with increasing T, while that occupied by the liquid grows, until at point *4* the substance is

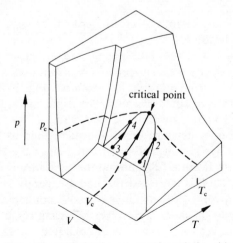

Fig. 1.8 When $V = V_c$ the isochore passes through the critical point.

wholly liquid. What remains constant along both these paths is the total volume of the *system*. If we have chosen one particular value V_c for the volume of the system (Fig. 1.8) then neither the liquid nor the gas grows in volume to fill the container. What we observe instead is that the usually clear boundary between the liquid and the gas above it becomes more and more indistinct until at $T = T_c$ we cannot tell one phase from the other. This is shown in Fig. 1.9 for carbon dioxide. In going from (a) to (e) we see the boundary disappear without changing its position in the tube. We now have a problem on our hands. At $T = T_c$, $V = V_c$, $T = T_c$ has the liquid turned into a gas, or has the gas turned into a liquid? All we can see is a single phase. It is purely a matter of conventions whether we call this single phase a liquid or a gas. The point (p_c, V_c, T_c) is called the *critical point*; p_c is called the *critical pressure*; V_c the *critical volume* (will of course depend on the mass of the substance present— doubling this will double V_c); T_c the *critical temperature*. Some triple and critical point values for a variety of substances are given in Table 1.1. To obtain

TABLE 1.1

Substance	$p_c/10^5$ Pa	$V_{c,m}/10^{-6}$ m^3 mol^{-1}	T_c/K	$p_{tr}/10^5$ Pa	$V_{tr,m}^1/10^{-6}$ m^3 mol^{-1}	T_{tr}/K
Ar	49	75	151	0·68	28	84
N$_2$	34	90	126	0·12	17	63
CO$_2$	74	94	304	5·10	42	216
H$_2$O	221	59	647	0·006	18	273·16 (by definition)
H$_2$	13	65	33	0·072	25	14

[1] $V_{tr,m}$ is the molar volume of the liquid phase which is in equilibrium with the solid and gaseous phases at the triple point.

the actual value of any quantity—say the critical pressure of N$_2$—you must equate the column heading, here $p_c/10^5$ Pa, to the appropriate numerical value for nitrogen, here 34. Cross-multiplying the equation so formed gives $p_c = 34 \times 10^5$ Pa. Exactly the same procedure is followed in reading the value of a physical quantity from a graph. For example, Fig. 1.7 tells us that at the point where the saturated liquid line meets the triple line $V_m/10^{-5}$ m^3 mol^{-1} = 1·8; that is $V_m = 1·8 \times 10^{-5}$ m^3 mol^{-1}.

The problem of nomenclature exists elsewhere than at the critical point. Consider the two ways shown in Fig. 1.10 to change the state of the system from state *i* to state *f*. If route *1* is followed the substance is initially present as liquid plus gas but as *T* is increased the liquid expands to fill the container. Thereafter only liquid is present. So we would confidently assert that the substance is a "liquid" at point *f*. However following route *2* leads to quite a different conclusion! We see that the amount of liquid decreases with increasing temperature to vanish on crossing the saturated gas line. Over the rest of route

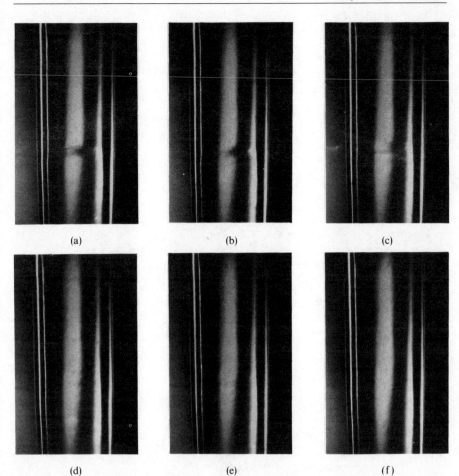

Fig. 1.9 A sealed tube ($V = V_c$) of carbon dioxide is heated through the critical point. The critical point (p_c, V_c, T_c) occurs around frame (d). (Reprinted with permission of the Open University from television programmes available from the university.)

2 only one phase is present which we would assert is a "gas". So it becomes a quibble over words what we call the single phase present at point *f*. The convention we shall adopt is to use the word *liquid* to describe the single phase present when the state of the system is represented by points lying on the portion of the surface shown shaded in Fig. 1.11. This figure is highly schematic for the pressures required to bring about the liquid to solid transition are enormous except very close to the triple line. Figure 1.11 also records the fact that there is no critical point associated with the "liquid" to solid transition. No matter what route you follow from "liquid" or "gas" to solid you will observe a phase separation occurring somewhere along the route. You cannot pass unknowingly from the gas or liquid phase into the solid phase.

11

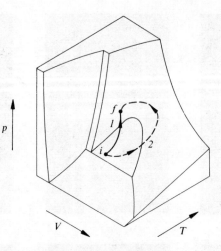

Fig. 1.10 Following route *1* from *i* to *f* leads to the conclusion that the substance is a liquid at *f*; following route *2* leads to the conclusion that it is a gas at *f*.

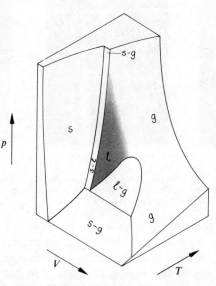

Fig. 1.11 A substance is in the liquid phase when its state is represented by points òn the shaded region of the *p–V–T* surface.

Exercise 1.2

Describe, in your own words, what happens to the phase of a substance as it is taken from state *i* to state *f* along the two routes shown in Fig. 1.12.

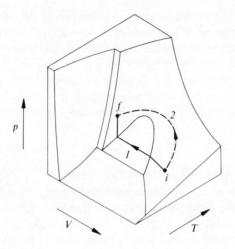

Fig. 1.12 Two different routes on the p–V–T surface.

1.3 Metastable states

We have been at some pains to point out that the p–V–T surface represents the *equilibrium* states of the system and that values of p, V, and T not lying on the surface correspond to non-equilibrium conditions in the system.

Attainment of equilibrium is normally a very rapid process. However under certain conditions the approach to equilibrium may be very slow. A gas held at a temperature T below T_c as in Fig. 1.13 will normally start to condense to form a liquid when the applied pressure equals the value appropriate to

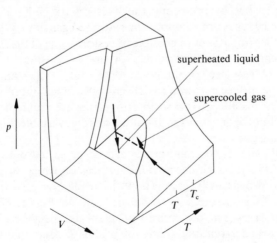

Fig. 1.13 Under certain conditions a substance may exist in metastable equilibrium as a super-cooled gas or as a superheated liquid.

13

temperature T on the saturated gas line. However if the system is dust-free it is often possible to increase p substantially beyond this value—pressures up to three or four times it have been realized—before condensation occurs and the system comes truly into equilibrium. A gas existing in such a "metastable state" is said to be *supercooled*. It is also often possible to reduce the pressure on a liquid held at a particular temperature to well below that at which evaporation should occur (Fig. 1.13). When this happens the liquid is said to be *superheated*.

1.4   Projections of the $p-V_m-T$ surface

A major disadvantage of recording equilibrium (p, V_m, T) values of a substance as a surface on two-dimensional paper is that it calls for a certain artistic flair! The obvious solution is to record the (p, V_m, T) values in tabular form— but it is difficult to spot overall trends from a table. Another technique is to project the $p-V_m-T$ surface onto the $p-V_m$, $p-T$, and $T-V_m$ planes. In projecting the surface onto, say, the $p-V_m$ plane we drop perpendiculars from each point on the surface onto this plane. All information about T is, of course, lost in carrying out this operation. Likewise we lose all information about V_m in projecting onto the $p-T$ plane and about p in projecting onto the $T-V_m$ plane. (Figure 1.2(a) shows how a point (p, V_m, T) projects onto each of these three planes.) Figure 1.14(a) shows the result of projecting the $p-V_m-T$ surface onto the $p-V_m$ plane. The plane is entirely peppered with points; the two independent variables p and V_m may be given any value we choose. (In examining this figure note that the surface is shown cut-off at finite values of p, V_m, and T.) So, as it stands, Fig. 1.14(a) tells us *nothing*! Fortunately, matters may be improved somewhat by projecting the lines on the $p-V_m-T$ surface which indicate phase changes (for example, the saturated gas line). When this is done we obtain Fig. 1.14(b). It is even possible to restore some of the missing information on the temperature of the system. A line of constant T on the surface (as in Fig. 1.5) will project unaltered onto the $p-V_m$ plane as shown in Fig. 1.14(c). The surface may well have been constructed out of such isothermal slices in the first instance, so no sculpturing skills are required! By this means we can record limited information about the missing variable. Figure 1.15 shows the results for argon.

In an exactly similar way the surface can be projected onto the $p-T$ plane as shown in Fig. 1.16(a). Notice how the surfaces on which two phases coexist in equilibrium project as lines and how the triple line projects as a point— the *triple point*. This projection is shown again in Fig. 1.16(b). It is worth reminding ourselves that the entire $p-T$ plane is "peppered with points"— the system may be given any values of p and T—and that this projection contains no information about the volume of the system. The results of experiments performed at constant volume could, of course, be projected onto

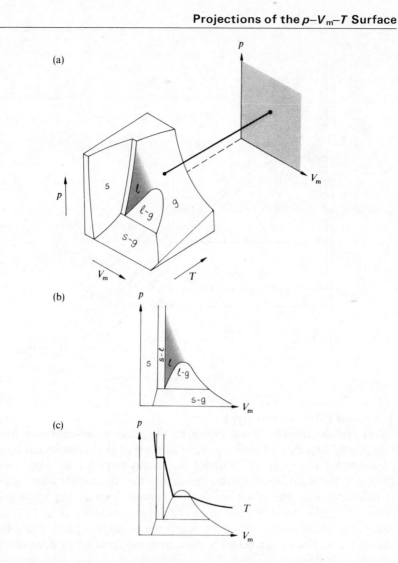

Fig. 1.14 (a) Projecting the p–V_m–T surface (which extends beyond that shown) onto the p–V_m plane. (b) Showing the regions of the p–V_m plane in which different phases are found. (c) An isotherm projects unaltered onto the p–V_m plane.

Fig. 1.16(b) to make good, in part, this deficiency. The line connecting the triple point to the critical point records how the boiling temperature (the temperature at which the liquid to gas phase transition occurs) varies with pressure. It is usually called the *vapour pressure* (or merely *vaporization*) *curve*. The line recording the pressure dependence of the temperature at which solid and liquid coexist is called the *fusion curve*. When solid and gas coexist we refer to the *sublimation curve* (Fig. 1.16(b)).

15

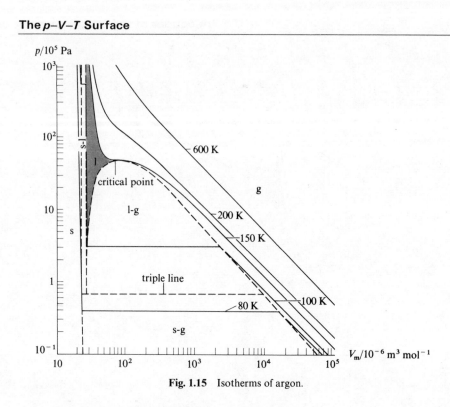

Fig. 1.15 Isotherms of argon.

1.5 The internal energy

In all our discussions about changing the state of a substance from that represented by a point *i* on the $p–V_m–T$ surface to that represented by a point *f* we omitted to say anything about the energy required to bring about this change. It turns out—perhaps unexpectedly—that the energy which is required is independent of the route which is followed. Exactly the same energy is required to take the substance from *i* to *f* along route *1* in Fig. 1.17, as along route *2*, as along route *3* (to name but three possible routes). Put differently, the change in the energy of the system in going from *i* to *f* does not depend on the route taken.

Measuring the change in energy

Figure 1.18 shows the type of apparatus which would allow us to measure the change in energy of a system in following a route like route *1* in Fig. 1.17. Here 1 mol of the substance is contained within a piston and cylinder apparatus whose walls are *adiabatic* (heat insulating). Even if we were to play a bunsen burner against the walls it would not affect the system (everything inside the cylinder). Notice that inside the cylinder is a stirrer in the form of a paddle wheel. This can be rotated by means of a piece of string which is connected via a frictionless, but leak-free seal, to a *Newton balance*; a spring

(a)

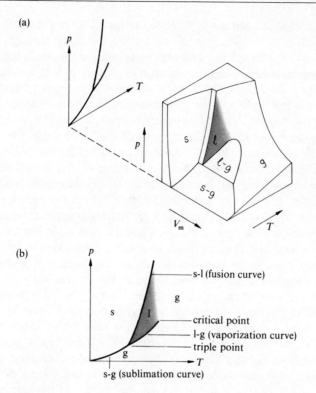

(b)

Fig. 1.16 (a) Projecting the p–V_m–T surface onto the p–T plane. (b) The p–T projection in more detail.

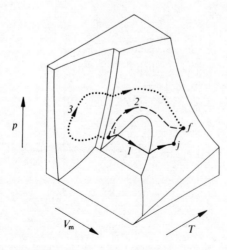

Fig. 1.17 Three different routes which take a system from state i to state f.

balance calibrated in newtons. If it takes a constant force F to pull the string, energy Fx will be fed into the system on pulling the string through a distance x. Energy may also be fed in—and removed—via the piston. If the combined mass of the piston plus weights is m an energy $mg|\delta y|$ will be added to the system if the piston is moved in by a distance $|\delta y|$. Energy $mg|\delta y|$ will be removed from the system if the piston moves out by a distance $|\delta y|$. Here $|\delta y|$ means "the magnitude of the change in the piston's position" (see Fig. 1.18). As an example, if $m = 2$ kg, $g = 10$ m s^{-2}, and $|\delta y| = 1\cdot5 \times 10^{-2}$ m the energy of the system will increase by $0\cdot3$ J if the piston moves in, and will decrease by $0\cdot3$ J if the piston moves out. The disadvantage of the formulation energy change $= mg|\delta y|$ is that we must couple to it the statement "added to" or "removed from" the system. A simpler formulation is to say energy change $= -mg\,\delta y$ where $\delta y = y_{\text{final}} - y_{\text{initial}}$ (Fig. 1.18). We shall say that when energy is added to the system the energy change is positive and when energy is removed the change is negative. It is necessary to insert a minus sign in front of $mg\,\delta y$ since if $y_f < y_i$ (that is, the piston moves down) δy is negative. The minus sign makes the energy change positive. If the piston moves up $\delta y = y_f - y_i$ is positive so the energy change is negative. Throughout this book we shall usually talk of "values" rather than "magnitudes"; the onus is on you to remember that when recording a value it must have a sign attached; such as $\delta y = +1\cdot5 \times 10^{-2}$ m or $\delta y = -1\cdot5 \times 10^{-2}$ m. All too many people merely record $|\delta y|$ only to discover later that their answers often have the wrong sign! Since $p = mg/A$ we may write the energy change in the system as $-pA\,\delta y = -p\,\delta V_{\text{m}}$ where δV_{m} is the value of the volume change of the system. It might be, say, -6×10^{-6} m^3.

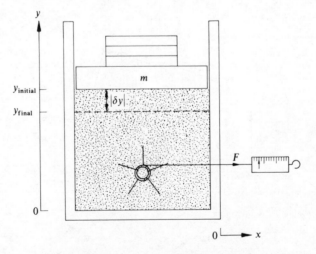

Fig. 1.18 Energy may be fed into the system via the stirrer. Energy may be fed in, and removed, via the piston. The system is contained within adiabatic walls.

It happens to be particularly easy to measure the energy change of the system in following route *1* of Fig. 1.17. We first hold p constant, leaving the weights unchanged on the piston, and keep adding energy via the paddle wheel until we reach point *j*. If the string is pulled out by x—as defined in Fig. 1.18 this will always be positive since the paddle wheel will never pull the string in— the system gains energy Fx. However some of this energy is removed to the Earth's gravitational field as the piston rises. If the volume change of the system in going from *i* to *j* is ΔV_m (e.g. $+5 \times 10^{-5}$ m^3 mol^{-1}) the net energy added is $Fx - p\Delta V_m$. The remainder of route *1* as it is shown in Fig. 1.17 is followed by only feeding energy in via the piston (the paddle wheel is not rotated). Since p keeps changing from *j* to *f* we must evaluate $-\sum p\,\delta V_m$. In practice we might do this by gradually increasing the weights on the piston, measuring the volume changes (e.g. $\delta V_m = -10^{-7}$ m^3 mol^{-1}) that results with each new value of p.

It is somewhat more tedious to follow route *2* in Fig. 1.17 (route *3* requires modifications to the apparatus). But whatever route is followed in going from *i* to *f* the change in the energy of the system is the same.

The internal energy function

These experiments argue strongly that there is some "function of state" U_m the difference between the value of which at *f* and *i* is the change in the energy of the system in going from *i* to *f*. In other words the change in energy is $U_m(f) - U_m(i)$, where $U_m(f)$ is the value of the function at *f* and $U_m(i)$ is its value at *i*. The name *molar internal energy* is given to the function U_m. Knowing the value of $[U_m(f) - U_m(i)]$ from experiment the value of $U_m(f) = U_m(i) + [U_m(f) - U_m(i)]$ follows immediately provided $U_m(i)$ is assigned some arbitrarily chosen value. We might, for example, decide to let $U_m(i) = 0$ at $T = 0$, $V_m = \infty$. (In practice we would have to start at a small, but finite, temperature and have a large, but finite, volume.) The measured value for $U_m(f)$ at a particular point (p, V_m, T) could now be "written in" on the surface. So we would end up with a p–V_m–T surface with values of U_m written in all over it.

There is however a much neater way to record the values of the internal energy. Once the values of the two variables V_m and T (or V_m and p) are specified for a given substance the p–V_m–T surface "does the rest"; it dictates the value of the third variable. The internal energy data may therefore be recorded as either a U_m–p–T surface, as a U_m–p–V_m surface, or as a U_m–V_m–T surface. Figure 1.19 shows the general form of the U–p–T surface of a substance which expands on melting. You can see that this surface "makes sense" by considering what happens as we follow a line of constant pressure (an *isobar*). In terms of the apparatus of Fig. 1.18 we keep a constant weight on the piston and note how the temperature of the system changes as energy is fed in via the stirrer. Some of the energy fed in via the stirrer promptly leaves via the piston (to the Earth's gravitational field) so the internal energy change as we move from *i* to *f* along the isobar shown in Fig. 1.19 will always be less than the energy fed in via the stirrer. Ignoring this "$-p\,\delta V$" loss—it is usually small in the solid and liquid phases where the volume does not change much as *T* is increased (Fig. 1.3)—we see that energy must be fed in as we first raise the temperature of the solid, melt it, raise the temperature of the liquid, evaporate it, and finally raise the temperature of the gas. This accords with our everyday experiences of the world.

1.6 The molar heat capacity

If you know of the work of Joule and others in the last century you will recall that they fed "heat" into water by stirring it with a paddle wheel. You might therefore wish to refer to the stirrer in Fig. 1.8 as a "heater" and call the energy $F\,\delta x$ fed in as the string is pulled through a distance δx the *heat* δQ added to the system. This is quite permissible *provided* the system is contained within adiabatic walls as it is in Fig. 1.18. When we talk, in this book, of "adding heat" to a substance we will always have this type of apparatus in mind. (In practice the stirrer would almost certainly be replaced by an "electrical heater". If the voltage across the heater is *V* volt and it carries a current of *I* amp the energy fed into the system in a time δt seconds is $VI\,\delta t$ joule. The conclusions we have so far come to—and will come to—are independent of the form of the heater.)

An obvious experiment is to feed a known amount of heat δQ into the system and measure the resulting temperature rise δT. We may do this in one of two ways; either we may keep the piston fixed in the apparatus of Fig. 1.18, thereby keeping the volume of the system fixed; or we may allow the piston to move, leaving the weights unaltered, thereby keeping the pressure fixed. Assuming there is 1 mol of substance present we define its *molar heat capacity at constant volume* as

$$C_{V,\mathrm{m}} = \left(\frac{\delta Q}{\delta T}\right)_V \tag{1.1}$$

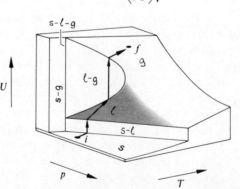

Fig. 1.19 The general form of a *U–p–T* surface of a substance which expands on melting.

The suffix V outside $\delta Q/\delta T$ denotes the fact that the volume is held constant. The *molar heat capacity at constant pressure* is defined as

$$C_{p,\text{m}} = \left(\frac{\delta Q}{\delta T}\right)_p \qquad (1.2)$$

where the suffix p tells us that the pressure is kept constant.

It is particularly easy to relate δQ to the internal energy change δU_m when the piston, and therefore V, is fixed. Since no energy is fed in or removed via the piston $\delta Q = \delta U_\text{m}$ and so

$$C_{V,\text{m}} = \left(\frac{\delta U_\text{m}}{\delta T}\right)_V \qquad (1.3)$$

Under a constant pressure regime energy will be removed via the piston and this must be subtracted from δQ to give the change in internal energy. In our later discussions of the molar heat capacity we will primarily be concerned with $C_{V,\text{m}}$.

Summary

1. When a simple substance is present as a single phase and is in equilibrium, fixing any two of p, V, and T will uniquely determine the value of the third quantity.
2. The equilibrium values of p, V_m, T can conveniently be represented as a *surface* in p–V_m–T space. The exact form of the surface depends on the substance.
3. When two (or three) phases are present at a fixed pressure and temperature there is some latitude in the choice of volume.
4. At temperatures greater than T_c a gas will not liquify—meaning no phase separation will occur—when subjected to increasing pressures. It is only a convention which labels the substance a "gas" and not a "liquid" at such temperatures.
5. The net change in the energy of a system in going from one point on the p–V_m–T surface to another point is independent of the route followed. This enabled us to introduce the molar internal energy function U_m.
6. Energy fed into an adiabatically enclosed system via a paddle wheel arrangement may be called heat. At constant volume the heat energy goes solely to change the internal energy of the system so that $C_{V,\text{m}} = (\delta U_\text{m}/\delta T)_V$.

PROBLEMS

1.1   Figure 1.6 shows the general form of the p–V–T surface of a simple substance which expands on freezing. Describe in your own words what happens as (a) the pressure is decreased at a fixed temperature $T < T_\text{tr}$, (b) the temperature is increased at fixed pressure $p_\text{c} > p > p_\text{tr}$, and (c) the temperature is increased at a fixed volume inter-

21

mediate in value between those at which the saturated liquid line and the saturated solid line (the line giving the state of a solid in equilibrium with a liquid) meet the triple line.

1.2   Make a rough sketch of the projection of the *p–V–T* surface of Fig. 1.3 onto the *V–T* plane. Record on this projection the phases which are present throughout. Also superimpose the results of experiments performed under conditions of constant pressure (that is, draw in isobars on the *V–T* plane).

1.3   You may well find that the mere act of sketching a *p–V–T* surface helps your understanding of what is represents. After tracing it a few times you will probably be able to draw it freehand (this makes quite a good party trick). In doing so always remember to label the axes! It is also helpful to draw in various routes over the surface and to ask yourself how the phase of the substance changes as these various routes are followed.

1.4   At a temperature T a mass M of a substance occupies a volume V_l when on the saturated liquid curve and a volume V_g when on the saturated gas curve. Calculate the fractions by mass of the system which are in the gaseous and liquid phases respectively, when the system has a total volume V intermediate between V_l and V_g and is at a temperature T (Fig. 1.4). Clues: It may help to draw a picture of the system showing the two phases. The total mass of the system is made up of the masses of.... These masses can be expressed in terms of volumes and densities. The densities are given by....

1.5   Figure 1.20 shows some isotherms of carbon dioxide close to the critical point. (a) What is the equilibrium temperature of carbon dioxide at $p = 7.4 \times 10^6$ Pa, $V_m = 11 \times 10^{-5}$ m^3 mol^{-1}? What phase is the substance in at this pressure and volume? (b) What volume would 10^{-2} mol of carbon dioxide occupy at $p =$

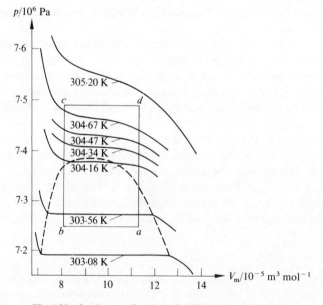

Fig. 1.20   Isotherms of carbon dioxide in the critical region.

$7{\cdot}25 \times 10^6$ Pa, $T = 303{\cdot}56$ K? (c) Describe in words the phase changes which occur as the state of the system goes from a to b to c to d to a. (d) Graph *isochores* (lines of constant volume) for $V_m = 8 \times 10^{-5}$ m^3 mol^{-1}, $V_m = 10 \times 10^{-5}$ m^3 mol^{-1}, and $V_m = 12 \times 10^{-5}$ m^3 mol^{-1} in the p–T plane. Indicate the phases which are present in different regions of the p–T projection. (e) Graph the isobar $p = 7{\cdot}43 \times 10^6$ Pa in the V_m–T plane. (f) At atmospheric pressure ($1{\cdot}0 \times 10^5$ Pa) carbon dioxide turns directly from the solid to the gaseous phase without passing through the liquid phase (i.e., it *sublimes*). What does this tell us about the triple point pressure of carbon dioxide?

1.6 A common method of obtaining low temperatures is to reduce the pressure over a boiling liquid. What is the lowest temperature that can be attained by boiling nitrogen under reduced pressure, and what pressure is required to attain this temperature? Use the data given in Table 1.1 (p. 10).

1.7 One could construct a hydrogen liquifier which operates by increasing the pressure on the gas while holding its temperature constant. The hydrogen might be contained in a copper piston and cylinder arrangement which is immersed in a suitable liquid boiling under reduced pressure. Which of the substances listed in Table 1.1 could be used to cool the hydrogen? Explain.

1.8 Consider the piston and cylinder arrangement shown in Fig. 1.21(a) which contains 1 mol of a certain substance. Energy may be fed in (as "heat") via the stirrer. The walls of the cylinder are made of copper (that is, they are diathermal) but they can be lagged (making them adiabatic). Energy may also be fed in, and removed, via the piston. A p–V_m diagram enables us to show how the molar volume of the system

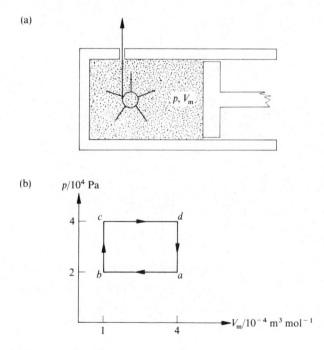

Fig. 1.21 The p–V_m diagram shown in (b) describes the state of the system illustrated in (a).

23

changes with pressure (Fig. 1.21(b)). (a) How much energy is transferred to the system in changing its state from a to b, assuming the walls are adiabatic and the stirrer is not rotated? (b) In going from b to c the walls are adiabatic and the piston is fixed. If the stirrer feeds in 5 J what is the total energy fed into the system in going from a to c? (c) In going from c to d no energy is added via the stirrer and the walls are adiabatic. Evaluate $U_m(d) - U_m(a)$. (d) The state of the system is restored to a by removing some of the lagging. How much heat will flow out through the diathermal wall? (e) If instead of 1 mol of the substance there is 5×10^{-2} mol how will this change your answers to (a) to (d)? (f) Can you guess in what phases the substance might be found during the cycle $abcda$?

1.9 The heat capacity $C_{p,m}$ of aluminium at $1 \cdot 0 \times 10^5$ Pa and 298 K is 24·4 J K^{-1} mol^{-1}. How much heat is required to increase the temperature of 10^{-3} mol of aluminium from 298 K to 300 K while keeping the pressure fixed at $1 \cdot 0 \times 10^5$ Pa?

1.10 On condensing a saturated vapour (a gas at $T < T_c$) to form a saturated liquid the volume of the liquid is typically 10^{-3} times that of the vapour at the same pressure and temperature. What is the ratio of the mean separation between molecules in the vapour to the mean separation between molecules in the liquid?

2. Characterizing Atoms

Now that we know the conditions under which a substance exists as a solid, a liquid, or a gas, we are almost ready to ask why "shoes and ships and sealing-wax" behave in the way they do. Why, for example, does glass shatter when hit? Why is golden syrup viscous? Why is it hard to compress a gas?

Answers to questions such as these—and we shall ask these questions later—can only be given in terms of a model: in our case an atomic model. Such questions must be rephrased as "Why, in terms of an atomic model, does glass shatter?" "What is going on at the atomic level to make a liquid viscous?" "How is the pressure in a gas related to the behaviour of the constituent atoms?" Which only begs the question as to how atoms behave.

While it would be perfectly possible to make *ad hoc* assumptions about the nature of atoms—much as did many a nineteenth century scientist—we are much better placed today to characterize atoms in terms of their mass and size, of how they interact one with another, and in terms of the laws of motion that they obey. In this chapter we will therefore look at some of the methods available for so characterizing atoms and at the results that they yield. Throughout we shall look for generalizations that apply to many atoms rather than attempting to characterize a few atoms in depth. We shall, so to speak, establish the ground rules for all that lies ahead.

2.1 Atomic masses

Measuring masses

The mass of an object is defined operationally by Newton's second law:

$$F = ma \tag{2.1}$$

If we can apply a known force F and measure the resulting acceleration a the mass m follows directly. Now acceleration—the rate of change of velocity—is one step removed from velocity and consequently the more difficult to measure. It therefore makes good sense to integrate eq. (2.1):

$$\int_0^s F\,dx = \int_0^s m\frac{dv}{dt}\,dx$$

$$\int_0^s F\,dx = \int_0^s m\,dv\,\frac{dx}{dt}$$

$$\int_0^s F \, dx = \int_0^v mv \, dv$$

Assuming F to be constant gives

$$Fs = \tfrac{1}{2}mv^2 \qquad (2.2)$$

You may know this equation as a statement of the conservation of energy; the left-hand side is the energy transferred to the object as a force F moves its point of application through a distance s; the right-hand side gives the kinetic energy of the object at its final velocity v. In fact, as we have just seen, eq. (2.2) follows logically from eq. (2.1) if we use a little calculus, so no discussion of energy is required!

Although there are many mass spectrometers which measure atomic masses via eq. (2.1), the one which we shall look at utilizes eq. (2.2).

The time-of-flight mass spectrometer

The most practical way to give an atom a known amount of energy is to *ionize* it—that is to remove one or more, say n, electrons—and then accelerate it through a known electrical potential difference. Figure 2.1(a) shows a piece of apparatus where this approach may be realized. A short burst of ionized atoms, each of mass m and each possessing a charge ne, where e is the charge of a proton ($+1.6 \times 10^{-19}$ C), is nudged through grid G_1 by momentarily making the backing plate B positive with respect to G_1. (These ions are produced by bombarding gas atoms with a transversely moving electron beam.) Once nudged through grid G_1 an ion will find itself in an electric field directed towards G_2 and so will be accelerated. If the potential difference between G_1 and G_2 is V the ion will possess an energy Vne on emerging through G_2. It will however only have acquired this energy if it has suffered no collisions on the way across; a condition ensured by having a near vacuum in the apparatus. If the ion enters G_1 with effectively zero velocity and leaves through G_2 with velocity v eq. (2.2) tells us that

$$Vne = \tfrac{1}{2}mv^2 \qquad (2.3)$$

So, provided we can measure v and can guess n correctly, we can deduce the value of m.

To measure the velocity of the ion we simply measure the time t it takes to travel across a field-free region of length l. By definition $v = l/t$ so eq. (2.3) becomes

$$Vne = \tfrac{1}{2}m(l/t)^2 \qquad (2.4)$$

It is because a determination of m involves measuring t that the apparatus is called a time-of-flight mass spectrometer. The flight time t is measured using a cathode-ray oscilloscope. At the instant the burst of ions is nudged through

G_1 the oscilloscope is triggered and a spot of light moves across its screen tracing out a straight line—straight until the pulse of ions passes through grid G_3. When this happens a signal is fed to the oscilloscope which momentarily deflects the spot upwards, producing a blip on the screen. Knowing the position of the blip and the sweep-rate of the oscilloscope t is easily found. (Allowance must be made for the fact that the trace starts before the ions emerge through G_2.)

If ions of different masses are present each of these species will have different flight times (see eq. (2.4)) resulting in a series of blips. Figure 2.1 (b) shows the trace obtained with singly ionized atoms of xenon. The left-hand superscript, as for example in ^{131}Xe, tells us the total number of protons and neutrons present in a nucleus; this total is called the *mass number*. Since the mass of a proton ($1·6726 \times 10^{-27}$ kg) and that of a neutron ($1·6749 \times 10^{-27}$ kg) are

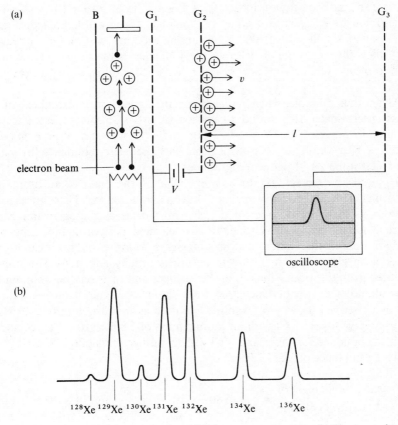

Fig. 2.1 (a) A schematic diagram of a time-of-flight mass spectrometer. (b) The trace obtained on the oscilloscope when naturally occurring xenon is analysed in the spectrometer.

27

practically identical it is usually a simple matter to deduce mass numbers—
we divide m, as deduced from the position of the maximum of the blip, by
1.67×10^{-27} kg and round off the result. If we wish to record the number
of protons present in a nucleus—that is the *atomic number*—we use the left
subscript position. By writing $^{131}_{54}Xe$, for example, we are stating that we are
dealing with an atomic species whose nucleus contains 54 protons and 131
protons-plus-neutrons (and therefore $131 - 54 = 77$ neutrons). The word
isotope is used to describe atomic species having the same atomic number
(that is, the same number of protons in their nuclei) but with different mass
numbers (that is, different numbers of protons-plus-neutrons in their nuclei).
Figure 2.1(b) therefore shows seven isotopes of xenon.

Exercise 2.1

When naturally-occurring sodium (atomic number = 11) is examined in a
time-of-flight mass spectrometer a single blip is observed on the screen
of the cathode-ray oscilloscope. A flight time of 5.46×10^{-6} s down a
0.5 m tube is recorded when the ions have been accelerated through a
potential different of 1000 V. Assuming the ions exist as Na^+ (meaning
they have a charge of $+1.6 \times 10^{-19}$ C) what is their mass? How many
protons and neutrons are present in a nucleus of this isotope of sodium?

As another example, when naturally-occurring carbon is examined in the
mass spectrometer it is found to consist of two stable isotopes; ^{12}C with
an atomic mass of 1.9926×10^{-26} kg and ^{13}C with an atomic mass of
2.1592×10^{-26} kg. The ^{12}C isotope has a 98.89 per cent abundance (by mass);
the ^{13}C isotope a 1.11 per cent abundance.

The question we set out to answer—what is the mass of an atom of a
particular element—does not appear to have a unique answer. There are as many
answers as there are isotopes of the element. So far as the chemistry of the
element is concerned all isotopes of that element behave in the same way,
notwithstanding their different atomic masses. For this reason the mean atomic
mass of an element as it occurs in nature is usually adequate. This can be
deduced from the atomic masses of the isotopes and their relative abundances.
(The abundances can be calculated from the area of each isotope's blip on
the oscilloscope.) By way of example, chlorine as found naturally consists of
two stable isotopes; ^{35}Cl with an atomic mass of 5.807×10^{-26} kg occurring
with an abundance of 75.5% and ^{37}Cl with an atomic mass of 6.138×10^{-26} kg
and an abundance of 24.5%. Therefore

$$\text{mean atomic mass of} \atop \text{natural chlorine} = \frac{75.5}{100}(5.807 \times 10^{-26}) + \frac{24.5}{100}(6.138 \times 10^{-26}) \text{ kg}$$

$$= 5.888 \times 10^{-26} \text{ kg}$$

2.2 Some definitions

For many purposes, comparative values of atomic masses are quite adequate. By an international agreement reached in 1961, atomic masses are expressed as a fraction of the atomic mass of the predominant isotope of carbon, ^{12}C, and this fraction is then multiplied by 12 exactly. The result, which is of course a dimensionless number, is called the *relative atomic mass* A_r of the element. Thus the relative atomic mass of, say, a ^{35}Cl atom is given by

$$A_r(^{35}Cl) = \frac{\text{mass of a } ^{35}Cl \text{ atom}}{\text{mass of a } ^{12}C \text{ atom}} \times 12$$

Substituting the measured values for the atomic masses as found using a mass spectrometer gives $A_r(^{35}Cl)$ as 34·9688. If one uses the mean mass of the chlorine atom found in naturally-occurring chlorine one obtains a relative atomic mass $A_r(Cl)$ of 35·453. With no left-hand superscript indicated—as in $A_r(Cl)$—the isotopic composition as found in nature is assumed.

In an exactly analogous way, the *relative molecular mass* M_r of a substance is defined as

$$M_r = \frac{\text{mass of a molecule of the substance}}{\text{mass of a } ^{12}C \text{ atom}} \times 12$$

Values for the masses of molecules may be found using the time-of-flight mass spectrometer. Using the measured atomic mass for a molecule of carbon dioxide, for example, one finds that $M_r(CO_2)$ is 44·009. Unless specified otherwise it is assumed that the atoms present in the molecule—in this case carbon and oxygen—have their natural isotopic composition. It is important to notice the presence of the word *relative* in our definitions of A_r and M_r. Without this word the phrases atomic mass and molecular mass will record, respectively, the mass of an atom of the element in question and the mass of a molecule of the compound in question. Both of these masses will normally be specified in units of the kilogram.

Because atomic masses range from about 10^{-25} kg to 10^{-27} kg there will be anything from 10^{25} to 10^{27} atoms in a kilogram of matter. Now in dealing with large numbers of anything, be they eggs or years, it is convenient to have a multiple unit as it keeps the numerical values small. So we would like to have something akin to the dozen or the century. Such a quantity is provided by the *mole*. We say that there is one mole (written 1 mol) of a substance present in a system when it contains as many *named* entities (be they atoms, molecules, ions, electrons, or any other named particles) as there are atoms of ^{12}C in 0·012 kg of ^{12}C. Therefore

$$N_A = \text{number of entities per mole} = \frac{0·012 \text{ kg}}{\text{mass of } ^{12}C \text{ atom in kg}} \qquad (2.5)$$

Substituting the mass of a ^{12}C atom as measured in a mass spectrometer gives a value of $6\cdot022 \times 10^{23}$ named entities per mole. (This number is usually called the *Avogadro constant*, N_A.) So if a vessel contains, say, 5 mol of water molecules it contains $5 \times (6\cdot022 \times 10^{23})$ water molecules. If there are 2×10^{24} electrons in a piece of metal it contains $(2 \times 10^{24})/(6\cdot022 \times 10^{23})$ mol of electrons. When using the mole we *must* state to what entities it refers. The vessel does *not* contain "5 mol of water"; it does contains 5 mol of *water molecules*. Remembering that water is H_2O it could be said to contain 5 mol of oxygen atoms and 10 mol of hydrogen atoms. Assuming the hydrogen is present as ^2_1H and oxygen as $^{16}_8O$ it could even be said to contain 50 mol of protons, 50 mol of neutrons, and 50 mol of electrons. Omit to say what the entities are and the statement is as meaningful as it would be to say of a farmer that he owns 5 dozen.

If a farmer decides to pick one dozen apples he merely stops picking when he reaches twelve. The problem about trying to obtain, say, 1 mol of atoms of an element X is that $6\cdot022 \times 10^{23}$ is rather a large number! Counting atoms is also rather a difficult pastime. Fortunately it so happens that if we measure out an amount, *in grams,* of X equal to its relative atomic mass, $A_r(X)$, we obtain 1 mol of atoms of X. This is easily proved:

$$\text{number of atoms in } A_r(X) \times 10^{-3} \text{ kg of element X} = \frac{A_r(X) \times 10^{-3} \text{ kg}}{\text{mass of atom of X in kg}}$$

Since

$$A_r(X) = \frac{\text{mass of atom of X in kg}}{\text{mass of } ^{12}C \text{ atom in kg}} \times 12$$

it follows that:

$$\text{number of atoms in } A_r(X) \times 10^{-3} \text{ kg of element X} = \frac{12 \times 10^{-3} \text{ kg}}{\text{mass of } ^{12}C \text{ atom in kg}}$$

which is, by definition (eq. (2.5)), the number of entities present in a mole. You should prove for yourself that if you measure out an amount, in grams, of a substance Y equal to its relative molecular mass you will have 1 mol of molecules of Y.

Just as the statement "1 dozen apples" only tells us how many apples are present and tells us nothing, for example, about their total volume or mass so "1 mole of molecules" only tells us about the number of molecules present. This deficiency is made good by defining the *molar volume* V_m of a substance as

$$V_m = \frac{\text{volume of the substance}}{\text{number of moles of molecules present}} \qquad (2.6)$$

In the case of an element the denominator is, of course, the number of moles of atoms present. The *molar mass M* is likewise defined as

$$M = \frac{\text{mass of the substance}}{\text{number of moles of molecules present}} \qquad (2.7)$$

By way of example, if 3 mol of lead has a volume of $5\cdot48 \times 10^{-5}$ m^3 and a mass of $0\cdot622$ kg the molar volume of lead is $1\cdot83 \times 10^{-5}$ m^3 mol^{-1} and its molar mass is $0\cdot207$ kg mol^{-1}. Terms like relative atomic mass, relative molecular mass, mole, and Avogadro constant will keep recurring throughout this book but rather than attempt to memorize their meaning now you would be well advised to keep referring back to these terms, as necessary, until you have fully grasped their meaning.

2.3 Atomic sizes

We have devoted some considerable space to discussing how atomic masses may be accurately measured. Such precision is entirely justified when dealing with a quantity as precisely defined as force/acceleration, a quantity whose value is independent of where the atom is located. Neither of these criteria apply to the size of an atom. All present-day models of an atom regard it as having a very diffuse electronic structure; so what do we mean by size? We can reach much the same position by thinking about a solid. In a solid the atoms are in close proximity—yet a solid *is* compressible. So the size of atoms will depend on how hard they are squeezed together. A rough estimate for an atomic size will therefore suffice, at least for the time being. We merely wish to know whether an atom is typically, say, 10^{-8} m, 10^{-9} m, 10^{-10} m, or 10^{-11} m in diameter; that is we want an *order of magnitude* estimate of the atomic diameter —one correct to the nearest power of ten.

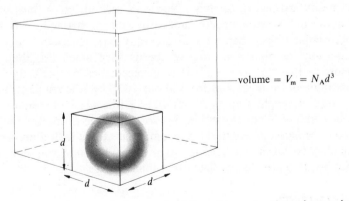

volume $= V_{\text{m}} = N_{\text{A}}d^3$

Fig. 2.2 If the atomic diameter is d one mole of the solid may be pictured as made up of N_{A} atoms each of volume d^3.

31

Roughly speaking we may picture a solid element X as a collection of tightly packed atoms (Fig. 2.2), not unlike lumps of sugar in a box. If d denotes the diameter of an atom each one will occupy a volume of order d^3. If there is 1 mol of the element it follows that there are N_A atoms present and that the mass of the solid is $A_r(X) \times 10^{-3}$ kg mol^{-1}. The total volume occupied by these N_A atoms—the molar volume— is $[A_r(X) \times 10^{-3}/\rho]$ m^3 mol^{-1} when ρ, the density of the solid, is measured in units of kg m^{-3}. Equating this volume with the total volume of all the atoms, $N_A d^3$, gives

$$d = \left(\frac{A_r(X)10^{-3}}{\rho N_A}\right)^{1/3}$$

As an example, solid lead has a density of $11\cdot3 \times 10^3$ kg m^{-3}. Since $A_r(\text{Pb}) = 207$ and $N_A = 6\cdot02 \times 10^{23}$ mol^{-1}, it follows that $d = 3\cdot1 \times 10^{-10}$ m.

Later on we shall meet other macroscopic properties, besides the density of a solid, which can be related to the diameter of the constituent atoms. The viscosity of a gas is one such property; its p–V_m–T behaviour is another. Very often these different properties yield different answers for the atomic diameter. Take argon; as deduced from the density of the solid phase $d = 4\cdot15 \times 10^{-10}$ m; from the gaseous viscosity $d = 3\cdot67 \times 10^{-10}$ m; from p–V_m–T data (via van der Waals' equation) $d = 2\cdot94 \times 10^{-10}$ m. The size really does depend on what the atom is up to! Clearly, the whole concept of the "size of an atom" will have to be looked at more carefully, and this we shall do later on. But, as measured in most laboratory experiments, atomic diameters lie mainly in the range 1×10^{-10} m to 5×10^{-10} m. So a good order-of-magnitude correct size to keep in mind is 10^{-10} m.

2.4 How atoms behave

An important question

Were we really justified in applying Newton's second law in measuring the mass of an atom? Newtonian mechanics was after all arrived at by studying how macroscopic objects behave. Our everyday experiences (which are based on observations of objects moving at speeds very much less than that of light) assure us that the laws of Newtonian mechanics are perfectly adequate to discuss the motion of masses from about 10^{-6} kg (the smallest mass in a chemist's box of weights) up to about 10^3 kg (the mass of a motor car). If these laws were not adequate within this sort of range of masses they would have been formulated differently! To assume that atoms with a mass of about 10^{-25} kg obey Newtonian mechanics involves making an extrapolation which would not be attempted in any field other than science.

A crucial experiment

Evidence that atoms do not obey the laws of Newtonian mechanics first came in the 1920s. In one experiment (developed by Stern from earlier work by Davisson and Germer) a beam of helium atoms all moving at effectively the same speed was directed at a lithium fluoride crystal and the angles at which the atoms were scattered for different settings of the crystal was studied. Figure 2.3 is a diagram of the apparatus used by Stern and his collaborators. We shall look in some detail at the experimental procedures for we shall meet very similar ones in later chapters. Helium gas from a furnace—a container of heated helium—passes out through an orifice O and a channel S_1 to form a parallel beam of gas atoms. This beam next encounters two discs, D_1 and D_2, spinning about a common axis. Each of these discs has in its circumference 408 equivalent radial saw cuts. The discs are placed so that the slots on one disc exactly face the slots on the other. With the discs at rest or rotating very slowly, atoms of all speeds can pass through both discs. At a somewhat higher rate of rotation the only atoms which can get through are those which cover the distance d between the discs (about 3 cm) in the same time as it takes the next following slot of D_2 to travel up to the line of OS_1S_2, i.e., the time it takes for a point on the circumference of D_2 to travel a distance equal

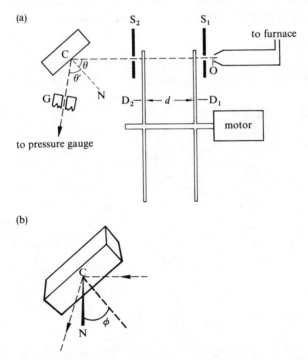

Fig. 2.3 (a) An apparatus in which the scattering of a beam of atoms by a crystal surface may be studied. (b) Showing the angle ϕ between the normal to the crystal surface and the plane of the incident and scattered beams (the plane of the paper in (a)). (After I. Estermann, O. R. Frisch and O. Stern, Z. Phys., **73**, 358 (1931) Fig. 11.)

33

to the separation of adjacent radial slots. Knowing the rotational speed of the discs and the separation of the radial slots it is a straightforward calculation to find the speed of those atoms in the beam which are allowed to pass through S_2 to strike the surface of the crystal C. Atoms scattered from the crystal surface are detected in a pressure gauge G which is set so that the angle of incidence (θ) of the beam equals the angle of reflection (θ'). What is changed in the experiment is the angle ϕ which the normal CN to the crystal surface makes with the plane containing the incident and the scattered beam (the plane of the paper in Fig. 2.3(a)). The angle ϕ is illustrated in the perspective sketch, Fig. 2.3(b).

Figure 2.4(a) shows how the scattered intensity changed with ϕ for a beam of helium atoms moving with a speed of 1230 m s^{-1} while Fig. 2.4(b) shows the corresponding variation for helium atoms moving with a speed of 1590 m s^{-1}.

A moments reflection should convince you that there are no real problems in interpreting the scattering at $\phi = 0$; it is how a ball—an object obeying Newtonian mechanics—would behave if thrown at a wall. Much more difficult to explain are the presence of the subsidiary maxima, particularly since their position depends on the speed of the helium atoms. Newtonian mechanics cannot adequately account for these subsidiary maxima.

de Broglie's hypothesis

The subsidiary maxima of Fig. 2.4 can only be explained if we assume that atoms behave not as particles obeying the laws of Newtonian mechanics but

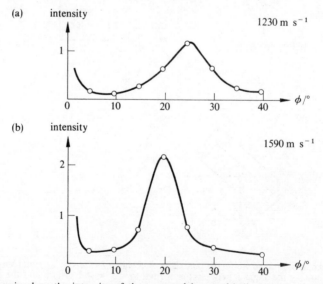

Fig. 2.4 Showing how the intensity of the scattered beam of helium atoms depends on ϕ. In (a) the helium atoms have a speed of 1230 m s^{-1} and in (b) a speed of 1590 m s^{-1}

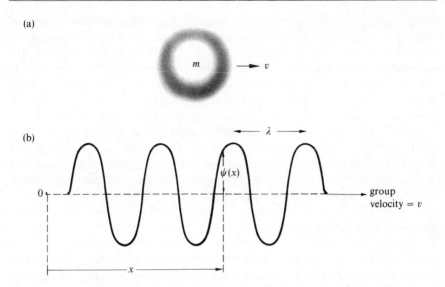

Fig. 2.5 (a) In Newtonian mechanics we consider a well-defined particle of mass m travelling at a speed v in a straight line. (b) In wave mechanics we consider a packet of waves of wavelength $\lambda = h/mv$.

in a way that is more reminiscent of waves. Instead of thinking of an atom as a well-defined particle of mass m moving in a straight line with a speed v (Fig. 2.5(a)) we must, according to the premises of wave mechanics, think of it rather as a packet of waves travelling as a group with a speed v (Fig. 2.5(b)). These waves are endowed with those properties, like momentum, which we have so far attributed to particles. It was in 1924 that de Broglie suggested that, at the microscopic level, matter might exhibit wave-like properties. In particular he suggested that the wavelength of these waves (see Fig. 2.5(b)) might be related to the momentum of the "particle" by

$$\lambda = \frac{h}{mv} \tag{2.8}$$

where h is a constant called Planck's constant ($6\cdot63 \times 10^{-34}$ J s). There was much debate in the 1920s as to what property is characterized by the *wave function* $\psi(x)$; the displacement of the wave at point x in Fig. 2.5(b). The current interpretation says that $|\psi(x)|^2$ (that is, the square of the magnitude of ψ at point x) is a measure of the probability of finding the particle at that point if a detector is placed there. Besides varying from point to point along the x-axis, the wave function will change with time (it must do so if it is to represent the particle of Fig. 2.5(a)). So we should really write the wave function as $\psi(x, t)$ to record the fact that we are dealing with the function at a particular point x and at a particular time t. In a three-dimensional situation we would write the wave function at point (x, y, z) at time t as $\psi(x, y, z, t)$. (Strictly

35

speaking $|\psi(x, y, z, t)|^2$ represents the relative probability *per unit volume* of finding the particle by an act of observation made at time t with a detector located at point (x, y, z). Therefore $|\psi(x, y, z, t)|^2 \delta V$ represents the relative probability of finding the particle within a volume δV. If $|\psi(x, y, z, t)|^2$ is $10^{-2}\,\mathrm{m}^{-3}$ and $\delta V = 10^{-6}\,\mathrm{m}^3$, which might well be the "active volume" of the detector, there is a one in a hundred million chance that the detector will "click".)

In 1927 Thomson and, independently, Davisson and Germer showed that de Broglie's relation holds true with electrons. It was with this knowledge and with the knowledge that the atoms at the surface of a crystal are arranged in a regular pattern that Stern and his colleagues had designed their experiment. How then can we interpret the results shown in Fig. 2.4?

Interpreting the results

To keep the discussion simple we will first consider the case where $\theta(=\theta') = 0$ and $\phi \neq 0$ in Fig. 2.3. (This particular geometry in which the incident and return paths of the beam are the same cannot be realized with the apparatus as shown in Fig. 2.3.) Figure 2.6 shows the situation. It is clear that atoms arriving at the detector which have been scattered by atom Q will have travelled a greater distance than those scattered by atom P. This difference amounts to $2QR$ (being RQ in and QR out). Denoting the separation of atoms P and Q by a (see Fig. 2.6) gives the path difference $2QR$ as $2a \sin \phi$.

If the signal at the detector is to be a maximum the de Broglie waves reaching the detector must be in phase. (When they are out of phase ψ, and therefore $|\psi|^2$, will be small, implying a small detector reading.) A maximum signal therefore demands that the path difference $2QR$ is an integral number n of wavelengths;

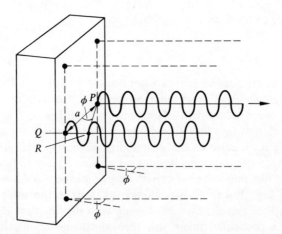

Fig. 2.6 The particular case in which the scattered beam is along the line of the incident beam.

$$2a\sin\phi = n\lambda \qquad (2.9)$$

or, substituting for λ from eq. (2.8), that

$$\sin\phi = \frac{nh}{2amv}$$

Although we have only considered the particular case where $\theta = \theta' = 0$ it is not difficult to show that in the more general case where $\theta = \theta' \neq 0$, which applies to Stern's apparatus,

$$\sin\phi \propto \frac{nh}{amv} \qquad (2.10)$$

Exercise 2.2

Figure 2.7 shows the results of a series of experiments performed by Stern in which he studied the dependence of ϕ on v. In this series of experiments $n = 1$ and the bombarding atoms were helium. Check

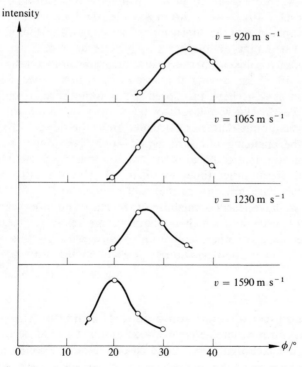

Fig. 2.7 The dependence of the detector reading on ϕ for beams of helium atoms moving at different speeds v.

37

whether Stern's results are compatible with de Broglie's relation as expressed in eq. (2.10).

A single series of experiments in which only two parameters—here ϕ and v—are studied is, of course, insufficient to prove the correctness or otherwise of eq. (2.10). But Stern and his colleagues did test the effects of changing n, a, and m. If $n = 2$, for example, a new maximum should occur at a higher value of ϕ; it was found. If a different crystal with a different interatomic spacing a is used ϕ should change according to eq. (2.10); it does. If hydrogen is used instead of helium then, since the mass of a hydrogen molecule ($^1H_2$) is half that of a helium atom (^4He), a hydrogen molecule travelling at twice the speed of a helium atom should produce a peak at the same value of ϕ; it does.

The dilemma
It begins to look as if we are going to have to abandon Newtonian mechanics in favour of wave mechanics. Not necessarily—we can always "chance our arm". We might reasonably expect to get away with it when the de Broglie wavelength is significantly less than the dimensions of the "surroundings". A car of mass 10^3 kg moving at 20 m s^{-1} will have a de Broglie wavelength $\lambda = h/mv = (6\cdot63 \times 10^{-34}/10^3 \times 20)$ m $= 3\cdot3 \times 10^{-38}$ m, which is utterly insignificant compared with the dimensions of anything with which the car might interact, be it a garage or another car. Newtonian mechanics is perfectly adequate to discuss collisions between cars! An argon atom, on the other hand, of mass $6\cdot6 \times 10^{-26}$ kg moving at a speed of 200 m s^{-1} (we shall see later that it will on average have this speed if the argon is at a temperature of 64 K) has a de Broglie wavelength of $0\cdot5 \times 10^{-10}$ m. Since this is roughly an eighth of the atomic diameter calculated from the density of the solid we may indeed be chancing our arm as we apply Newtonian mechanics to discussions of how matter behaves at the atomic level. Sometimes we shall get away with it; at other times we shall fail. The alternative is to adopt wave mechanics from now on, and that is just too terrible to contemplate!

Now that we have learnt something of the mass and size of an atom and of the laws of mechanics which it obeys we are ready to discuss how an atom interacts with another like atom. Armed with all this information we will then be in a good position to look at matter from a microscopic viewpoint.

2.5   Atomic interactions; some general considerations
Without some form of interaction between atoms it would be impossible to account for the fact that some hundred-odd atomic species produce the enormous variety of materials of which we are all aware. We may find out quite a lot about this interaction by carrying out a *thought experiment* in

which we interpret some large-scale or macroscopic properties of matter from a microscopic viewpoint.

The interatomic force

To begin with, we shall assume that all the interacting atoms are identical. In other words, we shall consider interatomic forces between the atoms of an element (X, say). Our aim is to show how the force $F(r)$ which one atom of X exerts on another atom of X varies with their separation, measured by the distance r between their centres.

In our imagination we take one atom of X and fix its position ("glue it to the paper" so to speak). We now take another atom of X to which we have—

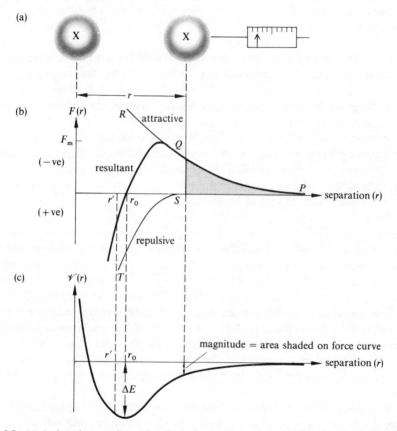

Fig. 2.8 (a) A thought experiment in which the position of the left-hand atom is fixed. The right-hand atom may be set at various separations r (measured between centres) from the left-hand atom and the force of attraction or repulsion "read" on a Newton balance. (b) The general form of the interatomic force between the two atoms of (a). Notice that negative forces are plotted along the upward ordinate and positive forces along the downward ordinate. (c) The corresponding variation in potential energy.

39

again in our imagination—attached a Newton balance and we place this second atom at various values of r from the fixed atom (Fig. 2.8a). For each setting of r we try to decide whether the force $F(r)$ between the two atoms is attractive (in which case the fixed atom will pull in the moveable one), is repulsive (in which case the fixed atom repels the moveable one), or is zero. Attractive forces are given negative values (e.g. -1.5×10^{-8} N), being directed in the opposite sense to that in which r is directed. Repulsive forces, being directed in the same sense as r, are given positive values. In Fig. 2.8(b) attractive forces are plotted along the upward ordinate and repulsive forces along the downward ordinate.*

In carrying out any thought experiment we must know some relevant basic facts; facts to be examined from a microscopic viewpoint to see what, if anything, they can tell us about the interaction between the two atoms of X. Here are several salient facts:

1. When they are well separated there is no detectable force between two similar lumps of matter. Two pieces of copper, for example, do not coalesce into a single lump when they are left close to each other on the bench.
2. To get two lumps of an element to "weld" together they must be brought into very close contact.
3. To "tear apart" solids and liquids requires external forces.
4. Under appropriate conditions of temperature and pressure (strictly speaking any two of p, V_m, T) all elements can exist in the solid phase.
5. If subjected to sufficient external stress solids and liquids can be compressed (but only by relatively small amounts).

Property 1 clearly tells us that at large separations there is no force between two atoms of X, and so $F(r)$ is zero at large r. Property 2 suggests that as r is reduced the force between two atoms of X becomes attractive—attractive since external forces are necessary to separate the atoms again (property 3). Because all elements can exist in the solid and liquid phases, each phase displaying properties 1, 2, and 3, it follows that short-range attractive forces are a general feature of interatomic forces between like atoms. Expressed in graphical form, as in Fig. 2.8(b), $F(r)$ will vary with r in the manner suggested by portion PQ of the curve. But curve PQ cannot continue ever upwards along path QR for, if it did, the attractive force between the two atoms would become increasingly strong as these atoms approach each other. With nothing to hinder them they would coalesce to form a single atom. All other atoms in the vicinity of X would behave likewise, and we would end

---

* The reason for not adopting the mathematically more usual convention of plotting positive forces along the upward ordinate and negative forces along the downward ordinate is that this leads to a force versus separation curve which superficially resembles the potential energy versus separation curve. The two curves are easily confused.

up with but a single "atom" of X! Since we are spared this catastrophe, repulsive forces must come into play at shorter distances. These are represented by curve *ST* in Fig. 2.8(b). Such repulsive forces also account for property 5; we need to apply an external compressional force acting against the repulsive interatomic forces as we push the atoms of liquid or solid ever closer together. The combined effect of these two interatomic forces—a short-ranged attractive force followed, at closer separations, by an even shorter-ranged repulsive force—is shown as a heavy line in Fig. 2.8(b).

So by means of very general arguments we have been able to establish that between two atoms of an element there is "a short-range attractive force followed by an even shorter-range repulsive force". In fact the arguments have a much greater validity and are equally true of the interaction between two molecules in a molecular material—provided that the molecules do not interact "chemically" in coming together to form the material.

The interatomic potential energy

Although we have expressed the interaction between two atoms in terms of forces, the interaction can also be expressed in terms of potential energy. We define the *potential energy* $\mathscr{V}(r)$ of two atoms a distance r apart as the energy *required* to bring one atom up from infinity to a distance r from the second one. (The choice of where to take the zero of potential is, of course, arbitrary; our definition of potential energy takes the potential energy to be zero when the atoms are an infinite distance apart. In later chapters we shall sometimes find it more convenient to choose a different location for $\mathscr{V}(r) = 0$.) This definition labels $\mathscr{V}(r)$ as positive if energy is required in the operation of bringing the moveable atom in from infinity to a distance r from the fixed atom. In terms of our thought experiment, the potential energy is positive if the "person" holding the movable atom provides a net amount of energy in performing the operation. The potential energy $\mathscr{V}(r)$ is labelled as negative if, on balance, energy is released in carrying out the operation of bringing the atom in from infinity to r; in terms of the thought experiment, if the "person" acquires a net amount of energy in the process.

There are two ways of obtaining the $\mathscr{V}(r)$ curve from the $F(r)$ curve. The first is formal and quick; the second is informal and slow. If you feel completely at ease with the formal approach, ignore the second one! If—like many people—you find potential energy a difficult concept to grasp then the second approach may illuminate the formalism of the first approach. Both are given because potential energy is an important concept which will keep recurring throughout this book.

Formally, the energy $d\mathscr{V}(r)$ required to displace the moveable atom in Fig. 2.8(b) through a distance dr is $[-F(r)] \, dr$. The minus sign in front of $F(r)$ arises because the "person" holding the moveable atom must provide a force equal in magnitude, but opposite in direction, to the interatomic force $F(r)$.

41

The resultant force on the moveable atom will then be zero and this will ensure that the moveable atom is brought in at constant speed (remember Newton's first law!). Therefore

$$\mathrm{d}\mathscr{V}(r) = -F(r)\,\mathrm{d}r \tag{2.11}$$

or

$$\mathscr{V}(r) = \int_{\infty}^{r} \mathrm{d}\mathscr{V}(r) = -\int_{\infty}^{r} F(r)\,\mathrm{d}r$$

$$\mathscr{V}(r) = \int_{r}^{\infty} F(r)\,\mathrm{d}r \tag{2.12}$$

You should be able to convince yourself that the potential energy curve shown in Fig. 2.8(c) follows on applying eq. (2.12) to the $F(r)$ curve of Fig. 2.8(b). In convincing yourself of this remember that we plotted negative (attractive) forces upwards in Fig. 2.8(b) and positive (repulsive) forces downwards.

The more informal approach starts by recalling that the magnitude of the energy transferred (or "work done") in a mechanical process is given by the magnitude of the area under the force-distance curve. Therefore as X is brought in from infinity to a position r the energy transfer has a magnitude equal to the area under the $F(r)$ curve between r and infinity. This area, shown shaded in Fig. 2.8(b), tells us the *magnitude* of the potential energy of the two atoms when a distance r apart. Since energy is released from the interatomic field in this particular operation the potential energy will be negative. The potential energy may now be plotted as a *single point*, as in Fig. 2.8(c). Notice that the ordinate value of this point tells us both the magnitude of the energy transfer *and* the direction in which energy is transferred.

We can repeat this entire operation of bringing X in from infinity to a different point r, measuring the area under the $F(r)$ curve between infinity and r and plotting this, with appropriate sign attached, as the potential energy $\mathscr{V}(r)$ at separation r. If the final separation is r_0, where the $F(r)$ curve crosses the force-axis, the total energy transfer is the area under the curve between infinity and r_0. Since this energy is again *all* transferred *to* the "person" holding the moveable atom, it is given a negative sign.

On repeating the operation yet again, but this time so that the final separation r' of X is such that the force on it is repulsive, an interesting change takes place. From infinity into position r_0 the force between the atoms is attractive so energy is transferred *to* the "person" involved. However from r_0 to r' (see Fig. 2.8(b)) the person must push; he provides the energy as he pushes against the repulsive force. Part of the energy he acquired as he was "pulled" in from infinity to r_0 must now be fed back as he reduces the interatomic separation from r_0 to r'. The net energy released from the interatomic field is given by the magnitude of the area between infinity and r_0 *minus* the magnitude of the area between r_0 and r'. Because the *net* amount of energy acquired from the field is reduced in magnitude the potential energy starts to increase at separations below r_0. This is a very important result; the minimum in the potential energy curve occurs at the separation r_0 where the force is zero. At some separation smaller than r' all the energy acquired from the attractive force will be spent in acting against the repulsive force and here the potential energy will be zero. At still smaller separations the energy gained from the attractive force will be insufficient to push X in against the repulsive force; the person must therefore provide the missing energy, so the potential energy will be positive at such separations.

It is always a good practice to invert arguments. Can the properties listed on p. 40 be explained from Fig. 2.8(b) and (c)? If they can it will not, of course, *prove* that our arguments are correct—mistakes can cancel. If these properties cannot be explained from the curve it will however show that mistakes have been made somewhere along the line.

A simple test of Fig. 2.8(b) is to see whether it is consistent with atoms joining together to form a solid (property 4). We know from Newton's first law that equilibrium of an atom demands there be no net force acting on it. Figure 2.8(b) shows that there is no net force when $r = r_0$, so equilibrium is possible (at least between a pair of atoms). This figure also shows that the equilibrium will be stable; increase the separation beyond r_0 and the attractive force will restore the atom towards r_0; decrease the separation below r_0 and the repulsive force will likewise restore the atom towards r_0. This then accounts for the essential stability of solids; compress them a little and they will return to their original form; extend them a little and they will also return. Figure 2.8(b) also asserts that there is a maximum restoring force, F_m, between two atoms. Should a force greater than F_m be applied the atoms will be unable to match such a force and so will fly apart. This accounts—or, at least, could account—for the limited strength of materials. (We shall see later that materials are in fact seldom as strong as we might expect from F_m.) Again Fig. 2.8(b) suggests that, because there is no "minimum" at separations less than r_0 that compares with the "maximum" at separations greater than r_0, materials will be stronger under compression than extension; they are. So Fig. 2.8 is consistent with the behaviour of materials.

Exercise 2.3

Figure 2.9 is a somewhat fanciful model of the interatomic force curve between two atoms; fanciful because nature would not introduce sharp kinks! Make a rough sketch of the corresponding potential energy curve. (You will find it helpful in drawing out the potential energy curve to use the same scale of r as in Fig. 2.9.) Identify on either the force, or potential energy, curve (or both if appropriate) the values of:

(a) the equilibrium separation of the pair,

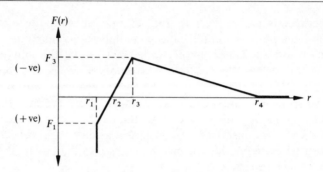

Fig. 2.9 A hypothetical interatomic force curve between two atoms.

(b) the maximum restoring force between the pair, and
(c) the energy required to completely dissociate a pair of atoms, initially at their equilibrium separation.

2.6 Modelling the interaction

Although Fig. 2.8 describes graphically how two atoms (or molecules) interact it is often more convenient to have this information in mathematical form since this allows one to discuss the interaction without having to resort to graphs. Our task then is to find some mathematical expression which reproduces the main features of Fig. 2.8(b) *or* (c). The word *or* is deliberate. We have just seen that $\mathscr{V}(r)$ is obtained by integrating $F(r)$ (eq. (2.12)). Put differently, $F(r)$ follows on differentiating $\mathscr{V}(r)$. Equation (2.11) says

$$F(r) = -\frac{\mathrm{d}\mathscr{V}(r)}{\mathrm{d}r} \qquad (2.13)$$

So once either $F(r)$ *or* $\mathscr{V}(r)$ is specified the other follows directly. Since differentiation is simpler to perform than integration it makes good sense to find a suitable expression to represent $\mathscr{V}(r)$ knowing that $F(r)$ follows via eq. (2.13).

We can always view the potential energy curve of Fig. 2.8(c) as being the sum of the potential energy curve due to attractive forces (portion PQR of Fig. 2.8(b)) and the potential energy due to repulsive forces (portion ST of Fig. 2.8(b)). This is illustrated in Fig. 2.10 where the component potential energies are indicated in light line and the total potential energy is indicated in heavy line. The positive component originates, of course, from the repulsive force component; the negative component of potential energy from the attractive force between the pair of atoms. Our programme is clear—to find some suitable mathematical representation of the two component energies and then to add them.

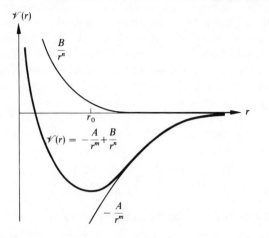

Fig. 2.10 The Mie potential model. The component B/r^n arises from interatomic repulsive forces; the component $-A/r^m$ from interatomic attractive forces. The resultant interaction is shown as the heavy line.

The Mie potential

Perhaps the simplest possible representation is that proposed by Mie in 1907. He represented the negative component by $-A/r^m$ and the positive component by B/r^n (see Fig. 2.10). Here A and B are positive constants and m and n are positive integers with $n > m$. It is necessary to have $n > m$ so that the positive term (the component due to the repulsive force) will dominate as r goes to zero and will vanish more rapidly than the negative term (due to the attractive force) as r goes to infinity. Adding together the two components graphically we obtain the required potential energy variation (Fig. 2.10). Adding them algebraically we obtain the following expression for the potential energy $\mathscr{V}(r)$ of two atoms a distance r apart:

$$\mathscr{V}(r) = -\frac{A}{r^m} + \frac{B}{r^n}, \quad \text{where} \quad n > m \tag{2.14}$$

If you are unconvinced that such an expression can indeed represent the general features of Fig. 2.8(c) you should, by way of an example, plot out $y = -(1/x) + (1/x^7)$ and compare the shape of your plot with the shape of Fig. 2.8(c).

The Lennard-Jones potential

Another expression for $\mathscr{V}(r)$ closely similar to Mie's is that of Lennard-Jones:

$$\mathscr{V}(r) = 4\varepsilon\left[-\left(\frac{\sigma}{r}\right)^p + \left(\frac{\sigma}{r}\right)^q\right] \tag{2.15}$$

where ε and σ are positive constants and p and q are positive integers. Like Mie's potential, Lennard-Jones' potential contains two continuously variable

45

constants, ε and σ. Unlike Mie's constants A and B, the constant ε is solely associated with energy, the constant σ solely with the interatomic separation. (Equation (2.15) shows that, say, doubling the value of ε doubles $\mathscr{V}(r)$. Trebling, σ, for example, stretches $\mathscr{V}(r)$ along the abscissa; to obtain the same value $\mathscr{V}(r)$ as before we now must go to $3r$.) This "division of responsibility" between ε and σ can be a real asset in some situations. In practice the Lennard-Jones potential is employed almost exclusively in modelling van der Waals' interactions where, as we shall see later, $p = 6$. A value of $q = 12$ is usually also assumed, so eq. (2.15) becomes

$$\mathscr{V}(r) = 4\varepsilon \left[-\left(\frac{\sigma}{r}\right)^6 + \left(\frac{\sigma}{r}\right)^{12} \right] \tag{2.16}$$

For obvious reasons this is called the *Lennard-Jones 6-12 potential*.

Getting rid of a constant

As they stand both the Mie and the Lennard-Jones potentials each contain four constants. It is however possible to eliminate either A or B from the Mie potential and σ from the Lennard-Jones potential—*provided* we agree to introduce the equilibrium separation r_0 of an isolated pair of atoms. (Experimentally it is easier to get at r_0 than, say, A or B so this move makes good practical sense.) We shall show how this reduction is carried out with a Lennard-Jones 6-12 potential, leaving you to deal with the Mie potential.

At the equilibrium separation r_0 we know that $F(r) = -\mathrm{d}\mathscr{V}(r)/\mathrm{d}r = 0$. Differentiating eq. (2.16) with respect to r gives

$$F(r) = -4\varepsilon \left[\frac{6\sigma^6}{r^7} - \frac{12\sigma^{12}}{r^{13}} \right] \tag{2.17}$$

Setting $F(r_0)$ (meaning, of course, $F(r)$ with $r = r_0$) equal to zero gives

$$2\sigma^6 = r_0{}^6 \tag{2.18}$$

$$r_0 = (2)^{1/6}\sigma = 1\cdot122\sigma \tag{2.19}$$

Substituting eq. (2.18) back into eqs. (2.16) and (2.17) gives

$$\mathscr{V}(r) = 4\varepsilon \left[-\frac{1}{2}\left(\frac{r_0}{r}\right)^6 + \frac{1}{4}\left(\frac{r_0}{r}\right)^{12} \right] \tag{2.20}$$

$$F(r) = -12\varepsilon \left[\frac{r_0^6}{r^7} - \frac{r_0^{12}}{r^{13}} \right] \tag{2.21}$$

As an illustration of the use to which eq. (2.20) may be put let us work out the energy required to completely dissociate a pair of atoms which are initially at their equilibrium separation r_0. This is known as the *dissociation energy* ΔE. In terms of Fig. 2.8, ΔE has a magnitude equal to that of the area under the force–separation curve between r_0 and infinity or, equivalently, the depth of the potential well at $r = r_0$ (Fig. 2.8(c)). Since $\mathscr{V}(r_0)$ is the energy required to *form* a pair so that they are at their equilibrium separation r_0 it follows that the energy to *dissociate* them is

$$\Delta E = - \mathscr{V}(r_0) \tag{2.22}$$

Substituting for $\mathscr{V}(r)$ from eq. (2.20) with $r = r_0$ gives

$$\Delta E = \varepsilon \tag{2.23}$$

Everytime we leave a kettle on the boil the energy fed in goes to separate completely water molecules from one another. Later on we shall make explicit the connection between the "boil away" energy and ΔE but, already, you can probably appreciate that the one is proportional to the other. (If ΔE could be doubled it would take twice the energy to boil the kettle dry.) In view of eq. (2.23) this means that the parameter ε of the Lennard-Jones 6-12 potential can be measured experimentally. In view of eq. (2.19) the other parameter σ can be found from r_0. (Roughly speaking r_0 is the same as the interatomic separation in a solid—which, as we have seen in section 2.3, can be estimated from the density of the solid.)

Exercise 2.4

By following through the same procedures as those just adopted in eliminating one constant from the Lennard-Jones 6-12 potential, show that the Mie potential (eq. (2.14)) can be written as

$$\mathscr{V}(r) = \frac{A}{r_0^m} \left[- \left(\frac{r_0}{r} \right)^m + \frac{m}{n} \left(\frac{r_0}{r} \right)^n \right] \tag{2.24}$$

where r_0 is the equilibrium separation of an isolated pair of atoms. Also show that the dissociation energy ΔE is

$$\Delta E = \frac{A}{r_0^m} \left(1 - \frac{m}{n} \right) \tag{2.25}$$

2.7 Theories of the interaction

To go beyond the stage of modelling the interaction of two atoms calls for a basic understanding of how atoms interact. To gain a full understanding requires a grounding in quantum mechanics and a mathematical facility well beyond that assumed in this book. Calculating the potential energy of an isolated pair of atoms would be relatively straightforward if we knew how the electrons are distributed between the two nuclei. Unfortunately a direct quantum-mechanical calculation of the electronic distributions involves knowing what this potential energy is!

Fortunately, there are two types of interaction which can be discussed without the need of quantum mechanics, but this is only possible because, in both cases, we assume the electronic distributions. The first of these types is ionic bonding, such as if found between ions in the alkali halides. The second type is the van der Waals interaction, as between inert gas atoms. Unfortunately neither of these types account for a significant proportion of the interatomic interactions existing in nature. The alkali halides—or any other substances in which the bonding is strictly ionic—and the inert gases are not very significant. In this sense our discussion of ionic forces is somewhat academic. However the form of the interaction between two isolated neon atoms is broadly similar to the form of the interaction *between* molecules in many solids and liquids; hence the importance of van der Waals' forces.

Ionic bonding
In a crystal of sodium chloride there is an effectively complete transfer of one electron from each sodium atom to each chlorine atom: The sodium atoms exist as Na^+ ions and the chlorine atoms as Cl^- ions. The electrostatic force $F(r)$ between a charge Q_1 and a charge Q_2 a distance r apart is given by Coulomb's law

$$F(r) = \frac{1}{4\pi\varepsilon_0}\frac{Q_1 Q_2}{r^2} \qquad (2.26)$$

where the constant $1/4\pi\varepsilon_0$ has a value (found experimentally) of $8 \cdot 99 \times 10^9$ N m^2 C^{-2}. (The constant ε_0 is known as the *permittivity* of free space—not to be confused with ε in the Lennard-Jones potential!) Since the Na^+ ion has a charge of value e and the Cl^- ion has a charge $-e$ the force $F(r)$ between an isolated $Na^+ - Cl^-$ ion pair is

$$F(r) = -\frac{e^2}{4\pi\varepsilon_0 r^2} \qquad (2.27)$$

Substituting this expression into eq. (2.12) gives

$$\mathscr{V}(r) = -\frac{e^2}{4\pi\varepsilon_0 r} \qquad (2.28)$$

Comparing eq. (2.28) with the first term in Mie's potential (eq. (2.14)) we see that $A = e^2/4\pi\varepsilon_0$ and $m = 1$. As to the value of n all that can simply be said is that because repulsive forces are very short-ranged—they really only come into play as the ions overlap—and because these forces increase very rapidly as r decreases, its value must be large. A value of $n = 9$ is often assumed. In fact, most calculations are very insensitive to the exact value of n. For example, the dissociation energy of an isolated NaCl molecule is, from eq. (2.25), given by

$$\Delta E = \frac{e^2}{4\pi\varepsilon_0 r_0}\left(1 - \frac{1}{9}\right) \qquad (2.29)$$

Substituting $1/4\pi\varepsilon_0 = 8.99 \times 10^9$ N m^2 C^{-2}, $e = 1.6 \times 10^{-19}$ C and taking $r_0 = 2.5 \times 10^{-10}$ m (the equilibrium separation in a NaCl molecule as measured in the gaseous phase) gives $\Delta E = 8.2 \times 10^{-19}$ J. This is within 4 per cent of the experimental value. Had we taken $n = \infty$ instead of $n = 9$ in eq. (2.29) it would only have changed ΔE by 10 per cent. An infinite value of n corresponds to what is called a *hard-sphere* model of the repulsive forces. By *hard* we mean that the spheres are incompressible; put differently, to compress them, even by an infinitesimal amount, requires an infinite energy. This effect that this hard sphere repulsive force has on $\mathscr{V}(r)$ is shown in Fig. 2.11 where it has been combined with the effect of a $1/r^2$ attractive force.

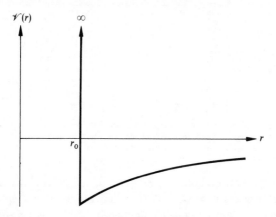

Fig. 2.11 The *hard-sphere* repulsion model showing how the potential energy between two hard spheres increases towards infinity at $r = r_0$.

van der Waals' forces

This type of force is found between inert gas atoms and represents the other extreme to ionic forces for there is no transfer of charge from one atom to the other.

We will start by considering a single isolated inert gas atom. The electron cloud is, on average, spherically symmetric about the nucleus (Fig. 2.12(a)). This means that the effective centre of the negative electron cloud coincides with that of the positive nucleus. Since the electron cloud and the nucleus have equal but opposite charges no resultant electric field should be produced outside the atom. Without an electric field it is hard to see how this atom could influence any other atom.

What we have said is true—but only true on average. At any instant there may be some asymmetry in the electron distribution. To put it simply (if somewhat misleadingly) the electrons are in motion around the nucleus. At any instant the effective centre of the electron cloud may not coincide with the nucleus. A "snapshot" would show a separation of charge (indicated schematically in Fig. 2.12(b)). The atom now consists of two charges $+q$ and

49

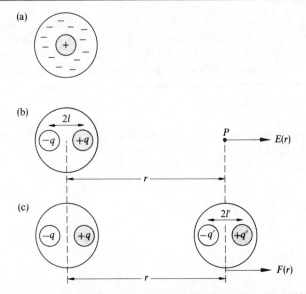

Fig. 2.12 (a) An isolated inert gas atom. The centre of the electron cloud coincides with that of the nucleus and the atom produces no external electric field. (b) The left-hand dipole produces an electric field. (c) This field polarizes the right-hand atom which leads to an attractive force between these atoms.

$-q$, say, separated by a distance $2l$. Such an arrangement in which equal but opposite sign charges are separated is called an *electric dipole* and is said to possess an *electric dipole moment* μ defined by

$$\mu = q(2l) \qquad (2.30)$$

We shall now show that this dipole produces an electric field and that this field will so distort the charge distribution in a second atom as to lead to a net attractive force between the two atoms.

Our first step is to calculate the electric field $E(r)$ produced at point P (Fig. 2.12(b)). This field is, of course, equal to the vector sum of the electric field due to charge $+q$ at distance $r - l$ from P and the field due to charge $-q$ at distance $r + l$ from P. Since the electric field $E(r)$ at a point is defined as "the force per unit positive charge placed at that point" it follows on applying Coulomb's law (eq. 2.26) that

$$E(r) = \frac{1}{4\pi\varepsilon_0}\left[\frac{q}{(r-l)^2} - \frac{q}{(r+l)^2}\right]$$

$$= \frac{q}{4\pi\varepsilon_0 r^2}\left[\frac{1}{[1-(l/r)]^2} - \frac{1}{[1+(l/r)]^2}\right]$$

$$E(r) = \frac{q}{4\pi\varepsilon_0 r^2}\left[\left(1-\frac{l}{r}\right)^{-2} - \left(1+\frac{l}{r}\right)^{-2}\right] \qquad (2.31)$$

On the assumption that $l \ll r$ we can expand eq. (2.31) by applying the binomial theorem, to give

$$E(r) = \frac{q}{4\pi\varepsilon_0 r^2}\left[\left(1 + \frac{2l}{r} + \cdots\right) - \left(1 - \frac{2l}{r} - \cdots\right)\right]$$

where we have ignored second and higher order terms. Therefore

$$E(r) = \frac{2(2ql)}{4\pi\varepsilon_0 r^3}$$

or, substituting for the electric dipole moment μ from eq. (2.30),

$$E(r) = \frac{2\mu}{4\pi\varepsilon_0 r^3} \tag{2.32}$$

We next examine the effect this field has on a second atom at point P. Since the field direction tells us the sense in which positive charge may move, it follows that the electric field $E(r)$ shown in Fig. 2.12(b) will move the positive nucleus in the field direction and the negative electron cloud in the opposite direction. This leads to a charge separation as shown in Fig. 2.12(c) in which charges of, say, $-q'$ and $+q'$ are separated by a distance of, say, $2l'$. When this charge separation takes place, the atom is said to be *polarized,* and the process is referred to as *induced polarization.* The field acting on the right-hand atom is not constant but varies from $E(r - l')$, acting on $-q'$, to $E(r + l')$ acting on $+q'$. The resultant force $F(r)$ acting on the right-hand dipole is given by

$$F(r) = [q'E(r + l') - q'E(r - l')] \tag{2.33}$$

where we have used the definition of the electric field as the force per unit *positive* charge. Substituting from eq. (2.32) for the electric field gives

$$F(r) = \frac{2\mu q'}{4\pi\varepsilon_0}\left[\frac{1}{(r + l')^3} - \frac{1}{(r - l')^3}\right]$$

$$F(r) = \frac{2\mu q'}{4\pi\varepsilon_0 r^3}\left[\left(1 + \frac{l'}{r}\right)^{-3} - \left(1 - \frac{l'}{r}\right)^{-3}\right] \tag{2.34}$$

Applying the binomial expansion formula to eq. (2.34) and neglecting second and higher order terms gives

$$F(r) = -\frac{12\mu q' l'}{4\pi\varepsilon_0 r^4}$$

Writing $\mu' = 2q'l'$ for the electric dipole moment of the right-hand atom gives

$$F(r) = -\frac{6\mu\mu'}{4\pi\varepsilon_0 r^4} \tag{2.35}$$

The value of $\mu' = 2q'l'$ will depend both on the strength of the polarizing field $E(r)$ and on the nature of the atom being polarized—just as the extension of a spring depends on the load and on the characteristics of the spring.

Since $+q'$ and $-q'$ are the nuclear and electronic charge, respectively, it is reasonable to suppose that these are fixed for a particular atomic species. If the atom obeys a form of "Hooke's law" (extension is proportional to load) we can expect $2l'$ to be proportional to $E(r)$. Both these assumptions are normally true, so we can say of $\mu'[= q'(2l')]$ that

$$\mu' \propto E(r)$$

or, substituting for $E(r)$ from eq. (2.32), that

$$\mu' \propto \frac{1}{r^3} \qquad (2.36)$$

Substituting eq. (2.36) into eq. (2.35) gives

$$F(r) \propto -\frac{1}{r^7} \qquad (2.37)$$

The negative sign, of course, indicates that the force is attractive. Integrating $F(r)$ via eq. (2.12) gives

$$\mathscr{V}(r) \propto -\frac{1}{r^6}$$

which justifies our earlier assumption that p in the Lennard-Jones potential could be given the value 6 when applied to the van der Waals interaction.

In arriving at eq. (2.37) we have advanced no adequate explanation as to the origin of the electric dipole moment of the left-hand atom of Fig. 2.12(b). What we have done in fact (perhaps without knowing it) is to calculate the attractive force between a permanent dipole—the left-hand atom of Fig. 2.12(c) —and an induced dipole—the right-hand atom of Fig. 2.12(c). Such an interaction between a permanent and an induced dipole features in the interaction between, for example, two HI molecules. But even here the forces arising from charge fluctuations in the molecules are some three hundred times greater. To fully investigate these so-called *dispersion forces* requires quite sophisticated quantum mechanics. However when the calculations are made a $-1/r^7$ force dependence or, equivalently $-1/r^6$ potential energy dependence, appears in the result. The attractive force between inert gas atoms arises exclusively from dispersion forces. Yet another type of interaction is that between permanent electric dipoles; the interaction between two water molecules is almost wholly of this sort. (In water the potential energy due to permanent dipole-permanent dipole interactions is some twenty times that due to permanent-induced interactions, and is also some four times that due to dispersion forces.) The name van der Waals' interaction may be given to all these forms of dipole–dipole interactions which are characterized by a $-1/r^7$ force dependence or, equivalently, a $-1/r^6$ potential energy dependence.

Covalent bonding

This type of bonding, by far the most prevalent in nature, is intermediate between ionic bonding, where there is an effectively complete transfer of an electron from one atom to the other, and the van der Waals interaction where there is no transfer at all of electrons. Put very simply, electrons are transferred to a "halfway house" between the two nuclei. This is shown pictorially in Fig. 2.13 for the H_2 molecule. Although the two nuclei repel one another, each is also attracted to the electron cloud whose "centre" is midway between them. (Two people pulling at opposite ends of a rope attract one another.) When covalent bonding occurs this attractive force will equal the repulsive force between the nuclei.

Because the attractive force between two ions varies as $1/r^2$ and that between two atoms in the van der Waals interaction varies as $1/r^7$, you might guess that in covalent bonding the attractive force would be proportional to $1/r^n$ where $7 > n > 2$. In fact when the calculations are made—and they are much too complex to be described—a simple inverse power law of force is never found. This means, of course, that any conclusions arrived at via a Mie or Lennard-Jones type of potential need not necessarily apply to covalently bonded materials. For this reason we shall normally take as our examples either the alkali halides or the inert gases.

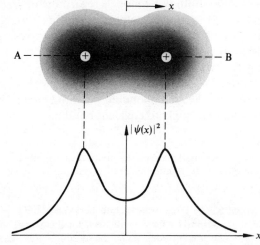

Fig. 2.13 A schematic representation of the electron cloud in a hydrogen molecule. This is suggested by shading and, more properly, by the probability density $|\psi(x)|^2$ at a point x along the line joining the centres of the two nuclei. The electron cloud is symmetrical about the line AB. The important point to note is the high probability of finding an electron at points between the two nuclei.

Summary

1. A mass spectrometer can measure both the absolute *atomic mass* and the *relative atomic mass* of an element. The relative atomic mass is calculated by dividing the atomic mass of the element by the atomic mass of ^{12}C and multiplying the result by 12 exactly. There is said to be 1 mole, written 1 mol, present if there are as many entities as there are atoms in 12×10^{-3} kg of ^{12}C; this number of atoms is called the Avogadro constant.

2. The *mass number* of an element measures the number of protons plus neutrons present in a nucleus of one atom of the element. The *atomic number* of an element measures the number of protons present in the nucleus; in an electrically neutral atom this also equals the number of electrons present. Two or more species of atom possessing the same atomic number but different mass numbers are referred to as *isotopes*. The mass number is written as a left superscript (e.g., ^{12}C), the atomic number as a left subscript (e.g., ^3_2He). The right subscript indicates the number of atoms present in a molecule of the substance (e.g., H_2).

3. Although it takes wave mechanics to fully describe how atoms interact one with another, Newtonian mechanics may be adequate if the de Broglie wavelength of an atom is insignificant compared to its size (as deduced from the density of the solid phase).

4. By very general arguments one can establish that between two like atoms or molecules there is "a short-ranged attractive force, followed by an even shorter-ranged repulsive force".

5. The interatomic potential energy may be conveniently modelled by a Mie or Lennard-Jones potential. Both these models regard the interatomic force as being composed of two separable components—one attractive and one repulsive—each of which can be represented by an inverse power of the interatomic separation.

6. In ionic bonding the attractive force varies as $1/r^2$; the corresponding potential energy varies as $-1/r$. With van der Waals' interaction the attractive force varies as $1/r^7$; the corresponding potential energy as $-1/r^6$. No simple power law relations apply to covalent bonding.

PROBLEMS

2.1 (a) Make an order-of-magnitude correct estimate of the number of atoms in your body. (b) Remembering that organic material is composed mainly of carbon and hydrogen make a rough estimate of the number of electron in your body. (c) If you could transfer 1 electron in 10^{10} of yours to a friend standing 1 m away what, roughly, would be the force of attraction between you? A 1 in 10^{10} loss of electrons could hardly seriously interfere with your biochemistry!

2.2 Make an order-of-magnitude estimate of the maximum area to which an oil drop could spread on water. Assume a drop volume of about 10^{-2} cm^3. Also assume that a molecule of the oil contains roughly ten atoms.

2.3 What is the flight-time for a Hg^+ ion in a time-of-flight mass spectrometer with an accelerating voltage of 60 V and a 0·5 m long drift tube? ($A_r(Hg) = 200$.)

2.4 Taking the density of solid sodium as 0.97×10^3 kg m^{-3}, estimate the diameter of a sodium atom. $(A_r(\text{Na}) = 23.)$

2.5 Roughly how many moles of water are there in the Mediterranean sea? Clue: use an atlas. (Water has a density of about 10^3 kg m^{-3}. Take $A_r(\text{H}) = 1$ and $A_r(\text{O}) = 16.$)

2.6 What is the de Broglie wavelength of a nitrogen molecule moving at 300 m s^{-1}? Through what electrical potential difference would a N_2^+ ion have to be accelerated to acquire this speed. $(A_r(\text{N}) = 14.)$

2.7 It is decided to model the interatomic force $F(r)$ between two atoms of an element in the manner shown in Fig. 2.14.
Here r represents the separation between centres of the two atoms. What, on this model, is (a) the equilibrium separation between two of these atoms, (b) the minimum force necessary to separate a pair of these atoms, and (c) the dissociation energy of the pair?

2.8 Sketch the potential energy variation corresponding to the force variation modelled in problem 2.7. Mark in on this curve: (a) the equilibrium separation of the pair, (b) the separation at which the restoring force is a maximum, and (c) the dissociation energy of the pair.

2.9 In the so-called *hard-sphere* model the repulsive force between two atoms becomes infinite at the instant of touching. Sketch the force variation and the corresponding potential energy variation between an Na$^+$ and Cl$^-$ ion assuming a hard-sphere repulsive interaction. Mark in on both curves (a) the equilibrium separation of the pair, (b) the separation at which the restoring force is a maximum, and (c) the dissociation energy of the pair.

2.10 Adopting a hard-sphere model write down an expression for $\mathscr{V}(r)$ between the two ions in an NaCl molecule that is valid at separations greater than the equilibrium value r_0. Calculate the dissociation energy of such a pair taking $r_0 = 2.5 \times 10^{-10}$ m.

2.11 Adopting a hard-sphere repulsion model, as in problem 2.10, calculate the maximum restoring force between the Na$^+$ and Cl$^-$ ions of a NaCl molecule. Assume $r_0 = 2.5 \times 10^{-10}$ m. Use your answer to calculate the tensional force required to break a grain of salt of cross-sectional area 10^{-6} m^2. Is this figure at all comparable with the sort of force which is required to smash a salt grain? (You

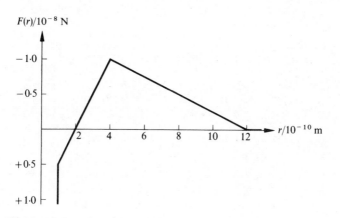

Fig. 2.14 A hypothetical interatomic force curve between two atoms.

55

surely must, at some stage, have crushed a grain of salt under a knife! In estimating the force you applied, remember that 1 newton is about equal to the weight of an average apple.)

2.12 Another model of the interatomic potential is that of Morse:

$$\mathscr{V}(r) = V_{\mathrm{e}}[e^{-2(r-r_{\mathrm{e}})/a} - 2e^{-(r-r_{\mathrm{e}})/a}]$$

where V_{e}, r_{e}, and a are constants.

(a) Show that the Morse potential does indeed fairly represent the interatomic interaction by plotting $\mathscr{V}(r)/V_{\mathrm{e}}$ against r/a for the case where $r_{\mathrm{e}} = 2a$.

(b) What is the equilibrium separation r_0?

(c) Calculate the restoring force for a value of r slightly different from r_0 and hence calculate the restoring force per unit displacement from r_0 (the so-called *force constant*).

2.13 Using a hard-sphere repulsion model write down an expression for $\mathscr{V}(r)$, valid at separations greater than the equilibrium separation r_0, for the potential energy of the two atoms in a NaCl molecule on the assumption that only gravitational (attractive) forces are present. Calculate the dissociation energy of the pair taking $r_0 = 2.5 \times 10^{-10}$ m. Compare your answer with that you obtained in problem 2.10. (You will remember that the force $F(r)$ of gravitational attraction between two spheres of masses m_1 and m_2 a distance r apart between centres is $F(r) = -Gm_1m_2/r^2$, where G is a constant of value 6.67×10^{-11} N m^2 kg^{-2}. Take $A_{\mathrm{r}}(\mathrm{Na}) = 23$ and $A_{\mathrm{r}}(\mathrm{Cl}) = 35.5$.)

3. Temperature

We must now face up to a key question: Why can one and the same substance sometimes exist as a gas, requiring an external pressure to contain it; sometimes as a liquid, capable of easy deformation; sometimes as a solid, capable of resisting large deforming forces? Asked these questions, the proverbial man in the street might well bring the word temperature into the discussion, pointing out that a substance exists as a solid at low temperatures, a liquid at "middling" temperatures, and a gas at high temperatures. We shall see that what is important in determining the phase of a substance is how the kinetic energy of its atoms or molecules compares with the dissociation energy of a pair, ΔE. This will lead us to consider how to relate our arguments, based on the microscopic, to temperature—something macroscopic, read on a dial. Finally we shall look at the heat capacities of gases—and find things that cannot be explained by the laws of classical mechanics.

3.1 Why solids, liquids, and gases?

Consider this statement for an answer? "Interatomic forces vary with temperature. At low temperatures they are strongly attractive. Proof? At low temperatures substances are solids—and solids require external forces to tear them apart. At high temperatures the interatomic forces are exclusively repulsive. Proof? At high temperatures substances are gases—and gases must be forcibly contained."

Such explanations were in fact advanced in the early part of the last century. We shall see that it is unnecessary to postulate any fundamental change in the form of the interatomic force—or, equivalently, in the form of the interatomic potential energy—as a substance changes from one phase to another. What is important in determining the phase of a substance is the kinetic energy of its atoms or molecules. Up to now we have only considered the potential energy of an isolated pair of atoms or molecules.

To see the effects of both kinetic and potential energies we will think about how a collection of atoms or molecules will behave. (For economy, we shall use the single word "atom" in what follows to mean either atom or molecule for whichever is appropriate to the substance under consideration.) We will suppose that between a pair of atoms there is "a short-ranged attractive force, followed by an even shorter-ranged repulsive force". In other words, we are assuming that the atoms interact according to Fig. 2.8(b) or (c).

We may expect that somewhere in the collection of atoms a bound pair will form—the atoms are, after all, attracted to one another. To separate such a pair into its component atoms requires an energy ΔE; the dissociation energy of the pair (Fig. 2.8(c)). In particular, let us consider the possible fates of any such bound pair (like the pair shown in Fig. 3.1). Because there are a great many other atoms in the system, each moving about with a kinetic energy $\frac{1}{2}mu^2$ (where m is the mass of one of the atoms and u its speed), it will not be long before another atom collides with the bound pair.

If $\frac{1}{2}mu^2$ exceeds the dissociation energy ΔE of the pair, then there is enough energy to dissociate the pair. Indeed if the average kinetic energy, written $\frac{1}{2}\overline{mu^2}$, of the colliding atom greatly exceeds ΔE, all (or virtually all) collisions will lead to dissociation of the bound pairs. Under these conditions no bound pairs can persist; the system will consist of individual atoms moving rapidly and with no apparent affinity for each other. In fact the atoms will have to be forced to occupy any given volume. These are just the properties which we associate with gases. On our microscopic model, a gas will therefore result when

$$\frac{1}{2}\overline{mu^2} \gg \Delta E \tag{3.1}$$

At the other extreme, when the average kinetic energy $\frac{1}{2}\overline{mu^2}$ of a colliding atom is very much less than the dissociation energy of the bound pair, no dissociation will result for there is not the energy available. The result is that the colliding atom may be captured by the pair.* Before long, this process will be repeated many times over and a large conglomeration of atoms will form. To dissociate such a conglomeration, energy must be fed in entirely from outside. Such a conglomeration of atoms—one that requires a significant amount of energy to dissociate it into a gas—is reminiscent of the solid phase. Therefore, on our microscopic model, the solid phase will occur when

$$\frac{1}{2}\overline{mu^2} \ll \Delta E \tag{3.2}$$

Lastly, when $\frac{1}{2}\overline{mu^2}$ is of the same order of magnitude as ΔE, we can expect some "clustering" to occur. Within the group of colliding atoms possessing an *average* energy $\frac{1}{2}\overline{mu^2} \approx \Delta E$ there will be some with energy less than ΔE. But there will also be some atoms present with a kinetic energy greater than ΔE and these will tend to dissociate any clusters which form. We can expect therefore to have a system in which a limited amount of association is possible;

---

*To be captured, the kinetic energy of the colliding atom must be removed in the collision. If this kinetic energy is not removed the colliding atom will be likely to rebound with no loss of energy, i.e., the collision will be elastic. A "cold" surface is, as we shall shortly see, a means of removing kinetic energy. In some types of atomic collisions, such as occur in hot flames, the collisions are sometimes inelastic; part of the translational kinetic energy of the colliding atoms goes to change their electronic configurations. These "excited" atoms may subsequently lose all or part of their energy by emitting light. This type of process will not concern us further in this text. In other types of inelastic collision translational kinetic energy is converted into vibrational energy in the colliding molecules; we shall see evidence of this effect in section 3.9.

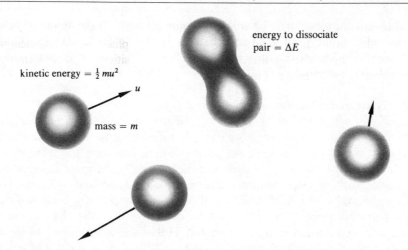

Fig. 3.1 Shows the competing roles of kinetic and potential energies in a system of many atoms.

a fluctuating system, part-bound, part-free. The system will not possess the rigidity of a solid nor the unrestrained freedom of a gas. These are the conditions characteristic of a liquid. Therefore the liquid phase may well occur when

$$\tfrac{1}{2}m\overline{u^2} \approx \Delta E \tag{3.3}$$

So by considering *both* the atoms' kinetic and potential energies we have been able to account for the solid, liquid, and gaseous phases.

There is a fourth phase of matter—the *plasma* phase—which consists of separated nuclei and electrons. This arises when the kinetic energy of the colliding atoms is so great that they knock each other asunder. The plasma phase is by far and away the most common—stars are plasmas—but it is also by far and away the most difficult to discuss quantitatively. For this reason we exclude it from further consideration.

As it stands this theory as to why a substance can exist in different phases is incomplete for it predicts that there should be a gradation of phases from solid through to gas (to plasma), depending on the value of $\tfrac{1}{2}m\overline{u^2}$. The theory would suggest that as one increases $\tfrac{1}{2}m\overline{u^2}$ the solid phase should change gradually and imperceptibly into the liquid phase. It does not explain why the three phases are normally so distinct and why phase transitions, as for example when a solid melts, are usually very sudden and occur at a well-defined temperature. Indeed there is no simple model to explain the sudden nature of phase transitions. It is perhaps hardly surprising that our model based, as it is, on how a *single pair* of atoms behave—relations (3.1), (3.2), and (3.3) involve the dissociation energy ΔE of a *pair*—is unsuccessful in this respect. Theories which do seek to take account of the mutual interactions of large collections of atoms (so called *many-body* theories) are very difficult to develop.

59

So although our model may be able to account for some of the main attributes of the solid, liquid, and gaseous phases it is clearly an inadequate model with which to discuss phase transitions. The limitations of a model must always be kept in mind.

3.2 A kinetic simulator

One way in which we might attempt to remove a serious deficiency of our model, namely its essentially two-particle nature, might be to write down just how each atom interacts with every other atom. Knowing the form of the interatomic force curve (Fig. 2.8(b)) and the disposition in space of the atoms we could work out the net force acting on each atom and therefore how each atom will move. Unfortunately there is no analytically exact solution even with only three atoms present. One can however "solve the equations" in step by step fashion using a computer. This is the technique of *molecular dynamics,* a technique which has been successfully applied to systems of several hundred atoms, and which we shall look at in more detail in chapter 11 when we come to discuss the liquid phase.

An equivalent approach is to build a simulator employing components which interact in the same way as do atoms. To be successful the simulator must employ "atoms" between which there is "a short-ranged attractive force, followed by an even shorter-ranged repulsive force" and which can be given variable kinetic energies. For "atoms" we may use steel balls (of the kind found in ball-bearings). The desired short-ranged attractive force may be simulated by coating the balls with oil. (If you have ever attempted to assemble a bearing you will know that oil-coated balls really do stick together.) The second feature which must be provided in the simulator is the means of giving kinetic energy to the balls. This may be provided by placing the oil-covered balls on a tray whose base is made of rough-moulded window glass containing an irregular pattern of pyramid-like peaks. When the tray is vibrated back and forth by means of a motor, kinetic energy is fed in throughout the system. (Because of energy dissipation in the oil films it is not sufficient to use a smooth-based tray and try to feed in energy only at the boundaries.)

On pouring the oil-coated balls on to the centre of the stationary tray they "crystallize" out into a regular two-dimensional pattern. This pattern persists at low vibrational speeds of the tray; that is, at low $\frac{1}{2}mu^2$ of the "atoms". Figure 3.2(a) shows this structure, present when $\frac{1}{2}mu^2 \ll \Delta E$. Later on we shall see that the atoms of a solid are arranged in a regular pattern.

As the speed of the tray, and therefore that of the balls, increases the regular pattern remains essentially intact until, at a well-defined value of $\frac{1}{2}mu^2$, the regularity suddenly disappears; the structure melts. Figure 3.2(b) shows what the system looks like when melting has occurred. This, one suspects, corresponds to the conditions existing in the liquid phase. If one measures the speed of u of each atom of the liquid and from it deduces the mean value

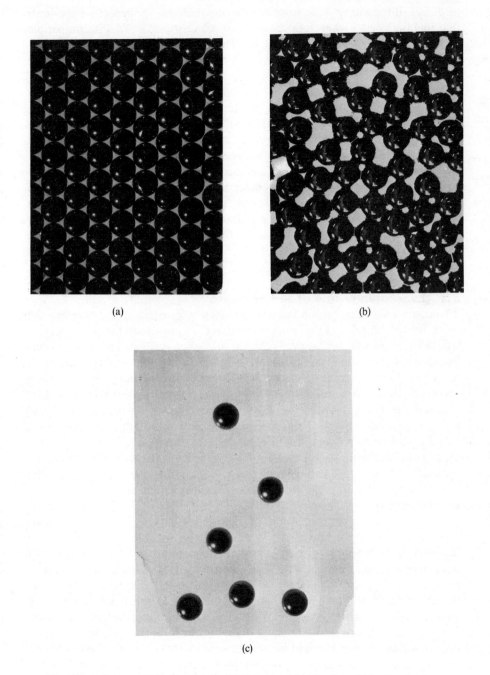

(a)   (b)

(c)

Fig. 3.2 A close up of (a) a simulated solid, (b) a simulated liquid, and (c) a simulated gas.

of u^2 for all the atoms—the so-called mean-square (m.s.) speed $\overline{u^2}$—one finds that melting occurs when $\frac{1}{2}m\overline{u^2}$ is some 20 per cent of ΔE. This is compatible with our two-particle model (eq. (3.3)). The speeds of the balls may be found by measuring how far each has moved in between successive frames of a cine film.

As the average kinetic energy of the balls is increased still further so that $\frac{1}{2}m\overline{u^2} \gg \Delta E$ the volume occupied by the liquid shrinks and the tray eventually contains a single phase which is undoubtedly gas-like (Fig. 3.2(c)). However this only happens when there are few balls on the tray—that is when the "molar area" (area per "N_A" balls) is large. With many balls present—so that the "molar area" is small—the liquid phase is seen to grow as $\frac{1}{2}m\overline{u^2}$ is increased until it fills the tray. You will remember from section 1.2 that no distinction can be made between a "liquid" and a "gas" at low molar volumes (in the shaded region of Fig. 1.11). So the simulator reproduces the conditions found in a real substance, thereby demonstrating the essential correctness of eqs. (3.1), (3.2), and (3.3).

3.3 Everyman's view of temperature

Throughout this chapter we have so far been very hesitant about using the word "temperature". Yet the "man in the street"—we will call him Everyman— would have no such hesitancy. To him a substance is a solid when the "temperature" is "low", is a liquid when the temperature is "middling", and is a gas when the temperature is "high". For our part, we would point out that a substance exists as a solid when $\frac{1}{2}m\overline{u^2}$ is very small (compared with ΔE); that it exists as a gas when $\frac{1}{2}m\overline{u^2}$ is very large (compared with ΔE); and that it exists as a liquid when $\frac{1}{2}m\overline{u^2}$ has some intermediate value (approximately equal to ΔE). Everyman's operational definition of a "high", a "middling", and a "low" temperature and our condition that (compared with ΔE) there should be a "high", a "middling", and a "low" translational kinetic energy, $\frac{1}{2}m\overline{u^2}$, of the constituent atoms or molecules of the substance, could be made consistent by writing that

$$\text{the temperature of a substance} \propto \tfrac{1}{2}m\overline{u^2} \tag{3.4}$$

Before rushing to adopt any such relation we should remind ourselves that we have only looked at part of what Everyman means by a temperature scale— that part dealing with steady conditions. Asked to describe what happens as bodies of different "temperature" are brought into contact, he might reply with some such illustration as this. If a poker at room temperature is plunged into a fire at a high (i.e., numerically high) temperature the appearance of the poker changes. Everyman, and we, might well say that the poker has acquired energy because it can now do "useful jobs" (such as scorching marks on a piece of wood) which it could not do previously. After being in the fire for a while nothing further happens to the poker. In our language there is no further net transfer of energy from the fire to the poker. In Everyman's language "the temperature of the poker is now the same as the fire".

If the poker is removed from the fire and plunged into a bucket of water the water sizzles. We declare that the state of the water has changed. It has acquired energy for it can now do useful jobs like cooking rice. The "reason" given by Everyman for such a change in the state of the water is that "the temperature of the poker is greater than that of the water". So a "temperature scale" contains within it the idea that if two bodies have numerically different "temperatures" energy will be transferred from the one of higher temperature to the one of lower temperature when the two bodies are placed in thermal contact. (Everyman would be quick to exclude cases where the bodies are separated by an adiabatic wall. Water inside a vacuum flask will not change its state if a hot poker is brought up to the outside of the flask.)

3.4   A microscopic view of temperature

Once we have examined, at the atomic level, the conditions governing the transfer of energy from one body to another we will be better placed to attempt to tie together our's and Everyman's idea of temperature.

A useful tactic to adopt in discussing any physical phenomenon is to try to break the discussion down into a series of discrete "chunks" each of which can be tackled with confidence. This is the tactic we shall discuss here and in later chapters.

A single collision

In imagination, leave a hot poker (a solid) to cool in the air (a gas). If we exclude radiant energy from further consideration (we do) the only other way that energy can be transferred from the solid to the gas is through collisions between atoms of the gas and atoms of the solid.

Figure 3.3(a) shows a gas atom of mass m moving up towards a solid composed of atoms of mass M. The ensuing collision will, in general, result in either a transfer of kinetic energy from the gas atom to the solid atom or from the solid atom to the gas atom. Figure 3.3(b) shows a single collision in more detail. Here U denotes the velocity of the solid atom (mass M) before impact and V its velocity after impact. The gas atom (mass m) has a velocity u before impact and a velocity v after impact. Following the usual convention we use the suffix x, y, or z to denote the components of velocity along the x-, y-, or z-axes respectively. Thus v_z, for example, means the z-component of the velocity v of m after impact.

The principle of conservation of energy tells us that any energy gained by, say, the gas atom as a result of the collision can only have been gained as a result of the solid atom losing energy. The energy $\Delta\varepsilon$ transferred from an atom

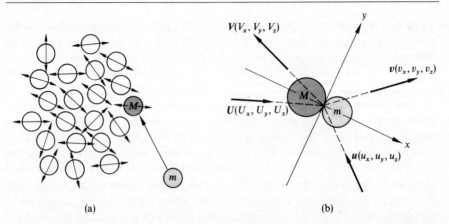

Fig. 3.3 (a) A gas atom of mass m approaches a solid composed of atoms of mass M. (b) The moment of impact between an atom of the gas and an atom of the solid. Here the x-axis is drawn along the line of centres of the atoms at impact. The y-axis lies in the tangent plane to each atom at impact. The z-axis (not shown) is mutually perpendicular to the x- and y-axes and comes out of the plane of the paper.

of the solid to an atom of the gas as a result of a collision is therefore given by*

$\Delta\varepsilon$ = (initial kinetic energy of the solid atom)

$\qquad\qquad\qquad$ − (final kinetic energy of the solid atom)

i.e.,

$$\Delta\varepsilon = \tfrac{1}{2}MU^2 - \tfrac{1}{2}MV^2 \tag{3.5}$$

As it stands, the right-hand side of eq. (3.5) only involves the condition of one partner in the collision—the solid atom. We would like to know how the other partner—the gas atom—is involved. To bring this into the picture we must appeal to the law of conservation of momentum as well as to the law of conservation of energy. As you will discover on studying appendix 1, appealing to both these conservation laws leads to the expression

$$\Delta\varepsilon = \frac{2mM}{(m+M)^2}\left[(MU_x^2 - mu_x^2) + (m-M)U_x u_x\right] \tag{3.6}$$

for the energy transferred from an atom of the solid to an atom of the gas in *one* collision (Fig. 3.3(b)).

---

* We assume that the solid atom does not move significantly while it and the gas atom are in contact. Should M move significantly the forces present between it and the other atoms of the solid will "do work" on m; so transferring some of the potential energy stored in the field between M and the other solid atoms to m. This would change its kinetic energy, of course. Put differently we are assuming that the duration of the collision between m and M is very much less than the vibrational period of an atom (such as M) of the solid.

64

An average collision

Needless to say, there are a great many collisions between atoms of the gas and atoms of the solid. What we really should be concerned with is the *average* energy $\overline{\Delta\varepsilon}$ which is transferred from the solid to the gas in a single collision. To find $\overline{\Delta\varepsilon}$ one would write down all the expressions like eq. (3.6) which describe each individual collision, sum them, and divide by the total number of collisions involved. It is not hard to show that this leads to the result:

$$\overline{\Delta\varepsilon} = \frac{2mM}{(m + M)^2} \left[(M\overline{U_x^2} - m\overline{u_x^2}) + (m - M)\overline{U_x u_x} \right] \qquad (3.7)$$

Now when a collision occurs, the x-component of velocity U_x of the atom of the solid may be either positive or negative. Since this atom remains as an atom of the solid it can have no continuous motion along the x-direction; it merely oscillates back and forth. So $\overline{U_x}$ must be zero. Therefore on averaging over many collisions, as we do in eq. (3.7), the average value of $U_x u_x$ will be zero. On the other hand, u_x^2 and U_x^2 are always positive (squaring a negative or a positive quantity gives a positive result), so $\overline{u_x^2}$ and $\overline{U_x^2}$ will be non-zero. Equation (3.7) therefore reduces to:

$$\overline{\Delta\varepsilon} = \frac{2mM}{(m + M)^2} (M\overline{U_x^2} - m\overline{u_x^2}) \qquad (3.8)$$

Assuming, as seems reasonable, that the fraction of atoms in the gas which have a particular speed is the same in all directions it follows that the mean square speeds resolved along the x-, y-, and z-directions will be equal, i.e., $\overline{u_x^2} = \overline{u_y^2} = \overline{u_z^2}$. We might also expect that along the surface of the solid equal numbers of atoms of the solid will be oscillating back and forth in all directions over a solid angle of 2π steradian, so that $\overline{U_x^2} = \overline{U_y^2} = \overline{U_z^2}$. This is much harder to justify than in a gas! However, accepting the result we can write down two further expressions involving the components of the initial speeds along the y- and z-axes respectively:

$$\overline{\Delta\varepsilon} = \frac{2mM}{(m + M)^2} (M\overline{U_y^2} - m\overline{u_y^2}) \qquad (3.9)$$

and

$$\overline{\Delta\varepsilon} = \frac{2mM}{(m + M)^2} (M\overline{U_z^2} - m\overline{u_z^2}) \qquad (3.10)$$

Adding together eqs. (3.8), (3.9), and (3.10) gives

$$3\overline{\Delta\varepsilon} = \frac{2mM}{(m + M)^2} \left[(\overline{U_x^2} + \overline{U_y^2} + \overline{U_z^2}) - m(\overline{u_x^2} + \overline{u_y^2} + \overline{u_z^2}) \right] \qquad (3.11)$$

Getting rid of component speeds

You will remember that u_x, u_y, and u_z are the magnitudes of the components of the velocity u of a gas atom resolved along the x-, y-, and z-axes respectively (Fig. 3.3(b)). In Fig. 3.4 the velocity vector u_i—we use the suffix i to indicate that we are talking about the velocity of a particular atom i—is shown resolved into three component velocities of magnitude u_{xi}, u_{yi}, and u_{zi}. The corresponding speeds, u_{xi}, u_{yi}, and u_{zi} are related to u_i by Pythagoras' theorem, namely

$$u_i^2 = [(u_{xi}^2 + u_{yi}^2)^{1/2}]^2 + u_{zi}^2$$

$$u_i^2 = u_{xi}^2 + u_{yi}^2 + u_{zi}^2 \tag{3.12}$$

If there are in all n_i atoms moving with speed u_i then on multiplying eq. (3.12) through by n_i, we obtain

$$n_i u_i^2 = n_i u_{xi}^2 + n_i u_{yi}^2 + n_i u_{zi}^2$$

or, summing over all speeds,

$$\sum_i n_i u_i^2 = \sum_i n_i u_{xi}^2 + \sum_i n_i u_{yi}^2 + \sum_i n_i u_{zi}^2 \tag{3.13}$$

If we now divide eq. (3.13) through by the total number of atoms $\left(= \sum_i n_i \right)$ present we obtain

$$\frac{\sum_i n_i u_i^2}{\sum_i n_i} = \frac{\sum_i n_i u_{xi}^2}{\sum_i n_i} + \frac{\sum_i n_i u_{yi}^2}{\sum_i n_i} + \frac{\sum_i n_i u_{zi}^2}{\sum_i n_i} \tag{3.14}$$

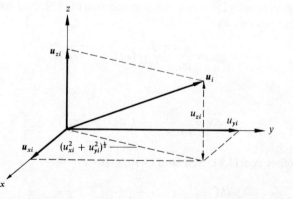

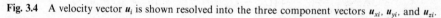

Fig. 3.4 A velocity vector u_i is shown resolved into the three component vectors u_{xi}, u_{yi}, and u_{zi}.

But by definition of mean square speed

$$\overline{u_x^2} = \frac{\sum\limits_i n_i u_{xi}^2}{\sum\limits_i n_i}$$

and similarly for the other components. Likewise

$$\overline{u^2} = \frac{\sum\limits_i n_i u_i^2}{\sum\limits_i n_i}$$

Therefore eq. (3.14) becomes

$$\overline{u^2} = \overline{u_x^2} + \overline{u_y^2} + \overline{u_z^2} \qquad (3.15)$$

A similar argument applies to the surface atoms of the solid, so

$$\overline{U^2} = \overline{U_x^2} + \overline{U_y^2} + \overline{U_z^2} \qquad (3.16)$$

Substituting eqs. (3.15) and (3.16) into eq. (3.11) gives the mean energy $\overline{\Delta\varepsilon}$ transferred from an atom of the solid to an atom of the gas as

$$\overline{\Delta\varepsilon} = \frac{2mM}{3(m+M)^2}(M\overline{U^2} - m\overline{u^2})$$

or

$$\overline{\Delta\varepsilon} = \frac{4mM}{3(m+M)^2}(\tfrac{1}{2}M\overline{U^2} - \tfrac{1}{2}m\overline{u^2}) \qquad (3.17)$$

Since m and M are constants eq. (3.17) may be written as

$$\overline{\Delta\varepsilon} \propto \tfrac{1}{2}M\overline{U^2} - \tfrac{1}{2}m\overline{u^2} \qquad (3.18)$$

In other words the average energy $\overline{\Delta\varepsilon}$ transferred in a collision from an atom of the solid to an atom of the gas is *proportional to the difference in the mean kinetic energy of the solid and gas atoms.* If $\tfrac{1}{2}m\overline{u^2} < \tfrac{1}{2}M\overline{U^2}$ then $\overline{\Delta\varepsilon}$ is positive so that energy is transferred from the solid to the gas. If $\tfrac{1}{2}m\overline{u^2} > \tfrac{1}{2}M\overline{U^2}$ then $\overline{\Delta\varepsilon}$ is negative so that energy is transferred from the gas to the solid. Finally, if $\tfrac{1}{2}m\overline{u^2} = \tfrac{1}{2}M\overline{U^2}$ then $\overline{\Delta\varepsilon} = 0$ so that there is no net transfer of energy from solid to gas; under these conditions *thermal equilibrium* is said to exist.

3.5 The two viewpoints compared

We are now in a position to compare our description of the processes that occur at the atomic level when a poker is placed in a fire, left till its state ceases to change, and then plunged into water, with the description involving "temperature" (which we shall denote by θ for short) given by Everyman.

67

These two different descriptions are summarized in Table 3.1. The suffix g refers to the gas (the flame), s to the solid (the poker), and l to the liquid (the water). The symbol m refers of course to the appropriate atomic (or molecular) mass: It does *not* refer to the mass of objects like the poker!

TABLE 3.1

Observation	Description at the atomic level	Description by Everyman
Poker placed in fire; poker changes (gets "hot")	Poker atoms acquire energy from gas atoms in flame: $\frac{1}{2}m_g\overline{u_g^2} > \frac{1}{2}m_s\overline{u_s^2}$	$\theta_g > \theta_s$
Poker ceases to change in fire	No net transfer of energy occurs between gas and poker atoms: $\frac{1}{2}m_g\overline{u_g^2} = \frac{1}{2}m_s\overline{u_s^2}$	$\theta_g = \theta_s$
Poker plunged into water; water changes	Water atoms acquire energy from the poker atoms: $\frac{1}{2}m_l\overline{u_l^2} < \frac{1}{2}m_s\overline{u_s^2}$	$\theta_l < \theta_s$

Inspecting Table 3.1 we see that two quite different descriptions—that of Everyman, with his different values of temperature θ, and the microscopic description involving different values of mean translational atomic kinetic energy—could be made compatible by writing

$$\theta \propto \tfrac{1}{2}m\overline{u^2} \qquad (3.19)$$

Adopting such a definition of temperature would make the statements of columns 2 and 3 agree. It would also be consistent with eq. (3.4), which was arrived at solely by considering the conditions under which a substance exists as a solid, as a liquid, or as a gas.

To be a worthwhile definition of temperature eq. (3.19) would have to be made operational. Although this equation is never in fact used to define temperature, it is nevertheless instructive to see how it might be made operational. Clearly one would have to devise a procedure for measuring $\frac{1}{2}m\overline{u^2}$—we shall shortly show that this may be done. One would also have to agree on a value for the constant of proportionality in eq. (3.19). The simplest choice would be to make it unity so that

$$\theta = \tfrac{1}{2}m\overline{u^2}$$

In such a régime temperature would be measured in the same units as energy; in the SI system of units temperature would be measured in joule (J).

In a somewhat more general vein we could write

$$\theta = C(\tfrac{1}{2}m\overline{u^2}) \tag{3.20}$$

where the constant of proportionality C could be given any value we fancy, and be measured in any units we care to use.

Exercise 3.1

As a *purely fanciful* idea we might decide to write C as 5 jean J^{-1} (introducing the "jean" as a quite arbitrary unit, named after Sir James Jeans who was one of the first authors to adopt the approach used in this chapter). Temporarily adopting this value for C, what would be the temperature of gaseous oxygen if the *root mean square* (r.m.s.) speed, meaning $(\overline{u^2})^{1/2}$, of the O_2 molecules is 600 m s^{-1}? ($A_r(O) = 16$).

This purely fanciful exercise will have emphasized that, on this approach, the units of temperature depend on the units given to the constant of proportionality C in eq. (3.20).

3.6 A time-of-flight "thermometer"

Even if we were to agree on a value for the constant C in eq. (3.20), there would still remain the problem of how to measure $\tfrac{1}{2}m\overline{u^2}$, or, assuming that we know the relative atomic (or molecular) mass of the substance, the problem of how to measure $\overline{u^2}$.

To find the temperature of, say, boiling water you might think it necessary to measure directly the speeds of the water molecules. Fortunately the problem may be eased if we immerse in the boiling water a cylinder made of a diathermal material like copper and containing a known gas, say mercury, at

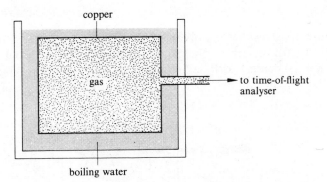

Fig. 3.5 A possible "thermometer" for measuring the temperature of, say, boiling water. The copper vessel contains a gas whose mean square speed can be measured using a time-of-flight analyser.

very low pressure (Fig. 3.5). If we could measure the mean kinetic energy of the gas atoms when thermal equilibrium is established, we know from our analysis that this is equal to the mean kinetic energy of the copper atoms, which is in turn equal to the mean kinetic energy of the water molecules. By virtue of eq. (3.20) we may say that at thermal equilibrium the temperature θ of the gas is the same as that of the copper, which is the same as that of the water.

The mean square speed of the gas atoms may be found using the apparatus shown in Fig. 3.6. The gas escaping through the hole in the copper container C (as in Fig. 3.5) is collimated into a fine beam by means of two slits S_1 and S_2. This beam next meets a rotating disc D_1 which has a narrow slot cut in it; this allows through a short burst of atoms once per revolution of D_1. This burst then travels on—the whole apparatus is highly evacuated—spreading out as it goes. The faster atoms move out ahead; the slower atoms trail behind (Fig. 3.6). On meeting the second revolving disc D_2, the only ones which will pass through the slot cut in it will be those which have covered the distance between D_1 and D_2 in the time it took for the slot in D_2 to move around to be in line with the burst. The number of those atoms which do get through the slot in D_2 is measured by allowing the beam, after it has passed through a third slit S_3, to strike a suitable recording detector R. In one early experiment the detector consisted of a glass plate cooled by liquid air. By timing how long it took for a visible deposit of mercury to form on the glass the intensity of the beam could be estimated.

In practice the discs D_1 and D_2 would contain many radial slots with those in D_2 displaced relative to those in D_1. By varying either the angle between the two sets of slots, or the speed of the motor M which drives the two discs, one can allow through atoms of various known speeds and then record the corresponding intensity at the detector. This type of experiment was pioneered by Stern and his students in the 1920s: You probably spotted a certain family resemblance between the apparatus of Fig. 3.6 and that of Fig. 2.3.

Exercise 3.2

Figure 3.7 shows results obtained in an actual experiment of the type we have just described. The gas was mercury ($A_r(\text{Hg}) = 200$) and it was in thermal contact with boiling water. What is the mean kinetic energy of the mercury atoms? What is the mean kinetic energy of the water

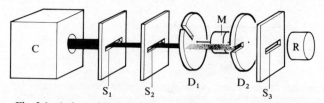

Fig. 3.6 A time-of-flight apparatus for measuring atomic speeds.

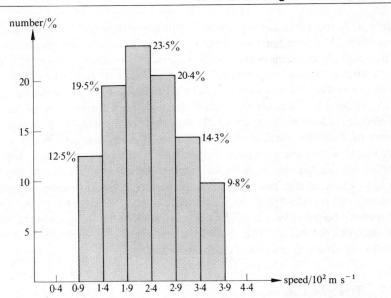

Fig. 3.7 Showing the distribution in speeds of gaseous mercury atoms in a beam emerging from a container which is in thermal equilibrium with boiling water. A time-of-flight instrument was used to measure the speed distribution. (Data from Lammert, *Z. Phys.*, **56**, 244 (1929).)

molecules? It should be pointed out that this type of experiment measures the speed of the mercury atoms in the *beam* which has emerged from C (Fig. 3.6). There is no guarantee that the distribution of speeds in this beam is the same as the distribution of speeds in the gas within C. In fact the two distributions are *not* the same. This is because the faster gas atoms within C make more collisions per unit time with the hole in C (thereby escaping) than do slower atoms. The emerging beam therefore contains a disproportionate number of fast atoms. It turns out (see problem 6.9) that the mean kinetic energy of the atoms within C is 3/4 of the mean kinetic energy of the atoms within the beam.

There is a technically much less sophisticated way to determine translational kinetic energies, one with an ancestry going back to 1807. In that year the English botanist Brown suspended grains of pollen in water. On examining the mixture through a microscope he saw the pollen grains dancing hither and thither without apparent rhyme or reason. The same erratic motion—now known as *Brownian motion*—is observed in particles of smoke suspended in a gas. If we regard each of these particles as being a rigid body of mass M we would expect them to move at a mean square speed $\overline{U^2}$ such that

$$\tfrac{1}{2}M\overline{U^2} = \tfrac{1}{2}m\overline{u^2}$$

$$(\overline{U^2})^{1/2} = \left(\frac{m}{M}\right)^{1/2} (\overline{u^2})^{1/2} \tag{3.21}$$

71

Here $\overline{u^2}$ is the mean square speed of the gas atoms and m is the mass of a gas atom. (A similar relation applies, of course, to the pollen grains in water.) Time-of-flight measurements—such as are made with the apparatus of Fig. 3.6— show that at "room temperature" an oxygen molecule has a root mean square (r.m.s.) speed $\left(\overline{u^2}\right)^{1/2} \approx 450 \text{ m s}^{-1}$. Now particles of tobacco smoke have a mass M of order 10^{-21} kg, which is some 2×10^4 times the mass m of an oxygen molecule. It follows from eq. (3.21) that the r.m.s. speed of Brownian movement of a smoke particle is about 3 m s^{-1}. Such a speed might easily be measured with a microscope equipped with a suitable scale and a stop watch. Although this particular form of "thermometer" is not used in practice, a related thermometer has been developed which relies on measuring electrical "noise" in a metal resistor. As we shall see in chapter 10 some of the electrons in a metal behave like a gas. The noise arises from fluctuations in the numbers of electrons present at either end of the resistor. These fluctuations depend on the mean square speed of the electrons in the "gas".

3.7 The gas thermometer

There is in fact no agreed constant C in eq. (3.20) which would enable us to use it as a definition of temperature. What is agreed internationally is how to measure temperatures using a device called a gas thermometer. Later on though we shall see how this device can, if we so wish, be used to yield a value for the constant C.

To give the full specification of a gas thermometer and to state exactly how a measurement is made would take a chapter in itself. The essential steps can however be described quite simply. We shall give the description in the form of a prescription.

The basic article

Take a fixed mass of gas and measure its pressure p and volume V when the container holding the gas is in thermal contact with water at its triple point (Fig. 3.8(a)). (You will recall from chapter 1 that at the triple point all the three phases—ice, water, and water vapour—coexist in equilibrium.) Now evaluate the product of p and V, written $(pV)_{tr}$. Call the temperature of the gas $T_{tr} = 273 \cdot 16$ K exactly.

To find the temperature T of, say, boiling sulphur, immerse the bulb in the sulphur, measure the new values of p and V, and calculate the product pV afresh. The temperature T of the sulphur is (roughly) given by

$$\frac{T}{T_{tr}} = \frac{(pV)}{(pV)_{tr}}$$

$$T = T_{tr}\frac{(pV)}{(pV)_{tr}} \tag{3.22}$$

Now because T_{tr} is defined as 273·16 K exactly this becomes

$$T = 273 \cdot 16 \text{ K} \frac{(pV)}{(pV)_{tr}} \tag{3.23}$$

There is a major snag to the thermometer as we have described it: Different observers would get different answers for the temperatures of the same bath of boiling sulphur. This might not matter much if we just wanted a rough and ready value for the temperature but discrepancies become very serious if we are trying to define operationally what is meant by *the* temperature of the system. If each device gives a different number, which device do we choose as standard? It is found that the number one obtains depends on how the thermometer is constructed (for example, on the material of the bulb and on how much of the thermometer's volume is "dead"—not in the bulb), on which gas is used (carbon dioxide and helium, for example, will in general give different answers for the temperature of our sulphur) and on how much gas is present in the thermometer.

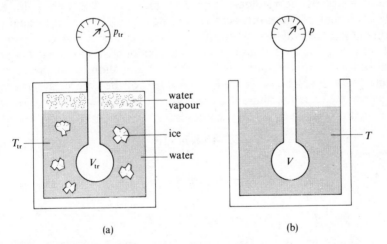

Fig. 3.8 A schematic diagram of the procedures involved in measuring a temperature on the gas scale. In (a) the bulb is immersed in water at its triple point. In (b) the bulb is immersed in the substance whose temperature is required.

Removing the snags

Over the years a great deal of effort has gone into refining the design of a gas thermometer, aimed at eliminating errors—such as that introduced by the dead volume, for example. Although these sources of errors can never be eliminated entirely they can be allowed for. There is however no one "approved" design of a gas thermometer. What exists is a consensus as to what constitutes good and bad practice. If you built a gas thermometer and obtained a value of 54·365 K for the triple point of oxygen your entire experimental procedures would be scrutinized by many critical eyes before that value was accepted as *the* triple point of oxygen on the gas scale. Not only are the "nuts and bolts" examined, but it is just as important to know how you eliminated errors introduced by having a particular amount of a particular gas in your thermometer.

As we have said, if you use any amount of any gas your answer for the temperature will depend on just what "any" is! Fortunately the answer gets less and less dependent on the nature and amount of the gas the smaller is the amount of gas present. The procedure, or rather one procedure, is to measure $(pV_m)/(pV_m)_{tr}$ first at one fill. Here V_m is the molar volume of the gas which is, of course, equal to the volume V of the gas divided by the number of moles, n, of gas present. Next one removes, say, half the gas (thereby halving n) and measures the ratio $(pV_m)/(pV_m)_{tr}$ again. One removes still more of the gas and measures the ratio afresh. To obtain the limiting value of $(pV_m)/(pV_m)_{tr}$ as the amount of gas present tends to zero we can plot $(pV_m)/(pV_m)_{tr}$ against p, the gas pressure at some convenient point such as the triple point of water. (If the volume occupied by the gas at the triple point is the same in all runs of the experiment p_{tr} will be very nearly proportional to n.) Extrapolating the graph to where it crosses the $p = 0$ axis gives the limiting value of $(pV_m)/(pV_m)_{tr}$ as p, and therefore the amount of gas present, tends to zero. This procedure is illustrated in Fig. 3.9 and shows that the measured boiling point of sulphur is indeed independent of the type of gas present in the thermometer as the amount of gas present tends towards zero. Adopting some such procedure eq. (3.23) becomes

$$T = 273 \cdot 16 \text{ K} \lim_{p \to 0} \left[\frac{(pV_m)}{(pV_m)_{tr}} \right] \tag{3.24}$$

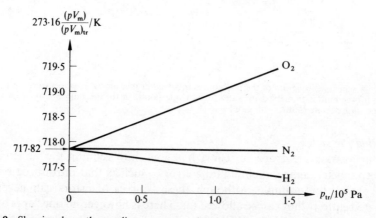

Fig. 3.9 Showing how the reading on a gas thermometer (actually a constant-volume gas thermometer) for the temperature at which sulphur boils (at a pressure of $1 \cdot 013 \times 10^5$ Pa) depends on the thermometric gas and on the amount of gas present, indicated by its pressure at the triple point of water.

which can be written as*

$$T = 273 \cdot 16 \text{ K} \frac{\lim_{p \to 0} (pV_m)}{\lim_{p \to 0} (pV_m)_{tr}}$$ (3.25)

This equation defines a temperature T on the *perfect gas scale* (also called the *ideal gas scale*). However it only defines T if all the "rules" have been followed. Lurking behind eq. (3.25) is a very complex piece of equipment which must satisfy many different criteria! Only when all these "rules" are obeyed is the value obtained for T independent of the device and of the gas employed in it.

Figure 3.10(a) shows the bulb of a constant-volume gas thermometer used at the National Physical Laboratory in England to measure temperatures in the range 2 K to 20 K. In a constant-volume gas thermometer one adjusts the pressure so as to keep the volume occupied by the gas constant. Figure 3.10(b) shows the ancillary equipment that goes with the constant-volume bulb! Inside the glass vessel in the top right-hand corner is the pressure measuring device—a piston carrying known weights mounted in a cylinder, exactly as in Fig. 1.1.

The gas constant
Equation (3.25) may be written as

$$\lim_{p \to 0} (pV_m) = RT$$ (3.26)

where

$$R = \frac{\lim_{p \to 0} (pV_m)_{tr}}{273 \cdot 16 \text{ K}}$$ (3.27)

is known as the *gas constant*. The value of the gas constant is, of course, obtained by measuring the limiting value of pV_m at the triple point as $p \to 0$ and dividing the result by $273 \cdot 16$ K. Such experiments currently give $R = 8 \cdot 31441 \pm 0 \cdot 00026$ J K^{-1} mol^{-1}. Because $\lim_{p \to 0} (pV_m)$ is an experimentally determined quantity (unlike the triple point temperature which is defined to be $273 \cdot 16$ K exactly) the value of R is subject to change as laboratory techniques are refined.

---

*As shown in practically any introductory text on calculus, if $f(x)$ and $g(x)$ are two functions of x such that $\lim_{x \to a} f(x)$ and $\lim_{x \to a} g(x)$ exist, then

$$\lim_{x \to a} \left[\frac{f(x)}{g(x)} \right] = \frac{\lim_{x \to a} f(x)}{\lim_{x \to a} g(x)}$$

provided $\lim_{x \to a} g(x) \neq 0$. These conditions hold true in our case.

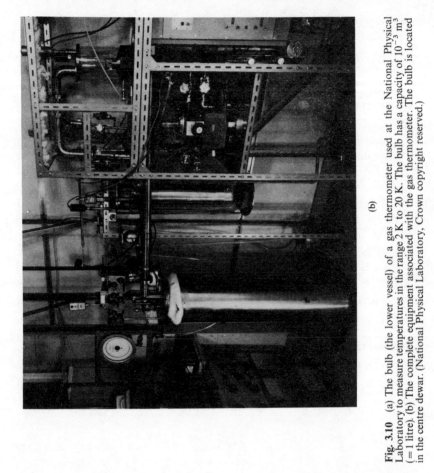

(b)

(a)

Fig. 3.10 (a) The bulb (the lower vessel) of a gas thermometer used at the National Physical Laboratory to measure temperatures in the range 2 K to 20 K. The bulb has a capacity of 10^{-3} m^3 (= 1 litre). (b) The complete equipment associated with the gas thermometer. The bulb is located in the centre dewar. (National Physical Laboratory, Crown copyright reserved.)

Boltzmann's constant

In the next chapter we shall discuss the origins of gas pressure. In so doing we shall adopt a particular model of a "perfect" gas—one which assumes that the interatomic potential energy is zero. This will only be true in a real gas when the atoms are a near-infinite distance apart (Fig. 2.8(c)); a condition approached as $p \to 0$. Therefore any relation derived on the basis of a model which assumes $\Delta E = 0$ must be qualified by the rider that $p \to 0$ before we can expect the relation to apply to a real gas. We shall later find that (eq. (4.23))

$$pV_m = \tfrac{2}{3}N_A\left(\tfrac{1}{2}m\overline{u^2}\right)$$

Modifying this equation so that it applies to a real gas gives

$$\lim_{p\to 0}(pV_m) = \tfrac{2}{3}N_A\left(\tfrac{1}{2}m\overline{u^2}\right) \qquad (3.28)$$

Substituting for $\lim_{p\to 0}(pV_m)$ from eq. (3.26) gives

$$RT = \tfrac{2}{3}N_A\left(\tfrac{1}{2}m\overline{u^2}\right)$$

or

$$T = \frac{2}{3k}\left(\tfrac{1}{2}m\overline{u^2}\right) \qquad (3.29)$$

where

$$k = \frac{R}{N_A} \qquad (3.30)$$

is called the *Boltzmann constant*. Since R, the gas constant, and N_A, the Avogadro constant, are both determined experimentally the value of k is firmly anchored in experiments; the currently accepted value is $1\cdot380662$ ($\pm$ $0\cdot000044$) $\times 10^{-23}$ J K^{-1}. You should satisfy yourself that the units of k are indeed J K^{-1}.

If you compare eqs. (3.29) and (3.20) you will see that both have fundamentally the same form. Equation (3.20), you will recall, was arrived at by relating Everyman's scale of temperature with the results of a microscopic analysis; eq. (3.29) was arrived at by relating the perfect gas scale of temperature with a microscopic analysis (yet to come). Why, you may ask, did we not make the constant C in eq. (3.20) equal to $2/3k$, adopting a fixed value for k (perhaps rounding it off to $1\cdot38 \times 10^{-23}$ J K^{-1})? Such a procedure would make temperatures as deduced by Everyman (who would perhaps use a "Brownian motion thermometer") agree with the values obtained by the professional using a gas thermometer. The professional physicist would, however, firmly resist any move to give k a fixed value. To give k, and therefore $2/3k$, an arbitrary *fixed* value in eq. (3.29) and to make this our prime definition of temperature would remove the definition of temperature from the realms of the macroscopic, as it is in eq. (3.24), to the realms of the microscopic. To make matters worse eq. (3.29) and (3.20) depends on the correctness or otherwise of one particular model of the behaviour of atoms in a gas. A macroscopic concept like temperature must not be at the mercy of any model of the microscopic world, because it can be defined and measured without any reference being made to the microscopic constitution of matter.

Exercise 3.3

On the assumption that the constant C of eq. (3.20) has a value $2/3k$, where $k = 1.38 \times 10^{-23}$ J K^{-1}, use the data given in exercise 3.2 (which you have already analysed) to calculate the temperature at which water boils.

Exercise 3.4

It is possible to boil a kettle of water by directing a high speed stream of gas at the base of the (stationary) kettle. Approximately what speed air blast is necessary to ensure that the water in the kettle will boil? (Water boils at about 373 K.) Assume that the still air is at 300 K. *Clues:* In still air the value of $\frac{1}{2}mu^2$ of the air molecules will, at equilibrium, equal the value of $\frac{1}{2}mu^2$ of the atoms in the base of the kettle, which will also equal $\frac{1}{2}mu^2$ of the water molecules in the kettle. If however an air blast of speed U is directed at the base of the kettle, the speed of the air molecules as they impinge on the kettle atoms is increased to something like $U + (\overline{u^2})^{1/2}$. (The kettle must be anchored firmly!) These air molecules have therefore more kinetic energy than they did when U was zero; so kinetic energy will be transferred to the base, and so to the water. When equilibrium is once more established . . . . You should have enough clues to tackle the problem.

3.8 The International Practical Temperature Scale

No one in their right mind would use a gas thermometer to see if, say, the cooking oil was at the right temperature to cook the chips. Quite apart from the size of the instrument, it takes several weeks of accurate observations to accurately measure a temperature on the perfect gas scale! And of course such precision is quite out of place in the kitchen—or, for that matter, in most laboratories.

The International Practical Temperature Scale (IPTS) is, as the name suggests, a scale of a somewhat more practical nature than the gas scale, yet one which is capable of very high precision. The scale *assigns* values to the temperatures of a number of reproducible equilibrium states (defining "fixed points") and lays down the type of instrument that is to be used to measure temperatures between these fixed points. As examples of fixed points, the scale adopted in 1968, and currently in use (called the IPTS-68 scale), fixes the triple point of hydrogen as 13.81 K, the boiling point of neon at 1.01325×10^5 Pa as 27.102 K, and the freezing point of zinc (equilibrium between solid and liquid phases) at $1 \cdot 01325 \times 10^5$ Pa as $692 \cdot 73$ K. (Figure 1.3 will remind you why it is necessary to specify the pressure of the boiling and freezing points.) These fixed point temperatures are not, of course, "plucked out of the blue"—they represent what are agreed to be the best determinations made on the gas scale. At roughly twenty year intervals an international group of scientists assesses the "state of the art", and may decide to change the value of any fixed point. In 1948, for example, they upped the freezing point of silver by $0 \cdot 3$ K from the value it had been assigned in 1927 (the year the IPTS scale was introduced). It is important to note that when a numerical value is *assigned* to a fixed point no "error" is attached to that value. Measurements made on the gas scale give the melting point of zinc as $692 \cdot 73 \pm 0 \cdot 03$ K—but IPTS-68 *fixes* the temperature as $692 \cdot 73$ K.

The second feature of the IPTS is that it lays down the instruments that are to be used in measuring temperatures between the fixed points. It says for example, that the standard instrument to be used from $13 \cdot 81$ K (the triple point of hydrogen) to $903 \cdot 89$ K (the freezing point of antimony at $1 \cdot 01325 \times 10^5$ Pa) is the platinum resistance thermometer. It is an experimental fact that the resistance of a metal varies with temperature, so this property can clearly form the basis of a thermometer. On the IPTS advice is offered on how to construct a thermometer. The criteria which the final product must satisfy are laid down, as is also the method of turning numbers—like the resistance of the platinum thermometer—into temperatures on the IPTS. Only when all these recommendations have been strictly adhered to can one claim to have measured a temperature on the IPTS.

Measuring a temperature on the IPTS is no joke. So one constructs a number of thoroughly practical thermometers, like the familiar mercury-in-glass thermometer, which can be calibrated against IPTS instruments. The usual mass produced thermometer is several steps removed from the standard instruments, being calibrated against "sub-standards" (which are not sub-standard in the sense that chipped cups are!).

3.9 The heat capacity of gases

In considering how a poker removed from the fire cools we looked at how energy was transferred from the solid poker to the gaseous air. Our discussion was concerned with what happened at the microscopic level. Anyone primarily concerned with the macroscopic properties of gases will be more interested in the molar heat capacity for this will tell him how much energy is required to produce a given temperature change in a given amount of gas. You will recall from chapter 1 that the molar heat capacity at constant volume is defined by (eq. (1.1))

$$C_{V,\text{m}} = \left(\frac{\delta Q}{\delta T} \right)_V$$

where δQ is the "heat" required to change the temperature of 1 mol of the substance by δT. You will remember how this energy δQ was pictured as being fed in via a "paddle-wheel" type of device (Fig. 1.18). You will also recall how we showed that in a constant-volume system δQ is equal to the change δU_m in the molar internal energy of the system eq. (1.3):

$$C_{V,m} = \left(\frac{\delta U_m}{\delta T}\right)_V \tag{3.31}$$

The questions we will now ask are these—starting with an atomic model of a gas, can we predict $C_{V,m}$? How is this prediction borne out in practice?

Monatomic gases

The rotating paddle wheel in the apparatus of Fig. 1.18 should do to a gas atom what a tennis racket does to a ball during a serve—increase its kinetic energy. In other words, in a constant-volume system energy δQ fed in via the paddle wheel, which manifests itself macroscopically as a change δU in internal energy of the system, should go to increase the translational kinetic energy of the gas atoms.

If there is 1 mol of gas present there are N_A atoms present, by definition. Since the average translational kinetic energy of a gas atom is $\frac{1}{2}m\overline{u^2}$ the total translational kinetic energy of all N_A atoms is $N_A(\frac{1}{2}m\overline{u^2})$. Assuming that the energy $\delta Q(=\delta U_m)$ fed into the gas only goes to increase the translational energy of the gas atoms we may write

$$\delta U_m = \delta\left[N_A\left(\tfrac{1}{2}m\overline{u^2}\right)\right] = N_A\delta\left(\tfrac{1}{2}m\overline{u^2}\right) \tag{3.32}$$

Now we also know that (eq. (3.29))

$$T = \frac{2}{3k}\left(\tfrac{1}{2}m\overline{u^2}\right)$$

where T is measured with a gas thermometer, so that

$$\delta T = \frac{2}{3k}\delta\left(\tfrac{1}{2}m\overline{u^2}\right) \tag{3.33}$$

Substituting eqs. (3.32) (which assumes the system is at constant volume) and (3.33) into eq. (3.31) gives

$$C_{V,m} = \frac{3kN_A}{2}\frac{\delta\left(\tfrac{1}{2}m\overline{u^2}\right)}{\delta\left(\tfrac{1}{2}m\overline{u^2}\right)} \tag{3.34}$$

$$C_{V,m} = \frac{3kN_A}{2}$$

or, since $R = kN_A$ (eq. (3.30))

$$C_{V,m} = \frac{3R}{2} \tag{3.35}$$

Besides predicting the value of $C_{V,m}$ eq. (3.35) also predicts that the molar heat capacity will be independent of temperature—R is a constant. It is not hard to see why theory predicts a constant value for $C_{V,m}$; a change in $\frac{1}{2}mu^2$ implies a proportional change in δU_m and in δT.

The fact that the measured value of $C_{V,m}$ for a monatomic gas does have a value of $3R/2(= 12\cdot5\,\mathrm{J\,K^{-1}\,mol^{-1}})$ which is independent of temperature should come as an unpleasant shock! Had we adopted a somewhat different approach, we might have argued (following up the tennis analogy) that part of the energy fed into the gas via the paddle wheel might indeed go to set the atoms moving about more rapidly, but part might go to set them spinning more rapidly, while part might well go "inside" the atoms to give the electrons more kinetic energy (and, in turn, more electrostatic potential energy as the electrons move further out from the nucleus). Some of the energy fed in might even set the nucleus vibrating more rapidly. Had we been more honest we would have written down not eq. (3.32) but

$$\delta U_{\mathrm{m}} = \delta \left[\sum_{\mathrm{atoms}} \left(\begin{array}{c} \text{translational kinetic energy + rotational kinetic energy +} \\ \text{electronic kinetic energy + electronic potential energy} \\ \text{+ nuclear kinetic energy + } \cdots \end{array} \right) \right]$$

(3.36)

where the summation is over all N_A atoms.
This is what we should have used in place of $N_A(\frac{1}{2}\overline{mu^2})$ in the numerator of eq. (3.34)! The fact that $C_{V,m}$ is constant at $3R/2$ independent of T—that is of $\frac{1}{2}\overline{mu^2}$—can only mean that

$$\frac{\delta(\text{rotational kinetic energy})}{\delta(\frac{1}{2}\overline{mu^2})} = 0$$

and similarly for all the following terms in eq. (3.36). Thus to get agreement with experiment one must be able to show why, for example, the rotational kinetic energy does not change as $\frac{1}{2}\overline{mu^2}$ changes; in other words we must be able to show why when two gas atoms collide more and more violently they do not spin more and more rapidly. It is true that we could explain this classically if the atoms happen to be quite smooth (perfect billiard balls colliding in *space* would not set one another rotating). What we cannot explain from the laws of classical mechanics is why the electrons do not run around more rapidly—even why the nucleus does not vibrate more rapidly—as the atoms collide more violently.

Diatomic gases

Unlike that of a monatomic gas, the heat capacity of a diatomic gas varies with temperature. Figure 3.11 shows how the molar heat capacity of hydrogen depends on temperature. Only at temperatures of less than about 50 K does $C_{V,m}$ have a value of $3R/2$, a value reminiscent of that of a monatomic gas.

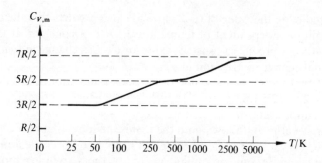

Fig. 3.11 The molar heat capacity at constant volume of gaseous hydrogen plotted against temperature.

As the temperature is raised above 50 K the molar heat capacity starts increasing, and by about 300 K it has levelled off at $5R/2$, only to start increasing again at around 1000 K towards $7R/2$. Why should something start to happen at about 50 K and again at about 1000 K? In other words why, at these temperatures, should the total energy of the molecules start to depend on T, that is on $\frac{1}{2}m\overline{u^2}$? You would expect from classical mechanics that as two dumb-bell-shaped molecules collide (hydrogen is a dumb-bell-shaped molecule, Fig. 2.13) they would spin (and vibrate) more rapidly the more violent the collision. Indeed classical mechanics, when applied in detail, shows that as $\frac{1}{2}m\overline{u^2}$ increases so does the average vibrational energy and the average rotational energy. They all increase in step—$C_{V,m}$ should be constant!

When one makes a classical calculation of the mean speed at which the two atoms in a hydrogen molecule vibrate back and forth—this is a straightforward classical problem which we look at (in a different context) in a later chapter—and from its speed calculates the de Broglie wavelength $\lambda = h/mv$ it turns out that λ is comparable to the molecular dimensions. Small wonder then that classical mechanics made wrong predictions! When brought to bear on the problem, wave mechanics can, in fact, fully account for the form of Fig. 3.11.

Summary

1. A substance exists as a gas when the mean translational kinetic energy $\frac{1}{2}m\overline{u^2}$ of its constituent atoms greatly exceed the dissociation energy ΔE of a pair of atoms, as a solid when $\frac{1}{2}m\overline{u^2} \ll \Delta E$, and as a liquid when $\frac{1}{2}m\overline{u^2} \approx \Delta E$.
2. If a system composed of atoms possessing a mean kinetic energy $\frac{1}{2}M\overline{U^2}$ is in thermal contact with a second system composed of atoms possessing a mean kinetic energy $\frac{1}{2}m\overline{u^2}$, there will be a net transfer of energy from the first to the second system if $\frac{1}{2}M\overline{U^2} > \frac{1}{2}m\overline{u^2}$, from the second to the first when $\frac{1}{2}M\overline{U^2} < \frac{1}{2}m\overline{u^2}$, and there will be no net transfer of energy when $\frac{1}{2}M\overline{U^2} = \frac{1}{2}m\overline{u^2}$.

3. A temperature T on the perfect gas scale is defined by

$$T = 273 \cdot 16 \text{ K } \frac{\lim_{p \to 0} (pV_m)}{\lim_{p \to 0} (pV_m)_{tr}}$$

and a set of "rules" about the design of the instrument and the computational procedures to be followed in processing the readings.

4. Provided one accepts a particular microscopic model of a gas, it can be shown that

$$T = \frac{2}{3k} \left(\tfrac{1}{2} m \overline{u^2} \right)$$

where k (Boltzmann's constant) is determined experimentally.

5. Classical physics can (with much "persuasion") explain the measured heat capacities of monatomic gases; it cannot explain the temperature dependent heat capacities of diatomic gases.

PROBLEMS

3.1 An atom of mass m moving with velocity u makes a head-on elastic collision with another atom of mass m which is at rest. Show that the impact will result in the moving atom coming to rest and the atom which was at rest moving off with velocity u.

3.2 An atom of mass m moving with velocity u makes an oblique collision with another atom of mass m which is at rest. (An oblique collision is one in which the path followed is not along the line joining the centres of the two atoms.) Show that if the collision is elastic, the paths of the two atoms after impact make an angle of 90° with each other. (Clues: Remember that momentum is a vector, so the momenta may be added vectorially. Also recall Pythagoras' theorem.)

3.3 Air consists mainly of a mixture of some 75% N_2 and some 23% O_2. What is the ratio of the mean translational kinetic energy of a nitrogen molecule to that of an oxygen molecule? ($M_r(N_2) = 28$, $M_r(O_2) = 32$.)

3.4 A pollen grain of mass 10^{-21} kg is observed to move with an r.m.s. speed of $3 \cdot 5$ m s^{-1} when it is suspended in water. What is the mean translational kinetic energy of the water molecules?

3.5 Figure 3.12 show an instrument for measuring the speeds of gas atoms. Atoms from the oven O are collimated into a fine beam by being passed through two slits S_1 and S_2. As they travel the distance d they will be bent downwards by the force of gravity. The faster they are travelling the less they will be deflected.

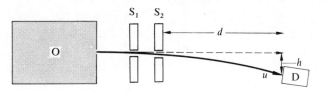

Fig. 3.12 An apparatus for determining the speed of gas atoms.

By moving the detector D in the vertical plane we can measure how many are deflected by a particular amount, and therefore how many atoms are moving with a particular speed. Derive an expression which relates the speed u of an atom arriving at the detector with the detector setting h and the flight path d.

3.6   What, roughly, is the r.m.s. speed of an oxygen molecule in the air surrounding you now?

3.7   The temperature reached during a hydrogen bomb explosion is some 10^8 K. Free nuclei of ^{1}H and ^{2}H are present during the explosion. Assuming thermal equilibrium to exist, what is the ratio of the r.m.s. speed of a proton to that of a deuteron (a ^{2}H nucleus)? Assume that a proton and a neutron have the same mass.

3.8(a) In one form of gas thermometer the volume of the gas is held constant—the pressure p of the gas being adjusted so as to maintain a constant volume. The pressure is recorded first with the bulb surrounded by water at its triple point, then with the bulb surrounded by the substance whose temperature is required. If the ratio of the second of these pressures to the first is 2·00, what is the temperature of the substance?

   (b) In another, more unusual, form of gas thermometer the pressure is held constant while the volume is recorded with the bulb surrounded first by water at its triple point, and then by the substance whose temperature is required. If the ratio of the second of these volumes to the first is 2·00 what is the temperature of the substance?

3.9   Assuming a hard-sphere repulsive model between a Na^+ and a Cl^- ion (as you did in problem 2.10) make a rough estimate of the melting (or fusion) temperature T_f of solid sodium chloride.

3.10   What roughly is de Broglie wavelength of a hydrogen molecule in gaseous hydrogen at a temperature of 50 K? ($A_r(H) = 1$.)

3.11   When 2 J of energy is fed into a fixed volume of a monatomic gas its temperature rises by 5 K. (a) How much gas is present? (b) What is the change in the molar internal energy? Assume the gas is contained within adiabatic walls.

3.12   Sketch the p–V_m–T surface of a perfect gas. You may find it helpful to first consider projections of, say, isotherms onto the p–V_m plane and of isobars onto the V_m–T plane.

3.13   What is the total kinetic energy of all the atoms present in 5 mol of a perfect gas at a temperature of 150 K?

3.14   Put an upper limit to the temperature that the skin of a supersonic aircraft flying at twice the speed of sound might reach. (Clue: Exercise 3.4.)

4. The Gaseous Phase

We have argued that between two like atoms there is a "short-ranged attractive force, followed by an even shorter-ranged repulsive force" and how, as a result of this interaction, it takes a finite energy ΔE to dissociate any pair of atoms which may form. We have also argued that in a many-atom system, clustering of atoms into groups will not occur if their mean translational kinetic energy $\frac{1}{2}m\overline{u^2}$ greatly exceeds ΔE. Under these conditions the system will consist of individual atoms (or molecules) moving about rapidly with no affinity for one another. Although we suggested that this is the situation in a gas, firm predictions rather than hunches are called for. So we shall try to predict, say, the pressure required to contain a gas. If the predictions are not confirmed by experiment we shall have to modify our model, make fresh predictions, and test them afresh. Only when we are satisfied with the level of agreement between "theory" and "experiment" do we call it a day. In a new subject area a 50 per cent discrepancy would often be tolerated—even regarded as providing firm proof that the underlying model was not seriously in error! In a venerable subject area—and gas pressure has been studied for well over a hundred years—one might not call it a day until discrepancies were down in the tenths of a per cent range. As we make a fairly detailed study of the gas pressure you will see something of the frustrations—and hopefully something of the joys—of trying to marry theory to experiment.

4.1   The perfect gas

The model of a gas summarized in the relation

$$\tfrac{1}{2}m\overline{u^2} \gg \Delta E \tag{4.1}$$

is not the only model which is compatible with the observation that to contain a gas requires an externally applied pressure—such as is provided by a piston loaded with weights (Fig. 1.1). Newton, and later Dalton, believed that "corpuscles" of a gas occupy *fixed* positions and fill the entire space available to them, contracting or expanding as the volume occupied by the gas is reduced or increased. The picture is of a piston and cylinder arrangement filled with something like spongy rubber balls. We must always bear in mind that there are, more often than not, several possible models which "explain" a given phenomenon. Were it not for the fact that this "fixed corpuscle" model is

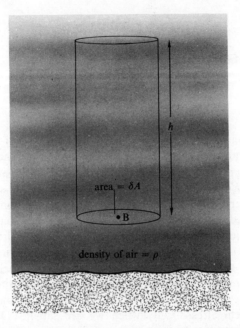

Fig. 4.1 Illustrating a commonly used "explanation" of atmospheric pressure. The pressure at B is supposed to derive from the *weight* of the air molecules overhead.

quite unable to account for the Brownian motion of smoke particles in a gas it would have to be considered further.

Exercise 4.1

Another explanation of gas pressure—an explanation to be found in certain textbooks—runs like this. Consider the situation at some point B in the Earth's atmosphere (Fig. 4.1). The pressure at B is *due to the weight of air overhead*. To find the pressure p we divide the weight of the column of air overhead—this equals the volume of the column ($h \, \delta A$), multiplied by the (mean) density of the air (ρ), multiplied by the acceleration due to gravity (g)—by the cross-sectional area δA. This gives

$$p = \rho g h \tag{4.2}$$

You may find the arguments leading to eq. (4.2) appealing. But in stating that pressure is due to the *weight* of air overhead one is assuming something about the nature of a gas. What is it? Can you think of any properties of a gas which are quite incompatible with this assumed nature of a gas?

Although eq. (4.1) seems to contain within it a possible explanation for why a pressure is required to contain a gas, as it stands the "equation" is difficult to handle. All it says is "consider both the kinetic and potential energy of the atoms, but pay particular attention to their kinetic energy". One simplification which we shall make, at least for the moment, is to assume that in a gas $\frac{1}{2}mu^2$ is so much greater than ΔE that, by comparison, ΔE may be taken as zero. We can naturally expect that predictions made adopting this restriction will be only approximately correct, becoming ever more untrustworthy as $\frac{1}{2}mu^2$ becomes comparable with ΔE. The only alternative would be to consider *ab initio* both the kinetic and the potential energies of the gas atoms. Were we to follow such a path we would soon land ourselves with formidable mathematical problems! So we shall assume that $\Delta E = 0$, calling a gas in which this would hold true a perfect gas. In developing the theory of how such a gas behaves we shall also assume that the atoms have effectively zero size; we incorporate this further assumption, in addition to the assumption that $\Delta E = 0$, in the label *perfect gas*.

4.2 The pressure of a perfect gas

Our goal is to derive an expression for the pressure p required to contain a perfect gas in terms of quantities like the mass of the individual gas atoms, their number per unit volume, and their speed. In other words, we shall try to relate a macroscopic property—here pressure—with the properties of the constituent atoms. Whatever relation we end up with it should be capable of experimental verification.

In essence, our explanation as to why we must keep pushing on a piston in order to contain a gas is that the gas atoms are continually colliding with the piston and we are continually having to send these atoms back into the body of the gas. If we do not send them back the gas will not remain contained! It is as if we are playing an endless game of tennis with the gas. Each time a gas atom strikes the piston we must first stop it, and then send it back; to do this, of course, requires a force. That then is the qualitative picture—we must now quantify it. In doing so we shall find it helpful to split the discussion up into a number of discrete chunks.

A single collision

Figure 4.2 shows a single gas atom colliding with a piston. We—and it may help to translate this to *I,* meaning yourself—must send that atom back into the body of the gas. Now we cannot send an atom back into the body of the gas without, at least, changing its direction and therefore its momentum. To change the momentum of an object requires an impulse. So we must consider how the force F which we exert on the piston changes with time (t).

Quite clearly, we exert no force on the piston until the colliding atom actually starts to make contact with the piston. As soon as contact is made, we

87

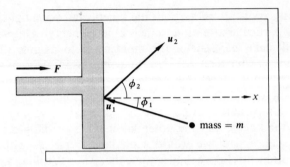

Fig. 4.2   A single atom of mass m strikes a piston with velocity $\boldsymbol{u}_1$ and rebounds with velocity $\boldsymbol{u}_2$.

must start pushing so as to slow the colliding atom down and to bring it to a temporary halt. To return the atom to the body of the gas we must *keep pushing in the same direction* until such time as the colliding atom has ceased to be in contact with the piston. We then stop pushing. So the force we must provide throughout the collision will vary in the manner suggested in Fig. 4.3. If you are still uncertain as to why it has this form follow through the arguments again, but this time think of the atom as a tennis ball and the piston as a racket. As the ball flattens itself on the strings you push, bringing the ball to a momentary halt. To make the ball leave the racket you keep pushing in the same direction, and only cease to push when the ball has left the racket.

Just as in the example of the tennis racket, it is unnecessary for the person holding the piston to move the piston inwards. We shall assume in fact that

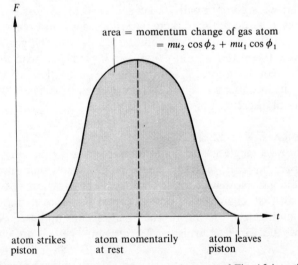

Fig. 4.3   Showing how the force F required to return the atom of Fig. 4.2 into the body of the gas might vary with time.

the position of the piston is fixed—were it to be moved in energy would be fed into the gas.

Newton's second law tells us that the change in the momentum of a body is equal to the impulse of the force causing that change. The impulse is defined as $\int F \, dt$ or—the same thing—as the area under the curve showing how the force varies with time. This area is shown shaded in Fig. 4.3. That is,

$$\int F \, dt = mu_2 - mu_1 \tag{4.3}$$

Since the force F is applied perpendicular to the piston face the net change in momentum of the atom will lie along this direction. Resolving the momentum of the atom, before and after impact, along this direction and equating the change to the impulse gives

$$\int F \, dt = mu_2 \cos \phi_2 - m(-u_1 \cos \phi_1)$$

i.e.,

$$\int F \, dt = mu_2 \cos \phi_2 + mu_1 \cos \phi_1 \tag{4.4}$$

where ϕ_1 and ϕ_2 are the angles between the normal to the piston and the incident and rebound directions respectively (Fig. 4.2) and u_1 and u_2 are the *speed* (that is, the magnitude of the velocity) of the atom before and after impact. The negative sign in $(-u_1 \cos \phi_1)$ indicates that the component of u_1 along the normal to the piston face (of magnitude $u_1 \cos \phi_1$) is directed towards the face. You can see that eq. (4.4) makes sense by considering what happens if a car of mass 10^3 kg strikes a wall at a speed of 5 m s^{-1} and bounces off at a speed of 5 m s^{-1}. Assuming $\phi_1 = \phi_2 = 0$ the change in momentum of the car is 5×10^3 kg m s^{-1} + 5×10^3 kg m s^{-1}. If there were a minus sign in eq. (4.4) the change in momentum of the car would be zero—the wall would exert no force on the car (and the car none on the wall)!

We also know that since there is no force acting parallel to the face of the piston there can be no change in momentum of the atom along this direction, i.e.,

$$0 = mu_2 \sin \phi_2 - mu_1 \sin \phi_1 \tag{4.5}$$

As just stated, eq. (4.5) is a lie! All we know is that on average—averaged over a great many collisions—there can be no net change in momentum in a direction parallel to the piston face. In any individual collision the colliding gas atom may well change its component of momentum parallel to the piston face—the gas atom is, after all, not colliding with the smooth piston we have indicated in Fig. 4.2 but with a very rough piston composed of individual atoms (as in Fig. 3.3(a)). So eq. (4.5) should have been written

$$0 = \overline{mu_2 \sin \phi_2} - \overline{mu_1 \sin \phi_1}$$

$$\overline{mu_1 \sin \phi_1} = \overline{mu_2 \sin \phi_2} \tag{4.6}$$

Equation (4.4) does apply at each individual collision, on the understanding that F is the force provided locally as the gas atom makes contact with the piston. Ultimately we want an expression for the mean force which the person pushing on the piston must provide. We are still a long way from this goal for, even if we knew u_1, u_2, ϕ_1, and ϕ_2 in eq. (4.4), we cannot calculate the force F without knowing how it varies with time. The problem is made no easier if we assume—for the sake of simplicity—that F remains constant during an impact time Δt as shown in Fig. 4.4. A constant F implies that the gas atom is decelerated to rest at a constant rate for a time $\Delta t/2$ and then accelerated away from rest at the same rate for time $\Delta t/2$. Under these circumstances eq. (4.4) becomes

$$F\Delta t = mu_2 \cos \phi_2 + mu_1 \cos \phi_1 \tag{4.7}$$

so, once more, we see that to determine F we seemingly must know Δt. The problem facing us is underlined in exercise 4.2. Only spend a minute or two at most on this exercise.

Exercise 4.2

A helium atom $(A_r(\text{He}) = 4)$ travelling at a speed of 500 m s^{-1} strikes a piston in a direction perpendicular to its face and rebounds in the same direction with unaltered speed. Given that the atom covered a distance of 3×10^{-6} m immediately prior to striking the piston, in a time 6×10^{-9} s, what force F must the piston provide? Assume that F remains constant throughout the collision?

There is in fact no easy way of finding Δt for a single collision. Newtonian mechanics insists that the time of impact be known if F is to be calculated.

Any new information is welcome! So far we have made no mention of the

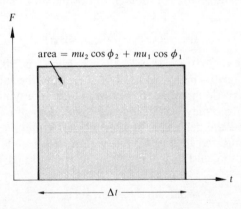

Fig. 4.4 A (hypothetical) collision where the force F required to return an atom into the body of a gas is assumed to be constant with time.

kinetic energy of the gas atom either before or after impact. Now we know that if thermal equilibrium exists—meaning that, on average, there is no net transfer of energy between the piston and the gas—the *average* kinetic energy of the gas atom must be the same before and after impacting with the piston (section 3.4); that is

$$\tfrac{1}{2}m\overline{u_1^2} = \tfrac{1}{2}m\overline{u_2^2} \tag{4.8}$$

We now have three equations with which to play about! Equations (4.6) and (4.8) only tell us about what happens on average—averaged over many collisions with the piston—while eq. (4.4) does tell us about an individual collision.

Before we discuss the effect of many collisions with the piston we are going to introduce a deliberate cheat. (The cheat is strictly speaking unnecessary but, without it, the ongoing mathematics gets extremely cumbersome.) We are going to assume that eqs. (4.6) and (4.8) hold, not on average, but in *each and every* collision of a gas atom with the piston. That is, we are assuming

$$mu_1 \sin \phi_1 = mu_2 \sin \phi_2 \tag{4.9}$$

and

$$\tfrac{1}{2}mu_1^2 = \tfrac{1}{2}mu_2^2 \tag{4.10}$$

On the basis of this assumption eq. (4.10) tells us that

$$u_1 = u_2 \tag{4.11}$$

Applying eq. (4.11) to eq. (4.9) gives

$$\sin \phi_1 = \sin \phi_2$$
$$\phi_1 = \phi_2 \tag{4.12}$$

Equation (4.4) therefore becomes, on using eqs. (4.11) and (4.12)

$$\int F \, dt = 2mu_1 \cos \phi_1 \tag{4.13}$$

The effect of many collisions

We now look at the consequences of many collisions, each of which produces an effect which is summarized in eq. (4.13). We shall concentrate our attention on a particular area δA of the piston and examine what is the net effect of the many collisions which occur with δA in a time interval of t. We shall start the discussion by classifying the gas atoms according to their speed and to the angle which their paths up to the piston make with the normal to the piston face. To begin with we shall look only at those atoms moving up towards δA with a particular speed u_i at an angle ϕ_i to the normal (Fig. 4.5) and shall ask how many collisions such atoms will make with δA in a time t.

The number of collisions may be found by drawing in a cylinder of length

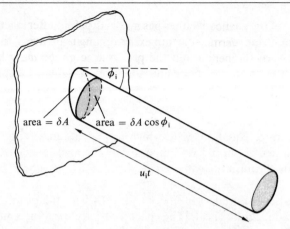

Fig. 4.5 The number of atoms moving at speed u_i and at angle ϕ_i with the normal that will strike δA during a time t is equal to all those within the cylinder shown of length $u_i t$ and cross-sectional area $\delta A \cos \phi_i$.

$u_i t$, as shown in Fig. 4.5, whose axis makes an angle ϕ_i with the normal to the piston. All those atoms lying within this cylinder moving at a speed u_i along a path parallel to the axis of the cylinder will strike δA in time t. (An analogue may help. Consider a single-lane road along which all the cars are travelling at a steady 50 m.p.h. The number of cars which will pass any point alongside the road within the next $\frac{1}{2}$ hour will be all those at present within a distance of $(50 \times \frac{1}{2})$ mile from the point in question.) There are, of course, other atoms which will strike δA in time t—they will be considered presently. Therefore:

the number of atoms possessing a velocity $\boldsymbol{u}_i$ that collide with δA in time t

= number within a cylinder of length $u_i t$ and cross-sectional area $\delta A \cos \phi_i$

= number within a cylinder of volume $u_i t \, \delta A \cos \phi_i$

= (volume of the cylinder) × (number of atoms per unit volume with speed u_i and moving at angle ϕ_i)

= $n_i' u_i t \, \delta A \cos \phi_i$ (4.14)

where n'_i is the number of atoms per unit volume possessing a speed u_i and moving at an angle ϕ_i to the normal with the piston.

Every time one of these atoms strikes the piston, as in Fig. 4.6, we must push, so changing the momentum of the atom. With many such atoms colliding we must provide a whole series of impulses as shown in Fig. 4.7. We have no knowledge of the shape of these "blips"—all we know is the area of each. It follows from eq. (4.13) that each "blip" has an area $\int F \, dt = 2mu_i \cos \phi_i$. We also know (eq. (4.14)) that there are $n'_i u_i t \, \delta A \cos \phi_i$ such "blips" in time t.

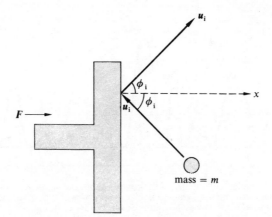

Fig. 4.6 Shows a single atom of mass m moving at speed u_i along a path making angle ϕ_i to the normal strike a piston and rebound with unchanged speed along a new path also making an angle ϕ_i to the normal. (Both paths shown are in the plane of the paper.)

So far we have only considered one particular "class" of atoms—those moving at a speed u_i along direction ϕ_i. However exactly the same arguments hold for all classes of atoms; every time an atom strikes the piston we must provide an impulse and each individual impulse equals the change in momentum of a particular atom. Overall we therefore provide a sequence of impulses as shown in Fig. 4.8.

But keeping the gas in a sealed bicycle pump requires a *constant* pressure!

The steady force

The apparently constant force $\bar{F}$ which we provide as we contain a gas is, in fact, of such a magnitude that the area $\bar{F}t$ is equal to the total area under all the "blips" (Fig. 4.8). That is, the observed impulse $\bar{F}t$ is equal to the sum of all the individual impulses. It is not easy to prove this result theoretically without

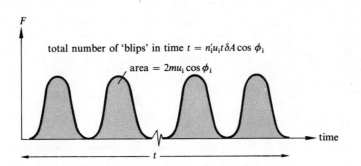

Fig. 4.7 Shows the sequence of impulses necessary to change the momentum of a stream of atoms incident on a piston. Each atom is supposed to have the same momentum and to behave as in Fig. 4.6.

93

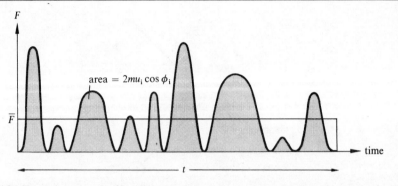

Fig. 4.8 Shows the sequence of impulses necessary to change the momentum of a stream of atoms. Each "blip" represents the impulse required to change the momentum of an individual atom. The atoms have different momenta but each is supposed to behave as in Fig. 4.6.

analysing the mechanics of the device supplying the force F. It is possible to check it out experimentally using large scale objects like marbles. If you drop an individual glass marble onto a horizontal plate attached to a suitable balance (Fig. 4.9(a)) then for it to rebound the balance spring must push up on the marble—it must provide the impulse shown in Fig. 4.9(b). This impulse can, of course, be recorded by observing how the force F provided by the balance changes with time. (Actually the balance records the reaction force of the marble on the plate and not the force of the plate on the marble—the action. However Newton's third law tells us the two forces are equal in magnitude.) Next we can drop, in rapid succession (Fig. 4.10(a)) a total of, say, N balls over a time t and measure the apparently constant force $\bar{F}$ which will be observed on the balance (Fig. 4.10(b)). One finds that $\bar{F}t = N(2MU)$, where U is the speed with which the marble strikes and leaves the plate. Applied to the problem of the gas in the cylinder (Fig. 4.8) we can therefore write

$$\bar{F}t = \text{total area of all the "blips" occurring in time } t$$

$$\bar{F}t = \sum (n_i' u_i t \, \delta A \cos \phi_i) \times (2mu_i \cos \phi_i) \qquad (4.15)$$

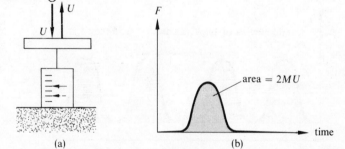

Fig. 4.9 (a) A glass marble dropped onto a massive plate rebounds with essentially unaltered speed. (b) Shows the impulse provided by the balance as it changes the momentum of the marble in (a).

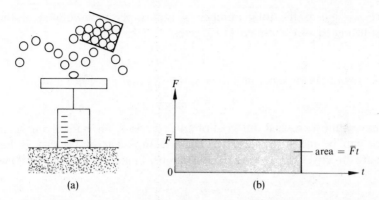

Fig. 4.10   (a) Showing a stream of N balls being dropped onto a massive plate during a time t. The balance reading remains sensibly constant .(b) The overall impulse provided by the balance.

The first term inside the summation of eq. (4.15) is the number of collisions of class i with the piston, that is the number of "blips" occurring in time t. The second term gives the change in the momentum of an atom of class i between striking and leaving the piston, that is it gives the area of an individual "blip". But $u_i \cos \phi_i$ is the component u_{xi} of the velocity of the atom along the normal to the piston face, which we shall take as the x-direction (Fig. 4.6). So eq. (4.15) becomes

$$\bar{F}t = 2 \sum mn'_i u^2_{xi} t \, \delta A$$

$$\bar{F} = 2 \, \delta A \sum mn'_i u^2_{xi} \qquad (4.16)$$

where n'_i is, you will recall, the number of atoms per unit volume with a speed u_i moving up towards the piston along a path making an angle ϕ_i with the normal to the piston (i.e., n'_i is the number of atoms per unit volume with a component speed u_{xi} such that $u_i \cos \phi_i = u_{xi}$). At any instant only half the population of the gas is, on average, moving towards the piston. If n_i is the total number of atoms per unit volume with a component speed u_{xi} it follows therefore that $n'_i = \frac{1}{2}n_i$. Equation (4.16) therefore becomes

$$\bar{F} = \delta A \, m \sum n_i u^2_{xi} \qquad (4.17)$$

This equation may be written somewhat differently by appealing to the definition of mean square speed:

$$\overline{u^2_x} = \frac{\sum n_i u^2_{xi}}{\sum n_i}$$

or

$$\sum n_i u^2_{xi} = \overline{u^2_x} \sum n_i = \overline{u^2_x} n \qquad (4.18)$$

The Gaseous Phase

where $n = \sum n_i$ is the total number of atoms per unit volume of the gas. Substituting eq. (4.18) into eq. (4.17) gives

$$\bar{F} = \delta A \, mn\overline{u_x^2}$$

Since pressure is force per unit area, it follows that $p = \bar{F}/\delta A$ and so

$$p = mn\overline{u_x^2} \tag{4.19}$$

We have almost reached our goal of an expression for p involving quantities which can be measured directly. The x-component of velocity is hard to measure directly. On the other hand u can be. In section 3.4 (eq. (3.15)) we saw that

$$\overline{u^2} = \overline{u_x^2} + \overline{u_y^2} + \overline{u_z^2} \tag{4.20}$$

where u_y and u_z are the magnitudes of the velocity components in the y- and z-directions. Since the measured pressure of a gas is the same in all directions, specifically in the x-, y-, and z-directions, it follows from eq. (4.19) that

$$\overline{u_x^2} = \overline{u_y^2} = \overline{u_z^2} \tag{4.21}$$

So eq. (4.20) becomes

$$\overline{u^2} = 3\overline{u_x^2}$$

$$\overline{u_x^2} = \tfrac{1}{3}\overline{u^2}$$

enabling eq. (4.19) to be written as

$$p = \tfrac{1}{3}mn\overline{u^2} \tag{4.22}$$

for the pressure required to contain a perfect gas whose atoms possess a mean square speed of $\overline{u^2}$ and in which there are n atoms (each of mass m) per unit volume. You should immediately check to see whether the units are the same on both sides of eq. (4.22). If they are different the equation is certainly wrong. If they are the same, the equation may still be wrong!

Equation (4.22) may be written somewhat differently by writing $n = N/V$, where N is the total number of atoms present and V is the volume of the gas:

$$p = \tfrac{1}{3}m\frac{N}{V}\overline{u^2}$$

$$pV = \tfrac{1}{3}mN\overline{u^2}$$

If there are n mol of gas present then, because each mole contains N_A atoms, $N = nN_A$, and so

$$pV = \tfrac{1}{3}mnN_A\overline{u^2}$$

$$pV_m = \tfrac{2}{3}N_A(\tfrac{1}{2}m\overline{u^2}) \tag{4.23}$$

where $V_m = V/n$ is the molar volume of the gas.

4.3   Experimental checks

As it stands eq. (4.22) does little more than herald the completion of a some-what lengthy cerebral exercise. Unless it can make predictions—predictions which can be tested experimentally—it is sterile.

Direct checks

Let us look for ideas. We know we can measure $\overline{u^2}$ using time-of-flight techniques (p. 70). Therefore we rewrite eq. (4.22) to give an expression for $\overline{u^2}$:

$$\overline{u^2} = \frac{3p}{mn}$$

Since m is the mass of an individual atom (or molecule) and n is their number per unit volume, it follows that mn is the density ρ of the gas. Therefore

$$\overline{u^2} = \frac{3p}{\rho} \tag{4.24}$$

If the experimentally measured value of $\overline{u^2}$ in a gas agrees with the value of $\overline{u^2}$ predicted by substituting the density and pressure of the gas into eq. (4.24) then this equation, and the assumptions underlying it, *may* be vindicated. But only *may*; two wrongs could have produced a right!

Using the type of apparatus shown in Fig. 3.6, the mean square (m.s.) speed of the atoms within the container C can be calculated from the m.s. speed of the atoms in the beam emerging from C (see exercise 3.2). This can then be compared with the m.s. speed calculated from eq. (4.24) (using the pressure p and density ρ of the gas in C). Both values agree to within the experimental errors; typically some 5–10 per cent. This particular test is hardly very searching since the gas pressure in the oven must be kept at a small fraction of atmospheric pressure.

If we are only interested in a rough and ready check of eq. (4.24) we do not need atomic beams; we simply measure the speed at which sound travels in a gas.

Without examining in depth how sound is transmitted through a gas it would be surprising if the speed of sound exceeded the mean speed of the gas atoms. It is they, after all, who pass on the message! So it seems reasonable to guess that the speed of sound is approximately equal to the mean atomic speed $\bar{u}$. Although $\bar{u}$ and $(\overline{u^2})^{1/2}$ are not identical they are close in value. (You can check that this is so by calculating $\bar{u}$ and $(\overline{u^2})^{1/2}$ from the data given in exercise 3.2.) We shall discover later (p. 209) that $(\overline{u^2})^{1/2} = 1\cdot08\bar{u}$ in a gas.

Exercise 4.3

At sea-level air has a density of about $1\cdot2$ kg m^{-3} and is usually at a pressure of about $1\cdot0 \times 10^5$ Pa. What value does eq. (4.24) predict for the r.m.s. speed of the air molecules? Try to measure the speed at which sound travels in air by timing an echo off, say, a distant wall. Remember that we are only looking for rough and ready agreement between the speed of sound and the r.m.s. molecular speed so a crude timing of the echo will suffice.

Introducing the temperature

You may have noticed that in this chapter we have avoided "temperature" like the plague! Now to inject into the discussion what we learnt in the last chapter.

To begin with, we showed in section 3.5 that at constant temperature (even as the word is understood by Everyman) $\frac{1}{2}m\overline{u^2}$ is constant. So eq. (4.23) becomes

$$pV_m = \text{constant, at constant temperature} \tag{4.25}$$

Figure 4.11 shows the results of experimental studies of how pV_m depends on p for gaseous hydrogen, nitrogen, oxygen, and carbon dioxide, all of which are maintained at the triple point of water. Evidently pV_m is anything but constant, independent of p, as it should be according to eq. (4.25). However notice that each pressure division in Fig. 4.11 is 2×10^7 Pa, which is some 200 times atmospheric pressure. At much lower pressures (up to about normal atmospheric pressure) pV_m does indeed remain nearly constant at a fixed temperature. This is shown in Fig. 4.12—you can see that with these gases pV_m changes by less than 1 per cent. This constancy of pV_m at a fixed temperature is probably already familiar to you as *Boyle's Law*.

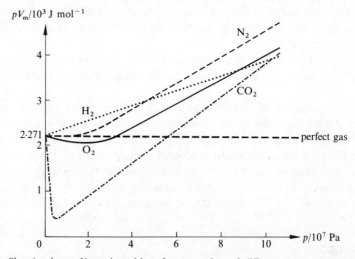

Fig. 4.11 Showing how pV_m varies with p for a number of different gases all maintained at 273·16 K. A perfect gas would have $pV_m = RT = 8·314 \times 273·16$ J mol^{-1} = $2·271 \times 10^3$ J mol^{-1}. A pressure of 10^8 Pa is about a thousand times normal atmospheric pressure.

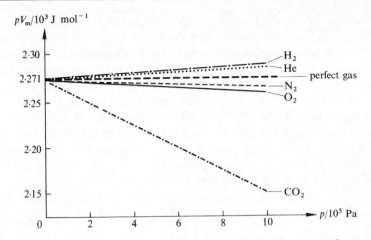

Fig. 4.12 Showing how pV_m varies with p for gaseous carbon dioxide, oxygen, nitrogen helium, and hydrogen all maintained at 273·16 K. Normal atmospheric pressure is about $1·0 \times 10^5$ Pa.

In chapter 3 we went on to define a temperature T on the perfect gas scale. To quote eq. (3.26), the temperature T of a real gas is related to the limiting value of (pV_m) as $p \to 0$ by

$$\lim_{p \to 0}(pV_m) = RT \qquad (4.26)$$

where R (defined by eq. (3.27)) is determined experimentally, and has a value of $8·314$ J K^{-1} mol^{-1}. Since the experiments shown in Figs. 4.11 and 4.12 were performed at the triple point, where $T = 273·16$ K, eq. (4.26) predicts that the limiting value of pV_m as $p \to 0$ is...easy on, we are about to fall into a trap! If you study p. 75 again you will see how R is measured experimentally using the very limiting procedure shown in Fig. 4.12! So we must look at what happens at temperatures other than the triple point.

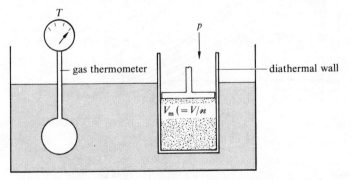

Fig. 4.13 An apparatus for obtaining (p, V_m, T) data on a gas. The piston and cylinder arrangement containing the gas under investigation is in thermal contact with a constant temperature bath, whose temperature can be measured with a gas thermometer.

Figure 4.13 shows the type of set-up one might use to explore how pV_m depends on T. The gas under investigation is contained in a piston and cylinder arrangement which is in thermal contact with a bath whose temperature is measured with a gas thermometer. Experimentally, we would fix T—measuring it with the gas thermometer—and study how V_m depended on p. We would next choose a new fixed temperature and repeat the study. We might decide to plot our data as a p–V_m–T surface—we would be much more likely though to represent it as a series of isothermal lines in the p–V_m plane. Figure 4.14 shows such isotherms for carbon dioxide. Were carbon dioxide a perfect gas it would satisfy eq. (4.26) at all pressures; we would not have to take the limit as $p \to 0$. It would therefore obey the relation

$$pV_m = RT \qquad (4.27)$$

the *equation of state of a perfect gas*.

Equation (4.27) predicts that the isotherms should be hyperbolic in shape ($pV_m = $ constant is the equation of a rectangular hyperbola). The dotted

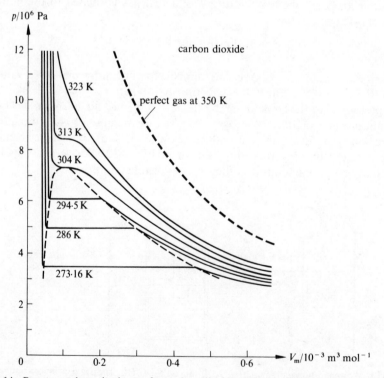

Fig. 4.14 Pressure–volume isotherms for carbon dioxide. The dotted lines show how carbon dioxide would behave were it a perfect gas.

isotherm labelled $T = 350$ K has been drawn assuming eq. (4.27). Quite clearly at low temperatures the isotherms are anything but hyperbolic! Something is very wrong.

If one is intentionally searching out departures from perfect gas law behaviour (eq. (4.27)) it is revealing to plot pV_m/RT against p at different T; revealing because, were the gas perfect, pV_m/RT would equal unity at all pressures and temperatures. Departures of a plot from unity are easy to spot. It is always good practice on checking out a theoretical prediction to plot the experimental data so as clearly to bring out any possible *departures* from the form predicted for it. (This advice is not so easy to follow when you yourself propound the theory!) The pressure and temperature dependence of pV_m/RT is shown in Fig. 4.15 for carbon dioxide. There is now no doubt as to the imperfect nature of the gas. At pressure below about 10^5 Pa, pV_m/RT departs from unity by less than 1 per cent, a fact already recorded in Fig. 4.12, albeit in a different form.

In passing it is worth noting that the equation of state of a perfect gas may be rewritten somewhat differently by substituting $R = N_A k$, where k is Boltzmann's constant (eq. (3.30)). Equation (4.27) then becomes

$$p = \frac{N_A}{V_m} kT$$

Since one mole contains N_A atoms and occupies a volume V_m it follows that N_A/V_m is n, the number of atoms per unit volume; giving

$$p = nkT \tag{4.28}$$

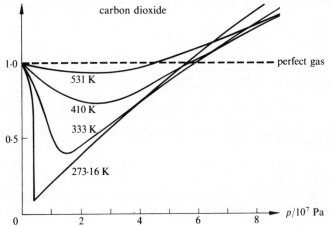

Fig. 4.15 The pressure dependence of pV_m/RT at different temperatures for carbon dioxide.

101

4.4 The assumptions analysed

Whenever one finds that theory and experiment disagree there are several possible courses of action. But before taking any action there are several precautions to be observed.

Are you really satisfied that the experiments were conducted properly? Suppose, for the sake of argument, that the gas cylinder were to leak at high pressures—could that explain the departure from the predicted behavior? So have you looked at results obtained in different laboratories using a variety of experimental techniques (they cannot all have leaky cylinders)? Is the breakdown specific to one substance—or is it more general? Then in looking at the theoretical side, are there any mistakes in the mathematics (this is not unknown)? More likely, have any mathematical approximations been introduced which limit the range of conditions over which the theory should apply (theoreticians do not always spell this out)? If these approximations could be removed, would this materially alter the theoretical predictions?

Assuming that these precautions—and this list is by no means complete—have been followed, disagreement between theory and experiment can usually only mean that something is wrong with the model on which the theory rests. To build a radically new model often calls for a touch of genius! But this is not the only path which is open. You might, and this is not to be dismissed out of hand, decide to "adjust" the theoretical expression so that it fits the experimental results. In following such an *empirical* (or *phenomenological*) approach one may sometimes, through the very act of trying to fit a variety of different expressions, get a clue as to what is wrong with the model. Yet another approach, and this is the one which we shall adopt, is to devise experiments to test the correctness, or otherwise, of the assumptions underlying the theory. When we know the results of these tests we can then decide on the most appropriate action. It might be that the model only requires touching up after all.

Exercise 4.4

List what you consider to be the key assumptions introduced in the course of developing eq. (4.22).

We are now ready to examine these assumptions; the order in which we do so is immaterial.

Immediate rebound

In sketching out how the force which the piston exerts on a gas atom varies with time (Fig. 4.3) we assumed that the gas atom is only momentarily at rest; as soon as it has been decelerated to rest it is immediately accelerated away again. But do gas atoms rebound immediately after being brought to rest?

Evidence that gas atoms do "stick" (or "dwell", or "linger") on a surface for some time before leaving first came from experiments performed in the 1920s. One type of apparatus used in these early studies is illustrated in Fig. 4.16. A narrow beam of gas atoms, which has been collimated in the usual way by being passed through a series of apertures, impinges on a rotating disc at a point S. If these atoms stick they will be carried along on the rotating surface. A movable detector enables one to measure the number which survive the journey to the point D on the disc, opposite the detector entrance, and which are desorbed at this point. By varying either the position of the detector, or the speed of rotation of the disc, the number of atoms that stick on the surface for various known times can be found. (The times are deduced, of course, from the angle DOS and the speed of rotation of the disc.) Early experiments showed that the average dwell times of an inert gas atom on a steel or glass surface were in the millisecond to microsecond range. Steel and glass are, of course, just the materials one might use in constructing a piston and cylinder arrangement or the bulb of a gas thermometer. Times of 10^{-3} s to 10^{-6} s are certainly long compared with, say, the 10^{-10} s that a molecule in air at room temperature and pressure spends in travelling up to a surface from the point in the gas when it last suffered a collision. Such long dwell times allow the colliding gas atoms to exchange momentum and energy with the atoms of the surface. Only with particularly clean surfaces which have been carefully prepared under high vacuum conditions does one observe dwell times of order 10^{-13} s (at 300 K).

Specular reflection

In the course of deriving the pressure formula we assumed that the angle of incidence ϕ_1 of an atom striking a piston equals the angle of reflection ϕ_2 after leaving the piston (Figs. 4.2 and 4.6). Since this is how a beam of light behaves on striking a mirror the situation when $\phi_1 = \phi_2$ is called *specular reflection*. The apparatus shown schematically in Fig. 4.17 enables us to test this assumption.

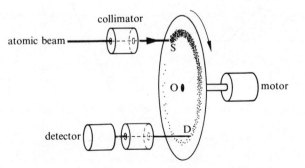

Fig. 4.16 An apparatus for measuring the time a gas atom dwells on a surface. A beam of atoms strikes a rotating disc at S. The number coming off at position D is measured with a detector.

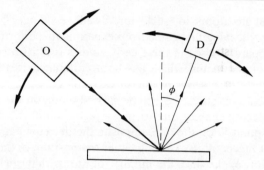

Fig. 4.17 Atoms from an oven O strike a surface. The number scattered in different directions is measured with a detector D.

After collimation, a beam of atoms from oven O strikes the surface of a solid, which may or may not be maintained at the same temperature as the oven. A moveable detector D (usually a bulb with a small hole in it, connected to a sensitive pressure gauge) allows one to measure the number of atoms scattered in different directions from the surface. Figure 4.18 shows the results obtained when a beam of nitrogen atoms incident along a direction IS strikes a polished glass surface. The number scattered (per unit time) along a direction SR is proportional to the length of line SR. Plotted in this way the results lie on a circle. By simple trigonometry, the intensity $I(\phi)$ of the beam scattered through an angle ϕ with the normal to the surface is $d \cos \phi$, where d is the diameter of the circle (Fig. 4.18);

$$I(\phi) \propto \cos \phi \qquad (4.29)$$

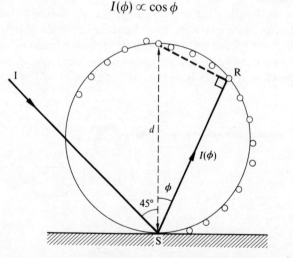

Fig. 4.18 The scattering of nitrogen molecules from a polished glass surface. The beam is incident along IS. The number scattered (per unit time) along a direction SR is proportional to the length of line SR. (Data: Courtesy of F. C. Hurlbut.)

104

Although the beam is shown incident along a particular direction in Fig. 4.18 this *cosine-law* behaviour is true, or nearly true, for all other angles of incidence. The law is closely obeyed by a wide variety of materials (e.g., sheet aluminium, steel, teflon) which have not been specially prepared, other than being "workshop" polished. With polished metal surfaces, for example, some 90–95% of the incident gas atoms are diffusely scattered according to the cosine law.

If, instead of using a piece of metal which has been lying around in the laboratory, one takes a single crystal of a metal and prepares it by raising its temperature to a high value, under an ultra-high vacuum, while it is *in situ* in the apparatus, then the scattered beam no longer obeys the cosine law. (Heating the crystal removes surface impurities; the ultra-high vacuum prevents these being absorbed again.) Figure 4.19 shows the results obtained for a tungsten single crystal at 300 K which is bombarded by a beam of hydrogen molecules at 300 K. When the hydrogen beam first impinges on the clean tungsten surface (Fig. 4.19(a)) approximately 80 per cent of the gas is chemisorbed (meaning it has a near-infinite dwell time) and most of the remaining 20 per cent is scattered diffusely according to the cosine law. Approximately 1 per cent of the incident beam is specularly reflected. Over a period of minutes the surface becomes completely covered with a monolayer of hydrogen. Figure 4.19(b) shows the scattering from such a saturated surface. Now only 35 per cent of the hydrogen molecules are diffusely scattered and most of the remaining 65 per cent are in the broad specularly-directed lobe.

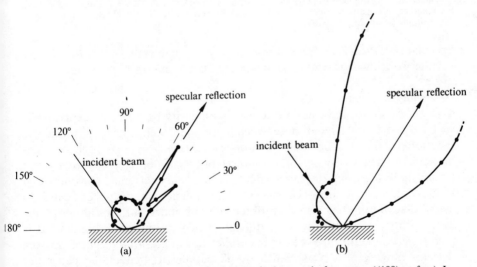

Fig. 4.19 Scattering of hydrogen molecules from a single crystal of tungsten ((100) surface). In (a) the surface is clean; in obtaining the results the surface was flashed to a high temperature between readings. In (b) the surface is covered with a strongly bound monolayer of hydrogen. Both beam and crystal are at 300 K. (Data from D. O. Hayward and M. R. Walters, *Jap. J. Appl. Phys.*, Suppl. 2, Part 2, p. 587, 1974.)

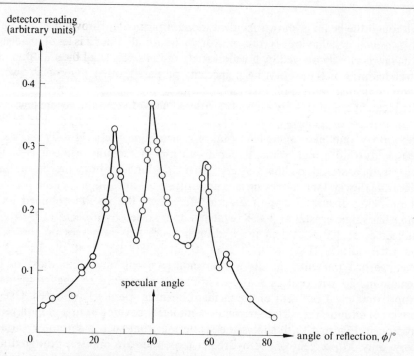

Fig. 4.20 Scattering of hydrogen molecules from a single crystal of tungsten ((100) surface). Both beam and crystal are at 300 K. The beam is incident at an angle of 40° with the normal to the face. The detector is moved in a plane parallel to, but not coincident with, that containing the incident beam and the normal to the surface. (Data from D. O. Hayward and M. R. Walters, *Jap. J. Appl. Phys.*, Suppl. 2, Part 2, p. 587, 1974.)

Specular reflection also occurs from polycrystalline metals *provided* they have been thoroughly degassed by heating them under an ultra-high vacuum.

Newtonian mechanics

You will no doubt have noticed a strong similarity between the experiments we have just described and those which Stern and his colleagues performed as they looked for evidence that de Broglie's relation $\lambda = h/mv$ applies to gas molecules. Their discovery of wave-mechanical scattering of hydrogen and helium molecules from the surface of alkali halide crystals must inevitably cast serious doubts on our use of classical mechanics in deriving eq. (4.22). Such non-classical scattering has also been observed from metal surfaces although the experiments are technically more difficult than with the alkali halides.* It is seen on repeating the type of experiment sketched in Fig. 4.17, this time with the detector moving in a plane which is still parallel to that of the paper but

---

* The potential energy of a gas atom varies much more strongly over the surface of an ionic crystal than over the surface of a metal. Stern *et al.* seem to have been lucky in their choice of material.

106

displaced from it. Figure 4.20 shows such a study for hydrogen molecules scattered from the saturated surface of a single crystal of tungsten. (Here the detector was moved so that the trajectories of molecules entering the detector orifice all made an angle of 9° with the plane of incidence—the plane of the paper in Fig. 4.17.) The maxima other than that at the specular angle can only be explained by wave mechanics. Classical mechanics is however able to account for the main features of in-plane scattering from clean surfaces and for diffuse scattering from dirty surfaces.

Zero dissociation energy and zero size

At the beginning of this chapter we defined a perfect gas to be one in which $\Delta E = 0$ and in which the atoms have effectively zero size. This is equivalent to assuming that the interatomic potential $\mathscr{V}(r)$ has the form shown in Fig. 4.21(b) or, if you prefer it, that the interatomic force $F(r)$ has the form shown in Fig. 4.21(a).

Figure 4.22(a) shows an apparatus designed to look for a finite ΔE. The left-hand chamber contains a gas at pressure p; the right-hand chamber is evacuated. Both chambers are surrounded by an adiabatic wall. The gas can be allowed to expand into the evacuated chamber by removing the dividing wall (Fig. 4.22(b)). If this divider is removed by pulling on it sideways no energy will be transferred from the gas from (or to) the person removing the wall. Under these circumstances the gas is said to undergo *a free expansion*. A

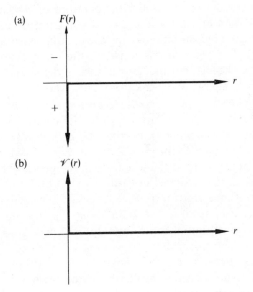

Fig. 4.21 (a) The form of the interatomic force assumed in the definition of a perfect gas. (b) The corresponding interatomic potential energy.

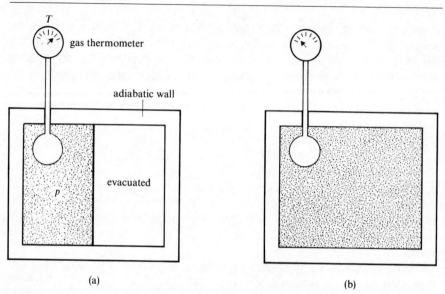

Fig. 4.22 On removing the dividing partition shown in (a) the gas undergoes a free expansion into the right-hand chamber as shown in (b). A thermometer enables one to assess $\frac{1}{2}m\overline{u^2}$ of the gas atoms before and after free expansion has occurred.

thermometer tells us the temperature of the gas—and so the value of $\frac{1}{2}m\overline{u^2}$ of the gas atoms or molecules—before and after expansion has occurred.

It is an experimental fact that the temperature of *all* gases falls as they undergo a free expansion. Since the gas is isolated and since no energy is transferred to or from the gas on removing the dividing partition, it follows that the *total* energy of the gas atoms must be the same before and after free expansion occurs. The fact that the temperature of the gas falls implies that the translational kinetic energy of the gas atoms falls. And if the kinetic energy falls, some other form of energy must increase to keep the total energy constant. The most likely candidate is the interatomic potential energy. So this experiment establishes, beyond reasonable doubt, that ΔE is finite. We should therefore modify Fig. 4.21(b) perhaps to the form shown in Fig. 4.23(a). This curve is also consistent with the observation that the drop in temperature falls towards zero as the starting pressure is reduced towards zero. At low starting pressures the initial mean interatomic separation is large and the potential energy gain to be had by further expansion is less than when the starting pressure is high (corresponding to small initial mean interatomic separation). Free-expansion experiments furnish no proof that atoms have a finite size. If their size were truly zero a gas condensing to form a solid would . . . disappear into nothingness! So Fig. 4.23(a) must be modified to the form shown in Fig. 4.23(b). In this "weakly attracting hard-sphere" model the equilibrium separation, measured between centres, of an isolated pair of atoms is the atomic diameter d.

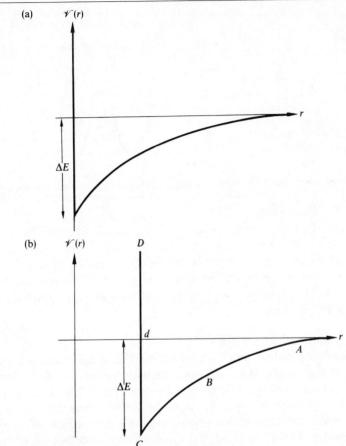

Fig. 4.23 (a) Shows the interatomic potential energy of a "semi" perfect gas. The atoms still have zero size but they are endowed with a finite dissociation energy ΔE. (b) The interatomic potential energy in a weakly attracting hard-sphere model of a gas.

4.5 The van der Waals equation of state

Now that we know the status of each assumption we must try to modify the original discussion of the pressure required to contain a gas so that it more accurately reflects the experimental facts. In performing this exercise we shall assume that the gas is contained in a vessel made from everyday laboratory materials like steel or glass, and not in a vessel made from, say, highly cleaned crystals of tungsten. For a start, this will allow us to continue to use Newtonian mechanics!

The effect of finite dwell time

The fact that a gas atom dwells on a dirty surface for some time before being released in no way affects the calculation. Instead of a single "blip" like

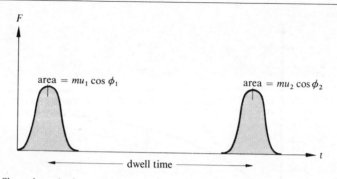

Fig. 4.24 Shows how the force which must be provided to send an atom back into the body of a gas varies with time if the atom dwells on the surface instead of rebounding immediately after being brought to rest.

that shown in Fig. 4.3 the force versus time curve should be drawn as shown in Fig. 4.24, where the time interval between the two "blips" is, of course, the dwell time. The first blip, during which the atom is decelerated to rest, has area $mu_1 \cos \phi_1$; the second blip, during which the gas atom is accelerated away from the piston, has area $mu_2 \cos \phi_2$. The combined area of both blips is the same as that of Fig. 4.3.

The effect of non-specular reflection

The evidence that gas atoms are scattered diffusely from a dirty surface, usually according to the cosine law, and not specularly, does not fundamentally change the discussion. It does dictate that the right-hand side of eq. (4.4) must be used in eq. (4.15) in place of the term $2mu_i \cos \phi_i$. When this correction is made to eq. (4.15) a further averaging procedure is necessary to allow for the diffuse scattering. This more exact, but more tedious, calculation leads to the same expression for the pressure as we obtained assuming specular reflection.

So we are left to make allowance for the fact that the interatomic potential does not have the form shown in Fig. 4.21(b). Although it might be an asset to adopt a "soft" interatomic interacton as in Fig. 2.8(c) the hard-sphere repulsive model of Fig. 4.23(b) does incorporate the key facts that atoms have a finite dissociation energy ΔE and a finite diameter d. In 1873 the Dutch physicist Johannes van der Waals (1837–1923) succeeded in modifying the equation of state of a perfect gas (eq. (4.27)) to allow for both these effects. Although he did not state the fact explicitly van der Waals tacitly adopted the potential of Fig. 4.23(b). His success lay in assuming that the effect of portion CD of the curve, attributable to the hard-sphere repulsion, could be treated quite separately from the effect of portion ABC, attributable to the weakly attractive force.

The effect of the hard-sphere repulsion

Figure 4.25(a) shows how the atoms of a *perfect* gas would behave in a piston

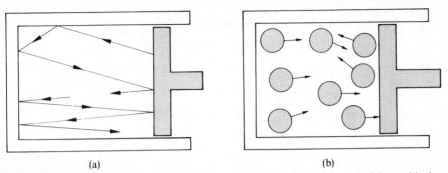

Fig. 4.25 (a) Atoms of a perfect gas will follow straight line paths between collisions with the containing walls. Since they have zero size they cannot collide with one another. (b) Giving atoms a finite size reduces the volume in which they can travel freely.

and cylinder apparatus. Because they have zero size they cannot collide with one another. They can only collide with the containing walls (whose atoms must have a finite size!). Physical intuition suggests that when the gas atoms are given a finite size, as in Fig. 4.25(b), there will be less free space in which the atoms can move and, as a consequence, the total number of collisions with the piston in unit time will increase. If your intuition suggests otherwise, try the following experiment. Place a number of small flat discs—small coins should do—on a horizontal tray. Vibrate the tray randomly back and forth, preferably over the surface of a table, and count the total number of collisions which occur with one of the sides in, say, thirty seconds. Now repeat the experiment, using the same vibrational speed, but this time with the same number of much larger discs on the tray. You should discover that there are more collisions per unit time with a side of the tray in the second experiment than in the first experiment. (You may find it difficult to vibrate the tray at the same rate in each experiment. If you do, vibrate two trays at once and ask someone to assist you with the counting.)

Although this simulation indicates that atoms of finite size make more collisions per unit time with the piston than do atoms of zero size it tells us nothing quantitative. To get hard facts we will consider a one-dimensional gas. This will be easier than considering a three-dimensional one! (It is often a good idea to start with a one-dimensional representation of a problem. If you have no idea how to tackle it you will be most unlikely to succeed with the real thing. If the one-dimensional discussion yields results you may be able to make an intelligent guess about how a three-dimensional gas behaves.)

Figure 4.26(a) shows a piston and cylinder arrangement in which an atom of *zero size* moves back and forth between the piston and the end of the cylinder. If its speed u is unchanged on colliding with the ends (this is the same assumption as we made in our earlier three-dimensional discussion) the time between successive collisions with the piston is $2l/u$, where l is the length of the cylinder. In other words, the number of collisions per unit time with the piston is

111

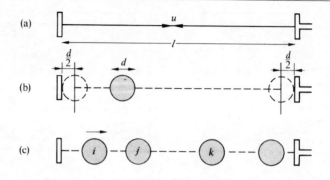

Fig. 4.26 (a) Shows a one-dimensional perfect gas (b) A single atom of finite size moves back and forth between the piston and the cylinder end. (c) A one-dimensional gas containing many atoms of finite size.

$u/2l$. If there are N atoms in this one-dimensional perfect gas the number of collisions per unit time f_0 with the piston will be given by

$$f_0 = N\left(\frac{u}{2l}\right) \tag{4.30}$$

Because of their zero size all N atoms can move along the same path without colliding with each other. To see what effect a finite size has on the behaviour of the gas we consider first that there is only one atom present (Fig. 4.26(b)). We can see immediately that the distance travelled by this one atom i between successive collisions with the piston is reduced from the value $2l$ for a perfect gas to the value $2l - 2(d/2) = 2l - d$ where d is the atomic diameter. With $N - 1$ additional atoms present (Fig. 4.26(c)) atom i is no longer able to travel freely from one end to the other. Before long i will collide with another atom j. At the moment of impact atom j may be moving to the right, or to the left. Since each alternative seems equally likely we will hazard the guess that, on average, the effect is the same as if j were at rest when struck by i. When i strikes j with speed u the two "swap places"; atom i stops dead and j moves off at speed u to strike atom k. Now j stops dead and k moves off with speed $u,\dots$ and so on. (You should be able to prove—perhaps you did in problem 3.1—that when an atom of mass m moving at a speed u makes a head-on elastic collision with a stationary atom of mass m the two swap places. The conversation piece called Newton's cradle demonstrates the same effect.)

When atom i, say, strikes atom j then atom j moves off *immediately* it is struck (assuming the spheres are perfectly hard—as they are in Fig. 4.23(b)). In other words, the momentum carried by i jumps a distance of $\frac{1}{2}d + \frac{1}{2}d = d$ in such a collision. Therefore, the effective distance which an atom has to travel between successive collisions with the piston is reduced from the single atom value of $2l - d$, as in Fig. 4.26(b) to a value $(2l - d) - 2(N - 1)d =$

$2l - (2N - 1)d$. The factor of 2 in $2(N - 1)d$ arises because an atom travels from the piston to the cylinder end *and back* between successive collisions with the piston; it makes $(N - 1)$ jumps, each of length d, on the outward journey, and $(N - 1)$, each of length d, on the return journey. As the speed of an atom remains constant at u throughout the sequence of collisions the number of collisions which this one atom makes with the piston per unit time is $u/[2l - (2N - 1)d]$. Since the same argument may be applied to all N atoms present it follows that the number of collisions per unit time f_d with the piston in a one-dimensional gas composed of atoms of diameter d is given by

$$f_d = \frac{Nu}{2l - (2N - 1)d}$$

which is clearly greater than the number of collisions in a one-dimensional perfect gas (eq. (4.30)). Therefore the number of collisions is increased by a factor of

$$\frac{f_d}{f_0} = \frac{l}{l - (N - \frac{1}{2})d}$$

or, when $N \gg 1$, by a factor of

$$\frac{f_d}{f_0} = \frac{l}{l - Nd} \tag{4.31}$$

We must now try to modify eq. (4.31) so that it can plausibly be applied to a three-dimensional gas. As in a one-dimensional gas the centre of an individual atom only has to approach within a distance of $d/2$ of a wall for a collision to occur (Fig. 4.27). Instead of a distance d which is "eliminated" in collisions

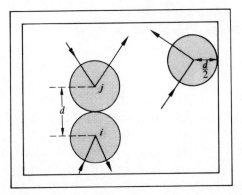

Fig. 4.27 In a three-dimensional gas composed of hard-sphere atoms of diameter d atoms can only approach to within a distance of $d/2$ from the wall. In addition, surrounding each atom is a sphere of volume $\frac{4}{3}\pi d^3$ which the centre of another atom cannot enter.

113

within the body of a one-dimensional gas, a volume $(4\pi/3)d^3$ is "eliminated" within the body of a three-dimensional gas; eliminated in the sense that momentum transfer occurs infinitely rapidly across this volume (see Fig. 4.27). So if the three-dimensional gas of hard spheres occupies a total volume V, the number of collisions with the piston will, by analogy with eq. (4.31) be increased by a factor of

$$\frac{f_d}{f_0} = \frac{V}{V - N(\frac{4}{3}\pi d^3)}$$

or, since an individual atom has a volume $v_a = (4\pi/3)(d/2)^3$, by a factor of

$$\frac{f_d}{f_0} = \frac{V}{V - 8Nv_a}$$

We may straight away multiply the right-hand side of eq. (4.22) by this collision "step up factor". (If the number of collisions with the piston were increased by a factor of 1·2 then p would increase by 1·2.) You may prefer to go back to eq. (4.14)—which is in essence an expression for f_0—and multiply its right-hand side by f_d/f_0. The conclusion is the same:

$$p = \tfrac{1}{3}mn\overline{u^2}\left(\frac{V}{V - 8Nv_a}\right)$$

It is important to note that the terms m, n, $\overline{u^2}$, and V have their origins in *perfect gas* theory. There n was the number of point atoms per unit volume and V was the volume of the gas. So nV is the number of perfect gas atoms in the volume V. If we now make the gas imperfect by giving the atoms a finite size this will not change the number of atoms which are present! Therefore nV represents the number N of *real* gas atoms present, giving

$$p(V - 8Nv_a) = \tfrac{1}{3}mN\overline{u^2}$$

If there is one mole of gas present this becomes

$$p(V_m - b) = \tfrac{1}{3}mN_A\overline{u^2} \tag{4.32}$$

where

$$b = 8N_A v_a \tag{4.33}$$

which is eight times the total volume of the (hard-sphere) gas atoms. Other treatments give an *excluded volume b* of four times the total volume of the atoms. Indeed it is possible to argue that we have overestimated b by a factor of two; we have forgotten that when atom i collides with atom j (as in Fig. 4.27) atom j necessarily collides with—excludes—atom i. Accepting this refinement as at least plausible gives

$$b = 4N_A v_a \tag{4.34}$$

If you prefer to stick with eq. (4.33) please do—it will not materially alter later discussions.

Now that we have taken account of the hard-sphere repulsion (portion CD of Fig. 4.23(b)) we next turn our attention to the weakly attractive force (portion ABC of Fig. 4.23(b)).

The effect of ΔE

Consider an atom i (Fig. 4.28(a)) which is just about to strike the piston. To have got there it will necessarily have left the vicinity of atoms like j, k, l, etc. In moving away from its neighbours atom i will have lost kinetic energy and this will have gone to increase the potential energy stored in the fields between atom i and atoms j, k, l, etc. Actually, the only gas atoms which need concern i as it strikes the piston are those whose centres lie within a hemisphere of radius D, where D is of the same order as the interatomic separation d of an isolated pair of atoms. (We shall shortly show that the force which the *piston* atoms exert on i can justifiably be neglected.) This statement is justified because the potential energy $\mathscr{V}(r)$ of an isolated pair of atoms varies so rapidly with r that once an atom has gone "a little further than d" away from its neighbour it has in effect said "goodbye"! You can see that this is so in the case of the $-1/r^6$ van der Waals interaction illustrated in Fig. 4.28(b). When $r = 1\cdot2d$ the potential energy has risen by 66 per cent of ΔE. Therefore as i strikes the piston (Fig. 4.28(a)) the only atoms it has lost kinetic energy to are those whose centres lie within the hemisphere of radius $D \approx d$ (D is often called the *range* of the force). If there is one mole of gas present then the number of atomic centres per unit volume is N_A/V_m. So the number of atoms—atoms

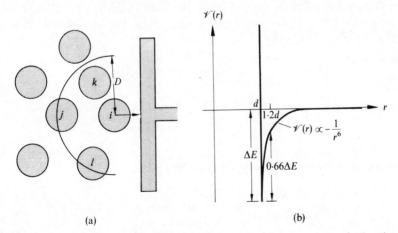

(a)	(b)

Fig. 4.28 (a) As atom i leaves the vicinity of j, k, l, etc., and moves up towards the piston its kinetic energy falls by an amount equal to the energy required to move away against the attractive forces from j, k, l, etc. (b) The interatomic potential energy $\mathscr{V}(r)$ of a pair of hard-sphere atoms with a $-1/r^6$ van der Waals interaction.

that matter—which i has left behind is approximately* $\frac{2}{3}\pi D^3(N_A/V_m)$. In leaving behind each of these atoms, atom i loses energy of order ΔE (Fig. 4.28(b)). Therefore the total energy lost by i in moving up to the piston is of order $\frac{2}{3}\pi D^3(N_A/V_m)\Delta E$. If i sets off from the bulk of the gas with a speed u_g and arrives at the piston face with a speed u_f then the law of conservation of energy tells us that

$$\tfrac{1}{2}mu_g^2 - \tfrac{1}{2}mu_f^2 = \tfrac{2}{3}\pi D^3\left(\frac{N_A}{V_m}\right)\Delta E$$

Actually the right-hand side really tells us about what happens to atom i on average. Sometimes it may escape from more neighbours, and sometimes from less neighbours, than $\frac{2}{3}\pi D^3(N_A/V_m)$—the hemisphere might be particularly full or even empty—so the left-hand side should also describe the average loss of kinetic energy:

$$\tfrac{1}{2}m\overline{u_g^2} - \tfrac{1}{2}m\overline{u_f^2} = \tfrac{2}{3}\pi D^3\left(\frac{N_A}{V_m}\right)\Delta E \tag{4.35}$$

Combining both corrections

In arriving at eq. (4.22)—and, by implication, the "half-corrected" eq. (4.32)—we asked what happened as a gas atom struck the piston. The speed u in eq. (4.32) is really the speed u_f, so this equation states

$$p(V_m - b) = \tfrac{2}{3}N_A(\tfrac{1}{2}m\overline{u_f^2})$$

We may now substitute for $\frac{1}{2}m\overline{u_f^2}$ from eq. (4.35). In so doing we shall take it that the range D of the interatomic force is equal to d, the hard-sphere diameter (see Fig. 4.28(b)). This gives

$$p = \frac{2N_A}{3(V_m - b)}\left[\tfrac{1}{2}m\overline{u_g^2} - \tfrac{2}{3}\pi d^3\left(\frac{N_A}{V_m}\right)\Delta E\right]$$

$$\left[p + \frac{N_A^2}{3V_m(V_m - b)}\tfrac{4}{3}\pi d^3\,\Delta E\right] = \frac{2N_A}{3(V_m - b)}(\tfrac{1}{2}m\overline{u_g^2})$$

Remembering that the temperature of a gas is related to the mean kinetic energy of its atoms by $\frac{1}{2}m\overline{u_g^2} = \frac{3}{2}kT$ (eq. (3.29)) gives

$$\left[p + \frac{N_A^2}{3V_m(V_m - b)}\tfrac{4}{3}\pi d^3\,\Delta E\right](V_m - b) = N_A kT = RT \tag{4.36}$$

---

* Even this is not quite correct. Since the atoms are hard spheres not *all* the hemisphere is available to atoms j, k, l, etc.; because i is where it is j, say, is prevented from being there. Introducing this further refinement here only corrects a correction term!

The second term inside the square bracket is but a correction to p. Because of this it introduces little error to replace $V_m - b$ in its denominator by V_m, giving

$$\left(p + \frac{a}{V_m^2}\right)(V_m - b) = RT \tag{4.37}$$

where

$$a = \frac{8N_A^2}{3}\frac{4\pi}{3}\left(\frac{d}{2}\right)^3 \Delta E = \frac{8N_A^2}{3}v_a \Delta E$$

Equation (4.37) is van der Waals' famous equation of state of a real gas.

An important question

Before examining the implications of van der Waals' equation there is one important question to be faced. Were we justified in neglecting the force which the *piston* exerts on a gas atom as that atom moves up to strike the piston? Since the piston is composed of atoms, each of which pulls on the gas atom, there will certainly be some resultant force of magnitude $|F_{pa}|$ acting on the atom as shown in Fig. 4.29. Surely this force will increase the speed u at which the atom strikes the piston, thereby increasing p? We must think carefully.

It is correct to suppose that because of the resultant force $|F_{pa}|$ of the piston on the gas atom (you may read the suffix as "piston on atom") that the momentum of the gas atom as it strikes the piston will be increased by $\int |F_{pa}|\, dt$, integrated over the interval during which the gas atom is accelerated. If the speed of the gas atom in the bulk of the gas, where $|F_{pa}| = 0$, is u then it will strike the piston with a momentum $(mu + \int |F_{pa}|\, dt)$. To reverse the motion of the atom the person pushing on the piston must therefore provide an impulse $2(mu + \int |F_{pa}|\, dt)$ which will be directed to the *right* in Fig. 4.29. Since the impulse required in a gas in which $|F_{pa}| = 0$ (the situation we have been

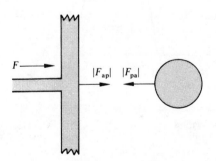

Fig. 4.29 As an atom approaches the piston the atom exerts a force F_{ap} on the piston and the piston exerts a force F_{pa} on the atom (which is equal in magnitude but opposite in direction to F_{ap}).

117

assuming up to now) is $2mu$ it does seem that the pressure required to contain a gas is greater than we previously calculated. However we have forgotten something.

What we have forgotten is that as the gas atom gets pulled in by the piston with a force $|F_{pa}|$ so the piston will get pulled out by a force $|F_{ap}|$ (Fig. 4.29). By Newton's third law $|F_{ap}| = |F_{pa}|$ but is oppositely directed; more concisely $F_{ap} = -F_{pa}$. To prevent the piston from moving into the gas the person holding it must tug the other way, that is he must provide an impulse $\int |F_{ap}|\, dt$ directed to the *left*. Now consider what happens as the gas atom leaves the piston to return to the body of the gas; it tries to drag the piston with it. To prevent this happening the person holding the piston must provide an impulse $\int |F_{ap}|\, dt$ again directed to the *left*. Figure 4.30 shows the time dependence of the force F provided by the person holding the piston during the collision sequence. The net impulse provided by the person is therefore $2mu + 2\int |F_{pa}|\, dt - 2\int |F_{ap}|\, dt$. Because $|F_{ap}| = |F_{pa}|$ the net impulse is $2mu$; the value we originally assumed. So the attractive force exerted by the walls of a container *can* be neglected in calculating the gas pressure.

4.6 Properties of van der Waals' equation

We will now look at the type of behaviour predicted by eq. (4.37). Rather than looking directly at a $p-V_m-T$ surface, it is easier to examine, say, isotherms in the $p-V_m$ plane. With this end in view we can conveniently rewrite van der Waals' equation as

$$p = \frac{RT}{V_m - b} - \frac{a}{V_m^2} \tag{4.38}$$

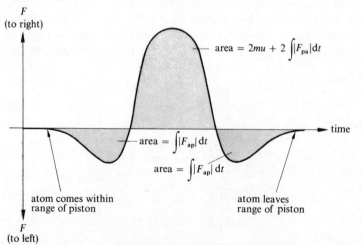

Fig. 4.30 Shows the form of the impulse required to reverse the motion of an atom colliding with the piston when the attractive force between the piston and the gas atom is taken into account.

118

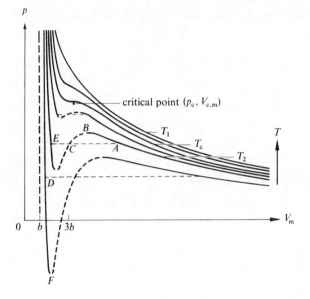

Fig. 4.31 Pressure–volume isotherms as predicted by van der Waals' equation.

We see that at high temperatures *and* high volumes the pressure approximates closely to the perfect gas expression $p = RT/V_m$, so the isotherms will be rectangular hyperbolas under these conditions. However as V_m approaches b the pressure becomes very large. Such a high temperature isotherm, labelled T_1, is shown in Fig. 4.31. At a lower temperature T_2 (Fig. 4.31) the pressure dips down with decreasing V_m before increasing towards infinity as V_m approaches b. The dip will occur if a/V_m^2 increases more rapidly with decreasing V_m than does $RT/(V_m - b)$. Whether or not there is a dip depends on how the value of RT compares with that of a and b. Clearly the dipping portion DB of the isotherm T_2 implies that an increase in p causes an increase in V_m (have you ever observed this?). It is possible to associate portion AB with a super-cooled gas and portion ED with a superheated liquid (cf. Fig. 1.13). We know from chapter 1 that supercooling and superheating are the exception rather than the rule; phase separation occurring along some such line as AE in Fig. 4.31.

At some temperature T_c which is intermediate in value between T_1 and T_2 the maximum and minima predicted by van der Waals' equation coalesce to yield a horizontal tangent at point $(p_c, V_{c,m})$, which is also a point of inflexion. The point $(p_c, V_{c,m}, T_c)$ can readily be associated with the critical point. Notice that at a temperature below T_c, such as T_2, there may be three positive real values of V_m for a given pressure (the volumes at A, C, and E in Fig. 4.31). As the temperature is increased above T_2 the three real values approach one another until, at $T = T_c$ they become equal, each with a value $V_{c,m}$. Therefore in the

119

neighbourhood of the critical point van der Waals' equation must take the form

$$(V_m - V_{c,m})^3 = 0$$

or

$$V_m^3 - 3V_{c,m}V_m^2 + 3V_{c,m}^2 V_m - V_{c,m}^3 = 0 \qquad (4.39)$$

This is to be compared with eq. (4.37) in which $T = T_c$ and $p = p_c$; that is, with

$$\left(p_c + \frac{a}{V_m^2}\right)(V_m - b) = RT_c$$

or, multiplying through by V_m^2, with

$$(p_c V_m^2 + a)(V_m - b) = RT_c V_m^2$$

$$V_m^3 - \left(b + \frac{RT_c}{p_c}\right)V_m^2 + \frac{a}{p_c}V_m - \frac{ab}{p_c} = 0 \qquad (4.40)$$

Comparing eqs. (4.39) and (4.40) we see that

$$3V_{c,m} = b + \frac{RT}{p_c} \qquad (4.41)$$

$$3V_{c,m}^2 = \frac{a}{p_c} \qquad (4.42)$$

$$V_{c,m}^3 = \frac{ab}{p_c} \qquad (4.43)$$

Dividing eq. (4.43) by eq. (4.42) gives

$$V_{c,m} = 3b \qquad (4.44)$$

Substituting eq. (4.44) into eq. (4.42) yields

$$p_c = \frac{a}{27b^2} \qquad (4.45)$$

Finally, substituting eqs. (4.44) and (4.45) into eq. (4.41) gives

$$T_c = \frac{8a}{27Rb} \qquad (4.46)$$

We are now in a position to substitute our expressions for $a(= 8N_A^2 v_a \Delta E/3)$ and $b(= 4N_A v_a)$ which were arrived at by purely microscopic arguments into eqs. (4.44), (4.45), and (4.46). This gives

$$V_{c,m} \approx 12N_A v_a \qquad (4.47)$$

$$p_c \approx \frac{\Delta E}{162v_a} \qquad (4.48)$$

$$T_c \approx \frac{16}{81} \frac{N_A \Delta E}{R} \tag{4.49}$$

It would be foolish to pay much attention to the numerical factors in these equations—particularly since some authors arrive at $b = 4N_A v_a$ and others at $b = 8N_A v_a$! Nevertheless it is fun to check them out to see if they are in the right ballpark.

In checking them out we shall assume that $N_A v_a$ (meaning the Avogadro constant times the volume of an atom) is the molar volume of the saturated liquid at a temperature well below the critical temperature—say at the triple temperature. So $N_A v_a = V_{tr,m}$. We may also use the fact that the energy required to dissociate a mole of such a liquid into its component atoms (or molecules) an infinite distance apart—the *molar latent heat of evaporation* (more properly called the *molar enthalpy of evaporation*) $H_{e,m}$—is approximately $\frac{1}{2} N_A \Delta E$. This latter relation arises because we may picture a mole of the liquid as being composed of $\frac{1}{2} N_A$ pairs of atoms, each of which requires an energy ΔE to dissociate it. Making these substitutions, eqs. (4.47), (4.48), and (4.49) becomes

$$\frac{V_{c,m}}{V_{tr,m}} \approx 12$$

$$\frac{p_c V_{tr,m}}{H_{e,m}} \approx \frac{1}{81} (= 0\cdot012)$$

$$\frac{RT_c}{H_{e,m}} \approx \frac{16}{40} (= 0\cdot4)$$

The experimental values for these ratios are set out in Table 4.1 for a variety of substances. Consider what we have been up to. We started off with a

TABLE 4.1

Substance	$V_{c,m}/V_{tr,m}$	$p_c V_{tr,m}/H_{e,m}$	$RT_c/H_{e,m}$	$RT_c/p_c V_{c,m}$
Ar	2·7	0·021	0·19	3·42
N_2	5·3	0·021	0·39	3·43
CO_2	2·2	0·012	0·10	3·65
H_2O	3·2	0·0095	0·13	4·11

model, in which $\Delta E = 0$ and $d = 0$, and arrived at the equation of state of a perfect gas. We next made ΔE and d finite and found out what this did to our equation of state. Next we took our "slightly corrected perfect gas" equation—which still assumed that atomic movement was largely unhindered—and applied it to a situation (the critical region) where the atoms are so tightly packed ($V_{c,m} \approx 12N_A v_a$) that they are tripping over one another's toes, so to speak. Under the circumstances, the factor of three or four difference between prediction and experiment revealed in Table 4.1 is nothing to worry about!

It should be pointed out that van der Waals introduced the terms a/V_m^2 and b as semi-empirical corrections to the perfect-gas law. He did not attempt to relate a and b in any detailed way to the interatomic potential $\mathscr{V}(r)$. Had we followed this empirical approach we would have started with eq. (4.37) and would have terminated the discussion at eqs. (4.44), (4.45), and (4.46). In fact using these three equations you can readily show that $RT_c/p_c V_{c,m} = 8/3 (= 2\cdot67)$, independent of a or b (and therefore of their origins). As the last column of Table 4.1 shows, this ratio more closely matches the theoretical value than do any of the other three, all of which depend on a particular microscopic interpretation of a and b.

It has always been something of a mystery as to why van der Waals'· equation should work as well as it does, considering the simplicity of the assumptions on which it rests. Its real strength lies in its ability to predict properties common to all gases and liquids. Its weakness lies in its inability to discuss any one substance in detail. We cannot for example, feed in the precise form of the interatomic potential; all we can hope to do is put in something about its range and its strength (meaning D and ΔE) into a and b. Later on we shall formulate another equation of state which does enable us to feed in this detailed information. The weakness of this new equation—the so-called Clausius virial theorem—is that it is hard to use it to spot overall trends. One equation's strength is often another's weakness.

We said at the beginning of this chapter that we would look in some detail at gas pressure to show something of what is involved in getting to grips with a problem. Seldom are there shortcuts to understanding!

Summary

1. A perfect gas is defined as one in which $\Delta E = 0$ and in which the atoms have zero size.
2. The pressure required to contain a gas arises because one must reverse the motion of atoms colliding with the containing walls. In a perfect gas $p = \frac{1}{3}mnu^2$, where m is the atomic mass, n is the number of atoms per unit volume, and $\overline{u^2}$ is their mean square speed. A term $2mu$ comes from the change in momentum of a single atom on striking a wall, and a term nu from the number of atoms striking unit area of the wall per unit time.
3. When gas atoms strike a dirty surface they are usually scattered diffusely, according to the cosine law. Specular reflection is only observed with clean crystalline specimens. In diffuse scattering the atoms dwell on the surface for some appreciable time before leaving: In the case of specular reflection the atoms dwell for a very much shorter time.

4. In arriving at van der Waals' equation, $(p + a/V_m^2)(V_m - b) = RT$, the atoms were regarded as possessing a weak interatomic attractive force and a hard-sphere repulsive force. They are given a non-zero radius. The attractive force leads to the a/V_m^2 correction; the hard-sphere repulsion to $-b$. The van der Waals equation of state reproduces the main features of the p–V_m–T surface of a real substance in the liquid and gaseous phases. It also leads to order-of-magnitude correct expressions for p_c, $V_{c,m}$, and T_c in terms of a and b.

PROBLEMS

4.1 A stream of balls, each of mass 2 kg and moving at a speed of 12 m s^{-1}, strike a wall and stop dead. In the course of 10 s fifty such balls hit the wall at right angles:
(a) What is the total change in momentum of the balls in 10 s?
(b) Show graphically how you would expect the force which the wall must exert to stop the balls to vary with time.
(c) Can you tell anything about the area under the graph of part (b)? Anything else?
(d) What is the average force which the wall exerts over the 10 s period?
(e) If, instead of stopping dead, the balls rebound with unaltered speed back along the direction in which they came in, will this change the mean force which the wall exerts? If so, by how much?

4.2 A child catches a ball of mass 0·25 kg which has been dropped from a height of 1·8 m. What force does the ball exert on the child's hand? (You may take $g = 10$ m s^{-2}.)

4.3 A single atom of mass m inside a piston and cylinder arrangement bounces back and forth between the piston face and the end of the cylinder with a constant speed u. (In other words, the piston face and the end of the cylinder are imagined as perfectly smooth and the atom is imagined always to strike and leave these two surfaces along a normal to each surface.) Derive an expression for the average force $\bar{F}$ which the gas atom exerts on the piston.

4.4 A (somewhat out of date!) engineer decides to build a "speaking tube" system so as to transmit sound as rapidly as possible. Would you advise him to fill the tube with a gas of high relative molecular mass or of low relative molecular mass? Should he maintain the tube at a high or at a low temperature? Explain.

4.5 You might try to simulate how atoms are scattered at the surface of a solid by throwing ping-pong balls at the surface of an egg carton (or other dimpled supermarket pack). Try to plot a graph showing the number coming off in different directions. It will help to get someone to look "sideways on" at what is happening. It also helps to carve up 180° into, say, six 30° sectors! What type of surface gives specular reflection?

4.6 How many molecules are present in a 10^3 m^3 gas holder which is at a pressure of $1·2 \times 10^5$ Pa and a temperature of 300 K. Assume the gas is perfect.

4.7 A gas, which you may suppose is perfect, occupies a volume of 10^{-2} m^3 at a pressure of 10^4 Pa. If there are 10^{23} molecules present in the gas, what is the mean kinetic energy of the gas atoms?

4.8 A gas is at a pressure of 10^{-3} Pa and the r.m.s. speed of its constituent molecules is 200 m s^{-1}. What is the density of the gas? Assume the gas is perfect.

123

4.9 In the last century Avogadro made the hypothesis that equal volumes of all gases kept at the same temperature and pressure contain equal numbers of molecules. Show that this follows from the kinetic theory of a perfect gas. Is *Avogadro's hypothesis* likely to hold good for an imperfect gas? Explain your reasoning.

4.10 To a good approximation, the pressure of a mixture of (near perfect) gases at a volume V is equal to the sum of the pressures which each gas would exert if it alone occupied the volume V. Show that this result, known as *Dalton's law of partial pressures,* follows from our discussions of gas kinetic theory.

4.11 A container of volume 0.2 m^3 is evacuated. Then 3×10^{-3} kg of water vapour is introduced. The pressure of the water vapour is found to be 5×10^5 Pa. What is the m.s. and r.m.s. speed of the water molecules?

4.12 An oxygen molecule strikes a surface and sticks. If the molecule comes to rest in a time of 10^{-15} s what is the mean force exerted by such a molecule on the piston when the gas is at 700 K? $(M_r(O_2) = 32)$.

4.13 Show that van der Waals' equation may be written in the form

$$\left(p_r + \frac{3}{V_r^2}\right)(3V_r - 1) = 8T_r$$

where the so-called *reduced pressure* p_r, *reduced volume* V_r and *reduced temperature* T_r are defined by

$$p_r = p/p_c, \qquad V_r = V_m/V_{c,m}, \qquad T_r = T/T_c$$

(Clue: you will need to bring in eqs. (4.44), (4.45), and (4.46).) You will notice that a and b have conveniently disappeared in this form of van der Waals' equation. As a result, if a variety of different substances—any substances—have the same value for two of p_r, V_r, and T_r the value of the third will be the same for all these substances. This is known as the *law of corresponding states.* If, for example, all the substances have the same *reduced* volume of 2/3 (the *actual* molar volumes being $2V_{c,m}/3$ would be different of course) and the same *reduced* pressure of 3/4 they will all have the same *reduced* temperature of . . . of what? If three of the substances present are argon, carbon dioxide, and hydrogen, what will be their actual temperatures? (The data you require is in Table 1.1.)

5. Transport Processes in Gases

So far we have been mainly concerned with equilibrium situations. In deriving the equation of state of a gas, for example, we assumed that there was no net transport of energy between the gas and the container; both were assumed to be at the same temperature. We now turn our attention to situations which are deliberately contrived to be non-equilibrium ones. We might have two different gases, as shown in Fig. 5.1(a), separated by a partition. On removing the partition the two gases interdiffuse. As we shall presently see, diffusion is characterized, at the atomic level, by a transport of mass. Alternatively we might have one gas sandwiched between two plates, as shown in Fig. 5.1(b). If the plates are at a different temperature, heat is conducted across the gas; at the atomic level thermal conduction is characterized by the transport of energy. If one plate is moved relative to the other—the lower one might be fixed and the upper one might move to the right—the gas is found to be "viscous"; to maintain the relative movement of the plates calls for a "shearing stress". We shall see that at the atomic level viscous flow is characterized by a steady transport of momentum from one plate to the other. A final possibility is to have the two plates at a different electrostatic potential. If the gas is partially ionized—all gases are in the earth's atmosphere—an electric current will flow; a process characterized by the transport of charge. These different transport processes are summarized in Table 5.1.

TABLE 5.1

Process	Requirement at macroscopic level	Characteristic
diffusion	density gradient	transport of mass
viscous flow	shearing stress	transport of momentum
thermal conduction	temperature gradient	transport of energy
electrical conduction	potential gradient (i.e., electric field)	transport of charge

Before discussing each of these processes in detail we must look at some characteristics underlying them all. To transport anything—be it mass, momentum, energy, or charge—the atoms must quite clearly move. But just how far can an atom move before it collides with another atom, perhaps thereby surrendering some or all of its momentum, energy, or charge?

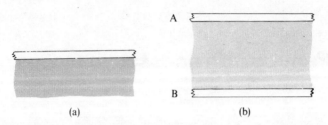

(a)   (b)

Fig. 5.1 (a) On removing the partition shown, the two different gases will interdiffuse. (b) If plate A is moved to the right and B is held stationary, momentum is fed into the gas by plate A and is removed by plate B. If A is at a higher temperature than B, energy is fed into the gas at A and removed at B. If B is at a higher electrical potential than A, and if the gas is at least partially ionized, negative ions will strike B and deposit their charge while positive ions will strike A and be neutralized by the electrons flowing through the external circuit from B to A.

Then again it is clear that the net amount of energy, momentum, or charge that is transferred to a plate in the gas will depend on the number of atoms colliding with the plate in unit time. Double this number and, all other things being equal, the net transfer will be doubled. So how many atoms do collide with unit area of surface in unit time?

5.1 The mean free path

In imagination let us follow the motion of any one atom i in a gas. We can expect the atom to follow some such tortuous path as that shown in Fig. 5.2. Between successive collisions with other atoms the atom i will travel freely through distances l_1, l_2, l_3, etc., distances known as *free paths*. What interests us is the mean distance it travels between consecutive collisions, the so-called

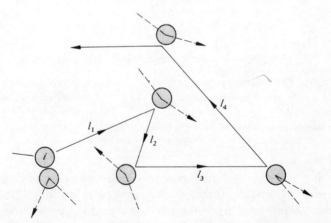

Fig. 5.2 Shows the tortuous path followed by atom i as it collides with other atoms of the gas. The paths l_1, l_2, l_3, etc., are called free paths.

126

mean free path (m.f.p.) λ. If we follow the motion of atom i for a time t then clearly

$$\lambda = \frac{\text{total distance travelled by atom } i \text{ in time } t\,(= l_1 + l_2 + l_3 + \text{etc.})}{\text{number of collisions made by } i \text{ in time } t} \tag{5.1}$$

Since the mean speed $\bar{u}$ of i is defined by

$$\bar{u} = \frac{\text{total distance travelled in time } t}{t}$$

it follows that eq. (5.1) may be written as

$$\lambda = \frac{\bar{u}t}{\text{number of collisions made by } i \text{ in time } t} \tag{5.2}$$

Had there been no other atoms present, atom i would have followed the straight line path shown in Fig. 5.3. But other atoms are, of course, present. If one of these other atoms is to collide with atom i then, as Fig. 5.3 shows, its *centre* must lie within a distance of $\frac{1}{2}d + \frac{1}{2}d = d$ from the path followed by the centre of atom i. (Atoms p and q will not collide with i; atom r will; atom s will just collide.) In other words:

number of collisions made by i in time t = number of atoms within cylinder of radius d and of length $\bar{u}t$

$$= (\pi d^2 \bar{u}t) \times n \tag{5.3}$$

Here n is the number of atoms per unit volume and $\pi d^2 \bar{u}t$ is, of course, the volume of the cylinder of length $\bar{u}t$ and radius d. Substituting eq. (5.3) into the denominator of eq. (5.2) gives

$$\lambda = \frac{1}{\pi d^2 n} \tag{5.4}$$

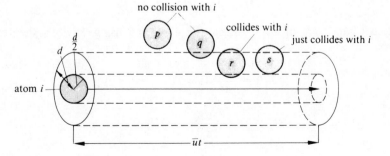

Fig. 5.3 As atom i attempts to travel the distance $\bar{u}t$ it will collide with all other atoms whose centres lie within a cylinder of radius d and of length $\bar{u}t$.

Although we chose to concentrate on a particular atom i the same argument applies to each and every other atom in the gas. In section 4.3 we showed that the equation of state of a perfect gas could be written as $p = nkT$ (eq. (4.28)). Substituting $n = p/kT$ into eq. (5.4) gives

$$\lambda = \frac{kT}{\pi d^2 p} \tag{5.5}$$

Exercise 5.1

Calculate the mean free path in nitrogen at a pressure of $1 \cdot 0 \times 10^5$ Pa and at a temperature of 300 K. At what pressure, again at 300 K, is the mean free path 10^{-1} m? Regard the nitrogen molecule as being a sphere of diameter $3 \cdot 5 \times 10^{-10}$ m.

5.2 The probability of a specified free path

The free paths of a gas atom are not, of course, all the same; the paths l_1, l_2, and l_3 are different in Fig. 5.2. What is the probability $f(l)$ that an atom will execute a free path that is *at least as great* as some specified value l? In other words, what is the probability $f(l)$ that an atom, setting off on its travels after suffering a collision, will travel a distance of between l and infinity before it suffers another collision?

After freely travelling a distance l since it last suffered a collision the chance that an atom will suffer a new collision in describing a further distance dl will be proportional to dl. (If dl is, say, doubled we would expect the chance of a new collision to be doubled.) That is, the chance of a collision in distance dl is $\alpha \, dl$, where α is the constant of proportionality. The chance that the atom will describe the distance dl *without* suffering a collision is therefore $(1 - \alpha \, dl)$. The chance that an atom will describe a distance l and then a further distance dl without suffering a collision is therefore $f(l)(1 - \alpha \, dl)$. This is equal to $f(l + dl)$, that is

$$f(l + dl) = (1 - \alpha \, dl) f(l) \tag{5.6}$$

The left-hand side of eq. (5.6) may be expanded using Taylor's theorem to give

$$f(l) + \frac{df(l)}{dl} dl = f(l) - \alpha \, dl \, f(l)$$

$$\frac{df(l)}{dl} = -\alpha f(l)$$

$$\frac{df(l)}{f(l)} = -\alpha \, dl \tag{5.7}$$

Integrating eq. (5.7) gives

$$f(l) = \beta\, e^{-\alpha l}$$

where the constant of integration, β, may be evaluated by noting that if $l = 0$ then $f(l) = 1$. (The atom has a complete certainty of colliding with another atom somewhere between 0 and ∞.) This gives $\beta = 1$, so

$$f(l) = e^{-\alpha l} \tag{5.8}$$

The constant α may be determined by evaluating the m.f.p. λ of an atom, as follows;

the probability of an atom having a free path between l and $l + dl$

$$= \text{(probability of freely travelling } l\text{)(probability of a collision in } dl\text{)}$$

$$= f(l)\alpha\, dl$$

If there are N atoms present it follows that:

the number of atoms having free paths between l and $l + dl = Nf(l)\alpha\, dl$ $\quad$ (5.9)

By definition

$$\lambda = \frac{\sum (\text{number of atoms with free path } l) \times l}{\text{total number of atoms}}$$

or, substituting from eq. (5.9) and eq. (5.8)

$$\lambda = \frac{1}{N} \int_0^\infty Nf(l)\alpha l\, dl$$

$$\lambda = \int_0^\infty e^{-\alpha l}\,\alpha l\, dl \tag{5.10}$$

Equation (5.10) may be readily integrated by parts:

$$\lambda = -\left[l\, e^{-\alpha l}\right]_0^\infty + \int_0^\infty e^{-\alpha l}\, dl$$

$$\lambda = 1/\alpha$$

Therefore $\alpha = 1/\lambda$ and so eq. (5.8) becomes

$$f(l) = e^{-l/\lambda} \tag{5.11}$$

—the probability that an atom will have a free path at least equal to l. Figure 5.4 shows the dependence of $f(l)$ on l/λ. It is clear that the free paths have all values and are not grouped closely on either side of the mean value

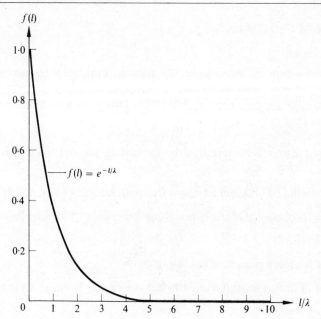

Fig. 5.4 Shows how the probability that an atom will have a free path at least equal to l varies with l/λ, where λ is the mean free path.

($l/\lambda = 1$). It is also worth noting that there is only a 0·37 chance that an atom will travel a distance of at least λ before suffering a collision; that is a 0·37 chance that an atom's free path will exceed λ.

5.3 Collisions with a surface

We now turn to the problem of calculating the number of atoms which strike unit area of a surface in unit time. Rather than undertake a serious calculation of this *collision frequency* we will see where a casual—even sloppy—train of thought takes us.

Let us say that a gas behaves *as if*, at any instant, $\frac{1}{6}$th of the atoms are moving in the $+x$ direction, $\frac{1}{6}$th in the $-x$ direction, $\frac{1}{6}$th in the $+y$ direction, $\frac{1}{6}$th in the $-y$ direction, and likewise for the z cartesian directions. If the total number of atoms per unit volume is n then there will be $n/6$ atoms moving in the $+x$ direction, etc. To find the number striking an area δA, in say the y–z plane, we draw in a cylinder of length $u_i t$ as shown in Fig. 5.5. All those atoms possessing a speed u_i which are within the cylinder of cross-sectional area δA and of length $u_i t$ will strike δA in time t. If the total number of atoms per unit volume possessing a speed u_i is n_i then, according to our approximations, $n_i/6$ will be moving up to strike δA. (Atoms moving in the other five directions will not strike δA.) Therefore

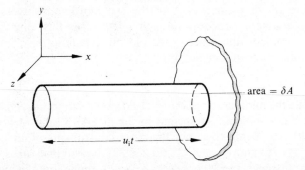

Fig. 5.5 All those atoms within the cylinder of length $u_i t$ and cross-sectional area δA which are moving parallel to the axis of the cylinder and towards the surface will strike δA in time t.

number of atoms of speed u_i colliding with δA in time $t = (u_i t \, \delta A)\left(\dfrac{n_i}{6}\right)$

Summing the effects of atoms of all speeds gives

$$\text{total number of atoms colliding with } \delta A \text{ in time } t = \frac{\delta A \, t}{6} \sum n_i u_i \quad (5.12)$$

By definition, the mean speed $\bar{u}$ of the gas atoms is given by

$$\bar{u} = \frac{\sum n_i u_i}{\sum n_i}$$

$$\bar{u} = \frac{\sum n_i u_i}{n} \quad (5.13)$$

Substituting for $\sum n_i u_i$ from eq. (5.13) into eq. (5.12) gives

$$\text{total number of atoms colliding with } \delta A \text{ in time } t = \frac{\delta A \, t}{6} n \bar{u}$$

Therefore

$$\text{total number of atoms striking unit area per unit time} = \tfrac{1}{6} n \bar{u} \quad (5.14)$$

If one makes an exact calculation* which avoids the assumption that $\frac{1}{6}$th of the atoms move along each of the six coordinate directions (acknowledging instead that equal number of atoms move in all directions in a gas) one concludes that

$$\text{total number of atoms striking unit area per unit time} = \tfrac{1}{4} n \bar{u} \quad (5.15)$$

Because of the close similarity of the two results, eqs. (5.14) and (5.15), we can say, with some justification, that a gas behaves *as if* at any instant, $\frac{1}{6}$th of

* The calculation is not difficult, but the integrations are somewhat tedious. You will find it discussed, for example, in R. D. Present: *Kinetic Theory of Gases*, p. 33, McGraw-Hill, New York, 1958.

the atoms are moving along each of the six coordinate directions. In our discussions of transport processes we shall in fact adopt this "one-sixth" model, being fairly confident that more exact, but more tedious, calculations would not substantially alter the predictions.

Exercise 5.2

Calculate the number of molecules striking the surface of a postage stamp, of size 2 cm × 2 cm, per second in air at 300 K and at a pressure of 1.0×10^5 Pa. Remember that the main constituents of air are nitrogen ($M_r(N_2) = 28$) and oxygen ($M_r(O_2) = 32$). By volume, air is roughly 80 per cent nitrogen and 20 per cent oxygen. Assume that the mean and the root mean square speeds of the gas molecules are identical. We shall see later (p. 209) that $\bar{u} = 0.92\overline{(u^2)}^{1/2}$.

5.4 Diffusion

The diffusion coefficient

For simplicity, we will only consider the diffusion of a gas into a radioactive isotope of the same gas. (The radioactive isotope will have atoms of approximately the same mass and size as the atoms of the non-radioactive form of the gas.) One might study how the two gases interdiffuse by removing a dividing partition separating the two gases and, using a suitable detector, measure the concentration of the radioactive gas at various points along the axis of the chamber. We will later describe how such an experiment is performed in practice. At time $t = 0$ (Fig. 5.6(a)) there is, of course, no inter-diffusion whereas at $t = \infty$ (Fig. 5.6(c)) the concentration of each species is constant throughout the chamber. At some intermediate time t (Fig. 5.6(b)) the radioactive gas will have partially penetrated the non-radioactive gas, and vice versa.

What interests us is the rate at which diffusion proceeds. We can measure what is called the *flux j*, defined as the number of atoms of one species crossing unit area per unit time. To help understand this definition imagine yourself standing at some point P in the chamber. With stopwatch in hand you count the net number of radioactive atoms moving through a known area δA in a time δt (Fig. 5.6(b)). You might find that, say, 5×10^7 atoms crossed an area $\delta A = 10^{-5}$ m² in time $\delta t = 2 \times 10^{-3}$ s. The flux—the number crossing unit area per unit time—therefore has a magnitude $|j| = 5 \times 10^7/(10^{-5} \text{ m}^2 \times 2 \times 10^{-3} \text{ s}) = 2.5 \times 10^{15} \text{ m}^{-2} \text{ s}^{-1}$. While conducting this thought experiment let us measure what is called the concentration gradient of the radioactive atoms at P. It might be that the concentration n of radioactive atoms changes from, say, $8.0 \times 10^{18} \text{ m}^{-3}$ to $9.6 \times 10^{18} \text{ m}^{-3}$, that is by an amount $|\delta n| = 1.6 \times 10^{18} \text{ m}^{-3}$, as you shift your position through a distance $|\delta x| = 10^{-4}$ m

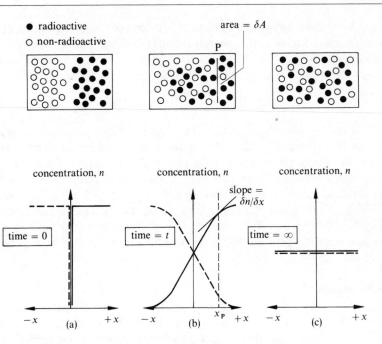

Fig. 5.6 Showing the interdiffusion of a gas and its radioactive equivalent. (a) The separating barrier is removed at time $t = 0$. (b) At some later time t interdiffusion is evident. (c) Eventually both atomic species attain the same uniform concentration.

along the axis of the chamber. The *concentration gradient*—the change in concentration per unit distance—therefore has a magnitude $|\delta n|/|\delta x| = 1\cdot6 \times 10^{18} \text{ m}^{-3}/10^{-4} \text{ m} = 1\cdot6 \times 10^{22} \text{ m}^{-4}$. (As can be seen from Fig. 5.6(b) the concentration gradient of the radioactive species is equal to the slope at $x = x_P$ of the curve of the concentration n of the radioactive species plotted against the position x.)

Experiments—real experiments of course—show that

$$|j| \propto \frac{|\delta n|}{|\delta x|}$$

or

$$|j| = D \frac{|\delta n|}{|\delta x|} \tag{5.16}$$

where the constant of proportionality D is called the *diffusion coefficient* (strictly speaking, in the present context, the *coefficient of self-diffusion*). In the case of our thought-experiment $D = 2\cdot5 \times 10^{15} \text{ m}^{-2} \text{ s}^{-1}/1\cdot6 \times 10^{22} \text{ m}^{-4} = 1\cdot6 \times 10^{-7} \text{ m}^2 \text{ s}^{-1}$. We must couple to eq. (5.16) the statement "diffusion

133

occurs down the concentration gradient". Instead of having to mix an equation involving magnitudes with a statement in words we can get away with the single expression

$$j = -D \frac{\delta n}{\delta x} \tag{5.17}$$

which deals with algebraic *values*. To see that this works look at the non-radioactive species in Fig. 5.6(b). Its concentration gradient $\delta n/\delta x$ has a negative value—if in doubt put in numbers on the graph of n against x—and it diffuses to the right. Assuming that we want "diffusion to the right" to be indicated by a positive value for j, and that we also want D to have a positive value, we are forced to insert the minus sign in eq. (5.17). The radioactive species in Fig. 5.6(b) has a positive concentration gradient and it diffuses to the left. This is consistent with eq. (5.17) when diffusion to the left is denoted by a negative value for j.

The mechanism

Our goal is to predict the value for D in terms of atomic parameters. To do this we focus our attention on an area δA drawn in the gas as shown in Fig. 5.7. If we can calculate the total number of atoms of one species crossing δA in unit time the flux will follow immediately. All those atoms which cross δA will, roughly speaking, have come from a region of the gas at a distance λ away from δA. (The truth—as expressed in eq. (5.11) and in Fig. 5.4—is that 37 per cent of the gas atoms will have a free path in excess of λ.) On this crude model *all* atoms starting from a greater distance than λ will be scattered and so will not pass through δA. It is clear that, because of the concentration gradient, more radioactive atoms will pass through δA moving to the left than will pass through δA moving to the right. (The reverse will, of course, be true

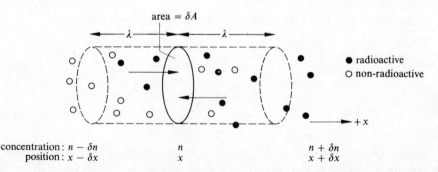

Fig. 5.7 Atoms crossing δA will have come from a region of the gas a distance λ away. Because of the concentration gradient more radioactive atoms will cross δA moving to the left per unit time than will cross δA moving to the right.

for the non-radioactive atoms.) If the local concentration of radioactive atoms at point $x - \delta x = x - \lambda$ (Fig. 5.7) is $(n - \delta n)$ then, accepting the "one-sixth" model (eq. (5.14)) the number of radioactive atoms moving to the right through δA per unit time is $\frac{1}{6}(n - \delta n)\bar{u}\,\delta A$. The number passing to the left through δA per unit time is $\frac{1}{6}(n + \delta n)\bar{u}\,\delta A$, where $(n + \delta n)$ is the concentration of radio-active atoms at point $x + \delta x = x + \lambda$. Therefore

$$\begin{array}{l}\text{net number of radioactive atoms passing}\\ \text{through } \delta A \text{ per unit time}\end{array} = \tfrac{1}{6}(n + \delta n)\bar{u}\,\delta A - \tfrac{1}{6}(n - \delta n)\bar{u}\,\delta A$$

$$= \tfrac{1}{3}\,\delta n\,\bar{u}\,\delta A$$

The number crossing per unit area per unit time—the flux—is therefore given by

$$j = -\tfrac{1}{3}\,\delta n\,\bar{u}$$

where we have inserted a minus sign to denote the fact that the radioactive species diffuse to the left. Multiplying the right-hand side by $\lambda/\lambda (=1)$ gives

$$j = -\tfrac{1}{3}\lambda\bar{u}\,\frac{\delta n}{\lambda}$$

or, since $\delta x = \lambda$

$$j = -\tfrac{1}{3}\lambda\bar{u}\,\frac{\delta n}{\delta x} \tag{5.18}$$

Comparing eqs. (5.17) and (5.18) we see that

$$D = \tfrac{1}{3}\lambda\bar{u} \tag{5.19}$$

By itself, eq. (5.19) is not very exciting. Indeed it is hardly unexpected. If you have ever watched people "diffusing" across a road, say, when another crowd of people were "diffusing" in the opposite direction you will have noticed that the faster everyone moves (i.e., the greater their $\bar{u}$) the faster do they get places. You will also have noticed that the fewer people there are trying to cross, the greater is their "mean free path" between successive collisions, and again the greater is their diffusion rate. Had eq. (5.19) come up as, say, $D \propto 1/\lambda\bar{u}$ we would have known that something was amiss. (You would also have known something was amiss because D and $1/\lambda\bar{u}$ are in quite different units.) As is so often the case, one can learn much from analogues.

Predictions
At a fixed temperature we know that $\bar{u}$ is constant and that $\lambda \propto 1/p$ (eq. (5.5)). Therefore we predict, from eq. (5.19), that

$$D \propto \frac{1}{p} \quad \text{at a fixed temperature} \tag{5.20}$$

135

At a fixed pressure $\lambda \propto T$ (eq. 5.5)). Furthermore $\bar{u} \propto \overline{(u^2)}^{1/2}$—a result we will establish later (p. 209)—and $\overline{(u^2)}^{1/2} \propto T^{1/2}$ (eq. (3.29)). So $\bar{u} \propto T^{1/2}$. Therefore we predict, from eq. (5.19), that

$$D \propto T^{3/2} \text{ at a fixed pressure} \tag{5.21}$$

Testing the predictions

Figure 5.8 shows an apparatus used by T. R. Mifflin and C. O. Bennett in 1958 to study self-diffusion in argon at a fixed temperature but at pressures up to 3×10^7 Pa (300 times normal atmospheric pressure). In fact they studied the diffusion of radioactive ^{37}Ar ($A_r = 36 \cdot 96$) through stable natural argon ($A_r = 39 \cdot 95$) so a small correction had to be applied to allow for the slight difference in atomic masses. Essentially, the apparatus consisted of two chambers P and Q separated by a plug of porous bronze of length $l = 3 \cdot 8 \times 10^{-2}$ m. To perform the experiment argon at the same pressure was introduced into the two chambers. Initially chamber Q contained natural non-radioactive argon and chamber P contained natural argon with a trace of ^{37}Ar. As time progressed the radioactive argon diffused from P to Q. The concentration of ^{37}Ar in each chamber was obtained by monitoring the currents i_p and i_q flowing between the electrodes p and q and the surrounding steel case (Fig. 5.8). As we shall see in section 5.7 the (saturation) currents i_p and i_q are proportional to the *rates* at which ions are produced in chambers P and Q respectively. Now the rate of production of ions is proportional to the concentration of ^{37}Ar; so i_p and i_q are proportional to a concentration of ^{37}Ar in chambers P and Q respectively. Currents of order 10^{-12} A were typical.

Now we must discuss how to turn data about i_p and i_q—which we have just seen is tantamount to data about the concentrations of ^{37}Ar in chambers P and Q—into information about D. To simplify the discussion we will suppose that initially ($t = 0$) chamber P contains only ^{37}Ar and that chamber Q contains only non-radioactive argon. (The fact that ^{37}Ar was only present as a tracer

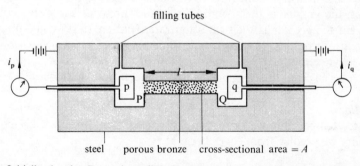

Fig. 5.8 Initially, chamber P contains radioactive argon and chamber Q contains non-radioactive argon. Interdiffusion occurs via the porous bronze plug.

in P does not fundamentally change the arguments.) If, at some later time t the concentration of ^{37}Ar is n_P in P and n_Q in Q the flux j of ^{37}Ar atoms through the plug is, from eq. (5.17), given by

$$j = -D(n_Q - n_P)/l = D(n_P - n_Q)/l \tag{5.22}$$

In applying eq. (5.17) in this manner we are assuming—justifiably as it happens —that the concentration gradient is confined to the plug and is linear.

The total number of ^{37}Ar atoms flowing per unit time through the plug of area A is, of course, given by Aj. But, since the system is in a state of (dynamic) equilibrium, the number of ^{37}Ar atoms flowing through the tube per unit time must equal the gain in Q of ^{37}Ar atoms per unit time and the loss in P per unit time. Both chambers P and Q had the same volume V so we can write

$$-\frac{d}{dt}(Vn_P) = Aj = AD\frac{(n_P - n_Q)}{l} \tag{5.23}$$

$$\frac{d}{dt}(Vn_Q) = Aj = AD\frac{(n_P - n_Q)}{l} \tag{5.24}$$

where we substituted for j from eq. (5.22). Combining eqs. (5.23) and (5.24) gives

$$\frac{d(n_P - n_Q)}{(n_P - n_Q)} = -\frac{2AD}{Vl}dt$$

which, when integrated, becomes,

$$\ln(n_P - n_Q) = \text{constant} - \left(\frac{2AD}{Vl}\right)t \tag{5.25}$$

Since the currents i_p and i_q—and it is these which are determined experimentally—are proportional to n_P and n_Q respectively, eq. (5.25) becomes

$$\ln(i_p - i_q) = \text{constant} - \left(\frac{2AD}{Vl}\right)t \tag{5.26}$$

A graph of $\ln(i_p - i_q)$ plotted against t should therefore be linear with a gradient of value $-2AD/Vl$. Figure 5.9 shows such a plot, obtained at a pressure of $1\cdot56 \times 10^7$ Pa and at a temperature of 323 K. This graph has a gradient of magnitude

$$\frac{3\cdot89 - 2\cdot77}{40} \text{ hour}^{-1} = 7\cdot8 \times 10^{-6}\,\text{s}$$

Equating this to $2AD/Vl$ and substituting the values of A, V, and l for the apparatus gives $D = 1\cdot48 \times 10^{-7}$ m^2 s^{-1}. This is, of course, the diffusion coefficient of ^{37}Ar in stable natural argon of relative atomic mass 39·95. A

137

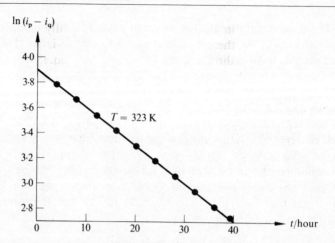

Fig. 5.9 Shows how the logarithm of the difference in the ion currents in chambers P and Q of the apparatus shown in Fig. 5.8 varies with time. (Data from T. R. Mifflin and C. O. Bennett, *J. Chem. Phys.*, **29**, 975 (1959).)

small correction is necessary to convert this coefficient to the self-diffusion coefficient of natural argon. When this correction is made the self-diffusion coefficient comes out as 1.45×10^{-7} m^2 s^{-1} at a pressure of 1.56×10^7 Pa and at a temperature of 323 K. When the experiment was repeated at different pressures p (which must, of course, be the same in both chambers P and Q) the results shown in Fig. 5.10 were obtained. Here Dp is plotted against p. According to our atomic model (eqs. (5.20)) Dp should be constant, independent of p, at a fixed temperature. (Why is this a better way of presenting the data than plotting D against $1/p$?) As Fig. 5.10 shows, Dp is indeed constant (to within at least about 25 per cent) over a four-fold change in pressure. The dashed line in Fig. 5.10 has been calculated on the assumption that argon

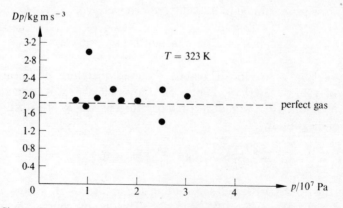

Fig. 5.10 Shows that Dp for argon is essentially independent of gas pressure. (Data from T. R. Mifflin and C. O. Bennett, *J. Chem. Phys.*, **29**, 975 (1959).)

obeys eq. (5.19) where λ is given by eq. (5.5). It has also been assumed that $d = 3\cdot3 \times 10^{-10}$ m and that $\bar{u} = 0\cdot922(\overline{u^2})^{1/2}$ (see page 209). Although Mifflin and Bennett did not change the temperature of the gas in their experiments other experiments show that, at constant pressure, D increases rather more rapidly with increasing T than the $\frac{3}{2}$-power suggested by eq. (5.21). We will shortly discover the reason for this discrepancy.

5.5 Viscous flow

The dynamic viscosity
We know from our everyday experiences that it takes an effort, albeit not a very great one, to pull a sheet of paper through the air. To make a less subjective study of such viscous properties we may contain a gas between two plates as shown in Fig. 5.11 and study how its flow characteristics depend on the applied force F, the area A of the moving plate, and on the velocity gradient of the gas. It is normally found that, at low values of F, the velocity gradient $\delta v_x / \delta y$ is the same throughout the gas, that is at all y. Here δv_x is the change in the value of the velocity v_x at which the gas *flows* as we shift a distance δy towards the moving plate. (One way to measure the velocity gradient is to introduce smoke at various levels between the plates and to photograph its position at two different times.) Experiments show that, at low flow rates,

$$\frac{F}{A} \propto \frac{\delta v_x}{\delta y}$$

$$\frac{F}{A} = \eta \frac{\delta v_x}{\delta y} \tag{5.27}$$

where the constant η is called the *dynamic viscosity* of the gas. As you can readily

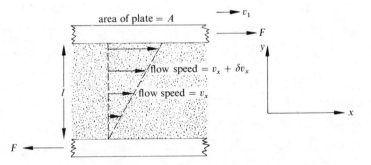

Fig. 5.11 A gas is contained between two parallel plates of (effectively) infinite area. The upper plate is pulled with a force F and the lower plate is kept stationary by applying an equal but oppositely directed force to that applied to the top plate. The vectors indicate the velocity of flow of the gas at various positions in the gas.

establish for yourself, in the SI system η is measured in units of Pa s or, the same thing, in units of kg m^{-1} s^{-1}. It is important to remember that v_x denotes the speed at which the *gas* flows. It does *not* refer to the r.m.s. speed of the gas *atoms,* which is usually many thousands of times greater than v_x. It is also important to note that $\delta v_x/\delta y$ is the velocity gradient *as measured in the gas.* As we shall shortly see, the layer of gas adjacent to each plate does not move with the speed of that plate; the layer adjacent to the top plate in Fig. 5.11 moves with a speed lower than v_1 and the layer adjacent to the lower plate is not at rest but moves to the right. Because of this "slip" the velocity gradient $\delta v_x/\delta y$ in the gas is *not,* in general, equal to v_1/l where v_1 is the speed of the moving plate and l is the separation of the plates. (The difference between $\delta v_x/\delta y$ and v_1/l is often so small that they can be taken as equal.)

An analogue

The following analogue suggests a mechanism which could account for the viscous properties of a gas. Consider four trains, A, B, C, and D, on parallel tracks. As they pass, passengers on each train throw missiles of mass m directly across to their neighbouring trains in the manner shown in Fig. 5.12(a). The person driving train A finds that every time a missile lands on his train the engine must provide the impulse necessary to change the momentum of that missile by $m(3\delta v_x - 2\delta v_x) = m \delta v_x$. When a fairly steady stream of missiles lands on his train the engine apparently provides a constant force $\bar{F}$ such that the area under the graph of $\bar{F}$ plotted against t is equal to the area of all the individual impulses provided in the time t (Fig. 5.12(b)). The driver of train A does *not* have to slow down the missiles which leave his train for train B—that is B's problem, not A's! Every time a missile arrives from A,

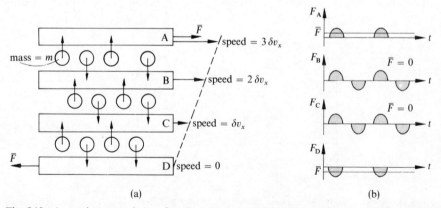

(a)   (b)

Fig. 5.12 An analogue to viscous flow in a gas. (a) As four trains A, B, C, and D moving at speeds $3\delta v_x$, $2\delta v_x$, δv_x, and 0, respectively, pass, missiles are fired from each train to its neighbouring trains. (b) The impulses required to keep the speed of each train constant.

train B provides the impulse of magnitude $m\,\delta v_x$ necessary to reduce its speed from $3\delta v_x$ to $2\delta v_x$. However, train B is also receiving missiles from train C and these must be speeded up by δv_x; so, on average, train B requires no force to keep it going at speed $2\delta v_x$ (assuming of course that it, like all the others, is frictionless). Exactly the same argument applies to train C (Fig. 5.12(b)). Train D, however, only receives missiles moving at speed δv_x and these must be brought to rest; as with A, the missiles leaving train D are no concern to D. So to remain at rest D's engine must provide a force equal and opposite to that provided by A's engine. These arguments implicitly assume that there is no accumulation of missiles on any train; for every missile that arrives, another one leaves that train. A moments thought will show that the net effect of this game is to produce a steady transfer of momentum from train A through to train D; a missile leaving A transfers momentum $m\,\delta v_x$ to B, another missile transfers momentum $m\,\delta v_x$ from B to C and, finally, yet another missile gives up momentum $m\,\delta v_x$ to D.

The mechanism in a gas
It is not difficult to see how the same basic mechanism might apply in a gas. Figure 5.13 shows a close-up of conditions near the plates of Fig. 5.11. Any atom which strikes a plate will, on average, have come from a distance of about λ into the gas. If we confine our attention to the top plate for the moment, an atom which strikes the top plate *and sticks* will have its flow (or drift) velocity increased from v', the flow velocity of the layer of gas at distance λ from the top plate, to v_1, the velocity of the top plate. In other

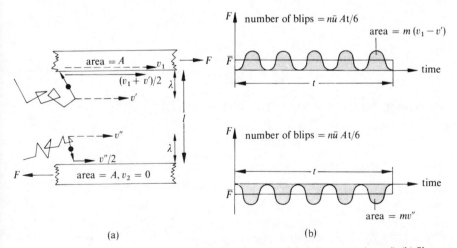

(a)   (b)

Fig. 5.13   An atom diffusing to the top plate will gain tangential momentum $m(v_1 - v')$. (b) Shows the series of impulses required to keep the top plate moving with speeds v_1, and to keep the lower plate stationary.

141

words, provided the atom sticks, even briefly, to the top plate its momentum to the right will have increased by $m(v_1 - v')$, where m is the atomic mass. This calls for an impulse of magnitude $m(v_1 - v')$ at each impact (Fig. 5.13(b)). What happens to these atoms when they eventually leave the top plate is of no concern to the person pulling the plate—*he* does not have to slow them down.

In a time t the total number of atoms impacting with the top plate is, adopting our "one-sixth" model (eq. (5.14)) given by $\frac{1}{6}(At n \bar{u})$, where A is the area of the plate and n is the number of atoms per unit volume in the gas. This therefore tells us the number of separate impulses—"blips" in Fig. 5.13(b)— to be provided by the person pulling the plate. Each "blip" has an area $m(v_1 - v')$, so the total area under all the "blips" in time t is $\frac{1}{6}(At n \bar{u}) m(v_1 - v')$. Just as we did in discussing the origins of gas pressure, we may equate this total area to $\bar{F}t$ where $\bar{F}$ is the apparently constant force provided by the person pulling the plate:

$$\bar{F}t = \tfrac{1}{6} At n \bar{u} m (v_1 - v')$$

$$\frac{\bar{F}}{A} = \tfrac{1}{6} n \bar{u} m (v_1 - v') \tag{5.28}$$

Now the mean flow velocity of the gas atoms immediately adjacent to the top plate will be the average of the flow velocity of an atom just before impact (v') and just after impact (v_1), that is $(v_1 + v')/2$ (see Fig. 5.13(a)). Since the velocity at a distance λ away is v', it follows that the velocity gradient is given by

$$\frac{\delta v_x}{\delta y} = \frac{\tfrac{1}{2}(v_1 + v') - v'}{\lambda}$$

$$\frac{\delta v_x}{\delta y} = \frac{v_1 - v'}{2\lambda} \tag{5.29}$$

Substituting for $(v_1 - v')$ from eq. (5.29) into eq. (5.28) gives

$$\frac{\bar{F}}{A} = \tfrac{1}{3} n m \bar{u} \lambda \frac{\delta v_x}{\delta y}$$

or

$$\frac{\bar{F}}{A} = \eta \frac{\delta v_x}{\delta y}$$

where η, the dynamic viscosity, is given by

$$\eta = \tfrac{1}{3} n m \bar{u} \lambda. \tag{5.30}$$

Although we looked at what happened at the top plate exactly the same expression for η would have been obtained had we chosen to look at the lower plate. You should satisfy yourself that this is so. In working this through for yourself you should note that the mean flow velocity immediately adjacent to the lower fixed plate is $v''/2$ where v'' is the flow velocity of the layer at $y = \lambda$ (Fig. 5.13(a)).

What we actually measure

In practice we never—well, hardly ever—measure the *true* velocity gradient $\delta v_x/\delta y$ present in the gas. What we measure is an *apparent* velocity gradient v_1/l; the velocity of the moving plate divided by its separation from the fixed plate. To relate these velocity gradients we look at the flow velocities of the gas immediately adjacent to each plate and at a distance λ away from each plate. These are shown afresh in Fig. 5.14. Looking, in turn, at triangles NPS, OPQ, and TRS we may immediately write down that

$$\frac{\delta v_x}{\delta y} = \tan \theta = \frac{1}{l}\left(\frac{v_1 + v'}{2} - \frac{v''}{2}\right) \tag{5.31}$$

$$\frac{\delta v_x}{\delta y} = \tan \theta = \frac{1}{\lambda}\left(\frac{v_1 - v'}{2}\right) \tag{5.32}$$

$$\frac{\delta v_x}{\delta y} = \tan \theta = \frac{1}{\lambda}\left(\frac{v''}{2}\right) \tag{5.33}$$

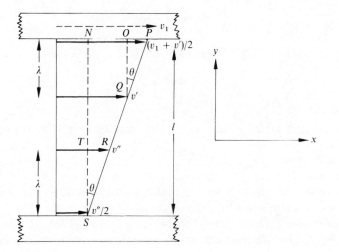

Fig. 5.14 Showing the true velocity gradient present during viscous flow. The apparent velocity gradient is v_1/l.

Substituting for v' and v'' as given by eqs. (5.32) and (5.33) into eq. (5.31) gives

$$\frac{\delta v_x}{\delta y} = \frac{v_1}{l + 2\lambda} \tag{5.34}$$

as the true velocity gradient in the gas. Substituting eq. (5.34) into our operational definition of dynamic viscosity (eq. (5.27)) gives

$$\frac{F}{A} = \eta \frac{v_1}{l} \left[\frac{1}{1 + (2\lambda/l)} \right] \tag{5.35}$$

Experiments tell us the apparent velocity gradient v_1/l with a known applied shear stress F/A. If we divide our value of F/A by our value of v_1/l we will be calculating an *apparent viscosity* η_{app}:

$$\eta_{app} = \frac{(F/A)}{(v_1/l)} \tag{5.36}$$

This is what all practical viscometers measure. Making use of eq. (5.35) gives

$$\eta_{app} = \eta \frac{1}{1 + (2\lambda/l)} \tag{5.37}$$

as the desired relation between the apparent dynamic viscosity which is measured experimentally (in eq. (5.36)) and the true dynamic viscosity which is required if we are to introduce the results of our microscopic discussion. In fact substituting for η from eq. (5.30) gives

$$\eta_{app} = \tfrac{1}{3} m n \bar{u} \left[\frac{\lambda}{1 + (2\lambda/l)} \right]$$

or, since $\lambda = 1/\pi d^2 n$ (eq. (5.4)) and $\bar{u} \approx (\overline{u^2})^{1/2} = (3kT/m)^{1/2}$ (eq. (3.29)),

$$\eta_{app} = \frac{1}{\pi d^2} \left(\frac{mkT}{3} \right)^{1/2} \frac{1}{1 + (2\lambda/l)} \tag{5.38}$$

For convenience later, λ has been left unaltered in the denominator.

Pressure dependence of η_{app}

As you saw in exercise 5.1, the mean free path λ of an nitrogen molecule in air at room temperature and at normal atmospheric pressure is about 10^{-7} m, which is much less than the separation l of the plates in any practical viscometer. Under such circumstances, where $\lambda \ll l$, eq. (5.38) predicts that the viscosity of a gas is independent of pressure. It should take the same effort to pull a card through the air whatever is the pressure of the gas (so long as $\lambda \ll l$)! The underlying reason for this prediction is not hard to find. If the

144

pressure p is, say, changed to $p/2$ this doubles the mean free path λ and halves the number density n. Doubling λ means an atom striking the plate has come from a point which is twice as far into the gas as before. It now comes from a region of lower flow velocity (Fig. 5.11) and arrives at the plate with only half the flow velocity it had at pressure p. To change its momentum to that of the top plate calls for double the impulse. However, because the value of n is halved the number of such impulses $(An\bar{u}/6)$ per unit time is halved. The person pulling the top plate therefore provides *half* the number of impulses as at pressure p, but each impulse is *double* its value at pressure p; so the average force $\bar{F}$ he provides is unaltered.

Figure 5.15 shows that the apparent viscosity of air is indeed constant, independent of pressure, over a range of pressures from 10^3 Pa to 10^6 Pa. At low pressures the viscosity starts to fall when λ becomes comparable with l. Such a fall in η_{app} is predicted from eq. (5.38) of course. However, when careful measurements are made η_{app} is found to decrease even more rapidly with increasing λ (which is related to p by eq. (5.5); $\lambda = kT/\pi d^2 p$) than is allowed for in eq. (5.38). Something has evidently not been allowed for in our discussions.

The effect of non-sticking atoms

Throughout our discussions we have assumed that when a gas atom strikes the moving plate it will "stick" for sufficient time for its flow velocity to be increased from v' to v_1 (Fig. 5.13(a)). However, we know from section 4.4 that while a large fraction, say σ, of atoms incident on a surface do stick, a certain fraction $(1 - \sigma)$ are specularly reflected with the result that their momenta parallel to the surface of the solid are unchanged in the collision (eq. (4.5)). So when many gas atoms, each with a flow velocity v' and therefore

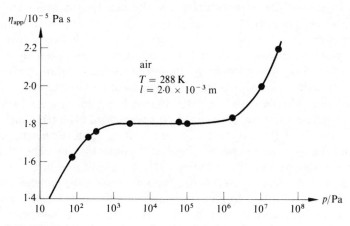

Fig. 5.15 Shows how the apparent viscosity of air depends on the pressure of the air.

145

a tangential momentum mv', arrive at the upper surface (Fig. 5.13(a)) which has a velocity v_1, the momentum of each atom will, on average, increase by

$$m[\sigma v_1 + (1 - \sigma)v'] - mv' = m\sigma(v_1 - v') \tag{5.39}$$

You can see that this makes sense by setting $\sigma = 0$, corresponding to wholly specular reflection (no change in tangential momentum) and by setting $\sigma = 1$, corresponding to every atom sticking, albeit temporarily. Equation (5.28) should therefore be replaced by

$$\frac{\bar{F}}{A} = \tfrac{1}{6}n\bar{u}m\sigma(v_1 - v') \tag{5.40}$$

If one now follows through the same detailed arguments as before one finds that eq. (5.38) becomes

$$\eta_{app} = \frac{1}{\pi d^2}\left(\frac{mkT}{3}\right)^{1/2}\frac{1}{1 + (2\lambda/l)[(2 - \sigma)/\sigma]}$$

Cross-multiplying this equation and setting $\lambda = kT/\pi d^2 p$ (eq. (5.5)) gives

$$\frac{1}{\eta_{app}} = \pi d^2\left(\frac{3}{mkT}\right)^{1/2} + \frac{1}{pl}\left(\frac{12kT}{m}\right)^{1/2}\left(\frac{2 - \sigma}{\sigma}\right) \tag{5.41}$$

A practical viscometer

To check out the correctness or otherwise of eq. (5.41) calls for some very careful measurements of η_{app} at a variety of pressures. In making any measurement of viscosity we would find it very inconvenient to use a straight parallel plate viscometer (Fig. 5.11). Quite apart from the fact that such an instrument would be inconveniently long we would be plagued with troubles at the leading and trailing edges of the moving plate. The size problem could be got over by replacing the moving plate with a long belt moving endlessly over rollers but this would still leave problems where the belt turned over. An obvious solution, which solves both problems, is to use two concentric cylinders as shown schematically in Fig. 5.16. The gas is confined between two vertical coaxial cylinders; one of which R is rotated at constant speed by a motor; and the other S is suspended by a fine tension wire W whose twist can be measured by shining a beam of light off a mirror and onto a scale.

The rotating cylinder feeds tangential momentum into the gas which is then transferred across the body of the gas to the suspended cylinder, which rotates until the torque of the suspension is sufficient to remove this momentum. When this happens the inner cylinder will come to rest. The suspended cylinder S is shorter than the rotating cylinder; above and below S are two fixed "guard" cylinders G_1 and G_2 of the same external diameter as S. The purpose of these guards is to greatly reduce end effects. The entire apparatus is located within a sealed container so that the pressure, temperature, and gas composition can be changed at will.

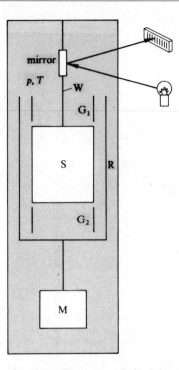

Fig. 5.16 A rotating cylinder viscometer. The outer cylinder R is rotated at constant speed by a motor M. The force necessary to keep the inner cylinder at rest is provided by a torsion wire W whose twist is measured by shining a beam of light off a mirror attached to the wire.

Because of the circular geometry, the relationship between the apparent viscosity, the speed of rotation of the outer cylinder and the separation of the cylinders is more complex than with parallel-plate geometry. Nevertheless theory predicts that at a fixed temperature a graph of $1/\eta_{app}$ (with a constant rotational speed of the outer cylinder η_{app} is proportional to the twist of the suspension wire supporting the inner cylinder) plotted against $1/p$ should be linear with a gradient proportional to $(2 - \sigma)/\sigma$. This is just what we predicted with parallel-plate geometry (eq. (5.41)).

Figure 5.17 shows results obtained for nitrogen and oxygen in a viscometer whose inner and outer cylinders were of aluminium. The best fit between theory and experiment is obtained by assigning $\sigma = 0.90$, i.e., by assuming that 90 per cent of the gas atoms striking the surface stick and that only 10 per cent are specularly reflected with no change in tangential momentum. This value for σ is compatible with the value obtained in beam-scattering experiments (p. 105).

You may have felt that this discussion of how momentum is transferred from a solid to a gas to have been obsessed with details and quite devoid of any real-life application. Yet the life-time of a satellite in (low) earth orbit

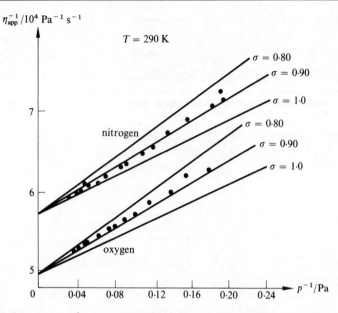

Fig. 5.17 Showing how η_{app}^{-1} varies with p^{-1} for N_2 and O_2 maintained at 290 K. The lines labelled $\sigma = 0.8$, $\sigma = 0.9$, and $\sigma = 1.0$ show the behaviour to be expected at these different values of σ. (Data from F. C. Hurlbut, *Phys. of Fluids*, **3**, 541 (1960).)

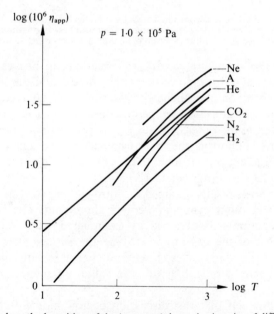

Fig. 5.18 Showing how the logarithm of the (apparent) dynamic viscosity of different gases varies with the logarithm of the temperature. All measurements were made at atmospheric pressure. The temperature T was measured in K and the viscosity η_{app} in Pa s.

depends on these fine details! We have seen (eq. (5.40)) that the tangential drag force per unit area ($|\bar{F}/A|$) on a plate moving through a gas is proportional to σ. To make an accurate prediction of the life-time of a satellite (or the precise trajectory of a high altitude missile) we must know the drag force, and therefore σ. In the ultra-high vacuum conditions of outer space surfaces will degas naturally and may very well become so clean that a large proportion of collisions with the surface are specular. Earth-bound simulations of conditions likely to be found in space give values of σ of around 0·5 when gold is struck by ionized inert gas atoms possessing velocities likely to be encountered in space. Such information on the values of σ is clearly of great value in deciding which material should be used for the exterior of, say, a satellite. What was an academic nicety in the 1930s has become of great practical importance in the 1970s.

Temperature dependence of viscosity

According to eq. (5.38) the apparent dynamic viscosity of a gas should be proportional to $T^{1/2}$ (provided $\lambda \ll l$), or a graph of $\log \eta_{\text{app}}$ against $\log T$ should be linear and have a gradient of 1/2. Figure 5.18 shows such a graph for a variety of gases (all at normal atmospheric pressure). Although roughly linear, as predicted, the gradients of these plots are greater than the value of 1/2 predicted by our simple model. Since (at $l \gg \lambda$) eq. (5.38) states

$$\eta_{\text{app}} = \frac{1}{\pi d^2}\left(\frac{mkT}{3}\right)^{1/2} \tag{5.42}$$

we could account for the discrepancy if πd^2 were to *decrease* with increasing T, that is with increasing atomic speed. Actually, this possibility is not so remote as it might seem. You will recall that the term $1/\pi d^2$ in eq. (5.42) arose from $\lambda = 1/\pi d^2 n$. You will also recall that in deriving this expression for λ we assumed the atoms were hard spheres of diameter d (Fig. 5.3)—

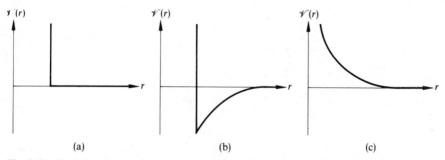

Fig. 5.19 The interatomic potential energy of (a) two hard spheres without any attractive force, (b) two hard spheres with an attractive force, and (c) two spheres with "soft" repulsion but without any attractive force.

149

in fact that the interatomic potential has the form shown in Fig. 5.19(a). Since this potential could not adequately account for the equation of state of a real gas it is hardly surprising that it is inadequate in discussing the details of viscosity. A better potential—the one that we assumed in deriving van der Waals' equation—is shown in Fig. 5.19(b). The effect of the attractive interatomic force (implicit in the negative potential energy in Fig. 5.19(b)) is to cause the hard-sphere atoms, which would otherwise have missed one another, to collide. Consider atom i in Fig. 5.20. Had the interatomic potential the form indicated in Fig. 5.19(a), atom i would have continued along the linear path AB shown in Fig. 5.20 and would have missed j. On "switching on" the attractive force—that is, adopting the potential model of Fig. 5.19(b)—atom i might still miss j (Fig. 5.21(a)), it might collide with j (Fig. 5.21(b)), or it might just miss j (Fig. 5.21(c)). Which happens will clearly depend on the speed of i (strictly speaking, it will depend on the relative velocity of i and j). If i is moving at a very high speed (as will happen if the gas is at a high temperature) then its path will not be bent much (Fig. 5.21(a))—the "cross-section" which j presents to i is really πd^2. If i is moving slowly (as will happen at low temperature) it can get "sucked into" j; so j presents a larger cross-sectional area. In other words, "πd^2" goes down as T goes up; or $1/\pi d^2$ goes up as T goes up. This can explain why η_{app} increases more rapidly than $T^{1/2}$ as predicted by eq. (5.42). A different approach is to assume the interatomic potential of Fig. 5.19(c). The argument now runs that the greater the kinetic energy of a colliding atom the deeper can it penetrate the repulsive force field of the atom with which it collides. In other words the greater their kinetic energy the smaller is the effective cross-sectional area of the atoms. Since $\frac{1}{2}mu^2 \propto T$ this decreasing area with increasing T could also account for the departures from eq. (5.42).

While both these approaches can separately be made quantitative, it is much more difficult to discuss analytically what happens when there is a weak attractive force followed by soft-sphere repulsion, that is, to combine two

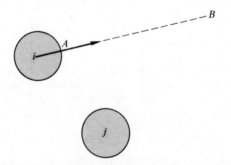

Fig. 5.20 With no attractive force between atoms i and j, atom i would follow path AB and would not collide with j.

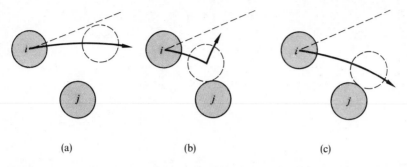

Fig. 5.21 With an attractive force present between atoms i and j one of three things may happen. As shown in (a), atom i may still miss j. It may, as in (b), collide with j or, as in (c), it may just miss j. Which happens depends on the velocity of i (relative to that of j).

curves; Fig. 5.19(b) and (c). Despite the difficulties it has been possible to determine the constants in a Lennard-Jones potential model (eq. (2.15)) by studying how the viscosity of a gas varies with temperature.

Exercise 5.3

This exercise enables you to check up on your understanding of the basic mechanism responsible for gaseous viscosity.

Three goods trains carrying coal move in the same direction along parallel tracks; the outer one at 50 m s^{-1}, the middle one at 45 m s^{-1} and the inner one at 40 m s^{-1}. As they pass, a team of men on each train shovel coal onto their nearest neighbouring train (two trains in the case of the two teams on the middle train). Every 3 s each of the teams shovels 10^3 kg of coal onto their neighbouring train. The total mass of each train therefore does not change. The driver of the fastest train finds his engine has to pull harder to maintain speed. Why, and by how much? The driver of the middle train finds that his engine does not have to pull any harder. Why? The driver of the slowest train finds he has to apply the brakes. Why, and what is the braking force applied to the train?

5.6 Thermal conduction

The thermal conductivity

If one encloses a gas between two parallel plates each of area A and separated by a distance l (Fig. 5.22) and if the plates are at temperatures T_1 and T_2 with $T_1 > T_2$ then one finds that heat is conducted through the gas at a rate $|\Phi|$ which is proportional to A and to the magnitude of the temperature gradient $|\delta T|/|\delta x|$ as measured *in the gas*, that is

151

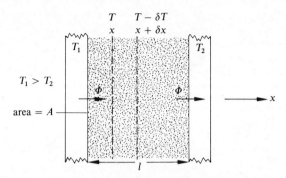

Fig. 5.22 A gas is contained between two parallel plates each of (effectively infinite) area A. The left-hand plate is maintained at temperature T_1; the right-hand plate at a lower temperature T_2. Heat energy flows at a rate Φ from the left to the right-hand plate.

$$|\Phi| \propto A \frac{|\delta T|}{|\delta x|}$$

$$|\Phi| = \kappa A \frac{|\delta T|}{|\delta x|} \tag{5.43}$$

where κ is called the *thermal conductivity* of the gas. Since Φ is measured in $J\,s^{-1}$, A in m^2, T in K, and x in m it follows that κ is measured in units of $J\,s^{-1}\,m^{-1}\,K^{-1}$ or, since watt (W) means $J\,s^{-1}$, in units of $W\,m^{-1}\,K^{-1}$. By way of example, if heat is conducted at a rate of $4 \times 10^{-3}\,J\,s^{-1}$ between the plates shown in Fig. 5.22 (each of area, say, $10^{-4}\,m^2$) and if the temperature in the gas at the left-hand dashed plane in Fig. 5.22 is 310 K and at the right-hand dashed plane, a distance 3×10^{-3} m away, is 310·6 K the temperature gradient *in the gas* has a magnitude $|\delta T|/|\delta x| = |310\,K - 310\cdot6\,K|/3 \times 10^{-3}\,m = 2 \times 10^2\,K\,m^{-1}$ and therefore $\kappa = (4 \times 10^{-3}\,J\,s^{-1})/(10^{-4}\,m^2)(2 \times 10^2\,K\,m^{-1}) = 0\cdot2\,W\,m^{-1}\,K^{-1}$.

To avoid having to couple the wordy statement "the heat flows from the region of higher temperature to the region of lower temperature" to eq. (5.43) we write

$$\Phi = -\kappa A \frac{\delta T}{\delta x} \tag{5.44}$$

The temperature gradient shown in Fig. 5.22 is negative (see Fig. 5.23) and heat flows to the right. The negative sign in eq. (5.44) therefore means that heat flow to the right has a positive value (κ is always taken as having a positive value). It is important to note that $\delta T/\delta x$ is the temperature gradient as it exists in the gas; it is not, in general, equal to the apparent temperature gradient $(T_1 - T_2)/(-l) = (T_2 - T_1)/l$.

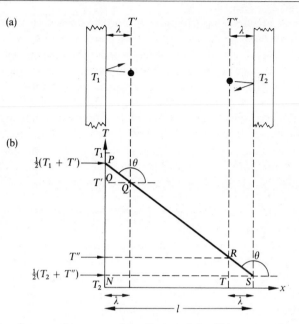

Fig. 5.23 (a) Gas atoms acquiring energy from the hot plate will have come from a distance of about λ into the gas. Atoms giving energy up to the cold plate will likewise have come from a distance of λ into the gas. (b) The temperature gradient present in the gas during thermal conduction.

How κ is measured

Equation (5.44) only applies if there are no convection currents present. These currents can be avoided by having large, parallel, closely-separated, horizontal plates with the upper plate at the higher temperature.

Almost all recent measurements of κ have been made using a *hot-wire cell*. This comprises a cylindrical tube which contains the gas to be studied. A fine wire, lying along the axis of the cylinder, is heated electrically. The energy Φ released per unit time in the wire is the product of the current i flowing through the wire and the potential difference across it (if i is in amp and V is in volt, Φ is in watt). The temperature of the wire is found from its resistance (V/i).

Once a steady state is reached $\Phi = Vi$ is measured, as is the temperature of the wire and the temperature of the surrounding cylinder (normally kept in a constant temperature bath). This enables κ to be calculated (via an integrated form of eq. (5.44)).

The mechanism in a gas

It is not difficult to guess how heat is conducted through a gas. Figure 5.23(a) shows a close-up of conditions near the two plates of Fig. 5.22. Any atom striking these plates will, on average, have come from a distance λ into the

153

gas. If we look at what happens near the hot plate (which is at temperature T_1) we see that when an atom strikes this plate its energy will, on average, increase from $\frac{3}{2}kT'$ to $\frac{3}{2}kT_1$. In other words, its energy will increase by $\frac{3}{2}k(T_1 - T')$. (If you have forgotten that the average energy of a gas atom is given by $\frac{1}{2}mu^2 = \frac{3}{2}kT$ see eq. (3.29).) However the gas atom does not hold on to its extra energy for ever. After leaving the hot plate it will suffer a collision in a "layer" distant λ from the plate. Energy acquired by this layer of atoms will be passed from "layer" to "layer" through the gas to the cold plate. Every time the cold plate is struck by a gas atom that atom will, on average, give up an energy $\frac{3}{2}k(T'' - T_2)$ to that plate. The net result is that there is a steady transfer of energy from the plate at temperature T_1 to the plate at temperature T_2.

In a time t the total number of atoms impacting with the hot plate is, adopting a "one-sixth" model (eq. (5.14)), given by $\frac{1}{6}(Atn\bar{u})$, where A is the area of the plate and $\bar{u}$ is the mean thermal speed. (In what follows we shall assume the temperature difference $T_1 - T_2$ is small in comparison with T_1 or T_2. This means that $\bar{u} \propto T^{1/2}$ may be taken as constant throughout the gas.) Since each atom has its energy increased by $\frac{3}{2}k(T_1 - T')$ on striking the hot plate, the energy given up to the gas per unit time is

$$\frac{1}{6}\left(\frac{Atn\bar{u}}{t}\right)\frac{3}{2}k(T_1 - T') = \frac{1}{4}An\bar{u}k(T_1 - T')$$

and this represents the heat flow Φ across the gas. Therefore

$$\Phi = -\tfrac{1}{4}An\bar{u}k(T' - T_1) \tag{5.45}$$

The average temperature of the gas atoms immediately adjacent to the hot plate is the average of their temperature (T') just before impact and their temperature (T_1) just after impact, that is the mean temperature is $\frac{1}{2}(T_1 + T')$. Since the temperature a distance $\delta x = \lambda$ away is T' it follows that

$$\frac{\delta T}{\delta x} = \frac{T' - \frac{1}{2}(T_1 + T')}{\lambda}$$

$$\frac{\delta T}{\delta x} = \frac{(T' - T_1)}{2\lambda} \tag{5.46}$$

Substituting for $T' - T_1$ from eq. (5.45) into eq. (5.46) gives

$$\Phi = -\tfrac{1}{2}n\bar{u}\lambda kA\frac{\delta T}{\delta x}$$

Comparing this with eq. (5.44) we see that κ, the thermal conductivity, is given by

$$\kappa = \tfrac{1}{2}n\bar{u}\lambda k \tag{5.47}$$

What we actually measure

In practice one never measures the actual temperature gradient $\delta T/\delta x$. What one measures is $(T_2 - T_1)/l$. To find the relation between the actual temperature gradient $\delta T/\delta x$ and the apparent temperature gradient $(T_2 - T_1)/l$ we (not surprisingly in view of the procedure we adopted in discussing viscous flow) write down three expressions for the temperature gradient. Looking in turn at triangles NPS, OPQ, and TRS we see that (Fig. 5.23(b))

$$\frac{\delta T}{\delta x} = \tan \theta = \frac{\frac{1}{2}(T_1 + T') - \frac{1}{2}(T_2 + T'')}{(-l)} = \frac{T_2 + T'' - T_1 - T'}{2l} \tag{5.48}$$

$$\frac{\delta T}{\delta x} = \tan \theta = \frac{\frac{1}{2}(T_1 + T') - T'}{(-\lambda)} = \frac{T' - T_1}{2\lambda} \tag{5.49}$$

$$\frac{\delta T}{\delta x} = \tan \theta = \frac{T'' - \frac{1}{2}(T_2 + T'')}{(-\lambda)} = \frac{T_2 - T''}{2\lambda} \tag{5.50}$$

Substituting for T' and T'' as given by eqs. (5.49) and (5.50) into eq. (5.48) gives

$$\frac{\delta T}{\delta x} = \frac{T_2 - T_1}{l + 2\lambda}$$

Substituting this expression for $\delta T/\delta x$ into the operational definition of thermal conductivity (eq. (5.44)) gives

$$\frac{\Phi}{A} = -\kappa \frac{(T_2 - T_1)}{l} \left[\frac{1}{1 + (2\lambda/l)} \right] \tag{5.51}$$

Experiments tell us the heat current flowing per unit area of plate Φ/A when the applied temperature gradient is $(T_2 - T_1)/l$. If we divide our measured Φ/A by our measured $(T_2 - T_1)/l$ we will be calculating an *apparent thermal conductivity* κ_{app}

$$\kappa_{app} = -\frac{\Phi/A}{(T_2 - T_1)/l}$$

Applying this definition of κ_{app} to eq. (5.51) gives

$$\kappa_{app} = \kappa \left[\frac{1}{1 + (2\lambda/l)} \right] \tag{5.52}$$

or, substituting for κ from eq. (5.47)

$$\kappa_{app} = \frac{1}{2} n \bar{u} \lambda k \frac{1}{1 + (2\lambda/l)}$$

Since $\lambda = 1/\pi d^2 n$ (eq. (5.4)) and $\bar{u} \approx (\overline{u^2})^{1/2} = (3kT/m)^{1/2}$ (eq. (3.29))

$$\kappa_{app} = \frac{k}{2\pi d^2} \left(\frac{3kT}{m} \right)^{1/2} \frac{1}{1 + (2\lambda/l)} \tag{5.53}$$

155

Pressure and temperature dependence of κ

As with viscosity, so the thermal conductivity of a gas should be independent of pressure provided $\lambda \ll l$ (eq. (5.53)).

Figure 5.24 shows that the apparent thermal conductivity of argon does indeed remain constant over a ten-thousand fold change in pressure. As with η_{app} (Fig. 5.15) the thermal conductivity κ_{app} starts to fall off when the m.f.p. λ of the gas atoms becomes comparable to the separation l of the plates in the conductivity cell.

Equation (5.53) also predicts that (provided $\lambda \ll l$) the apparent thermal conductivity of a gas should vary as $T^{1/2}$. Figure 5.25 shows that plots of $\log \kappa_{app}$ against $\log T$ are indeed nearly linear for neon, argon, and krypton but that their gradients are somewhat greater than 1/2. This is hardly surprising in view of the fact that η_{app} varies more rapidly than $T^{1/2}$. It is worth pointing out that although Fig. 5.25 records the apparent thermal conductivity κ_{app} of the gas, the pressure ($1 \cdot 0 \times 10^5$ Pa) is such that $\lambda \ll l$. Under these conditions κ_{app} and κ are identical (eq. (5.52)). Similarly, Fig. 5.18 may be taken as recording how $\log \eta$ varies with $\log T$ (see eq. (5.37) with $\lambda \ll l$).

Energy accommodation

In discussing the mechanism of thermal conduction we assumed that when gas atoms strike a solid surface they come into complete thermal equilibrium with it before they are returned to the gas phase. In terms of Fig. 5.23(a) we assumed that once an atom of kinetic energy $\frac{3}{2}kT'$ strikes a surface at temperature T_1 its energy on leaving that surface is $\frac{3}{2}kT_1$. Knowing, as we do, of the strange ways of atoms at surfaces, this assumption must be suspect.

Instead of supposing that, on average, an atom which strikes the surface with energy $\frac{3}{2}kT'$ leaves with energy $\frac{3}{2}kT_1$ we will (drawing on the procedure adopted in discussing viscous flow; in particular eq. (5.39)) suppose that it

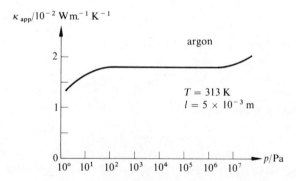

Fig. 5.24 Shows how the apparent thermal conductivity of gaseous argon remains constant despite a ten-thousand-fold change in pressure. (Data from F. G. Waelbroeck and P. Zuckerbrodt, *J. Chem. Phys.*, **28**, 523 (1958).)

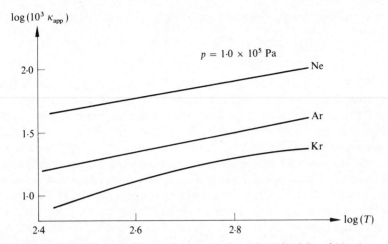

Fig. 5.25 Shows how the logarithm of the (apparent) thermal conductivity of Ne, Ar, and Kr varies with the logarithm of the temperature. The thermal conductivity κ_{app} is measured in units of $W\,m^{-1}\,K^{-1}$ and the temperature T in K. (Data from J. Kestin, W. Wakeham, and K. Watanabe, *J. Chem. Phys.*, **53**, 3773 (1970).)

leaves the plate with energy $\frac{3}{2}k[\alpha T_1 + (1 - \alpha)T']$; in other words that its energy has been increased by

$$\tfrac{3}{2}k[\alpha T_1 + (1 - \alpha)T'] - \tfrac{3}{2}kT' = \tfrac{3}{2}k\alpha(T_1 - T') \qquad (5.54)$$

The constant α is called the *accommodation coefficient*. If $\alpha = 1$ the energy of the colliding gas atom is increased from $\frac{3}{2}kT'$ to $\frac{3}{2}kT_1$—the maximum possible. If $\alpha = 0$ the gas atom acquires no energy from the surface. You can see that eq. (5.54) is consistent with this view of α. However tempting it is, in view of the similarities of eqs. (5.39) and (5.54), to equate α and σ, this cannot be done. The coefficient σ tells us about how a *vector* quantity—velocity (or momentum) —is accommodated at a surface. The coefficient α tells us about how a *scalar* quantity—energy—is accommodated at a surface. To change the momentum of an atom it is unnecessary to change its speed; you simply change its direction of motion. To change the kinetic energy ($\frac{1}{2}mu^2$) of an atom you *must* change its speed.

So, bringing α into the discussion, we should have written not eq. (5.45) but

$$\Phi = -\tfrac{1}{4}An\bar{u}k\alpha(T' - T_1)$$

This follows, of course, on adopting eq. (5.54) in place of the expression $\frac{3}{2}k(T_1 - T')$ for the energy increase of a colliding atom. On following through the same arguments as before one discovers that eq. (5.53) becomes

$$\kappa_{app} = \frac{k}{2\pi d^2}\left(\frac{3kT}{m}\right)^{1/2}\frac{1}{1 + (2\lambda/l)[(2 - \alpha)/\alpha]} \qquad (5.55)$$

157

or, cross-multiplying and substituting $\lambda = kT/\pi d^2 p$ (eq. (5.5)) that

$$\frac{1}{\kappa_{app}} = \frac{2\pi d^2}{k}\left(\frac{m}{3kT}\right)^{1/2} + \frac{1}{pl}\left(\frac{16mT}{3k}\right)^{1/2}\left(\frac{2-\alpha}{\alpha}\right)$$

A graph of $1/\kappa_{app}$ plotted against $1/p$ should therefore be linear with a gradient proportional to $(2-\alpha)/\alpha$. Figure 5.26 shows the results of such a study for air at 273 K. These results were obtained using a platinum hot-wire cell and indicate that the accommodation coefficient of air on platinum at 273 K is 0·8. The accommodation coefficient depends both on the gas and the surface and, in general, it varies with temperature. As a further example, the accommodation coefficient of helium on tungsten is 0·01 at 50 K; meaning that, on average, a helium atom only acquires 1 per cent of the energy it would have acquired were it to have come into thermal equilibrium with the tungsten surface. The practical significance of such low values for α should be obvious! At the domestic level the value of α determines for how long coffee will remain hot in a vacuum flask. (Thermal conduction through the residual gas in the evacuated walls is responsible for some—but not all—of the heat loss.)

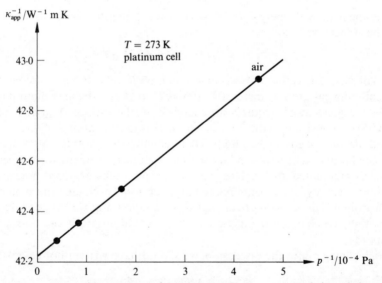

Fig. 5.26 Shows how κ_{app}^{-1} varies with p^{-1} for air. Measurements were made in a platinum hot-wire cell. (Data from W. J. Taylor and H. L. Johnston, *J. Chem. Phys.*, **14**, 219 (1946).)

5.7   Electrical conduction

Some basic facts

Let us think about what might happen in the experimental arrangement shown in Fig. 5.27(a). Here we have two parallel metal plates a distance l

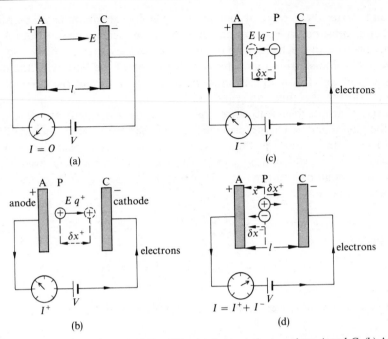

Fig. 5.27 (a) A constant electric field $E = V/l$ exists between the two plates A and C. (b) As the positive ion moves through δx^+ from position P, electrons flow in the external circuit. (c) As the negative ion moves through δx^- from position P, electrons flow in the external circuit. (d) When an ion pair is present the total current in the circuit is the sum of that in (b) and (c).

apart across which a battery of (fairly low) voltage V has been connected for some time. As you know, one of the plates (A) will be positively charged, the other (C) will be negatively charged, and there will be a steady electric field E of magnitude V/l between these plates. (If you like, we have a fully-charged capacitor.) Provided no ions are present in the gas between the plates, there will be no electric current I in the battery circuit.

Let us suppose that there is in fact a single positive ion of charge q^+ at some position P between the plates (Fig. 5.27(b)). Because of the electric field E this ion will experience a force Eq^+ directing it toward the negative plate. If, in the course of time δt, the positive ion moves a distance δx^+ along the field direction, it will acquire energy $(Eq^+)\delta x^+$ from the field (that is, "force × distance"). The ion is now closer to the negative plate—the *cathode* C—and further from the positive plate—the *anode* A—than it was formerly. As a result the electrical potential of C rises and that of A falls.* To restore

* You will recall that the electrical potential at a point is the energy required to bring unit *positive* charge up from infinity to the point in question. Having a positive ion close to C makes the task of bringing the unit positive charge up from infinity to C more difficult—the two repel one another. Moving the positive ion away from A lowers the potential of A since the task of bringing unit positive charge up from infinity to A is made easier.

159

C and A to their original potentials—thereby maintaining E constant—electrons must be driven through the external connecting circuit from A to C. (This transfer of electrons will, of course, raise the potential of A and lower that of C.) Transferring these electrons is the job of the battery. If the battery has a "voltage" V (or, strictly speaking an e.m.f. of V) and the current in the circuit during the time interval δt in question is I^+ (we use the $+$ sign to indicate that this (electron) current is induced by movement of a *positive* ion in the gas) then the energy provided by the battery is of magnitude $VI^+ \, \delta t$ ("volts $\times$ amps $\times$ time" in the SI system). This energy appears as the kinetic energy $Eq^+ \, \delta x^+$ which was acquired by the positive ion of charge q^+ as it moved through δx^+ in time δt in the field E. Conservation of energy clearly demands that

$$VI^+ \, \delta t = Eq^+ \, \delta x^+$$

or, since $E = V/l$

$$I^+ = \frac{q^+}{l} \frac{\delta x^+}{\delta t}$$

For consistency of later notation we shall write this in the form

$$I^+ = \frac{|q^+|}{l} \frac{\delta x^+}{\delta t} \tag{5.56}$$

as we may since $|q^+| = q^+$.

Because δx^+ is the distance gone by the ion in time δt it follows that $\delta x^+/\delta t$ is the velocity v^+ of the positive ion. Therefore

$$I^+ = \frac{|q^+|}{l} v^+ \tag{5.57}$$

Had there been a negative ion of charge q^- (that is a charge of magnitude $|q^-|$) at P in Fig. 5.27(c)... what would have happened? It would, of course, have been subjected to a force $E|q^-|$ and have moved in the opposite direction to that in which the positive ion moved. This movement would have lowered the potential of A and raised that of C. To restore A and C to their original potentials, electrons would yet again have had to be transferred from A to C. We will call this current, induced in the external circuit by the movement of the negative ion q^- in the tube, I^-. It is very important to note that I^+ and I^- are in the same sense (Figs. 5.27(b) and (c)). You should be able to show that the law of conservation of energy leads to

$$I^- = \frac{|q^-|}{l} \frac{\delta x^-}{\delta t} = \frac{|q^-|}{l} v^- \tag{5.58}$$

where δx^- is the distance q^- moves towards the anode in time δt, meaning its velocity is $v^- = (\delta x^-/\delta t)$.

160

Now consider the situation shown in Fig. 5.27(d). Here a pair of ions of equal, but opposite, charge have been created at point P. (You may like to picture an ionizing radiation knocking an electron out of one gas atom, turning that atom into a positive ion of charge $q^+ = e$. The ejected electron may then be captured by a neutral atom to form a negative ion of charge $q^- = -e$.) Clearly the *total* current I induced in the external circuit by movement of both these ions is given by

$$I = I^+ + I^-$$

$$I = \frac{1}{l}(|q^+|v^+ + |q^-|v^-) \qquad (5.59)$$

Finally, let us evaluate the *total charge* Q which flows in the external circuit in the situation shown in Fig. 5.27(d) in which q^+ travels from P to C and in which q^- travels from P to A. Since $dQ/dt = I$;

$$Q = \int I \, dt = \int (I^- + I^+) \, dt$$

or, substituting from eqs. (5.56) and (5.58) (expressed in the limit $\delta t \to 0$),

$$Q = \frac{|q^-|}{l} \int_0^x dx^- + \frac{|q^+|}{l} \int_x^l dx^+$$

As $|q^-| = |q^+|$ (remember they are an ion pair formed from a neutral atom) this becomes

$$Q = \frac{|q^+|}{l}[x + (l - x)]$$

$$Q = |q^+| = |q^-| \qquad (5.60)$$

In other words, the total *charge* which flows in the external circuit as a result of the formation of an ion pair in the gas, and the subsequent removal of the positive ion to the cathode and of the negative ion to the anode, has a magnitude equal to the charge of *one* of those ions.* The charge flowing through the external circuit is *not* $|q^+| + |q^-|$.

---

* This conclusion partially justifies a common description of what happens in the circuit of Fig. 5.27(d). This description runs as follows: the negative ion is attracted to the anode where it gives up its electron; the neutral atom so formed returns to the gas. The electron thereby released then travels through the external circuit to the cathode where it is deposited on a positive ion which has been attracted to this plate. Again a neutral atom results.

Our approach stresses the fact that, as positive ions move towards the cathode, electrons move through the wire to the cathode (where they will indeed eventually neutralize the positive ions). Likewise, negative ions approaching the anode will chase electrons away from that electrode. This enabled us to write the total current so "induced" as eq. (5.59). The more popular account of the process which ignores induced currents (we might call it the "dump-the-charge" approach) cannot predict the *current* in the circuit when a single negative ion travels to the anode and a single positive ion travels to the cathode.

The V–I characteristic

So far we have only considered how a single ion pair might behave in the circuit of Fig. 5.27(a). Figure 5.28 shows a set-up suitable for making a detailed study of how the circuit behaves when many ion pairs are present. Here a beam of X-rays ionizes the gas uniformly throughout its volume; apertures prevent the beam from falling onto the anode and cathode. The gas is enclosed within a glass bulb so that its composition, pressure, and temperature can be easily controlled. Because the resistance of the gas is (usually) very much greater than that of the rest of the circuit the potential difference across the tube may be taken as the battery voltage V.

If the applied voltage is gradually increased, keeping the intensity $\mathscr{I}$ of the X-ray irradiation constant, it is found that the current at first rises linearly, then more slowly, until it reaches a constant (saturation) value I_s (Fig. 5.29). If the intensity of the irradiation is doubled (we could do this by using two identical X-ray tubes operating under the same conditions to irradiate the gas) it is found that the initial linear rise in current is $2^{1/2}$ times more steep, and the saturation current is doubled. If the intensity of the irradiation is trebled, the linear region's slope goes up by a factor of $3^{1/2}$ and the saturation current is trebled, etc. With plates 10^{-1} m apart, 10^3 V might typically be required to produce saturation in air at atmospheric pressure.

We will content ourselves with trying to explain the initial linear rise in current and the constant saturation current which is observed at higher voltages (Fig. 5.29). Already you can probably guess that at saturation all the ions produced by the irradiation are collected by the anode and cathode. You can probably also guess that at lower voltages some of the positive and negative ions will recombine within the body of the gas before they can reach the plates. So we would expect the current to be lower when the voltage is reduced.

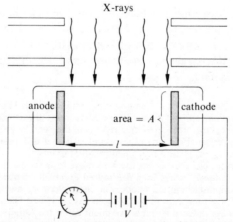

Fig. 5.28 A beam of X-rays uniformly irradiates gas contained between two plates. The current I is measured with different voltages V applied to the tube.

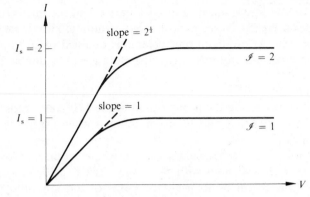

Fig. 5.29 The current-voltage characteristic of a partially ionized gas. If the intensity $\mathcal{I}$ of the X-ray beam in doubled the saturation current I_s is doubled but the slope of the initial linear portion of the characteristic only increases by a factor of $2^{1/2}$.

If the irradiation produces ions at a rate of dN/dt ion pairs per unit volume per unit time, it follows that the number of ion pairs being produced per unit time within the volume Al of the gas present in the tube (Fig. 5.28) is $(Al)\,dN/dt$. Therefore the number of positive ions being produced per unit time is $(Al)\,dN/dt$ and the number of negative ions being produced per unit time is $(Al)\,dN/dt$. (If a cook breaks 3 eggs s^{-1} he produces 3 yolks s^{-1} and 3 whites s^{-1}.) Since, at saturation, all the ions so produced are whisked off to the anode and cathode before they had the chance to recombine, it follows that the number of positive ions striking the cathode within a time t is $(Alt)\,dN/dt$. (The same number of negative ions will of course strike the anode.) Therefore the total charge Q_t which flows through the circuit in a time t is, appealing to eq. (5.60).

$$Q_t = Altq^+ \frac{dN}{dt}$$

where q^+ is the charge of an individual positive ion. The saturation current I_s in the circuit is therefore

$$I_s = \frac{Q_t}{t} = Alq^+ \frac{dN}{dt}$$

Now the rate of production of ions is proportional to the intensity $\mathcal{I}$ of the irradiation, so

$$I_s \propto \mathcal{I} \qquad (5.61)$$

which is in accord with experiment (Fig. 5.29). This saturated region of the V–I characteristic was that employed in the experiments of Mifflin and Bennett to measure the self-diffusion coefficient in argon. You will recall from p. 136 that in discussing these experiments we *assumed* that i_q, say, was proportional to the concentration of the radioactive ^{37}Ar in chamber Q

(Fig. 5.8). Since this ^{37}Ar concentration is a measure of the intensity $\mathscr{I}$ of the ionizing radiation, eq. (5.61) assures us that our assumption was in fact justified. (If the number of ^{37}Ar atoms in unit volume is doubled twice as many ions will be produced per unit volume of gas; therefore I_s will be doubled.)

A general result

As a prelude to considering the linear region of the $I-V$ characteristic we will look, generally, at what happens to an ion in a gas when the ion is subjected to an electric field.

In the absence of an electric field a gas ion will, of course, follow straight line paths in between collisions with gas atoms. As Fig. 5.30 shows, the effect of an electric field E will be to bend the paths of the ions into parabolas so that positive ions tend to move in the field direction, and negative ions in the opposite direction. A charge q^+ in an electric field E will, of course, be subjected to a force q^+E, that is it will accelerate at a rate q^+E/m in the field direction, where m is the mass of the ion.

If the ion travels freely for a time t_1 before it suffers a collision with a neutral atom, it will have acquired a final drift velocity of $(q^+E/m)t_1$ (that is, acceleration × time); in other words its average drift velocity during t_1 is $q^+Et_1/2m$. On colliding with a neutral atom the ion ceases to drift. It does not stop moving, it only stops drifting. The ion may now travel freely for a time t_2, say, collide and stop drifting yet again, and so on. This sequence of accelerations and collisions is shown graphically in Fig. 5.31. Since the average drift velocity in period t_1 is $q^+Et_1/2m$, in period t_2 is $q^+Et_2/2m$, in period t_3 is $q^+Et_3/2m$, etc., we may write down that

overall average drift velocity, v_d, over n collisions $= \dfrac{q^+E}{2m}\dfrac{(t_1 + t_2 + \cdots + t_n)}{n}$

$$v_d = \frac{q^+E\tau}{2m} \qquad (5.62)$$

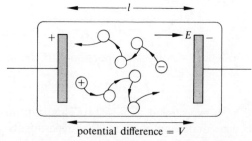

potential difference $= V$

Fig. 5.30 Shows how the free paths of a positive and a negative ion are bent under the influence of the electric field. As a result, the positive ion drifts in the field direction while the negative ion drifts in the opposite direction.

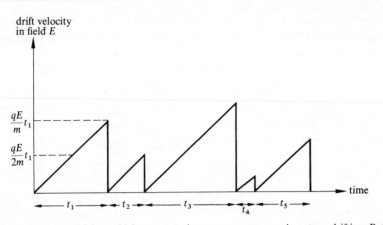

Fig. 5.31 After each collision, which occurs at times t_1, t_2, t_3, etc., an ion stops drifting. Between collisions it accelerates at a constant rate. So the mean drift velocity in any interval is one-half the maximum drift velocity attained by the ion in that interval.

where τ is the mean time between collisions of the ion with neutral atoms. Assuming that the drift velocity v_d is very much less than the mean thermal speed $\bar{u}$ we can write $\tau\bar{u} = \lambda$, or $\tau = \lambda/\bar{u}$, where λ is the ion's mean free path. Therefore

$$v_d = \frac{q^+ E \lambda}{2m\bar{u}}$$

or

$$\mu^+ = \frac{v_d}{E} = \frac{q^+ \lambda}{2m\bar{u}} \tag{5.63}$$

where μ^+ is known as the *mobility* of the ion—here the mobility of the positive ion. By definition, it tells us the drift speed of the ion in unit electric field. Since mobilities are normally quoted as positive quantities, the mobility μ^- of a negative ion must be written as

$$\mu^- = \frac{|v_d|}{E} = \frac{|q^-|\lambda}{2m\bar{u}} \tag{5.64}$$

The linear region of the I–V characteristic
Equation (5.59) tells us the current I induced in the external circuit of Fig. 5.28 when a *single* ion pair of charge $q^+ = -q^-$ (that is $|q^+| = |q^-|$) is present in the tube. If there are N ion pairs present per unit volume of the tube it follows that the total number of ion pairs present in the gas of volume Al is NAl and that the observed current I is

$$I = \frac{NAl}{l}\left(|q^+|v^+ + |q^-|v^-\right)$$

165

where v^+ and v^- are the *speeds* of the positive and the negative ions respectively. Substituting for the ions' speeds from eqs. (5.63) and (5.64) and recalling that $|q^-| = |q^+| = q^+$ gives

$$I = NAq^+(\mu^+ + \mu^-)E$$

If there are no "boundary effects" at the anode and cathode (akin to those in Fig. 5.23 which prevented us equating the true temperature gradient in a gas with $(T_2 - T_1)/l$), the electric field E has a magnitude of V/l, where V is the potential difference between the anode and cathode and l is their separation (Fig. 5.28). So

$$I = \frac{NAq^+}{l}(\mu^+ + \mu^-)V \qquad (5.65)$$

All that remains is to estimate N, the number of ion pairs present per unit volume of gas. At any instant we have

$$N = N^+ = N^- \qquad (5.66)$$

where N^+ and N^- are the number of positive and negative ions, respectively, present per unit volume of gas. (Remember that six eggs give six yolks and six whites.) Even if there were no electric field applied the number of ions present in the gas will not continue to grow indefinitely despite a constant *rate* dN/dt of ion production caused by the irradiation. This is because the greater N^+ and N^- the greater is the probability of a positive ion colliding with, and neutralizing, a negative ion. A state of equilibrium will soon be reached in which the rate of production of ion pairs by irradiation equals their rate of removal by neutralizing collisions. The probability of a particular positive ion colliding with a negative ion—any negative ion—is clearly going to be proportional to the negative ion concentration, N^-. The same is true for all N^+ positive ions in unit volume. So the overall rate at which neutralization occurs in unit volume will be proportional to the product of N^+ and N^-, that is to N^2 (see eq. (5.66)). Equating the rate of production to the rate of removal gives

$$\frac{dN}{dt} \propto N^2$$

$$\frac{dN}{dt} = \rho N^2 \qquad (5.67)$$

where the constant of proportionality ρ is called the *coefficient of recombination*. This equation only holds true in the absence of an external electric field. However it can be applied when there is a small current flowing through the gas, provided the number of ions neutralized by recombination in unit time is large compared with the number collected at the electrodes per unit time.

Substituting eq. (5.67) into eq. (5.65) gives

$$I = \frac{q^+ A}{\rho^{1/2}l}\left(\frac{dN}{dt}\right)^{1/2}(\mu^+ + \mu^-)V \qquad (5.68)$$

Since the rate of production of ion pairs dN/dt is proportional to the intensity $\mathscr{I}$ of the irradiation producing the ions, eq. (5.68) becomes

$$I \propto \mathscr{I}^{1/2} V$$

which accounts for the linear portion of the I–V characteristic (Fig. 5.29).

Boundary effects

When we discussed viscous flow and thermal conduction we concentrated on what happened at a solid surface. It was the *surface* which transferred momentum to (or received momentum from) the gas in the case of viscous flow. It was the *surface* which transferred energy to (or received energy from) the gas in the case of thermal conduction. So we are under some sort of obligation to see just how charge is transferred to (or from) the surface of an electrode in electrical conduction. On examining the consequences of these boundary effects we found that, in the case of viscous flow, the local velocity gradient was not v_1/l—the value calculated macroscopically (Fig. 5.14). In the case of thermal conduction the local temperature gradient at the plates was not $(T_2 - T_1)/l$ (Fig. 5.23). If, as we now do, we focus down on how charge is transferred to the anode (or from the cathode) we should be prepared to find that the local electric field is not V/l.

We will carry out this study by looking at the consequences of supposing that nothing strange happens in the vicinity of the anode and cathode of Fig. 5.28. We assume, in other words, that the electric field E is *constant,* of magnitude V/l at all points between the anode and cathode—or, equivalently, that the electrical potential increases linearly from cathode to anode (Fig. 5.32). This predicts that negative ions move up to the anode with a speed $\mu^- E$ (eq. (5.64)) and that positive ions move up to the cathode with a speed $\mu^+ E$ (eq. (5.63)). Since the total number of negative ions striking the anode within a time interval δt is all those within a cylinder of length $(\mu^- E)\,\delta t$ and area A, that is $N^-(\mu^- E\,\delta t)A$, it follows that the total charge deposited on the anode in time δt is $|q^-|N^-\mu^- E A\,\delta t$. Likewise the charge released at the cathode in time δt is of magnitude $q^+ N^+ \mu^+ E A\,\delta t$. Now dynamic equilibrium demands (as in eq. (5.60)) that these two charges be equal—that the charge deposited on the anode has the same magnitude as that given to the ions striking the cathode. But is

$$|q^-|N^-\mu^- E A\,\delta t = q^+ N^+ \mu^+ E A\,\delta t \tag{5.69}$$

or, since $|q^-| = q^+$ and $N^- = N^+$, is

$$\mu^- = \mu^+ ?$$

The answer is, in general, no; the mobility of positive and negative ions are usually different. This is because impurities "cluster" to a different extent about the positive and negative ions. As a result they have different masses and

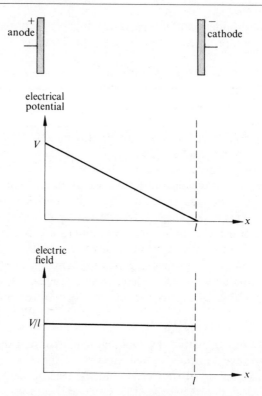

Fig. 5.32 A constant electric field of V/l results when the potential difference across the tube is V; *provided* there are no boundary effects at the anode and cathode.

therefore different mobilities (see eqs. (5.63) and (5.64)). We therefore cannot have a constant electric field throughout the tube; the electric field in the vicinity of the anode, E_a say, must be different to the field E_c in the vicinity of the cathode. Writing eq. (5.69) in a somewhat general form, the requirement that the same amount of charge be deposited on the anode as is released at the cathode in a given time interval becomes

$$N_a^- \mu^- E_a = N_c^+ \mu^+ E_c \qquad (5.70)$$

where N_a^- and N_c^+ are the number of negative and positive ions per unit volume of gas in the immediate vicinity of the anode and cathode respectively.

Figure 5.33 shows what does happen when an external electric field is applied to an ionized gas (Fig. 5.33(a)); the field moves the negative ions to the anode, the positive ions to the cathode (Fig. 5.33(b)). The effect of the positive charge is to raise the electrical potential in the vicinity of the cathode above the value it would have had were there no such "space charge" present; the effect of the negative charge is, of course, to lower the potential in the vicinity of the anode below the value it would have had with no space charge present

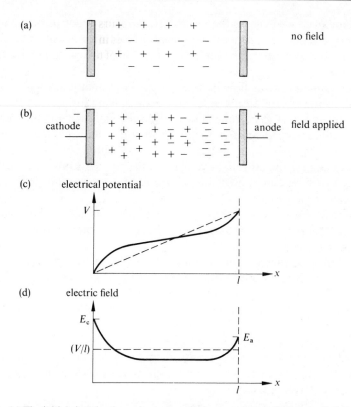

Fig. 5.33 (a) The initial situation in an ionized gas before an electric field is applied. (b) When a field is applied ions drift towards the anode and cathode. (c) The electrical potential in the gas. (d) The electric field in the gas. Notice how the local fields at the anode and cathode (E_a and E_c respectively) differ from the value of V/l which would apply were there no boundary effects.

(Fig. 5.33(c)). As a result of these space charges the local electric fields at the anode and cathode, E_a and E_c, differ from value E/l shown dashed in Fig. 5.33(d). We now have the wherewithal to satisfy eq. (5.70).

Summary

1. The probability that a gas atom will travel at least a distance l without suffering a collision with another gas atom is $\exp(-l/\lambda)$ where λ is the mean free path. On the assumption that gas atoms behave as hard spheres of radius d with no attractive force between them, $\lambda = 1/\pi d^2 n$, where n is the number of gas atoms per unit volume.

2. The number of atoms striking unit area of a surface per unit time is $\frac{1}{4}n\bar{u}$. Adopting a crude model in which, at any moment, $\frac{1}{6}$th of the gas atoms are imagined to be moving along the six cartesian coordinate directions, gives the number striking unit area per unit time as $\frac{1}{6}n\bar{u}$.

169

3. Diffusion occurs whenever there is a concentration gradient of a particular atomic species in a gas. As a result of a variable number density n throughout the gas more of these atoms will leave a region of high n than arrive there in unit time.

4. In maintaining viscous flow in a gas one is continually having to increase the momentum of gas atoms which strike the moving surface and to decrease the momentum of gas atoms which strike the stationary plate; one feeds momentum into a gas at the moving plate and removes it from the gas at the stationary plate. In an individual collision with a surface the gas atom usually acquires the tangential velocity of the surface. Only with very clean surfaces is there any appreciable failure for the momentum to be accommodated at the surface.

5. In thermal conduction energy is fed into the gas at the hot plate and removed from the gas at the cold plate. Energy accommodation at a surface is usually incomplete.

6. In electrical conduction in an ionized gas the current measured in the external circuit is the sum of the current induced as a result of movement of positive ions in the gas and the current induced as a result of movement of negative ions in the gas. Unless the current is saturated (constant independent of field) space charge effects near the plates will mean that the electric field is not equal to the potential difference between the plates divided by their separation. The field in the gas will be self-adjusting to ensure that the negative ion current striking the anode equals the positive ion current striking the cathode.

PROBLEMS

5.1 One way to simulate a two-dimensional gas is to vibrate randomly a tray of marbles back and forth over the surface of a table. If a tray has dimensions of $0.3 \text{ m} \times 0.3 \text{ m}$ and it contain 50 marbles, each of diameter 10^{-2} m, what will be the mean free path of a marble on the tray? What is the probability that a marble will travel the length of the tray without colliding with another marble? If you have a tray and marbles available you should try to make a rough and ready estimate of the mean free path. Is it in order of magnitude agreement with the theoretical value?

5.2 What is the mean free path of an electron moving through a gas composed of atoms of diameter d? Assume the electron has effectively zero diameter.

5.3 Invent a gas-kinetic problem for which the answer is "the mean free path is 10^{-5} m".

5.4 An oven contains silver vapour at a temperature of 1500 K. How many atoms will escape per second from a hole of area 10^{-7} m² cut in the wall of the oven? If you cannot answer this (or any other) problem because you feel inadequate information is given, state what further information is required to enable the problem to be solved.

5.5 A vessel is partially filled with liquid mercury and sealed, except for a hole of area 10^{-7} m², above the liquid level. This vessel is then placed in a highly evacuated (and continuously pumped) enclosure. After 30 days the vessel is reweighed and is found to be lighter by 2.4×10^{-5} kg. If the experiment was performed at a constant temperature of 273 K what is the vapour pressure of mercury at this temperature? ($A_r(Hg) = 200$.) Assume that the mean and the r.m.s. speed of a gas atom are equal and that eq. (5.15) applies.

5.6 Two vessels are separated from one another by a sheet of foil which is perforated with many holes each with a diameter and a length which is very much less than the gaseous mean free path. One chamber contains a gas of relative molecular mass M_1; the other contains a gas of relative molecular mass M_2. If both gases are at the same pressure, show that the initial rate at which the gas of relative molecular mass M_1 effuses into the gas of relative molecular mass M_2 is $(M_2/M_1)^{1/2}$ times the rate at which effusion occurs in the reverse direction. Assume the vessels to be at the same temperature. (*Effusion* differs from diffusion in that when a gas effuses it can "jump" from a region of constant pressure to another region of constant, and possibly different, pressure without colliding with another atom. In diffusion an atom suffers many collisions.)

5.7 Show that if the vessels of problem 5.6 contain a single species of gas atom, and if one vessel is maintained at a temperature T_1 while the other is maintained at T_2, the ratio of the pressure of the gas in the vessel at T_1 to the pressure in the vessel at T_2 is $(T_1/T_2)^{1/2}$ at equilibrium. This phenomenon is called *thermal transpiration*. It has important practical consequences in low temperature physics. Very often a vessel at a temperature of around 4 K is connected, via thin tubing of diameter very much less than the mean free path, to another vessel at room temperature where the pressure of the gas is measured. Many a physicist fails to realize he is not measuring the pressure in the low temperature vessel!

5.8 One way to simulate diffusion, as it occurs in say the apparatus of Fig. 5.8 is to line up eight pieces on one side of a chess board. Toss a coin to decide if the first piece advances a square: say "heads" for advance. Repeat the game for all eight pieces in turn. Now perform a second round of tosses but this time "tails" withdraw a piece one square (except when on the starting line). A round of tosses corresponds to the (constant) time of $\lambda/\bar{u}$ in the life of the gas as it diffuses. Plot a graph showing how the concentration varies with distance at different times after the commencement of diffusion. Your plot should display the main features sketched for one of the gases in Fig. 5.6. With a little ingenuity you may even be able to establish that eq. (5.25) is obeyed in this simulation. If it is obeyed, this simulation may be taken as vindicating the "random walk" nature of diffusion, as exhibited by the men on the chess-board.

5.9 Using the data given in Fig. 5.15 and any results reached in our discussion as to the microscopic origins of viscous flow, make a rough estimate of the diameter of an oxygen molecule.

5.10 As we have seen, heat conduction in a gas falls drastically when the gaseous mean free path becomes as large as the dimensions of the container. To what pressure should the 5×10^{-3} m space between the two glass envelopes in a vacuum flask be pumped? Assume that a nitrogen molecule has a diameter of 3.5×10^{-10} m and that the temperature is 300 K.

5.11 A layer of gas is sandwiched between two infinite parallel plates a distance l apart. One plate is fixed; the other moves with a velocity V. Assuming that the probability that an atom striking either plate will stick (for long enough for its tangential velocity to be increased to that of the plate) is σ, show that the true velocity gradient in the gas is $V/[l + 2\lambda(2 - \sigma)\sigma^{-1}]$. Clue: remember to calculate the mean flow velocity in the immediate vicinity of each plate.

5.12 Show that for a monatomic gas $\kappa m N_A/\eta C_{V_m} = 1$ and that $D\rho/\eta = 1$, where ρ is

171

the density of the gas. (The experimental ratios are closer to 2 than 1 for most substances.)

5.13 If a cannon ball is fired horizontally with a very high velocity it will not, in theory at least, strike the earth. At very low velocities the free path of the ball is terminated by the earth. At what speed will the ball just not collide with the earth? (This problem was first solved by Newton.) You should spot the relevance of this type of calculation to any discussion of gaseous mean free paths.

5.14 A saturated current of 10^{-7} A is measured when a discharge tube is being irradiated with X-rays. Assuming the ions are singly charged, how many ion pairs are being produced per second by the radiation?

6. The Maxwell-Boltzmann Distribution

In the main we have so far been content to talk of the mean square, or the root mean square, speed of the atoms in a gas without asking what range of speeds contributes to the mean. It is true that we discussed a time-of-flight technique which enables one to measure the spread in speeds directly. However, our interest in the distribution of speeds was really only secondary; our interest in the technique lay in the fact that it enables the mean square speed to be determined. In this chapter we will address ourselves to the problem of finding the precise form of the velocity distribution function, that is, the function which tells us what fraction of the molecules in a gas have any given speed (to be exact, the fraction whose speed lies within unit range of any specified speed).

We will start by looking at how the velocity distribution function can be obtained by means of a simulation. Since this is necessarily based on a small number of particles we will attempt to perform the simulation on paper, with the hope that, once we have learnt the ground rules, it can be extended to deal with many particles. We will find that as the number of particles keeps increasing—there are 6×10^{23} in a mole, remember—so the "game" keeps getting longer to play. We will be forced to play the game mathematically. This will lead to an expression for the velocity distribution function. Finally, we will see how this expression can be put to good use as we examine how a chemical reaction proceeds in the gaseous phase.

6.1 Simulating a gas

We have already discussed (in appendix 1) what happens when two atoms collide. We know that, given the initial momenta of two atoms which collide elastically, one can readily calculate the momenta, and therefore the speeds, of the atoms when the collision is over. Although the problem is straight-forward when there are only two atoms present it becomes very tedious when there are many atoms. And "many"—even in 10^{-20} mol of a substance—means just that!

One way out of the problem is to build a suitable simulator. Perhaps the simplest way to simulate a two-dimensional gas—for the moment let us content ourselves with simulating such a gas—is to randomly vibrate a tray of, say, 30–50 marbles over the surface of a horizontal table. Another possibility is a tray of small diameter coins. You should try to construct some such simulator for yourself.

Using your simulator, try to answer the question "In a two-dimensional gas how many atoms would move with what speed?" You may well find this is a very difficult question to answer—the situation keeps changing. All right, let us rephrase the question. "How many atoms *on average* move with what speed?" At least you should be able to decide whether the average—meaning time-averaged—situation is represented most closely by Figs. 6.1(a), (b), (c), or (d). As you look at the simulator ask yourself questions like these: Have all the coins (or marbles) the same speed, as in (d)? Are there many more with a high speed than with a low speed, as in (b), or is it the other way round, as in (a)? Or do most coins have a "middling" speed, as in (c)?

In carrying out this experiment you should have noticed that there were very few stationary coins on the tray; for a coin to be stopped requires a very fortuitous set of collisions. You should also have observed that very few coins moved at very high speeds; again, to possess a speed greatly above the mean requires an improbable sequence of collisions. Thus the simulator will have demonstrated that there are not many coins, and therefore gas atoms, with very low and with very high speeds. Probably all that you could say about intermediate speeds is that the majority of marbles had "in-between" speeds. Only an "up and down" curve—one such curve is shown in Fig. 6.1(c)—is compatible with the results of the simulation.

Exercise 6.1

There is a problem connected with the labelling of the ordinates in Fig. 6.1 which you may have already spotted. To highlight this problem,

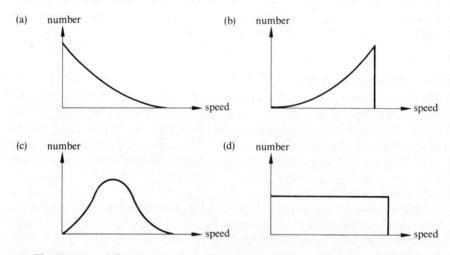

Fig. 6.1 (a) to (d) Four hypothetical velocity distributions in a two-dimensional gas.

try to draw out a graph showing (what you suspect to be) the number of students in your class in college with any particular height, as a function of height.

Just as it is pointless to plot the number of people having any exact height—there only is one person with such and such a height exactly—so it is pointless to plot the number of atoms having an *exact* speed against that speed. We must plot the number within a specified *range* of speeds against the speed intervals. Once we have found what such a speed plot looks like we could readily convert it to an energy plot which would tell us the number of atoms with energies within a specified range of energy. (The conversion is not difficult since kinetic energy is $\frac{1}{2}mu^2$.) Because of the importance, to our later discussions, of the energy distribution we will concentrate largely on looking at the number of atoms within a particular energy interval, knowing that the conversion to a speed distribution is readily accomplished. But first we must refine our simulator so that it relies on more than inspired guesses!

6.2 An air-table simulation

Refinements are desirable on two counts. Not only should we improve our method of measuring the speeds, and therefore the energies of the particles, but we should also take more care to ensure that the particles really do behave like gas atoms. A coin or marble on a tray has the unfortunate tendency to slow down as it moves across the tray between collisions! An improvement is to use pucks on an air-table. In such a device the pucks—short cylindrical discs—float on a cushion of air which is forced up through holes in the surface of the table. In essence the device behaves as an "inverted" hovercraft. Pucks can travel a distance of several metres over such a table with but a few per cent loss of speed. Such small losses as do occur are made good by vibrating the bounding walls of the air-table back and forth by means of a motor drive. Another advantage of pucks over marbles is that we can label them A, B, C, etc. In labelling them we are not, of course, saying that each atom in a gas actually carries a label. We label them because in classical physics each atom of a gas *is* unique, that is, identifiable. In principle at least it is quite possible to label each and every atom in a gas so that it is uniquely identified.

To measure the speeds of the pucks, which is going to be a necessary preliminary to measuring the pucks' energies, we may take a time-exposure photograph of the simulator while it is being illuminated with light from a stroboscope (a device which produces short bursts of light at fixed time intervals). Successive images on the film will then show where the puck was at each flash from the stroboscope. Figure 6.2(a) shows a photograph obtained by this technique. During the time that the camera shutter was open, the

175

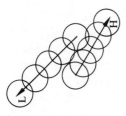

Fig. 6.2 (a) Pucks on an air-table photographed under stroboscopic illumination. (Reprinted with permission of the Open University from television programmes obtainable from the University.) (b) Showing vectors representing velocity superimposed on the images of the pucks in Fig. 6.2(a).

strobe-light flashed five times. The separation of two consecutive images of a puck tells us how far that puck has travelled between flashes and so this separation, and therefore the total length of the track, is a measure of the speed of that puck. Knowing the speed u of each puck it would now be a simple matter to work out the energy of each puck. However, just to measure up the speeds, to work out the energies and to plot an appropriate histogram would, at this stage, throw away some of the information which is contained within the photographs—we would throw away all the information we have about the direction in which the pucks are moving. We should retain the information about the velocity u of each puck, in other words, the information we have on its momentum mu. Later on we shall wish to distinguish between particles having the same speed but different momenta.

Recording the information

To preserve the full information which is contained within Fig. 6.2(a) vectors may be drawn over the tracks as shown in Fig. 6.2(b). The length of the arrow is proportional to the track length and its direction is along that of the track. Where a collision has appeared in the photograph the velocities have been recorded before or after the event, not both. Although Fig. 6.2(a) does not allow us to detect the sense of movement of a puck there are techniques for obtaining this information. One technique is to reduce manually the camera's

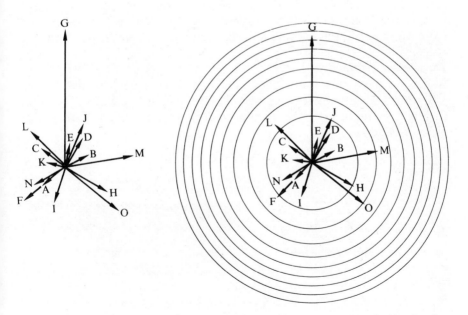

Fig. 6.3 (a) The velocity vectors of Fig. 6.2(b) transposed to a common origin. (b) Showing rings of constant energy superimposed on the vectors of Fig. 6.3(a).

aperture during the time-exposure; the puck then moves in the sense in which the image intensity on the negative decreases. In Fig. 6.2(b) the senses of movement were assigned arbitrarily by tossing a coin.

These velocity vectors may now be brought to a common origin as shown in Fig. 6.3(a). To find the number of pucks possessing a kinetic energy within a particular range of energies a series of rings is superimposed on the vector representation as shown in Fig. 6.3(b). If any one ring has a radius of u, say, and the next one out has a radius of $u + \delta u$ then all those named pucks whose vector tips lie in the annulus between radii u and $u + \delta u$ will have kinetic energies within a range of energy

$$\delta E = \tfrac{1}{2}m(u + \delta u)^2 - \tfrac{1}{2}mu^2 \approx mu\,\delta u \qquad (6.1)$$

about the energy

$$E = \tfrac{1}{2}mu^2 \qquad (6.2)$$

in the limit of small δu. In drawing the ring system of Fig. 6.3(b) δE has been taken to be the same in each annulus, that is, the number of named tips in the inner circle gives the number of pucks with energies within the range 0 to 1 δE; the number of tips falling within the first annulus gives the number of particles with energies between 1 δE and 2 δE, etc. Counting up the number of distinct vector tips which fall within each annulus gives the energy distribution shown in Fig. 6.4. Here the energy of those pucks whose velocity vector tips fall within the inner circle is taken as 0; the energy of those whose vector tips fall within the first annulus as 1, and so on.

The average distribution

So far we have only learnt about the particular energy distribution that was present when one particular photograph—that of Fig. 6.2(a)—was taken. Clearly it would be foolish to attempt to draw any conclusions from a single piece of evidence.

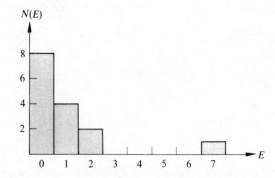

Fig. 6.4 Shows the number $N(E)$ of pucks of Fig. 6.2 with an energy E.

178

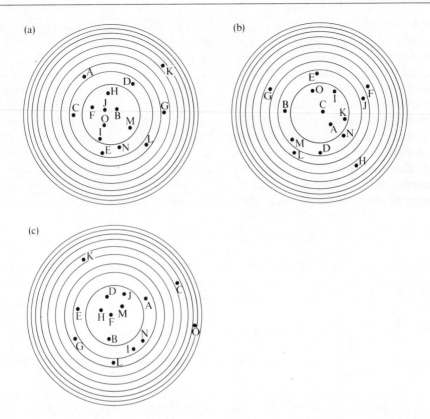

Fig. 6.5 (a), (b), (c). Shows the distribution of velocity vectors from three photographs of the air table. The dot adjacent to each letter indicates that the velocity of that puck is represented by the vector joining the centre of the ring system to the dot in question.

To obtain a feel for the average energy distribution the simulated gas must be photographed many more times and the results obtained from individual photographs then averaged. Figures 6.5(a) to (c) shows the results obtained on carrying out the same procedures which led to Fig. 6.3(b) on three more photographs of the table. Here instead of drawing in the velocity vectors in full only the terminating points of the vector heads are shown. (The dot adjacent to letter B, for example, in Fig. 6.5(b) indicates that the velocity of puck B when the photograph was taken is represented by a vector joining the centre of the ring system to the point in question. It also tells us, and this is more relevant for our present purposes, that the energy of B lies between $1\, \delta E$ and $2\, \delta E$, and so has an energy which we call 1 unit.) The photographs from which the representations of Fig. 6.3(b) and of Figs. 6.5(a) to (c) were constructed were not specially selected. These photographs were "as they happened" and were not taken when conditions "looked good" on the table. We therefore have an unbiased record of what was happening on the table at four randomly selected moments of time. To obtain the average number of named pucks lying within any energy interval, say that between $1\,\delta E$ and $2\,\delta E$, and hence in our notation the number having an energy of 1 unit, one simply counts the total number of tips (i.e., the number of labels A, B, C, etc.) falling within the appropriate annulus in all the representations and one then divides this by the number of representations concerned. On carrying out this procedure with the four velocity distributions contained in Fig. 6.3(b) and in Figs. 6.5(a) to (c) the average energy distribution shown in Fig. 6.6 was obtained. So we now have some indication of how a two-dimensional gas would behave. As Fig. 6.6 shows, there would be a steady fall off in the number of atoms possessing a specified energy (or, rather, within a unit range of energy) as the energy is increased. Real gases are, however, three-dimensional!

Exercise 6.2

How might you set about simulating a three-dimensional gas? What problems would be encountered in trying to perform this simulation on Earth? Remember to read the comments on p. 458, after you have come to your conclusions, and before you read on.

As in two dimensions, vectors would be erected along the three-dimensional tracks and then these vectors would be transposed to a common origin. This time, however, instead of drawing in annuli we would have to draw in spheres as in Fig. 6.7.

If the radii of a spherical shell are u and $u + \delta u$ then all those named vector tips which fall within the shell of thickness δu will (see eqs. (6.1) and (6.2)) have energies within a range

$$\delta E = mu\,\delta u \qquad (6.3)$$

about the energy

$$E = \tfrac{1}{2}mu^2 \qquad (6.4)$$

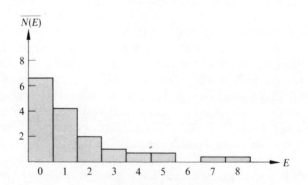

Fig. 6.6 Showing the average number $\overline{N(E)}$ of pucks with an energy E. The average is taken over the representations of Fig. 6.3(b) and of Figs. 6.5(a), (b), and (c).

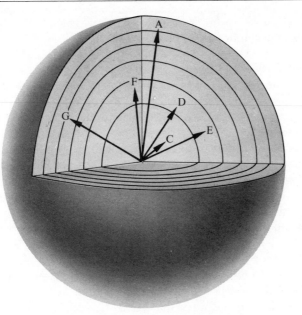

Fig. 6.7 A hypothetical distribution of velocity vectors for a three-dimensional simulated gas.

Were such an experiment performed we would, as in two dimensions, photo-graph the simulated gas at several randomly chosen times. To find the average number of particles in the energy range E to $E + \delta E$ we would then count the total number of named tips lying within the appropriate shell in all the velocity representations (like Fig. 6.7) and then divide this total by the number of photographs concerned. As it stands, this "thought experiment" will never, of course, tell us the form of three-dimensional energy distribution function.

6.3 Predicting the photographs

Even with the highly practical two-dimensional simulator all we can hope to do is to *sample* the behaviour of the gas. It would clearly be advantageous to have as "complete" a set of distinct pictures as is possible in trying to predict the average energy distribution in the gas. Rather than trying to obtain such a set by taking endless photographs of the air-table, could we not perhaps generate the pictures without recourse to experiment? If pictures like those of Fig. 6.5 can be generated on paper we may be able to do more than sample the gas at random moments; we may generate every conceivable picture. Furthermore, if the technique works in two dimensions we may be able to extend it to three dimensions where simulations are well-nigh impossible. An added advantage—assuming of course that we can find the correct rules

181

for playing this "game"—is that we should be able to extend it to include many more particles than can be employed in a simulator.

The ground rules

One feature of the sequence of pictures shown in Fig. 6.3(b) and Fig. 6.5 is that the *total energy* of all the named pucks is constant. What changes from picture to picture is the *way* that this constant energy is shared out. So we shall assume that the total energy is constant. Assuming a constant total energy for a fixed number of atoms is, of course, equivalent to assuming a constant *average* translational kinetic energy for the gas atoms, and therefore a constant temperature (section 3.4). To summarize, the ground rules for our game are: (1) each gas atom is unique (and so can be labelled A, B, C, etc.), (2) the total number of gas atoms is constant, and (3) the total energy of all the atoms is constant.

Exercise 6.3

Consider a two-dimensional gas containing, for arguments sake, four atoms A, B, C, and D which share out a total of five units of energy. Try to predict *all* the ways that A, B, C, and D can share out this total of five units of energy. First though, draw out about ten ring systems like that shown in Fig. 6.8. (If you measure up the radii of successive rings you will discover that they are in the ratio $1:2^{1/2}:3^{1/2}:4^{1/2}:$ etc. Since $E = \frac{1}{2}mu^2$ it follows that the ratio of the energy of those atoms whose vector tips end on the first circle to those whose vector tips end on the second circle is $1:2:3:\ldots$, and so on.) Now try to draw out the *complete* set of pictures (cf. Fig. 6.5) showing how A, B, C, and D share out five units of energy. Take the energy of an atom whose vector tip lies anywhere in the inner circle to be 0 units; the energy of an atom

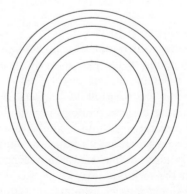

Fig. 6.8 A ring system on which to draw the velocity vectors for a two-dimensional gas.

whose vector tip lies in the first annulus to be 1 unit, etc. (You may find it necessary to draw out quite a few more ring systems as the game progresses.)

In carrying out this exercise—and you are strongly advised to attempt it if you have not done so already—a couple of problems will have arisen. Firstly, just how many blank ring systems does one need in trying to draw in the complete set of pictures? Secondly, and closely related, when is one picture different from another?

An additional rule

There is no doubt that Figs. 6.9(a) and (b) represent physically different situations. There is also no doubt that Figs. 6.10(a) and 6.10(b) represent physically different situations since the atoms are distinct; in Fig. 6.10(a) atom A is moving in a roughly north-westerly direction and C is moving in a roughly south-westerly direction, whereas in Fig. 6.10(b) it is C which is moving in the north-westerly direction while A is moving south-west. If you are still in doubt, thinking back to the "photographs" that these "pictures" represent should convince you that the two situations are physically distinguishable. Now look at the two pictures shown in Fig. 6.11. Careful scrutiny will convince you that the velocity of A is slightly different in the two cases. Although the speed u, and therefore the energy ($\frac{1}{2}mu^2$), is the same in each case the direction of motion of A, and therefore its momentum mu, is different in the two cases. Through just how small a distance can the point of the vector tip be moved to generate a new picture? If the answer is through an infinitesimal distance—this is what you may have decided—there will be an infinity of pictures. To keep the number of distinct pictures finite, we must introduce some rule; another rule in our game.

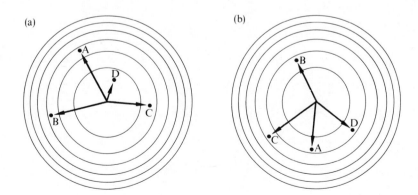

Fig. 6.9 (a) and (b). Two different arrangements of velocity vectors for four atoms of a two-dimensional gas sharing out five units of energy.

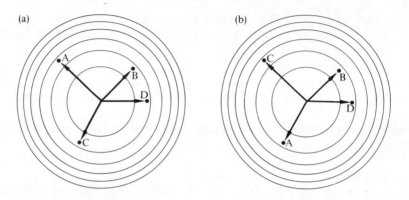

Fig. 6.10 (a) and (b). Two different arrangements of velocity vectors of four atoms of a two-dimensional gas sharing out five units of energy.

The rule for deciding whether two arrangements of vectors, two pictures, are different is, ultimately, arbitrary. Operationally, here is what the rule says:

The space in which the velocity vectors are drawn (*velocity space*) is to be carved up into *cells* of equal "size"; in two dimensions the cells are to have equal area; in three dimensions the cells are to have equal volume. If you change the position of a vector tip corresponding to a named atom keeping the tip within a cell, you *do not* get a new picture. If you change the position of the vector tip so as to move it to a *new cell* you *do* get a new picture.

There is nothing in the rule about the shape of the cells, provided that they have equal size throughout velocity space and do fill the space. Figure 6.12 shows the carving up procedure applied in two dimensions. By way of illustration of the rule, if the vector representing the velocity of particle A, which at present has its tip at point i in Fig. 6.12, is moved to i' we *do*

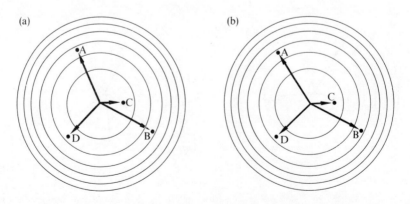

Fig. 6.11 In (b) the velocity of atom A differs slightly from its velocity in (a).

184

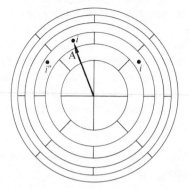

Fig. 6.12 Showing the division of two-dimensional velocity space into cells of equal area. Moving the tip of the velocity vector of atom A from point i to point i' does generate a new picture; moving it from i to i'' does not generate a new picture.

obtain a new picture. If, however, the tip only moves to point i'' within the same cell as i, while the other vectors are kept fixed, we *do not* obtain a new picture. Although the rule may appear somewhat arbitrary at this stage our subsequent development will show that the final form of the energy distribution does not depend on the size of the cell which may therefore (at least according to classical physics) be made as small as we wish.

Having established the rule we may now generate the complete set of distinct pictures in which the total energy of all the named particles is a constant.

6.4 The bookshelf method in two dimensions

A little bit of calculus will show that if the energy rings in two dimensions are divided up into cells of equal area, each energy ring contains the same number of cells. If two adjacent circles drawn in velocity space have radii u and $u + \delta u$, corresponding to energies E and $E + \delta E$, then the area of the enclosed ring is $2\pi u\, \delta u$ (that is, the length $2\pi u$ multiplied by the thickness δu). If each cell has constant area A_0 then the number $\mathcal{N}_2(E, A_0)$ of cells in the ring whose radii correspond to energies E and $E + \delta E$ is given by

$$\mathcal{N}_2(E, A_0) = \frac{2\pi u\, \delta u}{A_0}$$

or, substituting $u\, \delta u = \delta E/m$ from eq. (6.1),

$$\mathcal{N}_2(E, A_0) = \frac{1}{A_0}\left(\frac{2\pi}{m}\right)\delta E \tag{6.5}$$

Therefore in a ring system in which δE is the same in each ring—as it is in the ring system which we have adopted—the number of cells is the same in each ring. (In Fig. 6.12 it is, of course, four cells per ring.)

Before attempting to generate the complete set of distinct pictures it is convenient to transform the velocity space diagram of Fig. 6.12 into a rectangular diagram as shown in Fig. 6.13—this we shall call a "book-shelf" diagram. If particle A, for example, has an energy of two units (which means, of course that the tip of its velocity vector falls in the second ring in Fig. 6.12) then it is shown in the shelf labelled 2 in Fig. 6.13. You may well like to think of it as a "book" on a shelf. The actual "module" in which the "book" resides depends, of course, in which cell its velocity vector tip ends in Fig. 6.12.

Adopting the language of the library, the question we posed earlier (as in exercise 6.3) now become:

1. How many distinct arrangements of a given number of books (say 4; A, B, C, and D) can be made such that total energy of each arrangement sums to a given number (say 5)? A book on the lowest shelf is taken to have energy 0; a book on the next shelf is taken to have energy 1, etc. One such arrangement, or "picture", is shown in Fig. 6.13.
2. Averaged over all the distinct arrangements or "pictures" (equally weighted) what is the mean number of books appearing on a given shelf, that is, what is the mean number of atoms in a two-dimensional gas possessing a given energy?

If you try to answer the first question—perhaps you should—you will soon discover that even with each shelf divided into only four modules (that is, each ring in velocity space is carved up into only four cells) there are a daunting number of distinct arrangements. We first try a simpler problem.

Exercise 6.4

Considering only a single vertical column of shelf modules draw out all the distinct arrangements, or pictures, in which four books, A, B, C, and D, share out a total of five units of energy. A typical arrangement using

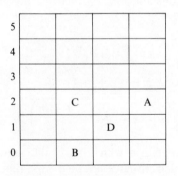

Fig. 6.13 A "bookshelf" representation of the cells of Fig. 6.12.

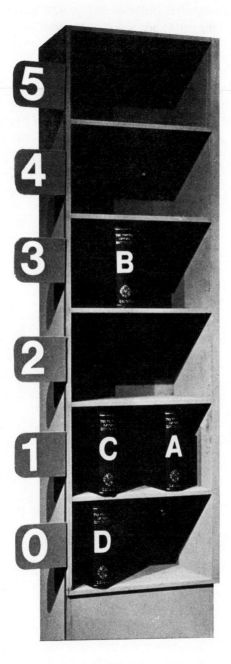

Fig. 6.14 Four identical labelled books sharing out five units of energy. (Reprinted with permission of the Open University from television programmes available from the University.)

actual books and shelves is shown in Fig. 6.14. You are to assume that rearranging books *within* a given module does not produce a new picture; CA, for example, is the same as AC. You may find it helpful to put the bookshelf method into practice!

You should have found that with four books sharing out five units of energy there are 56 distinct pictures or arrangements. The full 56 are displayed diagrammatically in Fig. 6.15. These arrangements may be grouped, for convenience, as shown in Table 6.1. The arrangement (5, 0, 0, 0) means that one book is in level 5 and the other three in level zero (hence the three zeros). Similarly, (3, 1, 1, 0) as in Fig. 6.14, means one book in level 3, two in level 1 and one in level 0. The second column of Table 6.1 records the number of pictures of each type.

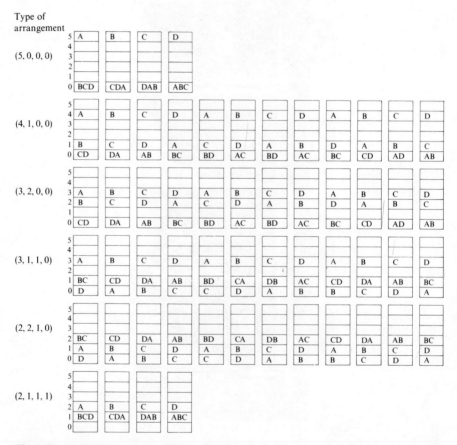

Fig. 6.15 All 56 distinct arrangements (of which Fig. 6.14 is one) showing how four identical labelled books share out five units of energy.

TABLE 6.1

Arrangement type	No. of occurrences
(5, 0, 0, 0)	4
(4, 1, 0, 0)	12
(3, 2, 0, 0)	12
(3, 1, 1, 0)	12
(2, 2, 1, 0)	12
(2, 1, 1, 1)	4

To answer the second question—what is the mean number of books appearing on a particular shelf—the number of appearances of a book on that shelf must be counted and this number must be divided by the total number of pictures (56). As an example, the total number of book appearances in level 3 is given by 12 books appearing in the (3, 2, 0, 0) arrangement and by 12 books appearing in the (3, 1, 1, 0) arrangement. You should identify these appearances in Fig. 6.15. So the mean number of books in level 3, averaged over all 56 pictures, is $(12 + 12)/56 = 0.43$. You should be able to work out the mean number of book appearances on the other shelves. Your results should agree with those given in Table 6.2. (These results may also be calculated directly from Table 6.1 rather than from Fig. 6.15.) The mean number of books per shelf (column 3 of Table 6.2) is shown plotted as a histogram in Fig. 6.16.

TABLE 6.2

Energy shelf (E/arbitrary unit)	Total of book appearances $N(E)$	Mean number $\overline{N(E)}$ of books per shelf $\overline{N(E)} = N(E)/56$
5	4	0.07
4	12	0.22
3	24	0.43
2	40	0.71
1	60	1.07
0	84	1.50
		Total 4

Now we must return to the original problem posed by Fig. 6.13 (that is, by Fig. 6.12) with its four modules at each level. We shall discover that while the complete set of arrangements is much larger than 56, a histogram identical to Fig. 6.16 will emerge from the calculation. For *each* of the original 56 arrangements (an example of which is given in Fig. 6.17(a)), 3 new arrangements can be generated by moving book A horizontally as shown in Figs. 6.17(b), (c), and (d) giving four arrangements in all. By moving both books A and B, we get 16 possible arrangements, and by moving all four books we get

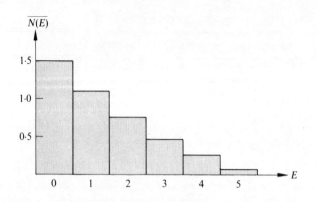

Fig. 6.16 Showing the mean distribution of four atoms of a two-dimensional gas sharing out five units of energy.

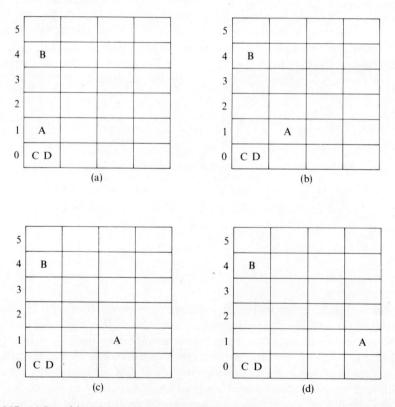

Fig. 6.17 (a) One of the original arrangements of Fig. 6.15. The three new arrangements shown in (b), (c), (d) result from the movement of book A in Fig. 6.17(a).

$4 \times 4 \times 4 \times 4$ or 256 arrangements for each arrangement generated with a single column of modules. This means that when we come to evaluate the number of appearances of a book on a given energy shelf, we find that each number of the original calculation (column 2 of Table 6.2) is multiplied by 256, only to be divided (as in column 3 of Table 6.2) by 56×256. The result is that the histogram of Fig. 6.16 remains unchanged. Since the form of the distribution function is not altered by scaling up the number of modules per shelf by a common factor, it is clear that the fineness of division of the energy rings (which is equal to the number of modules per shelf) is irrelevant to the form of the energy distribution. The distribution of Fig. 6.16 which we got with each energy annulus as a single cell (represented in Figs. 6.8 and 6.14) will therefore be the same as that which we would get with the finest sub-division imaginable. Such a sub-division would represent all the possible energy states of the moving pucks on the air table or of atoms in a hypothetical two-dimensional gas. If you compare the form of Fig. 6.16 with the energy distribution obtained from the simulator study (Fig. 6.6), you will note the similarities in the two histograms; high at the low-energy end, low at the high-energy end, and a monotonic decrease with increasing energy.

6.5 The bookshelf method in three dimensions

Simulating a three-dimensional gas poses so many problems that it is well-nigh impossible to build a simulator capable of yielding quantitative data. This alone forces us to concentrate on how to predict the "photographs" in three dimensions, that is, the ways that the velocity vectors might be arranged in space. We will therefore try to predict the complete set of arrangements of the type shown in Fig. 6.7. By way of example, we will concentrate on the problem of 4 atoms of a three-dimensional gas sharing out 5 units of energy. The question to be answered is this: On average, how many atoms have 0, 1, 2, 3, 4, or 5 units of energy?

The first step is to determine the form of the "bookshelf diagram" for a three-dimensional gas. You will remember that the problem in two dimensions was to ascertain how many "cells" of equal area could be put into an annulus in velocity space. The corresponding problem in three dimensions is to ascertain how many cells of equal volume V_0 can be put into a shell in velocity space between two spheres of radii u and $u + \delta u$ (such as between two spheres shown schematically in Fig. 6.7).

The volume δV of a shell contained between spheres of radii u and $u + \delta u$ is

$$\delta V = \frac{4\pi}{3}(u + \delta u)^3 - \frac{4\pi}{3} u^3$$

$$\delta V \approx 4\pi u^2 \, \delta u \tag{6.6}$$

Now since $E = \frac{1}{2}mu^2$ it follows that $\delta E = mu\,\delta u$ (eq. (6.1)). Therefore

$$\delta V = 4\pi \left(\frac{2E}{m}\right)^{1/2} \frac{\delta E}{m}$$

$$\delta V = \left(\frac{32\pi^2}{m^3}\right)^{1/2} E^{1/2}\,\delta E \qquad (6.7)$$

Dividing δV by the cell volume V_0 gives the number $\mathcal{N}_3(E, V_0)$ of cells of volume V_0 in the spherical shell between energies E and $E + \delta E$ as

$$\mathcal{N}_3(E, V_0) = \frac{1}{V_0}\left(\frac{32\pi^2}{m^3}\right)^{1/2} E^{1/2}\,\delta E \qquad (6.8)$$

i.e.,

$$\mathcal{N}_3(E, V_0) = CE^{1/2}\,\delta E \qquad (6.9)$$

where C is a constant.

Notice that in three dimensions $\mathcal{N}_3(E, V_0)$ is not constant in all shells of constant δE but varies as $E^{1/2}$. Contrast this with the situation in two dimensions where the number of cells was constant in all annuli of constant δE (see eq. (6.5)). This means that in setting up the bookshelf diagram, the number of modules on each energy shelf must be proportional to $E^{1/2}$. Such a diagram is shown in Fig. 6.18. In drawing this particular diagram the constant C in eq. (6.9) has been given a value of 2, while δE is unity in the present problem. The values so calculated for $\mathcal{N}_3(E, V_0)$ have been rounded off to the nearest integer.

Exercise 6.5

You may, if you wish, draw out a series of bookshelves like the set shown in Fig. 6.18 and proceed to find the total number of distinct ways of sorting four atoms, A, B, C, and D, such that their energy always totals

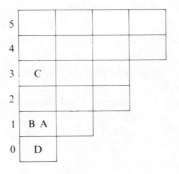

Fig. 6.18 A book-shelf representation for a three-dimensional gas.

to five units. However, be warned, there are 676 distinct arrangements! To really simplify matters, use this series of shelves to sort only two atoms, A and B, such that their energy always totals to three units. In playing the game, remember the rule that changing the order of the vector tips *within* any cell, which in our representation means changing the order of the letters within a module, does *not* produce a new picture. To produce a new picture, one or more vector tips must change modules. Once you have drawn out all the distinct arrangements, find the total number of atoms occurring in each level and then divide these totals by the number of distinct arrangements to obtain the mean number of atoms with energies of 0, 1, 2, 3, etc., units. Plot your results as a histogram.

As you may have discovered for yourself in working through this exercise, it is actually unnecessary to take the trouble to draw out every single picture. In fact the calculation can be broken down into two parts.

We first find the number of pictures of a *given type* using the first *column* of modules only. This will, of course, be the same as in two dimensions. As an example, for the (3, 1, 1, 0) type there are 12 distinct arrangements (see Table 6.1). We must next work out how many pictures may be formed by moving the books horizontally among the modules on a given shelf. For *each* of the 12 arrangements of the (3, 1, 1, 0) type (see Fig. 6.18) three pictures may be generated by moving the book in level three along the shelf. There is no freedom of movement on level zero. In level one, book B may be in either of two modules, as may book A. Four possible pictures may therefore be generated by moving the books in level one. Rearranging the books within a single module at any level leads to no new pictures (e.g., the arrangement BA in the first module of level one is equivalent to the arrangement AB in the first module of level one). The total number of pictures of the (3, 1, 1, 0) type there-

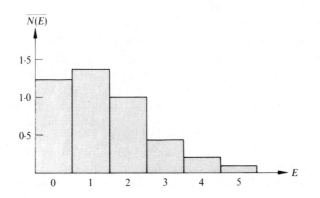

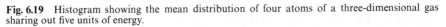

Fig. 6.19 Histogram showing the mean distribution of four atoms of a three-dimensional gas sharing out five units of energy.

fore comes to $(3 \times 4 \times 1)$ multiplied by the original number of arrangements using the first column of modules only (12), giving 144 distinct pictures of the (3, 1, 1, 0) type in all. The total number of pictures for each of the other types can be worked out similarly. For example, for the (5, 0, 0, 0) type there are 16 distinct pictures. To obtain the mean number of books appearing at a particular level, and therefore the mean number of atoms with a particular energy, we must, of course, find the total number of book appearances in this level and then divide by the total number of pictures (this is set out in column three of Table 6.3). Figure 6.19 shows the resulting energy distribution histogram.

TABLE 6.3

Energy shelf (E/arbitrary unit)	Total number of book appearances $N(E)$	Mean number $\overline{N(E)}$ of books per shelf $\overline{N(E)} = N(E)/676$
5	16	0·02
4	96	0·14
3	252	0·37
2	636	0·94
1	888	1·31
0	816	1·21

There is just the hint of a peak in the distribution which was not present in the energy distribution histogram of a two-dimensional gas (Fig. 6.16). This difference in the two distributions stems from the variable number of modules at each energy level in three dimensions, which is absent in two dimensions (where the number of modules is constant at each energy level). With a variable number of modules, the total number of pictures obtained with arrangements of types such as (5, 0, 0, 0) which place many books in a *low* energy shelf, is but little changed from the number of pictures obtained with a single column of modules. (In the case of the (5, 0, 0, 0) arrangement there are now four modules —see Fig. 6.18—into which the single book at level 5 may be moved. The three books at level 0 are unable to move, and we "miss out" on a lot of new pictures.) On the other hand the total number of pictures for arrangements—like (2, 2, 1, 0)—which place the books in the middle range of energies is significantly greater than the number of pictures obtained with a single column of modules. (In the case of the (2, 2, 1, 0) arrangement there are now three modules—see Fig. 6.18—for each of the two books in level 2, and two modules for the book in level 1.) So the effect of the variable number of modules in three dimensions is to give greater contributions to the middle range of energy values ($E = 1$ and 2) and relatively lower contributions to the extreme high and low values ($E = 0$, 3, 4, and 5). This effect may be seen on comparing Figs. 6.16 and 6.19.

Extending the game

We are starting to get some intimations that the energy distributions are different in two- and three-dimensional gases. In three dimensions there is the suggestion of a peak in the distribution. However, with the small number of atoms in the gas and with the rough and ready way we have carved up the energy shells into cells it would be unwise to be too dogmatic about the peak being there. When the calculation is repeated with a bookshelf representation subdivided so that successive shelves differ by half a unit of energy, as shown in Fig. 6.20, the histogram shown in Fig. 6.21 is obtained. On comparing Fig. 6.21 with Fig. 6.19 we see that the effect of having more finely divided energy levels is to enhance the peak in the histogram.

As the energy levels are divided ever more and more finely the number of *types* of arrangement increases. If, for example, three atoms share out 4 units of energy, the *types* of arrangement are; (2, 1, 1), (3, 1, 0), (2, 2, 0), and (4, 0, 0). If the three atoms share out 8 half-units of energy (again totalling to 4 units) the *types* of arrangement are (4, 3, 1), (5, 2, 1), (3, 3, 2), (4, 2, 2), (5, 3, 0), (6, 1, 1), (6, 2, 0), (7, 1, 0), (4, 4, 0), and (8, 0, 0). If they share out 12 one-third units of energy the *types* of arrangement are (5, 4, 3), (6, 4, 2), ... you should be able to complete this list! What is more important than the increase in the number of types of arrangement is the fact that *one type* of arrangement becomes relatively ever more and more important as the energy levels become ever

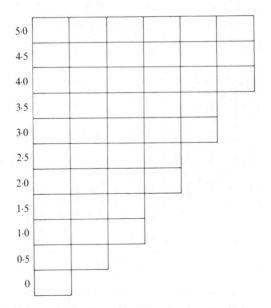

Fig. 6.20 A bookshelf representation for a three-dimensional gas in which successive shelves differ by half a unit of energy.

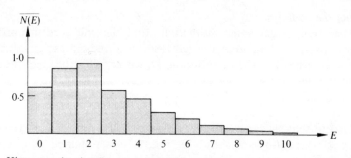
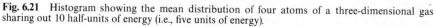

Fig. 6.21 Histogram showing the mean distribution of four atoms of a three-dimensional gas sharing out 10 half-units of energy (i.e., five units of energy).

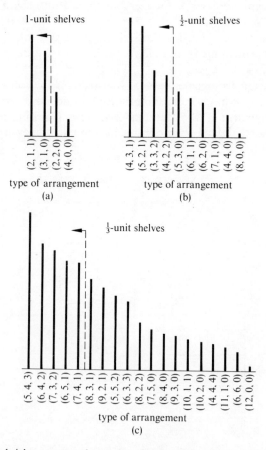

Fig. 6.22 The bar heights represent the number of pictures belonging to each type of arrangement when three atoms share out four units of energy. In (a) the energy is shared out as single units— meaning each shelf is one unit wide. In (b) the energy is shared out in units half that of (a). In (c) the energy units are one-third that of (a).

more and more finely divided. Figure 6.22 shows what happens on sorting out all the pictures illustrating the ways three atoms share out four units of energy, (a) when the energy shelves are 1-unit wide, (b) when they are $\frac{1}{2}$-unit wide, and (c) when they are $\frac{1}{3}$-unit wide. If you like the image, the pictures are stacked in letter trays, each of which carries the label of one permitted type of arrangement. You can see that as the energy levels become narrower the pictures collect into a smaller fraction of the trays. The dotted line separates off the smallest number of trays (types of arrangement) needed to contain 50 per cent of all the pictures. In scheme (c) only 5 out of 19 types are necessary to contain 50 per cent of the pictures, whereas in scheme (a) two out of four are necessary. In a sufficiently finely divided system containing very many atoms there will be a *single* type of arrangement that contains an overwhelming percentage of the pictures—so much so that pictures in other trays can be discarded in evaluating the mean number of atoms with a specified energy. One letter tray contains pictures "a mile high", the others each have "the odd one or two" pictures.

Playing the "bookshelf game" with ever increasing numbers of atoms and with ever increasing fineness of division of the energy levels is, to put it mildly, tedious. We are now going to try to predict the mean energy distribution of a large population in which the energy levels are (virtually) infinitely finely divided, but without resorting to "hand sorting" of the atoms. This will introduce you to the ideas of statistical mechanics. Although our arguments will not do justice to the power of statistical mechanical arguments they will give you a taste of the subject. If the taste seems bitter you can always regard the relations we shall derive as empirical—they do fit the experimentally determined distribution functions arrived at in time-of-flight studies.

6.6   The energy distribution function

The shelves and the modules
The first step is to redraw Figs. 6.8 and 6.7 so that the rings in two dimensions and the shells in three dimensions are much closer together than we have considered up to now. If one surface of the shell has a radius u and the next surface has a radius $u + \delta u$, where $\delta u/u \ll 1$, the energy E of atoms whose vector tips end in this cell will lie between E and $E + \delta E$, where δE is related to δu by eq. (6.3),

$$\delta E = mu\,\delta u$$

Since $E = \frac{1}{2}mu^2 = \dfrac{1}{2m}(mu)^2$ it follows that $mu = (2mE)^{1/2}$ and so

$$\delta E = (2mE)^{1/2}\,\delta u \qquad (6.10)$$

As $\delta u \to 0$, the energies of all atoms whose vector tips end in this shell therefore tend to the same value, E. We have already seen (eq. (6.8)) that the

197

number of cells, each of volume V_0, which are contained within this shell is (in the limit as $\delta E \to 0$) given by

$$\mathcal{N}_3(E, V_0) = \frac{1}{V_0}\left(\frac{32\pi^2}{m^3}\right)^{1/2} E^{1/2}\,dE \qquad (6.11)$$

We have also seen (eq. (6.5)) that for a two-dimensional gas the number of cells, each of area A_0, which are contained within an annulus of thickness δu in velocity space is given by

$$\mathcal{N}_2(E, A_0) = \frac{1}{A_0}\left(\frac{2\pi}{m}\right)dE \qquad (6.12)$$

Suppose that we write

$$\mathcal{N}_2(E, A_0) = g_2(E)\,dE \qquad (6.13)$$

and

$$\mathcal{N}_3(E, V_0) = g_3(E)\,dE \qquad (6.14)$$

then comparing eq. (6.13) with eq. (6.12), and eq. (6.14) with eq. (6.11), gives

$$g_2(E) = \frac{1}{A_0}\left(\frac{2\pi}{m}\right) \qquad (6.15)$$

and

$$g_3(E) = \frac{1}{V_0}\left(\frac{32\pi^2}{m^3}\right)^{1/2} E^{1/2} \qquad (6.16)$$

It follows from eq. (6.13) that $g_2(E)$ is equal to the number of cells within an annulus of unit width (expressed in units of energy) at energy E. Likewise it follows from eq. (6.14) that $g_3(E)$ is equal to the number of cells within a shell of unit width (again expressed in units of energy) at energy E. In formal statistical mechanics $g(E)$ is called the *density of states* (the name density arises because, from eqs. (6.13) and (6.14), $g(E)$ is the number of cells per unit range of energy).

In Fig. 6.23 we have drawn out a "shelf" and its cells for a three-dimensional gas in "bookshelf and module" fashion. In saying that the number of modules in this shelf is equal to $g(E_i)$ ($= g_i$, say,) we are taking $dE = 1$ (eq. (6.14)). The subscript i is used to denote the conditions pertaining to this general shelf; that is the energy of an atom on this ith shelf (or, rather, the energy of an atom whose vector tip ends in the shell the shelf represents) is denoted by E_i and the number of atoms with this energy is denoted by n_i. (This numbering system has an analogy in the British system of numbering floors in a building. So the ground shelf, where the energy is zero, is the 0th shelf, the 1st shelf corresponds to an energy E_1, the 2nd shelf to an energy E_2, etc.)

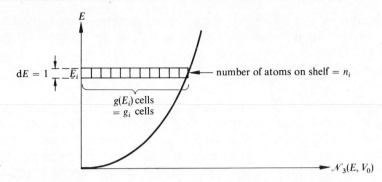

Fig. 6.23 Showing a general "shelf" for a three-dimensional gas.

Filling the shelves

The problem would seem to be to somehow write down or "draw out" the full range of pictures in which the energy of the atoms totals to a specified value, and then to compute the average number on each shelf, that is, the average number of atoms possessing a specified energy. This would be just the procedure we adopted in the problem of four atoms of a three-dimensional gas sharing out five units of energy. If we were to play the same game, this time in thought only, we would first compute the number of pictures, say W, which corresponds to a given *type* of arrangement, one with n_i atoms on shelf i (each with an energy E_i), n_j on shelf j (each with an energy E_j), etc. So let us do just that—set up a particular type of arrangement where the number n_i of atoms on each level i is specified.

Figure 6.24 shows the blank row of cells into which we are going to place the specified number n_i of atoms (or rather of vector tips). These atoms must come from the total number of atoms, N, present in the gas. Since all N atoms must be located on the shelves it follows that:

$$N = n_1 + n_2 + n_3 + \cdots$$

that is

$$N = \sum_i n_i \tag{6.17}$$

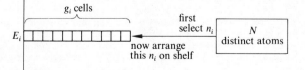

Fig. 6.24 Illustrating the procedures involved in placing n_i atoms on a shelf at energy E_i containing g_i cells.

The number of ways in which the n_i atoms can be selected as *would-be occupants* for shelf i—atoms still to be placed on this shelf—is given by $_NC_{n_i}$ where*

$$_NC_{n_i} = \frac{N!}{n_i!(N-n_i)!} \tag{6.18}$$

Having selected the n_i would-be occupants these must now be placed "on the shelf". The first of these n_i can go into any of the g_i (where $g_i = g(E_i)$) cells at this level. The same is true of the second atom, of the third atom, and so on for all n_i atoms. Therefore the number of distinct ways of arranging the n_i atoms selected for level i is $(g_i)^{n_i}$. But there are, as we have seen, $_NC_{n_i}$ ways of selecting these n_i atoms from our population so the total number of possible distinct arrangements of atoms on level i is given by

$$W_i = {}_NC_{n_i} \times (g_i)^{n_i}$$

$$W_i = \frac{N!}{n_i!(N-n_i)!}(g_i)^{n_i} \tag{6.19}$$

In selecting the n_j atoms for level j we have fewer to choose from—fewer because n_i have already been allocated to level i—in fact, we have only $(N-n_i)$ left from which to select n_j. This selection may be made in $_{N-n_i}C_{n_j}$ ways and each of these selected atoms can be placed in any of the g_j cells in level j, giving $(g_j)^{n_j}$ distinct ways of arranging the n_j atoms selected for this level. Therefore the number W_j of distinct arrangements of atoms on level j is given by

$$W_j = {}_{(N-n_i)}C_{n_j} \times (g_j)^{n_j} \tag{6.20}$$

For levels k the n_k atoms must be selected from the $(N-n_i-n_j)$ unallocated atoms remaining. This leads to W_k distinct arrangements where

$$W_k = {}_{(N-n_i-n_j)}C_{n_k} \times (g_k)^{n_k} \tag{6.21}$$

---

* A box contains $N = 5$ different chocolates (orange, brazil, lemon, wafer, and fudge). You are told you can select $n = 3$ different chocolates from the box. How many *different* selections can you make? For your first choice you have five chocolates to choose from—you might choose lemon. For your second choice you have 4 to choose from (the lemon is gone). For your third choice you have only 3 to choose from. The total number of choices appears to be $5 \times 4 \times 3$, which can be written as $5 \times 4 \times 3 \times 2 \times 1/(2 \times 1) = 5!/(5-3)!$, or more generally $N!/(N-n)!$ (If in doubt write down all 60 selections.) However, certain of the selections which you have made are really the same. Picking out an orange, followed by a fudge, followed by a brazil is no different than picking out a fudge, followed by an orange, followed by a brazil—the order within the choice of three is immaterial. So the number of initial selections must be divided by the number of ways the three chocolates can be arranged among themselves; this number is $3 \times 2 \times 1$ = $3! = n!$ (If in doubt write down all six ways of arranging three different chocolates.) Only 1 in 6 of our original selections therefore passes the test of being a unique selection. The total number of ways of selecting $n = 3$ chocolates out of $N = 5$ different varieties, written $_NC_n$, is therefore given by

$$_NC_n = \frac{N!}{(N-n)!n!} \left(= \frac{5!}{2!3!} = \frac{5 \times 4 \times 3 \times 2 \times 1}{(2 \times 1)(3 \times 2 \times 1)} = 10 \right)$$

Since any one of the W_i distinct arrangements of atoms on level i may coexist with any one of the W_j distinct arrangements on level j and with any one of the W_k distinct arrangements on level k, and so on, it follows that the total number W of pictures of the type characterized by n_i atoms in level i, n_j atoms in level j, and so on, is given by

$$W = W_i W_j W_k \ldots \tag{6.22}$$

Substituting from eqs. (6.19), (6.20), and (6.21) this becomes

$$W = \frac{N!}{n_i!(N - n_i)!} \cdot \frac{(N - n_i)!}{n_j!(N - n_i - n_j)!} \cdot \frac{(N - n_i - n_j)!}{n_k!(N - n_i - n_j - n_k)!} \ldots$$

$$\times (g_i)^{n_i}(g_j)^{n_j}(g_k)^{n_k} \ldots$$

or, on cancelling terms,

$$W = \frac{N!}{n_i! \, n_j! \, n_k! \ldots}(g_i)^{n_i}(g_j)^{n_j}(g_k)^{n_k} \ldots \tag{6.23}$$

Equation (6.23) tells us the number of pictures belonging to *one* particular type—that type of arrangement which places n_i atoms in level i, n_j atoms in level j, and so on. Were we to follow the same procedure as we employed in playing the bookshelf "game" we would now write down similar expressions for all other permitted types of arrangement. Each one of those permitted types must be such that the *total* energy of all the atoms taken over all levels is constant and equal to the specified energy of the system. So we should perhaps find W for a new permitted type of arrangement, with say n_i' atoms in level i, n_j' in level j, and so on. In fact we shall do nothing of the sort! We will do nothing of the sort because in a large population (a mole of gas, for example, contains 6×10^{23} molecules) one particular type of arrangement will have overwhelmingly more pictures associated with it than with any other; so much so that all the other pictures arising from all other types of arrangements may be ignored in computing the mean energy distribution. The problem facing us is to find this *one* type of arrangement which yields the *greatest number of pictures*. Once we know this type of arrangement the energy distribution follows immediately. In experimental practice we would be interested in the time-averaged distribution in a real gas. What we have been calculating is a "picture-averaged" distribution (in formal statistical mechanics this is called an ensemble-averaged distribution). It is an axiom of elementary statistical mechanics that the time- and the ensemble-averaged distributions give the same results.

Exercise 6.6

Suppose it to be true that, for a large number of atoms, one *type* of arrangement occurs overwhelmingly more often than any other so that all the pictures belonging to other types of arrangement may be ignored. (In the language adopted in describing Fig. 6.22, only one tray of pictures matters.) Assuming that this one type of arrangement is known, what further calculations are necessary to give the mean energy distribution?

Finding the all-important type of arrangement

We must now find the type of arrangement which yields the greatest number of pictures (or, if you prefer it, the tray in Fig. 6.22 which has greatest number of pictures).

Taking the logarithm of eq. (6.23) gives

$$\ln W = \ln N! - \sum_i \ln n_i! + \sum_i n_i \ln g_i \qquad (6.24)$$

By using a result, known as Stirling's formula, for the logarithm of the factorial of a large number, namely

$$\ln(n!) \approx n \ln n - n \qquad (6.25)$$

eq. (6.24) becomes (remembering also that the total number of atoms, N, is constant—and so $\ln N$ is constant)

$$\ln W = \text{constant} - \sum_i (n_i \ln n_i - n_i) + \sum_i n_i \ln g_i$$

$$\ln W = \text{constant} + \sum_i (n_i \ln g_i - n_i \ln n_i + n_i) \qquad (6.26)$$

Since the total number of atoms, N, is constant

$$N = \sum_i n_i \qquad (6.27)$$

In addition, the total energy, E, of all the atoms is constant:

$$E = \sum_i n_i E_i \qquad (6.28)$$

Our problem is to find the set of numbers (n_0, n_1, n_2, etc.) which maximizes the number of pictures W, and hence maximizes $\ln W$, subject to the two constraints contained in eqs. (6.27) and (6.28). To find the maximum value of $\ln W$ as the n_i vary, eq. (6.26) must be differentiated with respect to n_i and the result equated to zero. This gives

$$d(\ln W) = \sum_i (dn_i \ln g_i - dn_i - dn_i \ln n_i + dn_i) = 0$$

$$\sum_i \ln(g_i/n_i)\, dn_i = 0 \qquad (6.29)$$

But eq. (6.29) is subject to the constraints that, as n_i changes, eqs. (6.27) and

202

(6.28) must still be satisfied. Differentiating eqs. (6.27) and (6.28) with respect to n_i gives:

$$dN = \sum_i dn_i = 0 \tag{6.30}$$

and

$$dE = \sum_i E_i \, dn_i = 0 \tag{6.31}$$

since N and E are constant. If we now multiply eq. (6.30) by a constant, α, we obtain $\sum_i \alpha \, dn_i = 0$. If we multiply eq. (6.31) by a constant, β, we obtain $\sum_i \beta E_i \, dn_i$. Subtracting these modified forms of eqs. (6.30) and (6.31) from eq. (6.29) gives*

$$\sum_i (\ln (g_i/n_i) - \alpha - \beta E_i) \, dn_i = 0 \tag{6.32}$$

Since the dn_i are now in effect independent, the coefficient of each must vanish, so for all i

$$\ln (g_i/n_i) - \alpha - \beta E_i = 0$$

$$\frac{g_i}{n_i} = e^{\alpha + \beta E_i}$$

$$n_i = g_i \, e^{-\alpha} e^{-\beta E_i} \tag{6.33}$$

These n_i describe the *type* of arrangement which possesses the largest number of pictures. According to our assumptions, this type of arrangement describes conditions as they exist on (time-) average in a gas. Now you will remember that, to keep the notation simple, we took the number of cells at energy E_i to be equal to $g_i (= g(E_i))$; in other words we assumed $dE = 1$ in eqs. (6.13) and (6.14). Introducing the actual number of cells at energy E within a range dE (which is given by eq. (6.12) for a two-dimensional gas and by eq. (6.11) for a three-dimensional gas) in place of g_i in eq. (6.33), and writing dN for the number of atoms n_i within the energy range dE at energy $E = E_i$ gives

$$dN = \text{constant } e^{-\beta E} dE \tag{6.34}$$

for a two-dimensional gas, and

$$dN = \text{constant } e^{-\beta E} E^{1/2} dE \tag{6.35}$$

for a three-dimensional gas. (The constants include not only the constants in eqs. (6.11) and (6.12) but also $e^{-\alpha}$ which is, of course, constant since α is a constant.)

* Properly speaking one should multiply eq. (6.27), rather than eq. (6.30), through by α and eq. (6.28), rather than eq. (6.31), through by β and then subtract these modified equations from eq. (6.26). Only now should one differentiate with respect to n_i and set the result equal to zero. This proper approach—known as the method of Lagrange multipliers—leads to the same conclusion, eq. (6.31), as does our sloppy treatment.

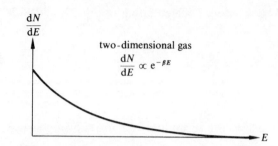

Fig. 6.25 The energy distribution function for a two-dimensional gas.

A check up

Before proceeding to evaluate the constants in eqs. (6.34) and (6.35) we should check up on whether or not the energy distributions predicted by these equations agree with the distributions obtained by manual sorting. To this end, we divide these equations through by dE so that the left-hand sides become dN/dE, that is, the number of atoms with an energy E per unit range of energy. This gives

$$\frac{dN}{dE} = \text{constant } e^{-\beta E} \text{ (two dimensions)} \tag{6.36}$$

and

$$\frac{dN}{dE} = \text{constant } E^{1/2}\, e^{-\beta E} \text{ (three dimensions)} \tag{6.37}$$

Equation (6.36) is shown in Fig. 6.25 and eq. (6.37) in Fig. 6.26. Comparing these plots with the results we obtained by manual sorting (Figs. 6.16 and 6.21) we see that the two techniques do yield broadly similar results. Because the statistical mechanical analysis has been applied to a much larger population than was our manual analysis, we shall take eq. (6.36) as describing conditions prevailing in an (albeit hypothetical) two-dimensional gas and eq. (6.37) as describing conditions prevailing in a real (three-dimensional) gas. The name *energy distribution function* is usually given to dN/dE.

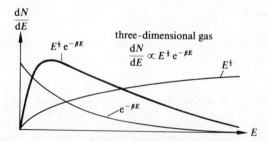

Fig. 6.26 The energy distribution function for a three-dimensional gas.

6.7   The velocity distribution function

Although we have carried through the discussion in terms of the energy of the atoms we may, since the energy E and the velocity u are related by $E = \frac{1}{2}mu^2$, convert the energy distribution function to a *velocity distribution function*, meaning the number of atoms per unit range of velocity about a particular velocity u. (Properly speaking, the function should be called the speed distribution function since u is actually the speed, and not the velocity, of the atom.) Differentiating E with respect to u gives

$$\mathrm{d}E = mu\,\mathrm{d}u$$

Substituting this, along with $E = \frac{1}{2}mu^2$, into eqs. (6.34) and (6.35) gives

$$\frac{\mathrm{d}N}{\mathrm{d}u} = \text{constant } u\,e^{-\beta(\frac{1}{2}mu^2)} \text{ (two dimensions)} \tag{6.38}$$

and

$$\frac{\mathrm{d}N}{\mathrm{d}u} = \text{constant } u^2\,e^{-\beta(\frac{1}{2}mu^2)} \text{ (three dimensions)} \tag{6.39}$$

Figure 6.27 shows the form of eq. (6.38). Unlike the energy distribution function for a two-dimensional gas (Fig. 6.25) we see that there is a peak in the velocity distribution function. Figure 6.28 show the form of the velocity distribution function for a three-dimensional gas (eq. (6.39)). Although this, like the energy distribution function (Fig. 6.26), has a peak, the detailed shape of the two distribution functions is different.

Evaluating the constants

There are still two unknown constants to be determined in eqs. (6.38) and (6.39) (and therefore in eqs. (6.36) and (6.37)). To evaluate both these constants we are going to need two other pieces of information about each gas. In fact we will only evaluate the constants for the three-dimensional gas; it will be left as an exercise for you to evaluate them for a two-dimensional gas.

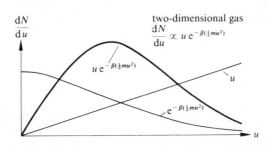

Fig. 6.27   The velocity distribution function for a two-dimensional gas.

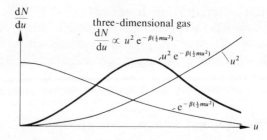

Fig. 6.28 The velocity distribution function for a three-dimensional gas.

The first piece of information we make use of is the total number of atoms, N, in the gas. Clearly

$$N = \int_0^\infty \frac{dN}{du} \, du \tag{6.40}$$

or, substituting from eq. (6.39) with the constant written as A,

$$N = \int_0^\infty A u^2 \, e^{-\beta(\frac{1}{2}mu^2)} \, du \tag{6.41}$$

To evaluate eq. (6.41) we appeal to the result that*

$$I_2 = \int_0^\infty u^2 e^{-\lambda u^2} \, du = \frac{1}{4} \left(\frac{\pi}{\lambda^3} \right)^{1/2} \tag{6.42}$$

This and other integrals of the same form are tabulated in Table 6.4. In our case the constant $\lambda = \beta m/2$ so that eq. (6.41) becomes

$$N = A(\pi/2)^{1/2} (\beta m)^{-3/2} \tag{6.43}$$

The other piece of information is the fact that the average kinetic energy of the gas atoms, $\frac{1}{2}\overline{mu^2}$, is related to the temperature T of the gas by eq. (3.29);

$$\tfrac{1}{2}\overline{mu^2} = \tfrac{3}{2}kT$$

But, by definition,

$$\tfrac{1}{2}\overline{mu^2} = \frac{\int (\tfrac{1}{2}mu^2) \, dN}{\int dN}$$

$$= \frac{1}{N} \int_0^\infty \tfrac{1}{2}mu^2 \frac{dN}{du} \, du$$

---

*This integral can only be evaluated from $u = 0$ to $u = \infty$. If interested, you will find it and other like integrals discussed in more detail in, for example, M. Born, *Atomic Physics*, 6th edn, Blackie, London, 1957 (Appendix 1). When $n = 1, 3, 5, 7$, etc. (Table 6.4) the integral can be evaluated "by parts".

TABLE 6.4

$$I_n = \int_0^\infty u^n e^{-\lambda u^2}\, du$$

n	I_n	n	I_n
0	$\dfrac{1}{2}\left(\dfrac{\pi}{\lambda}\right)^{1/2}$	1	$\dfrac{1}{2\lambda}$
2	$\dfrac{1}{4}\left(\dfrac{\pi}{\lambda^3}\right)^{1/2}$	3	$\dfrac{1}{2\lambda^2}$
4	$\dfrac{3}{8}\left(\dfrac{\pi}{\lambda^5}\right)^{1/2}$	5	$\dfrac{1}{\lambda^3}$
6	$\dfrac{15}{16}\left(\dfrac{\pi}{\lambda^7}\right)^{1/2}$	7	$\dfrac{3}{\lambda^4}$

or, substituting for dN/du from eq. (6.39) (where the constant is A)

$$\tfrac{1}{2}m\overline{u^2} = \tfrac{3}{2}kT = \frac{Am}{2N}\int_0^\infty u^4\, e^{-\beta(\frac{1}{2}mu^2)}\, du \tag{6.44}$$

In evaluating the integral we use another standard form, namely

$$I_4 = \int_0^\infty u^4 e^{-\lambda u^2}\, du = \frac{3}{8}\left(\frac{\pi}{\lambda^5}\right)^{1/2}$$

with $\lambda = \beta m/2$. Equation (6.44) therefore becomes

$$\tfrac{3}{2}kT = \frac{3}{2\beta}$$

$$\beta = \frac{1}{kT} \tag{6.45}$$

Substituting this expression for β into eq. (6.43) gives

$$A = N\left(\frac{2}{\pi}\right)^{1/2}\left(\frac{m}{kT}\right)^{3/2} \tag{6.46}$$

Finally, when these expressions for A and β are substituted back into eq. (6.39) (where the constant is A) we obtain

$$\frac{1}{N}\frac{dN}{du} = \left(\frac{2}{\pi}\right)^{1/2}\left(\frac{m}{kT}\right)^{3/2} u^2\, e^{-mu^2/2kT} \quad \text{(three dimensions)} \tag{6.47}$$

as the expression for the fraction of the atoms present in a gas at temperature

207

T possessing speeds which lie within unit range of u. When plotted out graphically at different temperatures eq. (6.47)—called the *Maxwell–Boltzmann velocity distribution*—has the form shown in Fig. 6.29.

To make an accurate experimental test of the Maxwell–Boltzmann distribution (more accurate than is posible with the data contained in Fig. 3.7) involves painstaking work. Figure 6.30 shows the results of such a study which measures the time-of-flight of potassium atoms emerging from an oven at 430 K and at a pressure of 0·11 Pa. The continuous curve has been computed assuming eq. (6.47). (Being inversely proportional to the flight time the velocity increases to the right along the abscissa of Fig. 6.30.) The close agreement between prediction and experiment clearly vindicates the Maxwell-Boltzmann distribution—at least at the temperature and pressure at which the experiment was performed!

It is a straightforward matter to convert the velocity distribution of eq. (6.47) into an energy distribution; one merely substitutes $E = \frac{1}{2}mu^2$ and $dE = mu\,du$. This leads to

$$\frac{1}{N}\frac{dN}{dE} = \frac{2}{\pi^{1/2}}\left(\frac{1}{kT}\right)^{3/2} E^{1/2}\, e^{-E/kT} \quad \text{(three dimensions)} \qquad (6.48)$$

The mean and the r.m.s. speeds compared
Before leaving the velocity distribution it is worthwhile using it to evaluate the

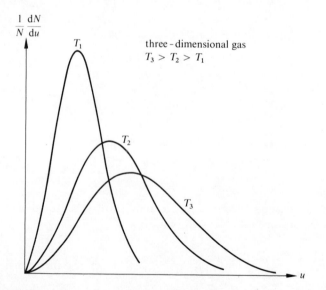

Fig. 6.29 The velocity distribution function for a three-dimensional gas at three different temperatures, $T_3 > T_2 > T_1$.

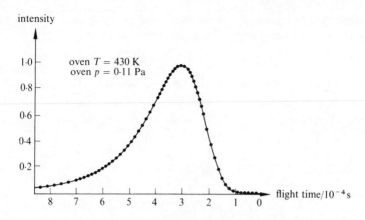

Fig. 6.30 The intensity (shown as dots) recorded in a time-of-flight apparatus for potassium at 430 K and 0·11 Pa. The curve has been calculated assuming the Maxwell-Boltzmann velocity distribution function (eq. (6.47)). (Data: P. M. Marcus and J. H. McFee.)

mean speed $\bar{u}$ and the root mean square speed $(\overline{u^2})^{1/2}$ in a gas. By definition

$$\bar{u} = \frac{\int u \, dN}{\int dN} = \frac{1}{N} \int_0^\infty u \frac{dN}{du} \, du$$

$$(\overline{u^2})^{1/2} = \left(\frac{\int u^2 \, dN}{\int dN} \right)^{1/2} = \left(\frac{1}{N} \int_0^\infty u^2 \frac{dN}{du} \, du \right)^{1/2}$$

Substituting for dN/du from eq. (6.47) and making use of the standard integrals in Table 6.4 gives

$$\bar{u} = \left(\frac{8kT}{\pi m} \right)^{1/2}$$

$$(\overline{u^2})^{1/2} = \left(\frac{3kT}{m} \right)^{1/2}$$

Therefore $(\overline{u^2})^{1/2}/\bar{u} = (3\pi/8)^{1/2} = 1·08$. The fact that $(\overline{u^2})^{1/2}$ and $\bar{u}$ only differ by 8 per cent justifies the assumption, made so often in the last chapter, that $\bar{u} \approx (\overline{u^2})^{1/2}$. In finding that the root mean square speed is $(3kT/m)^{1/2}$ we are, of course, only recovering the relation $\frac{1}{2}mu^2 = \frac{3}{2}kT$ which we fed into the calculation (eq. (6.44)). Had we obtained a different result, eq. (6.47) would be a lie.

6.8 The one- and two-dimensional gases

Exercise 6.7

Carry out the same type of procedure to that which we have just employed in three dimensions to evaluate the unknown constants occurring in the

209

velocity distribution of a two-dimensional gas (eq. (6.38)). The temperature T of a two-dimensional gas is defined by

$$kT = \tfrac{1}{2}\overline{mu^2}$$

and not by $\tfrac{3}{2}kT = \tfrac{1}{2}\overline{mu^2}$ as in three dimensions. (In three dimensions we know from $\tfrac{1}{2}\overline{mu^2} = \tfrac{3}{2}kT$ that $kT = \tfrac{1}{3}\overline{mu^2}$ or, since $\overline{u^2} = 3\overline{u_x^2}$, that $kT = \overline{mu_x^2}$. Defining $kT = \tfrac{1}{2}\overline{mu^2}$ tells us, since $\overline{u^2} = 2\overline{u_x^2}$ in two dimensions, that $kT = \overline{mu_x^2}$; the same as in three dimensions.)

You should have obtained the result that

$$\frac{1}{N}\frac{dN}{du} = \left(\frac{m}{kT}\right) u\, e^{-mu^2/2kT} \quad \text{(two dimensions)} \qquad (6.49)$$

The corresponding energy distribution is

$$\frac{1}{N}\frac{dN}{dE} = \left(\frac{1}{kT}\right) e^{-E/kT} \quad \text{(two dimensions)} \qquad (6.50)$$

as follows immediately from eq. (6.49), since $mu\,du = dE$ and $\tfrac{1}{2}mu^2 = E$.

Exercise 6.8

A useful exercise, which allows you to check up on your understanding of this section, is to deduce the velocity and energy distribution functions of a hypothetical one-dimensional gas. It will be sufficient to deduce the number of "modules" within an energy range dE at energy E and to substitute this for g_i in eq. (6.33). You should then evaluate the two unknown constants as we did in three dimensions. Assume that the temperature T of one-dimensional gas is related to the mean kinetic energy of the gas atoms by $\tfrac{1}{2}kT = \tfrac{1}{2}\overline{mu^2}$. (Since $\overline{u^2} = \overline{u_x^2}$ in a one-dimensional system, this defines $kT = \overline{mu_x^2}$; the same as in two and three dimensions.)

You should have found that

$$\frac{1}{N}\frac{dN}{du} = \left(\frac{2}{\pi}\right)^{1/2}\left(\frac{m}{kT}\right)^{1/2} e^{-mu^2/2kT} \quad \text{(one dimension)} \qquad (6.51)$$

or, in terms of the energy distribution function,

$$\frac{1}{N}\frac{dN}{dE} = \frac{1}{\pi^{1/2}}\left(\frac{1}{kT}\right)^{1/2} E^{-1/2}\, e^{-E/kT} \quad \text{(one dimension)} \qquad (6.52)$$

210

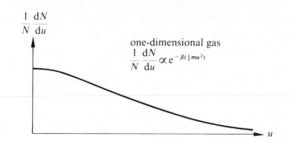

Fig. 6.31   The velocity distribution function for a one-dimensional gas.

The one-dimensional velocity distribution function is shown in Fig. 6.31 and the corresponding one-dimensional energy distribution function is shown in Fig. 6.32. Having arrived at the form of the velocity distribution function in a gas, we should now ask whether introducing this function into the discussion of the so-called transport coefficients, D, η, and κ, would have materially altered our expressions (eqs. (5.19), (5.30), and (5.47)) for these coefficients. The answer is that (apart from being multiplied by a factor close to unity) the transport coefficients are unaltered. A rough and ready explanation of why this is so is that the term $n\bar{u}$ which occurred in all our discussions (see, for example, eq. (5.28)) is replaced by $\int \mathrm{d}n\, u$, that is, by $\int u(\mathrm{d}n/\mathrm{d}u)\,\mathrm{d}u$. But, by definition, $\bar{u} = (\int u(\mathrm{d}n/\mathrm{d}u)\,\mathrm{d}u)/n$, i.e., $\int u(\mathrm{d}n/\mathrm{d}u)\,\mathrm{d}u = n\bar{u}$. This happy state of affairs only comes about because the limits of integration in $\int u(\mathrm{d}n/\mathrm{d}u)\,\mathrm{d}u$ are zero and infinity in expressions for the transport coefficients. If the integration is from a finite velocity to infinity the form of the answer is drastically changed. Such integrals occur in chemical reaction theory.

6.9   Gaseous phase chemical reactions

Up to now we have only considered what happens when like hits like in a gas. When two argon atoms collide, for example, two argon atoms emerge unscathed from the collision. However when gaseous hydrogen (H_2) and iodine

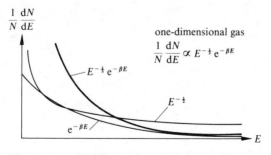

Fig. 6.32   The energy distribution function for a one-dimensional gas.

(I_2) are present together, the hydrogen and iodine molecules may not emerge unscathed from the collision. What may happen is that two molecules of hydrogen iodide (HI) are formed. As another example, when an atom of ^2H (called deuterium, symbol D) collides with a molecule of H_2 (properly written $^1H_2$) a molecule DH and an atom H may be formed. It is this second example which we shall consider further.

Clearly, the minimum condition which must be satisfied by a D atom and an H_2 molecule which are to react chemically is that they collide. If they do not collide they cannot interact! In section 5.1 we derived an expression (eq. (5.3)) for the number of collisions made by an atom of diameter d per unit time as it moved in a gas composed of like atoms. Applying the same arguments to an atom of type A, of diameter d_A, moving through a gas composed of atoms of type B, each of diameter d_B, leads directly to (and you should be able to prove this for yourself (studying Fig. 5.3 will help))

$$\text{number of collisions of atom A per unit time} = \pi\left(\frac{d_A}{2} + \frac{d_B}{2}\right)^2 \bar{u}\, n_B \quad (6.53)$$

where n_B is the number density of atoms of type B. If, instead of there being only a single atom of A present, there are n_A per unit volume, the total number of collisions between atoms of type A and atoms of type B in unit volume per unit time—the so-called *collision frequency* Z_{AB}—is found by multiplying eq. (6.53) through by n_A:

$$Z_{AB} = \frac{\pi}{4}(d_A + d_B)^2 \bar{u}\, n_A n_B \quad (6.54)$$

Strictly speaking, eq. (6.54) only applies if both types of atom are moving at the same speed. This will be so in the case of the reaction between ^2H (i.e., D) and H_2 where the mass of an ^2H atom is virtually identical to that of an H_2 molecule. Under such conditions we may write, as we have done on so many previous occasions,

$$\bar{u} \approx (\overline{u^2})^{1/2} = \left(\frac{3kT}{m}\right)^{1/2} \quad (6.55)$$

Now the rate at which DH (and H) are formed in the reaction between D and H_2 should be equal to the number of collisions (Z_{AB}) between atoms of D and molecules of H_2 in unit volume per unit time. We may therefore write that, from eqs. (6.54) and (6.55),

$$\text{reaction rate} = \frac{\pi}{4}(d_D + d_{H_2})^2 (3kT/m)^{1/2} n_D n_{H_2} \quad (6.56)$$

Here rate means the rate of change of the number density of DH (or H). Experimentally the reaction rate can be studied by determining the composition (using a mass spectrometer) at different times. While it is found that the reaction rate does indeed depend on the product of the instantaneous concentrations of D and H_2, as is predicted by eq. (6.56), the rate is found to increase much more rapidly with increasing temperature than the predicted $T^{1/2}$ dependence. In addition, the observed reaction rates are many orders of magnitude less than the rates given by eq. (6.56). There is evidently a serious flaw somewhere in our arguments.

The flaw lies in our assumption that each and every collision can, and indeed does, lead to a reaction. We have implicitly assumed a hard-sphere model (in eq. (6.53)) yet we have allowed the H_2 molecule to split and one of its atoms to pair with the deuterium atom. It is possible to argue that under these circumstances the potential energy curve between the reacting species should actually have the form shown in Fig. 6.33. At large separations to the left in Fig. 6.33 the H_2 molecule and the D atom exert no forces on one another and their potential energy may be taken as zero. As they approach closely we would expect them to resist further compression; repulsive forces should come into play and therefore the potential energy will rise. As they approach still closer, the attractive forces which enable the atoms to rearrange themselves come into play, and therefore the potential energy starts to fall again. At large separations (to the right in Fig. 6.33) the potential energy between the H atom and the DH molecule will again fall to zero. (If the reactant and the product molecules are quite different, as they are when H_2 and I_2 react to form HI, the potential energy "plateaus" will have different values on either side of the hill.) You will notice that the word "separation" has been set in inverted commas in Fig. 6.33. At separations much larger than the size of either molecule there is no problem about what is meant by the "separation" between an H_2 molecule and a D atom, or between an H atom and a DH molecule. However, at small "separations" when the atoms are very close (symbolized by D–H–H in Fig. 6.33) there is no one "separation". If the D–H–H molecule which is "formed" as soon as the reactants

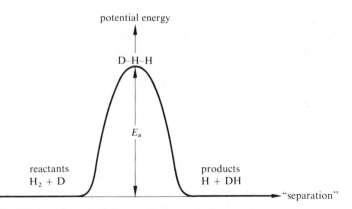

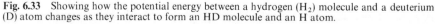

Fig. 6.33 Showing how the potential energy between a hydrogen (H_2) molecule and a deuterium (D) atom changes as they interact to form an HD molecule and an H atom.

213

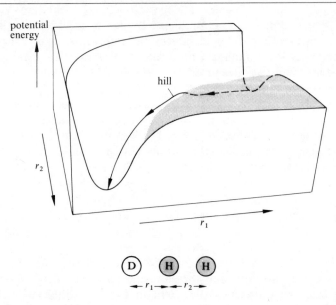

Fig. 6.34 Schematic potential energy surface for the interaction between a hydrogen molecule and a deuterium atom.

start to interact is linear we must be able to specify the potential energy as a function of the D–H separation r_1 and of the H–H separation, r_2. To do this requires a surface. In fact the surface has the form shown in Fig. 6.34. For such a linear D–H–H intermediate, fixing r_1 and r_2 uniquely fixes the potential energy so the surface can indeed be constructed. You will notice that there is a col or hill along the valley, and it is this col which is represented by the peak in Fig. 6.33. In moving from left to right in Fig. 6.33 we are really moving "up the valley and over the hill" as shown in Fig. 6.34. To specify the route requires a point by point specification of (r_1, r_2). Fortunately, as we shall presently see, we can discuss the reaction without knowing precisely what route is followed; Fig. 6.33 will be quite adequate for our purposes.

It is clear from Fig. 6.33 that for a collision between a hydrogen molecule and a deuterium atom to lead to the formation of an HD molecule and an H atom, the energy of the colliding particles must equal or exceed E_a, the so-called *activation energy* of the reaction. What we must do is work out the fraction of collisions which possess this necessary energy and then to multiply our former expression, eq. (6.56), by this fraction. Now we should, of course, treat the problem as a three-dimensional one. However in view of the simplifications we have already introduced into the discussion it will be quite adequate to regard the reaction as taking place in two dimensions. (A three-dimensional discussion is quite tedious and does not materially alter the final result.) Equation (6.50) tells us that the fraction of atoms which possess an energy within the range dE at an energy E is given by

$$\frac{dN}{N} = \frac{1}{kT} e^{-E/kT} dE \tag{6.57}$$

We are interested in the fraction with an energy in excess of E_a. Integrating eq. (6.57) gives

$$\text{fraction of atoms with energy} \geq E_a = \int_{E_a}^{\infty} \frac{1}{kT} e^{-E/kT} dE = \int_{E_a}^{\infty} - d(e^{-E/kT})$$

$$\text{fraction of atoms with energy} \geq E_a = e^{-E_a/kT} \tag{6.58}$$

Finally, multiplying the right-hand side of eq. (6.56) by this fraction—the fraction of particles which collide with the necessary energy to react—gives

$$\text{reaction rate} \left(\frac{dn_H}{dt}\right) = \frac{\pi}{4}(d_D + d_{H_2})^2 n_D n_{H_2} (3kT/m)^{1/2} e^{-E_a/kT} \tag{6.59}$$

When the calculation is carried out in three dimensions the same dominant exponential temperature dependence appears again (which is hardly surprising in view of eq. (6.48)). Much the same analysis applies to the reaction between H_2 and I_2 and to several other reactions. Figure 6.35 shows an experimental study of $\ln \left[(dn_{HI}/dt)/2n_{H_2} n_{I_2} \right]$ plotted against $1/T$. As eq. (6.59) (applied to the reaction between molecular hydrogen and hydrogen iodide) predicts, the

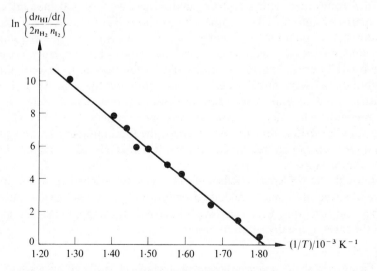

Fig. 6.35 Showing the temperature dependence of the reaction between molecular hydrogen and molecular iodine which leads to the formation of hydrogen iodide. Here n_{H_2}, for example, is the number density of molecular hydrogen. (For convenience a constant has been added to all the values plotted along the ordinate. This will not, of course, affect the value of the gradient.)

215

graph is indeed linear. When one calculates absolute reaction rates on the basis of a refined version of eq. (6.59) they agree, to within a factor of about two, with the experimentally determined values in the reaction between molecular hydrogen and iodine. Considering all the approximations which must be made in this type of theoretical discussion, such a measure of agreement must be regarded as highly satisfactory.

To emphasize a remark made earlier, one *can* discuss quite adequately how gases behave without appealing explicitly to the velocity (or energy) distribution function *provided* there is no activation energy involved in the process under discussion. Virtually all processes in solids and in liquids involve an activation energy of one sort or another.

Summary

1. There is no literal interpretation to the question: In a perfect gas how many atoms possess one particular specified speed (or energy)? It can only be answered if the question is phrased to include a range of speeds or energies.
2. Using an air table it is possible to simulate a two-dimensional gas. Stroboscopically-lit photography enables one to determine the time-averaged energy distribution for such a gas. The technique is impractical in three dimensions.
3. Using the idea of energy cells we were able to predict the ensemble-averaged (or "average over all possible arrangements") energy distribution for a low population two- and three-dimensional gas.
4. When confronted with a high population gas we saw that manual sorting of particles among cells becomes very tedious. Fortunately we found that with such populations one particular *type* of arrangement predominated so that pictures contributed by all other types of arrangement could be ignored. By appealing to this technique of finding the most probable distribution we were able to derive expressions for the velocity and energy distributions of one-, two-, and three-dimensional gases. Each of these expressions, when derived, contain two undetermined constants which can be found by writing down expressions for the total number of atoms present and for the mean atomic kinetic energy, which is related to the temperature in a known way.
5. Although the transport coefficients in a gas are insensitive to the form of the Maxwell–Boltzmann velocity distributions, processes like gaseous phase chemical reactions, which involve an activation energy, must take account of the form of the distribution function.

PROBLEMS

6.1 Figure 6.36 shows a time-exposure photograph of pucks on an air table taken under stroboscopic illumination. Using the information contained in this photograph draw a histogram showing the energy distribution of the pucks. You will have to make your own decisions about what size energy intervals to employ. You should

216

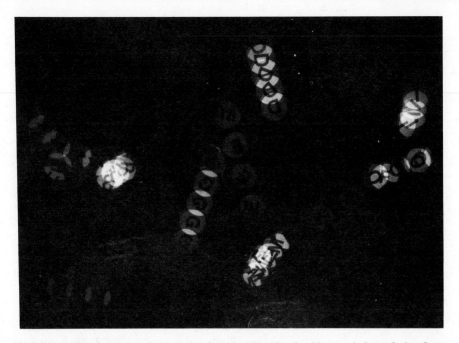

Fig. 6.36 A time-exposure photograph of pucks. (Reprinted with permission of the Open University from television programmes available from the University.)

also decide what to do when pucks are involved in a collision! The histogram will, of course, only tell you about what is happening at one particular time on the table.

6.2 By playing the "bookshelf game" sketch out all the ways that three atoms, A, B, and C of a two-dimensional gas can share out four units of energy. Because all energy rings of constant δE possess the same number of cells in two dimensions you need only sort the atoms among a single column of modules; one at level 0 (i.e., where the energy is 0); one at level 1, etc. Remember that changing the order of the atoms *within* a given module does not give rise to a new picture. When you have obtained all the distinct pictures, calculate the mean number of atoms at each level and plot the results as a histogram.

6.3 Three atoms A, B, and C of a three-dimensional gas share out between them a total of four units of energy. By adopting the bookshelf technique sketch all the distinct pictures showing the ways that the energy can be shared out. Assume that in velocity space the inner sphere, where the energy is 0, contains only one cell; that the first shell, where the energy is 1, contains two cells; that there are three cells in the second shell where the energy is 2; that there are three cells in the third shell, where the energy is 3; and four cells in the fourth shell where the energy is 4 units. (This number of cells is arrived at by assuming that the constant $(32\pi^2/m^3)^{1/2}/V_0 = 2$ in eq. (6.16) and by rounding off the answers to the nearest integer.) Once you have obtained all the distinct pictures work out the average number of atoms within each energy level and plot your results as a histogram. (You will find it helpful to work out the basic types of arrangement first; rather than just drawing pictures "as they come".)

217

6.4 (a) Solve the problem posed in exercise 6.3 but this time with two atoms A and B sharing out three units of energy. (b) Repeat the exercise with A and B sharing out four units of energy.

By raising the total energy from three to four units we are increasing the mean kinetic energy per atom from 3/2 to 2 units. This is equivalent to raising the temperature of the gas by a factor of $2/(3/2) = 4/3$. By comparing the histogram you obtain in (b) with the histogram you obtain in (a) you should be able to see, in a rough sort of way, how raising the temperature affects the energy distribution in a two-dimensional gas.

6.5 The *most probable speed* of atoms in a gas is that at which the Maxwell–Boltzmann velocity distribution function is a maximum. Show that in a three-dimensional gas the most probable speed is $(2kT/m)^{1/2}$. By how much is the r.m.s. speed in a gas greater than the most probable speed of the gas atoms?

6.6 Using the data given in Fig. 6.35 evaluate the activation energy for the reaction between molecular hydrogen and molecular iodine that leads to hydrogen iodide.

6.7 Plot out graphically the Maxwell–Boltzmann velocity distribution function, eq. (6.47), for molecular oxygen at a temperature of 300 K. $(M_r(O_2) = 32.)$

6.8 In a two-dimensional gas at a temperature of 100 K (a) what fraction of the atoms have an energy lying between $2 \cdot 0 \times 10^{-21}$ J and $2 \cdot 1 \times 10^{-21}$ J? (b) what fraction have an energy greater than $1 \cdot 38 \times 10^{-21}$ J? and (c) what fraction have an energy greater than $3 \cdot 76 \times 10^{-21}$ J?

6.9 A gas is contained within the vessel C (Fig. 6.37) which is sealed except for a small hole of area A. The space outside C is evacuated. Show that the mean translational kinetic energy of the gas atoms which escape into the vacuum is 4/3 times that of the gas atoms within C. (In other words, show that the escaping gas atoms have a mean kinetic energy of $\frac{4}{3}(\frac{3}{2}kT) = 2kT$.) Some help: By assuming a "$\frac{1}{6}$th-model" (section 5.3) you can avoid having to consider atoms which impact on A from all directions. (This will save tedious integrations.) In a time t the number of atoms with speeds between u and $u + du$ which escape are one-sixth of the total number with speeds between u and $u + du$ contained within a cylinder of length ut and cross-sectional area A. This total is $dn\,(utA) = (dn/du)utA\,du$, where dn/du is the number of atoms per unit volume with speeds, within unit range of speed, of u. Now each atom which leaves possesses an energy $\frac{1}{2}mu^2$, so the total energy carried away in time t by atoms with speeds between u and $u + du$ is one-sixth of $\frac{1}{2}mu^2[(dn/du)utA\,du]$. Integrating from $u = 0$ to $u = \infty$ gives expressions for the total energy and the total number of atoms leaving C in time t. Dividing the total energy by the total number of atoms leaving will, of course, give the mean energy of the departing atoms. You will need to use integrals given in Table 6.4.

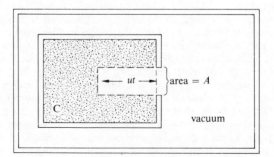

Fig. 6.37 Atoms escape from vessel C into a vacuum.

7. The Solid Phase

We have argued that when the mean translational kinetic energy $\frac{1}{2}m\overline{u^2}$ of an atom greatly exceeds the interatomic dissociation energy ΔE, atoms can only have the most fleeting association with one another and the substance will be in the gaseous phase. We have also argued that when $\frac{1}{2}m\overline{u^2} \ll \Delta E$ there is insufficient kinetic energy to prevent the atoms attracting one another to form a tightly bound conglomeration which is characteristic of the solid phase. Just as we chose to define a perfect gas as one in which $\Delta E = 0$, $\frac{1}{2}m\overline{u^2} > 0$, so it would seem reasonable to define a perfect solid as one in which $\Delta E > 0$, $\frac{1}{2}m\overline{u^2} = 0$. And this is the definition we shall adopt in the present chapter. We shall refer to such a solid as a "thermally perfect" solid. (Later on we will use the word perfect to denote the absence of those defects in the structure of a crystal in which atoms are permanently displaced from their proper sites.) Our immediate concern is to look at some of the possible ways in which atoms are arranged in crystalline solids. Our survey of crystallography will necessarily be fairly superficial; indeed we will only look in any detail at those structures which are relevant to later discussions.

7.1 Order or disorder?

The first, rather obvious, question to ask is how atoms should be arranged in a thermally perfect solid. One way of answering this question is to pour some oil-covered bearings ($\Delta E > 0$) onto a tray and to see how the balls arrange themselves once they come to rest ($\frac{1}{2}m\overline{u^2} = 0$). Figure 3.2(a) tells us the answer: they are arranged in a regular and endlessly repeating pattern. In fact it is possible, without having to resort to experiment, to argue that in a thermally perfect solid the atoms should be arranged in such a regular way rather than conglomerating together in a haphazard fashion. The argument is a *reductio ad absurdem* one.

Suppose that the stationary atoms are not arranged in a regular pattern but are disposed at random as shown in Fig. 7.1. Now consider any two atoms, i and j. Because the local arrangement of atoms is, in general, different about atoms i and j the net force acting on i will differ from that on j. If it were of immediate interest we could, of course, calculate the resultant force acting on any atom from the form of the interatomic force curve and the local arrangement of atoms about the atom in question. The only way to

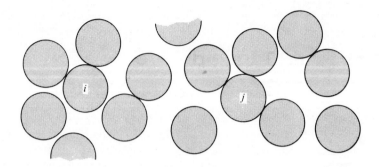

Fig. 7.1 In a non-crystalline solid each atom, i, j, etc., is subjected to a different net force due to the random arrangement of their neighbouring atoms. If i is in equilibrium the odds are that j will not be in equilibrium.

ensure that all the atoms are at rest (making $\frac{1}{2}m\overline{u^2} = 0$) is to have zero resultant force acting on each atom. In a random arrangement of atoms we might expect that the local arrangement of atoms about some *one* atom might indeed lead to zero resultant force on that atom. However, the resultant force acting on any other atom would, in general, be non-zero. So the random arrangement illustrated in Fig. 7.1, with all its atoms at rest, is an absurdity! To have zero resultant force on each atom demands that the local (but as yet undetermined) arrangement of atoms about each and every atom be the same. In other words the structure must be periodic; the "wallpaper pattern" must repeat.

If this argument is correct why then do *amorphous* substances like glasses and certain plastics—substances with a non-periodic structure—exist? Actually the argument never said that such substances would not exist; it only asserts that such structures will not be in equilibrium. Indeed, it is a fact that, over a period of centuries glass may crystallize out. If the glass is kept close to its softening temperature the crystallization is much more rapid—as will be known to anyone with experience of glass blowing. By rapidly quenching molten sulphur in water *plastic sulphur* is formed. This may happen when the mean translational kinetic energy of the atoms (i.e., the temperature) is reduced in a significantly shorter time than the time it takes for the atoms to find their true equilibrium positions. In most plastics crystallization is made difficult by having long chain molecules which can become so intertwined that the time required for crystallization to take place can be very large indeed. This may be helped by introducing a spread in the chain lengths or by introducing side chains at random. Under these conditions practically every molecule is different; the intermolecular forces will therefore be different throughout the substance and so periodicity is not required to ensure stability. Another trick is to introduce additives (plasticizers) which separate the chains and so prevents them interacting strongly with one another. Celluloid consists of nitrocellulose, which is normally crystalline, plasticized with camphor. Cellophane consists of cellulose plasticized with glycerol. The disadvantage of these now largely superseded plastics was that the plasticizers could evaporate, allowing the chains to come together and so to crystallize. You may have noticed how cellophane goes brittle with age.

7.2 Periodic arrays of atoms

Even before the atomic hypothesis had gained widespread acceptance the regularity of crystal faces had suggested that crystals are formed by the regular repetition of identical "building blocks". However it was not until 1912 that X-ray diffraction studies vindicated these conjectures and enabled the structure of crystals to be determined unequivocally. Before looking at this experimental evidence we shall introduce a few—but only a few—of the terms that had been introduced into the subject during the years prior to 1912.

Figure 7.2 shows a hypothetical two-dimensional crystal structure. Properly speaking, the figure shows a *lattice*—an arrangement of points (denoted by ·) in space—which has a *basis*—a group of atoms (denoted by⌒)—associated with each lattice point. The whole—the lattice plus its associated basis—is referred to as a *structure*. So we may describe the structure of a crystal by stating the form of the underlying lattice *and* the basis that is to be associated with each point of the lattice. Remember that the lattice as such does not exist; it is merely an arrangement of points in space which tells one where to locate the basis. The basis may, as in copper for example, consist of a single atom or it may consist of several atoms. In crystallized proteins the basis may contain some tens of thousands of atoms.

In practice it is unnecessary to go to the trouble of drawing out a vast array of points to indicate what the lattice is like. The lattice can be constructed provided one is given the form of the *primitive cell*. This is the smallest cell which, when repeated endlessly throughout space, will fill all space and reproduce the lattice. Figure 7.3(a) shows four possible primitive cells for

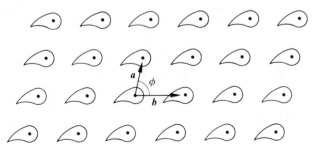

Fig. 7.2   A crystal structure results on associating a basis (⌒), which may be a single atom or perhaps a protein molecule, with each point (·) of a lattice.

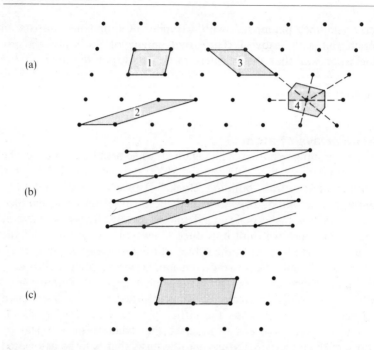

Fig. 7.3 (a) Showing four primitive cells of a lattice. (b) Once a primitive cell is known the lattice may be constructed by regular and endless repetition of that cell. (c) The cell shown shaded contains more than one lattice point and is called non-primitive.

the lattice of Fig. 7.2. The construction of cells 1, 2, and 3 is clear enough. Cell 4 was constructed by drawing lines to connect a given lattice point to all neighbouring lattice points and then, at the midpoint of each line, drawing in normal lines. (Such a cell is called a Wigner–Seitz primitive cell.) Figure 7.3(b) shows how repeating just one of these primitive cells throughout space does indeed reproduce the lattice. A characteristic of a primitive cell is that it contains but one lattice point. This is obviously true for cell 4 in Fig. 7.3(a). In the other cells there are lattice points at the four corners of the cells but each point is shared by the four cells which meet at that point (see Fig. 7.3(b)). Applied to a structure it follows that the number of atoms in a primitive cell is equal to the number of atoms in the basis. This is a consequence of the fact that the basis is associated with each lattice point.

It is sometimes more convenient in describing a lattice to specify a cell which is larger than the minimum size cell (primitive cell). Such a cell is, not surprisingly, called *non-primitive*. Figure 7.3(c) shows an example of such a non-primitive cell for the lattice of Fig. 7.2.

Lattice types

By changing the magnitude of the so-called *primitive translation vectors* **a** and **b** in Fig. 7.2—the name arises because starting at any lattice point we may reach *any* other lattice point from integral combinations of **a** and **b**—and the magnitude of the angle ϕ, one can generate an unlimited number of lattices which all differ from one another. However, as one generates ever more and more lattices one soon discovers that, in two dimensions, they all fall into five fundamentally different types. All others are "variations on a theme". We might decide for example to start off with the lattice illustrated in Fig. 7.2 and to increase the magnitude of **a** by 5 per cent, to decrease that of **b** by 2 per cent, and to increase ϕ by 2 degrees. However this new lattice is not of a fundamentally different type to that of Fig. 7.2. If, on the other hand, we had made $a = b$ and $\phi = 90°$ then we would have produced a quite different type of lattice (Fig. 7.4). The distinction between these two types of lattice is that the lattice of Fig. 7.4, unlike that of Fig. 7.2, is unaltered on rotating it through 90° about a lattice point. The square lattice can also be "reflected" without alteration about a plane passing through a lattice point and parallel to **a**. It is also unaltered on being reflected about a plane passing through a lattice point and parallel to **b**. (So "fundamentally different" actually means "with different lattice symmetry properties".) The five fundamentally different two-dimensional lattices are illustrated in Fig. 7.5(a). Within any of the lattice types shown as (2), (3), (4), and (5) in Fig. 7.5(a), where ϕ is fixed, one is free to choose the magnitude of a and/or b—provided these are consistent with the type of lattice. For example, in the case of the hexagonal lattice a must have the same magnitude as b although this can be anything we wish. In the case of the oblique axis, where $a \neq b$, we must, of course, avoid making $\phi = 90°$. (To do so would generate the rectangular lattice.) By ringing all the permitted changes one can produce an infinite number of *lattices*; however all these lattices fall into the five fundamental *types* shown in Fig. 7.5(a). In studying these lattice types remember that a lattice does *not* represent a crystal structure. The structure is only achieved when we associate a basis of one or more atoms with each lattice point.

In three dimensions it turns out that there are fourteen fundamentally different lattices. These are illustrated by the cells, some of which are non-primitive,

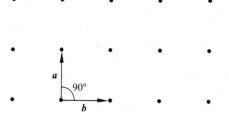

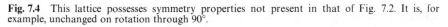

Fig. 7.4 This lattice possesses symmetry properties not present in that of Fig. 7.2. It is, for example, unchanged on rotation through 90°.

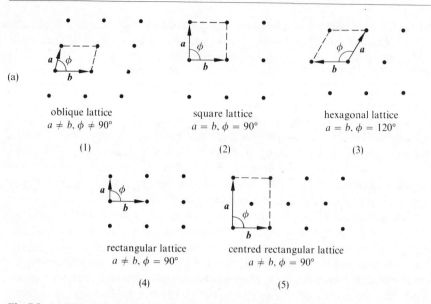

(a)

oblique lattice
$a \neq b, \phi \neq 90°$

(1)

square lattice
$a = b, \phi = 90°$

(2)

hexagonal lattice
$a = b, \phi = 120°$

(3)

rectangular lattice
$a \neq b, \phi = 90°$

(4)

centred rectangular lattice
$a \neq b, \phi = 90°$

(5)

Fig. 7.5 (a) All two-dimensional lattices fall into one or other of the five types shown. The cell shown in (5) is non-primitive. (b) All three-dimensional lattices fall into one or other of the fourteen types shown. The cells shown in outline are the conventional ones, which are not always primitive. The letters P, I, C, F serve to distinguish the details of the lattice; for example I denotes a body-centred cell.

in Fig. 7.5(b). As in two dimensions, endless repetition of these cells through-out space will generate the lattice. Associating a basis with each lattice point will yield the structure.

Describing lattice planes

The lattice points of the various lattices we have just described may be thought of as lying on various sets of parallel lines in two dimensions and on various sets of parallel planes in three dimensions. Figure 7.6 shows several ways of drawing in sets of parallel lines in a two-dimensional square lattice. Figure 7.7 shows two different planes in a three-dimensional lattice (for clarity most of the lattice points have been omitted). In both the two- and three-dimensional lattices, axes have been drawn in along the directions of the primitive translation vectors, namely a and b in two dimensions and a, b, and c in three dimen-sions. Now, to determine the position and orientation of a line in two dimensions requires the coordinates of two points. To determine the position and orientation of a plane in three dimensions requires the coordinates of three points which must not be collinear. The plane shown shaded in Fig. 7.7, for example, is determined by the points (2, 0, 0), (0, 3, 0), and (0, 0, 1), where the coordinates are measured in units of the lattice constants a, b, and c.

It is more usual to specify the orientation of a plane in a lattice by its so-called *Miller indices*. If plane ABC in Fig. 7.7 makes intercepts Ha, Kb,

(b)

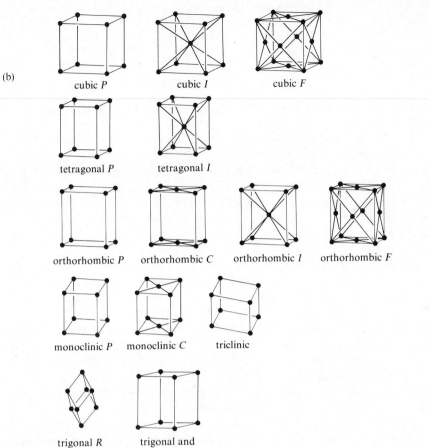

cubic P cubic I cubic F

tetragonal P tetragonal I

orthorhombic P orthorhombic C orthorhombic I orthorhombic F

monoclinic P monoclinic C triclinic

trigonal R trigonal and hexagonal P

and Lc on the three axes it follows that for this plane, or for any parallel plane,

$$OA:OB:OC = Ha:Kb:Lc$$

$$= \frac{Ha}{HKL} : \frac{Kb}{HKL} : \frac{Lc}{HKL}$$

$$= \frac{a}{KL} : \frac{b}{HL} : \frac{c}{HK}$$

$$OA:OB:OC = \frac{a}{h} : \frac{b}{k} : \frac{c}{l} \tag{7.1}$$

Because H, K, L are integers it follows that $h(=KL)$, $k(=HL)$ and $l(=HK)$ are integers. In the case of plane ABC illustrated in Fig. 7.7 $H = 5$, $K = 4$,

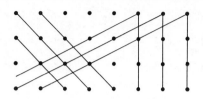

Fig. 7.6 Shows three different sets of parallel lines in a two-dimensional square lattice.

and $L = 2$; so $h = 8$, $k = 10$, and $l = 20$. It is normal to reduce the three integers h, k, and l to the smallest three integers having the same ratio. The result, written in parentheses as $(h\,k\,l)$, is referred to as the Miller indices of the plane. The Miller indices of plane ABC and parallel planes are therefore (4 5 10). For a plane whose intercepts are $H = 4$, $K = 3$, $L = 2$ the reciprocals $h(=KL) = 6$, $k(=HL) = 8$ and $l(=HK) = 12$. Dividing these values by 2 gives the Miller indices of this, or any parallel plane, as (3 4 6). Given the Miller indices of a plane and, of course, the lattice vectors a, b, and c the plane is most easily constructed by appealing to eq. (7.1). For plane $(h\,k\,l)$ one divides a by h, b by k, and c by l and then draws a plane through the three points so obtained. This, or any parallel plane, is the plane with Miller indices $(h\,k\,l)$. It follows that a Miller index of zero means the plane only intersects a particular axis at infinity. Figure 7.8 shows some important planes in a cubic crystal labelled by their Miller indices. A minus sign placed above an index as in $(\bar{1}00)$ denotes that a plane cuts the axis on the negative side of the origin. You should be able to show that the faces of a cube lying in a cubic lattice are (100), (010), (001), $(\bar{1}00)$, $(0\bar{1}0)$, and $(00\bar{1})$. These *set* of cube faces may be written as $\{100\}$ for convenience.

To specify a certain direction in a lattice one need only specify the coordinates of a line lying in this direction. If the line passes through the origin and through the lattice point with coordinates ua, vb, and wc the line is determined when u, v, and w are specified. It is usual to divide such a set of integers through by a common factor so as to give the set of smallest possible integers.

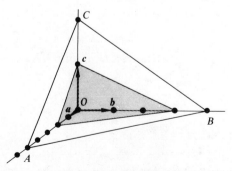

Fig. 7.7 Two different planes in a three-dimensional lattice. For clarity most of the lattice points have been omitted.

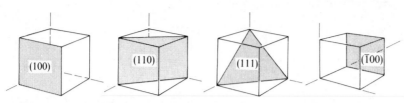

Fig. 7.8 Some important planes in a cubic lattice indicated by their Miller indices.

If $u = 12$, $v = 8$, and $w = 6$ we would write the lattice direction in square brackets as $[6\ 4\ 3]$. In a cubic crystal, for example, the x-axis is the $[1\ 0\ 0]$ direction.

Exercise 7.1

Sketch lines having Miller indices of $(1\ 0)$, $(\overline{1}\ 0)$, and $(2\ 3)$ in a two-dimensional square lattice (where $a = b$ and $\phi = 90°$). Also indicate the lattice direction $[2\ 5]$.

7.3 X-ray diffraction

To determine the structure of a crystal we must be able to ascertain the form of the underlying lattice and the basis which is associated with each lattice point. Both of these pieces of information may be obtained from X-ray diffraction measurements although, of the two, it is always much easier to determine the form of the lattice.

Experimental procedures

In Germany in 1912 Friedrich and Knipping, acting on a suggestion from Laue, directed a narrow beam of X-rays at a single crystal. A photographic plate placed behind the crystal recorded a pattern of discrete spots. Shortly afterwards, Bragg in England performed a somewhat different experiment which was capable of a more ready interpretation. Whereas Friedrich and Knipping used a beam of "white" X-rays, containing a wide range of wavelengths, to illuminate a stationary crystal, Bragg used a beam of single wavelength ("monochromatic") X-rays and a rotating crystal. A modern version of Bragg's apparatus is illustrated in Fig. 7.9. The film is placed in a cylindrical holder which is concentric with a spindle on which is mounted the specimen in the form of a single crystal. Unless one has been lucky one finds that with the crystal stationary no diffraction spots are recorded on the film when a (structurally) perfect crystal is illuminated by a very well collimated beam of very monochromatic X-rays. It is only on rotating the crystal (either continuously through 360° or by rotating it back and forth through a more limited range of angles) that diffraction spots are normally obtained. Each spot (or group of spots) corresponds to a unique position of the crystal relative to the beam.

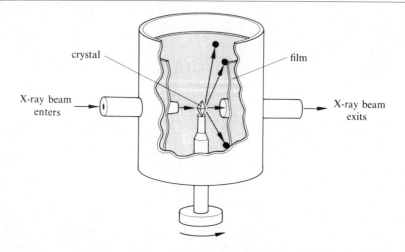

Fig. 7.9 A crystal mounted on a rotating spindle is struck by a narrow beam of monochromatic X-rays. When the crystal is in particular orientations strong diffraction maxima are produced along particular directions. These strongly reflected beams are recorded on the emulsion which is concentric with the axis of the spindle.

Even when such diffraction maxima are present most of the radiation striking the crystal continues straight and is allowed to exit through a hole cut in the film (Fig. 7.9).

Obtaining the lattice

When a beam of X-rays strikes a crystal each and every atom in the crystal (or rather the electrons of each and every atom) scatters the beam through a wide angle. Along certain directions, and for particular settings of the crystal, the scattered beams may be in step, so producing a strong diffraction spot. In other directions they will be out of step and so cancel one another. Figure 7.10 shows a parallel beam of monochromatic X-rays striking a single crystal. For simplicity we have assumed a simple cubic lattice whose c-vector is perpendicular to the plane of the paper. The basis ($\bigcirc$) associated with each lattice point might be a single atom or it might be a very complex molecule containing many tens of thousands of atoms. In thinking about what happens it is convenient to regard all the basis units as lying on a set of parallel planes. There are, of course, many different ways of drawing in such planes and only one such possible way is illustrated in Fig. 7.10. These planes will be denoted by the appropriate Miller indices $(h\,k\,l)$ of the plane; as drawn the parallel planes have Miller indices of $(1\bar{1}0)$.

Let us consider how radiation scattered from each basis lying in plane AB can interfere with the radiation scattered from each basis in the adjacent parallel plane CD. In particular, let us consider the radiation which is scattered at an angle θ equal to the glancing angle of the radiation on these planes.

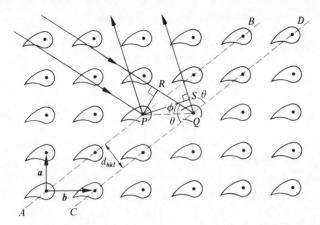

Fig. 7.10 A beam of X-rays strikes a crystal and is scattered by the basis associated with each lattice point. Here we consider the radiation scattered in a direction which makes the same angle θ with two parallel planes as does the incident beam.

Should the X-rays scattered from the basis at P reinforce those scattered from the basis at Q it follows that the radiation scattered from all other similar pairs will also reinforce, and so the intensity of the beam reflected in direction θ will be finite. For radiation scattered from the basis at P to interfere constructively with radiation scattered from the basis at Q the path difference $RQ + QS$ (Fig. 7.10) must be an integral number of wavelengths. (Since the incident radiation is in phase—"in step"—along the front PR and is in phase again along PS, radiation striking the basis at Q travels the extra distance $RQ + QS$ over that scattered from the basis at P.) So for constructive interference

$$RQ + QS = n\lambda \qquad (7.2)$$

where n is an integer, 1, 2, etc.
From triangle PQR

$$RQ = PQ \cos \phi$$

Also, since angle $PQS = 180° - 2\theta + \phi$,

$$QS = PQ \cos (180° - 2\theta + \phi)$$

$$QS = -PQ \cos (2\theta - \phi)$$

Therefore,

$$RQ + QS = PQ(\cos \phi - \cos (2\theta - \phi))$$

$$= 2PQ \sin \theta \sin (\theta - \phi)$$

Since the perpendicular distance d_{hkl} between adjacent $(h\,k\,l)$ planes is equal to $PQ \sin(\theta - \phi)$ it follows that

$$RQ + QS = 2d_{hkl} \sin \theta \qquad (7.3)$$

Substituting eq. (7.3) into eq. (7.2) we see that the condition for a strong diffracted beam is

$$2d_{hkl} \sin \theta = n\lambda \qquad (7.4)$$

—the famous result known as *Bragg's law*. Notice that d_{hkl} does *not* measure the distance PQ between the basis at P and Q on adjacent planes in the lattice; it measures the separation between adjacent $(h\,k\,l)$ planes in the lattice. Since $\sin \theta$ has a maximum value of unity, eq. (7.4) tells us that Bragg reflection can only occur for wavelengths $\lambda \leq 2d_{hkl}$. This explains why visible light cannot be used! Equation (7.4) also explains why an arbitrary chosen crystal setting is most unlikely to produce Bragg reflection with a mono-chromatic X-ray beam; the chances are that, with λ fixed, there will be no planes within the lattice which have a separation d_{hkl} and which make the correct angle θ with the incident beam to satisfy Bragg's law.

From the position of each diffraction spot on the developed film it is a simple matter to work out the angle θ (the angle between the incident and the reflected beam in Fig. 7.10 is $180° - 2\theta$). It is somewhat more difficult to obtain the order n which produced the spot at θ but we are helped by the knowledge that n must be an integer. We also know from Bragg's law that at low θ (meaning that spots lie close to the straight through position on the film) n is low. So guessing n may do the trick. Knowing n and θ the spacings of various lattice planes follow from Bragg's law. By such means the lattice is obtained.

Obtaining the basis

It is important to realize that, by itself, Bragg's law only enables the under-lying *lattice* to be determined. It tells us nothing about the nature of the basis which is associated with each lattice point. This is because it is solely concerned with the *positions* at which diffraction spots of non-zero intensity are found. The discussion omitted any reference to the absolute intensity of these diffraction spots. Figure 7.11 shows two different structures possessing the same *lattice*. In (a) the basis is a single atom; in (b) the basis is a group of several atoms—a molecule. It would be very surprising if the single atoms of (a) scattered X-rays in the same way as the molecules of (b). We might expect (wrongly as it happens) that the single atom would scatter X-rays equally well in all directions, so producing diffraction spots of constant intensity. We would certainly not expect the molecules in (b) to scatter X-rays equally in all direc-tions; there is clearly the possibility of constructive or destructive interference occurring between the radiation scattered by individual atoms within a

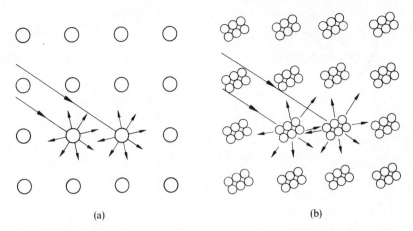

Fig. 7.11 Showing how the form of the basis influences the intensity of the X-rays scattered in different directions. In (a) the scattering is assumed to be equal in all directions. In (b) Bragg reflection within the basis leads to strong scattering in particular directions.

molecule. Bragg's law, if you like, may be satisfied by the atoms of an individual molecule as well as by the molecules of the lattice. As a result the overall intensity of the diffraction spots will vary throughout the photograph. From the measured intensities of the spots the basis can usually—but not always—be elucidated. Knowing the lattice and the basis the structure is fully determined.

7.4   Some simple crystal structures
The structures of many crystalline materials are often surprisingly simple. We will look at just a few representative structures.

Hexagonal close-packed (hcp) structure
This is one of the most commonly occurring type of crystal structure. In fact some 25 per cent of all elements crystallize with this structure. Examples are hydrogen, magnesium, and zinc.

To understand this structure we consider first a single plane (*A*) of atoms which are packed together as closely as possible. Such a plane is shown by the open circles in Fig. 7.12(a). In imagination we now place another plane (*B*) of atoms on top of this plane so that each atom of *B* touches three atoms of plane *A*. In placing a third plane (*C*) of closest-packed atoms on top of plane *B* so that each atom of *C* touches three atoms of *B*, we have two possible choices. If we place plane *C* so that its atoms are directly above those of plane *A* we produce a hexagonal close-packed structure. For obvious reasons the packing is often referred to as *ABAB*. Figure 7.12(b) is a sketch of a small portion of the hcp structure with the atoms drawn to scale. Figure 7.12(c) shows the positions of the atoms somewhat more clearly.

231

(a) 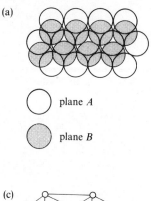 (b)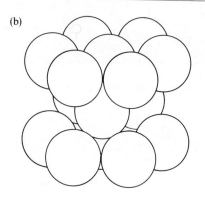

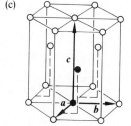

(c)

Fig. 7.12 The hcp structure in an element. (a) Two closest-packed planes of atoms are stacked on top of one another so that each atom of plane B makes *contact* with three atoms of plane A. (b) A portion of an hcp structure with the atoms drawn to size. (c) For clarity the atoms are represented by points. The lattice is hexagonal and the basis consists of an atom at $\bigcirc\bigcirc\bigcirc$ and at $\frac{2}{3}\,\frac{1}{3}\,\frac{1}{2}$. (The coordinates are expressed as fractions of a, b, and c.)

Face-centred cubic (fcc) structure

This structure results when closest-packed planes of atoms are stacked in a slightly different sequence to that which leads to the hcp structure. The first two planes go in the AB sequence. The third plane (C) however is located so that the atoms in this plane are over the holes in the first plane (A) which are not occupied by atoms of the second plane (B). This is illustrated in Fig. 7.13(a). Figure 7.13(b) shows the relative positions of the atoms in the closest-packed planes A, B, C, and A. (The packing in the fcc structure may be said to be $ABCABC \ldots .$) Although the cell which is shown in Fig. 7.13(b) is not the primitive cell its convenience is that it is cubical. A more usual way of drawing this cube is shown in Fig. 7.13(c) and in Fig. 7.13(d) where the atoms have been drawn to scale. A minor disadvantage of these drawings is that, unlike Fig. 7.13(b), they fail to bring out the stacking sequence $ABCABC$ which is so evident in Fig. 7.13(a). Some 20 per cent of the elements crystallize with fcc structures. Perhaps the most noteworthy examples are the inert gases (except for helium which crystallizes with a hcp structure).

Sodium chloride is an example of a compound whose lattice is fcc. The basis consists of one sodium ion and one chlorine ion separated by one

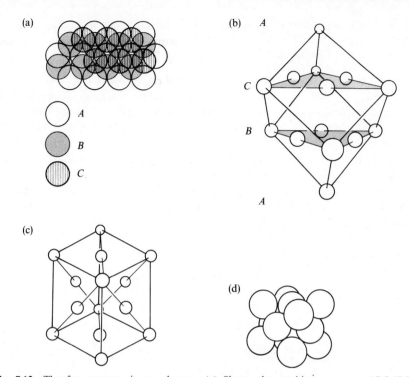

(a)

A

B

C

(b)   A

C

B

A

(c)

(d)

Fig. 7.13 The fcc structure in an element. (a) Shows the stacking sequence $ABCABC$ of adjacent planes. (b) The relative positions of atoms on adjacent planes may be seen. (c) On rotating the cell shown in (b) we see the fcc nature of the cell. (d) Here the atoms have been drawn to size.

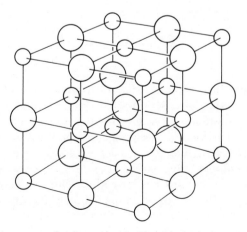

Fig. 7.14 The crystal structure of sodium chloride. The chlorine ions are larger than the sodium ions.

half the body diagonal of the fcc cell. This basis, you will recall, is to be associated with *each* lattice point. When this association is made the structure shown in Fig. 7.14 results.

Body-centred cubic (bcc) structure

The *ABAB* . . . and *ABCABC* . . . sequences for stacking closest-packed planes exhaust the ways of repetitively stacking such planes. As we have seen, the hcp and fcc structures together account for some 45 per cent of all elements. Of the remaining elements, some 15 per cent crystallize with a body-centred cubic structure. The most notable examples are the alkali metals, Li, Na, K, Rb, and Cs. Tungsten is another example.

The body-centred cubic structure for the elements results on associating a single atom with each point of the bcc lattice. A single cell of this structure is illustrated in Figs. 7.15(a) and (b). Notice that in this structure the atoms touch only along a cube diagonal and not along an edge as in the fcc structure. In other words the structure is *not* the result of stacking closest-packed planes of atoms.

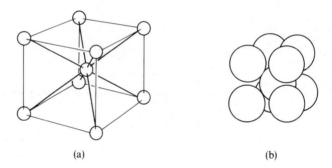

(a)   (b)

Fig. 7.15 The bcc structure of an element. In (b) the atoms have been drawn to size.

Simple cubic structure

This is undoubtedly the simplest structure to visualize and to appeal to in calculating the properties of a perfect solid. Teachers must often regret that only one *element*—polonium—crystallizes with a simple cubic structure! (And even the structure of polonium is simple cubic only within a restricted temperature range.) This structure is formed by associating a single atom with each point of the simple cubic lattice. Figure 7.16 shows a single cell of the structure. Notice how the atoms only touch along the cube edges. If you like, this structure is formed by stacking, directly on top of one another, planes of atoms in each of which an atom only makes contact with four neighbouring atoms. Crystal structures with simple cubic lattices are by no means rare among *compounds*. Caesium chloride is an example. Here the basis

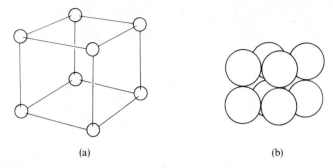

(a)   (b)

Fig. 7.16 (a) The simple cubic structure of an element. In (b) the atoms have been drawn to size.

consists of one Cs^+ ion at 0 0 0 and one Cl^- ion at $\frac{1}{2}\frac{1}{2}\frac{1}{2}$ (Fig. 7.17). (In giving the coordinates of a point *within* a cell it is usual to omit commas between the coordinates, which are expressed in fractions of the axial lengths a, b, and c, and also to omit brackets.)

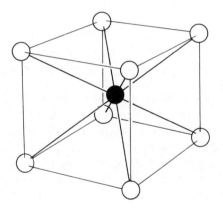

Fig. 7.17 The crystal structure of caesium chloride. The lattice is simple cubic. The basis has one Cs^+ ion at 000 and one Cl^- ion at $\frac{1}{2}\frac{1}{2}\frac{1}{2}$.

Diamond structure

The diamond structure, shown in Fig. 7.18, results when we associate a basis of two atoms with each point in an fcc lattice. We start with the (non-primitive) cell of the fcc lattice (called cubic F in Fig. 7.5(b)). The basis—to be associated with *every* point of the *lattice*—is an atom at 0 0 0 and an atom at $\frac{1}{4}\frac{1}{4}\frac{1}{4}$. Affixing this basis to each lattice point produces the diamond structure—a single cell of which is shown in Fig. 7.18. Besides carbon in the form of diamond, silicon, germanium, and gray tin all crystallize in the diamond structure.

235

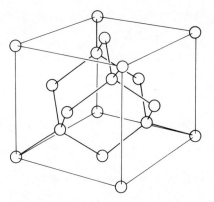

Fig. 7.18 The crystal structure of diamond.

Summary

1. Arguments based on classical physics suggest that, at absolute zero (where $\frac{1}{2}m\overline{u^2} = \frac{3}{2}kT = 0$) the atoms of a solid would be arranged in a regular fashion. X-ray diffraction studies show that the time-averaged structure of a crystal is regular.

2. The structure of a crystal may be described in terms of a lattice (an array of points in space) and a basis (an atom or group of atoms) which is associated with each lattice point. The location of the spots on an X-ray diffraction photograph enables the lattice type of the crystal to be found. The intensities of the spots may enable the basis to be found.

3. In two dimensions there are five fundamentally different types of lattice (Fig. 7.5(a)); in three dimensions the number is fourteen (Fig. 7.5(b)).

4. The Miller indices of a plane are inversely proportional to the intercepts which the plane makes with three crystal axes. The axes are taken to lie along the directions of the three primitive translation vectors a, b, and c and the intercepts are measured in units of a, b, and c.

PROBLEMS

7.1 Which of the cells shown in Fig. 7.5(b) are non-primitive? Remember that a primitive cell contains one lattice point.

7.2 Show that in a simple cubic lattice the distance between adjacent planes of Miller indices $(h\,k\,l)$ is $a(h^2 + k^2 + l^2)^{-1/2}$, where a is the lattice constant (here the separation between neighbouring points on the lattice).

7.3 A monochromatic beam of X-rays of wavelength 1.54×10^{-10} m is incident on a crystal whose lattice is simple cubic with a lattice constant of 4.0×10^{-10} m. At what angle θ will first-order Bragg reflection occur from the $(1\,0\,0)$ planes of the crystal? At what angle will third-order reflection occur?

7.4 Show that the structure of sodium chloride (Fig. 7.14) can be described as a combination of a fcc lattice with a sodium ion as basis and a fcc lattice with a chlorine ion as basis. By how much is one lattice displaced relative to the other?

7.5 Show that the diamond structure is really two fcc structures displaced from one another by one-quarter of the body diagonal of the fcc cell. The zinc blende (ZnS) structure results when Zn atoms are placed on one of these fcc lattices and S atoms on the other fcc lattice. What are the coordinates of the Zn and S atoms in a cubic cell of the zinc blende structure?

7.6 For hexagonal close packing of rigid spheres what is the c/a ratio (see Fig. 7.12(c))?

7.7 Show that in a bcc lattice the nearest neighbour distance is $3^{1/2}a/2$ and that in a fcc lattice it is $a/2^{1/2}$. Here a is the side of the cube edge in the cells labelled cubic I and cubic F in Fig. 7.5(b).

7.8 What is the maximum proportion of the available volume which can be filled by hard spheres when these spheres are arranged on (a) a simple cubic lattice, (b) a fcc lattice, and (c) a bcc lattice?

8. Thermal Properties of Solids

You will recall how once we had elucidated the properties of a perfect gas we introduced the fact that ΔE really is finite. This led to new expressions which were in much better agreement with the experimental results. Now seems the opportune moment to refine our model of a perfect solid—to acknowledge that $\frac{1}{2}m\overline{u^2}$ really is finite. We will give the atoms of our solid a finite kinetic energy and see what happens. But wait, surely we already know from X-ray diffraction studies made at around room temperature that the structure *is* regular; a finite $\frac{1}{2}m\overline{u^2}$ hardly seems to make much difference! We must remember though that an X-ray diffraction photograph (which may take several hours exposure) only tells us about the time-averaged structure. What is the situation like at any instant? We shall see that we can learn much about what the atoms are up to by studying how the molar heat capacity at constant volume varies with temperature. In fact we shall make something of a case study of the heat capacity of solids. We shall do so partly to illustrate how an in-depth enquiry proceeds; partly because we shall later appeal to some of the results arrived at during the enquiry. We shall also look at why solids expand and at a mechanical model of melting.

8.1 Heat capacity of non-metals: classical theory

Feeding energy into a solid

Figure 8.1(a) shows an apparatus which would enable the heat capacity of a solid to be measured. The solid is surrounded by a small volume of gas in which is located a paddle wheel and the bulb of a gas thermometer. If we rotate the paddle wheel (via a Newton balance pulled through a known distance) we feed a known amount of energy into the system—everything within the surrounding adiabatic walls. (We may take it that—as near as makes no difference—all the energy fed in goes to the massive lump of solid.) Rather than try to imbed a gas thermometer bulb in the solid lump we leave the bulb in the gas, confident that, at equilibrium, the temperature of the gas in the bulb is equal to the temperature of the surrounding gas, which is equal to the temperature of the solid.

No one would nowadays use a paddle wheel; an electrical heater is the obvious choice. However, the paddle wheel does remind us that feeding energy into a gas increases the average kinetic energy of the gas atoms. (The atoms

238

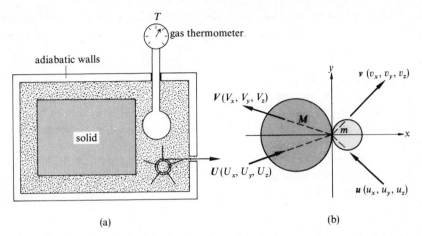

Fig. 8.1 (a) Energy may be fed into the solid by means of a paddle-wheel arrangement located in the surrounding gas. Rotating the wheel increases the translational kinetic energy of the gas atoms. This energy may then be transferred to the solid. (b) An individual collision between a gas atom of mass m and a solid atom of mass M.

get "slammed" by the paddles.) When this happens the atoms of the solid will be struck by atoms with an increased kinetic energy. In terms of Fig. 8.1(b) the solid atoms (mass M) are struck by gas atoms (mass m) which have an $\frac{1}{2}m\overline{u^2} > \frac{1}{2}M\overline{U^2}$. As a result, the kinetic energy of the solid atoms will increase until $\frac{1}{2}M\overline{U^2} = \frac{1}{2}m\overline{u^2}$. Once this stage is reached the solid and gas will be in equilibrium.

The motion of a solid atom

Unlike an atom in a gas, an atom in a solid is not free to move throughout the volume of the solid. In a solid an atom is bound by interatomic forces to its surrounding neighbours. It is as if each atom is connected by springs as shown in Fig. 8.2. When this atom is given kinetic energy it will be set moving around some complicated orbit. Despite appearances, this complex

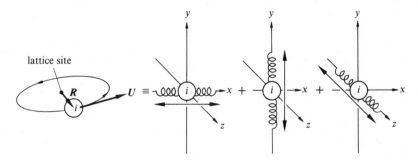

Fig. 8.2 Although atom i follows some complicated orbit the motion may be resolved into three individual vibrational motions.

orbital motion can be resolved into three individual motions as shown in Fig. 8.2. By suitably combining the vibrational motions along the x-, y-, and z-axes the actual orbit of atom i can be reproduced. (An, albeit two-dimensional, demonstration of how two "simple harmonic" motions combine to produce a complicated two-dimensional pattern is provided by Lissajous' figures. In the usual form of the demonstration a voltage which varies sinusoidally with time is applied to the x-input of a cathode-ray oscilloscope, while another sinusoidally-varying voltage is applied to the y-input. The pattern on the screen—the path followed by the electron beam—depends on the relative amplitude, frequency and phase of the two signals, and can be highly complicated.) We may therefore picture the actual motion of an atom in a solid as being the resultant of vibrational motions along three mutually-perpendicular directions.

Before we attempt to calculate the kinetic and potential energies of the solid atom we ought surely to begin with a simpler problem: what is the equation of motion of an atom in a one-dimensional structure? And, if we know its equation of motion—that is, how its position varies with time—can we deduce the energy of the atom?

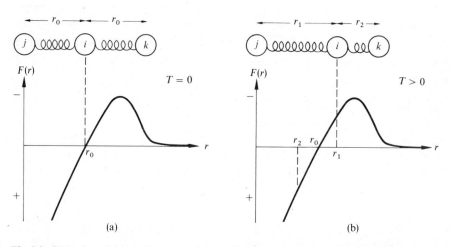

Fig. 8.3 In (a) the solid is at $T = 0$ and the equilibrium separation r_0 is such that atoms j and k exert no net force on i. In (b) the solid is at a finite temperature. Besides possessing kinetic energy, atom i now possesses potential energy in the fields between i and j and between i and k.

Consider atom i in Fig. 8.3(a). At $T = 0$ it will (according to classical physics) be at rest midway between atoms j and k at a distance r_0 from each. (In Fig. 8.3 $F(r)$ is the interatomic force characteristic of an *isolated pair* of atoms.) We now give energy to the structure, making $T > 0$, and take a "snapshot" of atom i. Figure 8.3(b) is the result. (It is a bit of a cheat because it ignores the motion of j and k. We will be more honest in section 8.3.) We see that $r_1 > r_0$ and that $r_2 < r_0$. Atom i is therefore subjected to a restoring force from atom j, *and* to a restoring force from atom k. Remember that the restoring force appears whenever r is increased *or* decreased from its equilibrium value r_0. Atom j pulls back on i; atom k pushes back on i. (In visualizing interatomic forces as "springs" the image must be of a spring which requires an effort both to extend it and to compress it. A suspension spring found in certain car suspensions is a good one to keep in mind.) At low temperatures the *amplitude* of vibration—the maximum displacement reached from the equilibrium position—is sufficiently small that we may approximate the interatomic force curve by a straight line in the vicinity of r_0 (Fig. 8.4). As a result, the restoring force exerted on i per unit displacement from its equilibrium position —the so-called *force constant*—is $2k_s$, where k_s is the force constant when only one neighbour is present. The factor of two arises, of course, because j is "pulling back" on i while k is "pushing back" on i (Fig. 8.4). Applying Newton's second law to the motion of i gives

$$M \frac{\mathrm{d}^2 x}{\mathrm{d}t^2} = -2k_s x \qquad (8.1)$$

The negative sign is necessary to ensure that the atom, of mass M, decelerates ($\mathrm{d}^2 x/\mathrm{d}t^2$ is negative) as x increases. (The spring constant k_s is always taken to be positive.) Let us guess the following solution of eq. (8.1);

$$x = A \sin \omega t = A \sin (2\pi t/T_v) \qquad (8.2)$$

Here A is the amplitude of vibration since x must lie between $\pm A$. Also T_v is the *period* of the vibration since x—that is atom i—is back to where it was at time t at a later time $(t + T_v)$; you know that $\sin [2\pi(t + T_v)/T_v] = \sin [2\pi t/T_v + 2\pi T_v/T_v] = \sin (2\pi t/T_v)$. The name *circular frequency* is given to

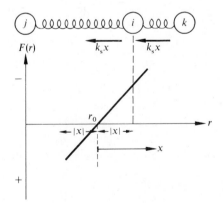

Fig. 8.4 On displacing atom i from its equilibrium position it is subjected to restoring forces from atoms j and k. For small displacements the interatomic force characteristic may be taken as linear.

$\omega = 2\pi/T_v$. (In the past ω was called the *angular frequency*.) To see if eq. (8.2) is indeed a solution of eq. (8.1) we substitute it into eq. (8.1)

$$M \frac{d^2}{dt^2} (A \sin \omega t) = -2k_s(A \sin \omega t)$$

$$-MA\omega^2 \sin \omega t = -2k_s A \sin \omega t$$

$$\omega = \left(\frac{2k_s}{M}\right)^{1/2} \tag{8.3}$$

or

$$T_v = \frac{2\pi}{\omega} = 2\pi \left(\frac{M}{2k_s}\right)^{1/2} \tag{8.4}$$

For it to be a solution of eq. (8.1), eq. (8.2) must therefore be written

$$x = A \sin \left[\left(\frac{2k_s}{M}\right)^{1/2} t\right] \tag{8.5}$$

Figure 8.5(a) shows how x varies with t.

The energy of a solid atom

We are interested not so much in the displacement *per se* of atom i as in its potential and kinetic energies.

To increase the separation between i and j from r_0 to r_1 (Fig. 8.3) calls for energy; energy is required to move i out in the face of the attractive (negative) force between i and j. This energy is stored as potential energy in the field between i and j; its magnitude is the area under the $F(r)$ curve between r_0 and r_1. Likewise energy is required to reduce the separation between i and k from r_0 to r_2, and this energy is stored in the field between i and k. If we define the potential energy (P.E.) to be zero when $r = r_0$ in Fig. 8.4 the P.E. of atom i at displacement x is merely the energy *required* to displace i by an amount x. Therefore

$$\text{P.E.} = \int_0^x (2k_s x)\,dx = k_s x^2 \tag{8.6}$$

By choosing to define the zero of potential energy to be at $x = 0$ (meaning $r = r_0$, Fig. 8.4) we are saved the trouble of having to carry a constant through subsequent calculations—as would be necessary if we still defined the P.E. to be zero at $r = \infty$.

Substituting eq. (8.2) into eq. (8.6) gives

$$\text{P.E.} = k_s A^2 \sin^2 \omega t \tag{8.7}$$

and this is shown in full line in Fig. 8.5(b).

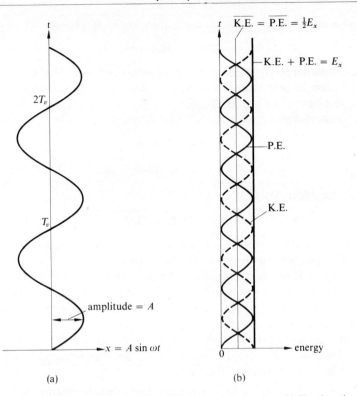

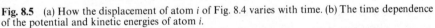

Fig. 8.5 (a) How the displacement of atom i of Fig. 8.4 varies with time. (b) The time dependence of the potential and kinetic energies of atom i.

The kinetic energy (K.E.) of atom i can be readily evaluated since

$$\text{K.E.} = \tfrac{1}{2}MU_x^2 = \tfrac{1}{2}M\left(\frac{\mathrm{d}x}{\mathrm{d}t}\right)^2 \tag{8.8}$$

Substituting from eq. (8.2) gives

$$\text{K.E.} = \tfrac{1}{2}MA^2\omega^2\cos^2\omega t$$

or, appealing to eq. (8.3),

$$\text{K.E.} = k_s A^2 \cos^2 \omega t \tag{8.9}$$

This is shown in dashed line in Fig. 8.5(b).

The total energy E_x of atom i due to its vibrational motion along the x-axis is, of course, the sum of its potential energy (given by eq. (8.7)), and its kinetic energy (given by eq. (8.9)). Thus

$$E_x = k_s A^2 \sin^2 \omega t + k_s A^2 \cos^2 \omega t$$

$$E_x = k_s A^2 \tag{8.10}$$

243

If we wish to, we may substitute for k_s from eq. (8.3), giving

$$E_x = \tfrac{1}{2} M A^2 \omega^2 \tag{8.11}$$

So the total energy E_x is constant, *independent of time*. This total energy is shown by the heavy line in Fig. 8.5(b). Since the time-averaged values of $\sin^2 \omega t$ and of $\cos^2 \omega t$ are each equal to $1/2$ (you can see that this is so from Fig. 8.5(b)) it follows from eqs. (8.7) and (8.9) that

$$\overline{\text{P.E.}} = \tfrac{1}{2} k_s A^2$$

$$\overline{\text{K.E.}} = \tfrac{1}{2} k_s A^2$$

and therefore, from eq. (8.10), that

$$E_x = 2 \overline{\text{P.E.}} = 2 \overline{\text{K.E.}} \tag{8.12}$$

What we want to know, of course, is the total mean energy $\overline{E}$ of an atom of the solid. In deriving an expression for $\overline{E}$ we shall assume that the restoring force acting on atom i is spherically symmetric; that is, at any given distance R of atom i from its lattice site, the restoring force is independent of the orientation of $\mathbf{R}$ relative to the x-, y-, and z-axes. This assumption allows us to write the potential energy of i (see eq. (8.6)) as $k_s R^2 = \tfrac{1}{2}(2k_s)R^2$, where $2k_s$ is the (resultant) force constant for atom i (Fig. 8.4). Had the restoring force been dependent on the direction of $\mathbf{R}$ we could not have written the potential energy merely as $k_s R^2$. Since, by Pythagoras' theorem, $R^2 = x^2 + y^2 + z^2$, the potential energy of i becomes $k_s x^2 + k_s y^2 + k_s z^2$. If the instantaneous velocity of i is U (Fig. 8.2) its kinetic energy is $\tfrac{1}{2} M U^2$. Because $U^2 = U_x^2 + U_y^2 + U_z^2$ (eq. (3.12)), the kinetic energy of i may be written as $\tfrac{1}{2} M U_x^2 + \tfrac{1}{2} M U_y^2 + \tfrac{1}{2} M U_z^2$. The (instantaneous) total energy E of i is therefore given by

$$E = k_s x^2 + k_s y^2 + k_s z^2 + \tfrac{1}{2} M U_x^2 + \tfrac{1}{2} M U_y^2 + \tfrac{1}{2} M U_z^2$$

or, regrouping terms, by

$$E = (k_s x^2 + \tfrac{1}{2} M U_x^2) + (k_s y^2 + \tfrac{1}{2} M U_y^2) + (k_s z^2 + \tfrac{1}{2} M U_z^2)$$

Each of these bracketed expressions is equal to the energy of a one-dimensional oscillator (being the sum of its potential and kinetic energies; see eqs. (8.6) and (8.8)). We may therefore write

$$E = E_x + E_y + E_z$$

as the instantaneous energy of atom i. If i executes at least one orbit (Fig. 8.2) before its energy is changed, it follows that each of the equivalent oscillators along the x-, y-, and z-axes will execute at least one cycle during which their energy is constant. This allows us to write (see eq. (8.12))

$$E_x = 2\,\overline{\text{K.E.}} = 2(\tfrac{1}{2} M \overline{U_x^2}) = M \overline{U_x^2}, \quad E_y = M \overline{U_y^2} \quad \text{and} \quad E_z = M \overline{U_z^2}.$$

Therefore

$$E = M\overline{U_x^2} + M\overline{U_y^2} + M\overline{U_z^2}$$

If we follow the motion of i over a long time-interval we can expect its energy to change as it interacts with its neighbours. The mean energy $\overline{E}$ of i during this interval will be given by

$$\overline{E} = M\overline{U_x^2} + M\overline{U_y^2} + M\overline{U_z^2} \qquad (8.13)$$

where $\overline{U_x^2}$ is the mean value of U_x^2 during the interval, and likewise for $\overline{U_y^2}$ and $\overline{U_z^2}$.

What really interests us is not the energy of a *single* atom averaged over a long time interval but, rather, the mean energy of *all* the atoms in the solid (at a particular instant). We shall take it—although we shall not attempt to justify the assumption—that the time-averaged energy of a single atom of the solid is equal to the mean energy deduced from a single "snapshot" of all the atoms of the solid. This allows us to appeal to eq. (3.15)—which was obtained by averaging over all the atoms in the system—and so to write $\overline{U^2} = \overline{U_x^2} + \overline{U_y^2} + \overline{U_z^2}$. Equation (8.13) therefore becomes

$$\overline{E} = M\overline{U^2} \qquad (8.14)$$

The molar heat capacity predicted
In section 1.6, eq. (1.3), we saw that the molar heat capacity of a substance at constant volume is given by

$$C_{V,m} = \left(\frac{\delta U_m}{\delta T}\right)_V$$

where U_m is the molar internal energy of the substance. When there is one mole of a solid element present each of the N_A atoms has, on average, an energy $M\overline{U^2}$, eq. (8.14). Therefore the molar internal energy of U_m of the solid may be written as

$$U_m = N_A(M\overline{U^2}) = 2N_A(\tfrac{1}{2}M\overline{U^2})$$

Now the temperature of the solid is defined operationally as the reading on a gas thermometer which is in thermal contact with the solid. It is therefore eminently proper to relate the temperature T of the solid to the average kinetic energy $\tfrac{1}{2}\overline{mu^2}$ of the gas atoms via eq. (3.29); $T = 2(\tfrac{1}{2}\overline{mu^2})/3k$. So

$$C_{V,m} = \frac{\delta U_m}{\delta T} = 3kN_A \frac{\delta(\tfrac{1}{2}M\overline{U^2})}{\delta(\tfrac{1}{2}\overline{mu^2})}$$

$$C_{V,m} = 3R \frac{\delta(\tfrac{1}{2}M\overline{U^2})}{\delta(\tfrac{1}{2}\overline{mu^2})} \qquad (8.15)$$

245

Now we know from section 3.4 that as you increase the kinetic energy $\frac{1}{2}m\overline{u^2}$ of the gas atoms impacting on the solid (Fig. 8.1(b)) so you increase the kinetic energy $\frac{1}{2}M\overline{U^2}$ of the atoms of the solid; the two go hand-in-hand, with $\frac{1}{2}M\overline{U^2} = \frac{1}{2}m\overline{u^2}$. Equation (8.15) therefore becomes

$$C_{V,\mathrm{m}} = 3R \qquad (8.16)$$

So classical physics predicts that $C_{V,\mathrm{m}}$ for all solid elements should have the same value $3R$, which is constant *independent of temperature*. Experiments show that at sufficiently high temperatures $C_{V,\mathrm{m}}$ is indeed constant and with a value $3R(= 24\cdot9 \text{ J K}^{-1} \text{ mol}^{-1})$; an observation known as Dulong and Petit's law. However, as the temperature is lowered $C_{V,\mathrm{m}}$ is found to fall off, tending towards zero as T tends to zero. Figure 8.6(a) shows results for diamond and Fig. 8.6(b) for copper. (The measurements were actually made at constant pressure. However, the difference between $C_{p,\mathrm{m}}$ and $C_{V,\mathrm{m}}$ is usually negligible in solids and may be neglected. If energy is fed into a solid at constant pressure very little of the energy is fed out again as the solid expands against the external pressure p—simply because solids expand but little as their temperature is raised.)

Something seems amiss with classical theory! It begins to look as if the assumption that $\frac{1}{2}M\overline{U^2} = \frac{1}{2}m\overline{u^2}$ is wrong. If only we could somehow "insulate" the atoms of the solid so that their energy fails to change as the energy of the gas atoms falls (that is as the temperature falls) we would have explained the drop-off in $C_{V,\mathrm{m}}$ (eq. (8.15)). However, classical mechanics predicts quite unequivocally that, at equilibrium, the mean translational kinetic energy of the gas atoms equals the mean vibrational kinetic energy of the solid atoms, which, in turn, equals the mean vibrational potential energy of the solid atoms. Something really is amiss with classical mechanics.

8.2   Heat capacity of non-metals: Einstein's theory

The model

The first explanation of the breakdown of Dulong and Petit's law came from Einstein in 1906, who capitalized on an earlier result of Planck. In 1900 Planck had assumed that the atoms of a solid are not in fact free to gradually change their energy with every small change in temperature. Instead of picturing an atom as vibrating in, say, the x-direction with an energy $E_x = 2(\frac{1}{2}M\overline{U_x^2})$ (eq. (8.12)), Planck assumed that E_x could only have certain discrete values, given by

$$E_x = n\frac{h}{2\pi}\omega = nh\omega \qquad (8.17)$$

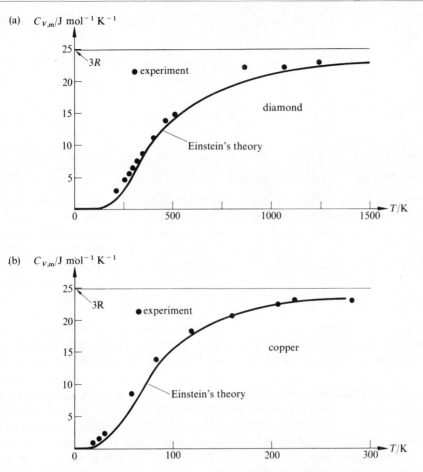

Fig. 8.6 (a) The molar heat capacity of diamond. The curve has been calculated from Einstein's theory (section 8.2) assuming $\theta_E = 1320$ K. (b) The molar heat capacity of copper. Here $\theta_E = 240$ K has been assumed.

where n is an integer, 0, 1, 2, 3, etc., h is a constant known as Planck's constant (for brevity we write $\hbar$ for $h/2\pi$), and ω is the circular frequency of vibration of an atom as calculated classically.

The average energy of an atom

Our goal is an expression for the average energy of an atom of a solid which shares out its total internal energy according to Planck's rules. Having found this average energy we will then multiply it by N_A and differentiate with respect to T to obtain $C_{V,m}$—just as we did before.

As a preliminary we consider how, say, four "Planck oscillators" A, B, C, and D share out a total of, say, five units of energy. One possible way is

247

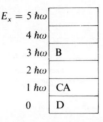

Fig. 8.7 One possible way in which four Planck oscillators A, B, C, and D can share out a total of five units of energy. It would make no difference had we written AC in shelf $1\hbar\omega$ since this would still tell us that A has energy $1\hbar\omega$ and C has energy $1\hbar\omega$. So rearranging letters within a module does not provide new pictures.

shown in Fig. 8.7. Here oscillator B has an energy $E_x = 3\hbar\omega$; oscillators C and A each have energy $1\hbar\omega$ and oscillator D has zero energy. What we must now do is to draw out all the possible "pictures" which correspond to physically distinct situations and then find the average number of oscillators with energy 0, $1\hbar\omega$, $2\hbar\omega$, etc. This problem is formally equivalent to one we discussed in section 6.4 in considering a two-dimensional gas. In the present context Fig. 6.15 shows all the ways in which four oscillators can share out five units of energy. To find the mean number of oscillators with a particular energy, say $E_x = 3\hbar\omega$, we count up the total number of appearances at this level (24) and divide by the total number of pictures (56). On carrying out this operation at each level we obtain the histogram shown in Fig. 8.8 (which is, of course, similar to Fig. 6.16). Quite clearly the mean number $\overline{N(E_x)}$ of oscillators with a particular energy E_x falls off steadily with increasing energy. It would, of course, be unwise to assert that this is how a large population of oscillators would behave. Happily it is not difficult to predict the behaviour of a large population. We will have a quick look at how this is done.

Figure 8.9 shows a blank column of cells. Into the cell at level E_i we are going to place n_i oscillators. There are $_NC_{n_i}$ ways of selecting the n_i oscillators from a population of N. (Changing the order of the letters within a cell does

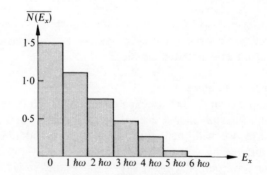

Fig. 8.8 The energy distribution of four Planck oscillators sharing out five units of energy.

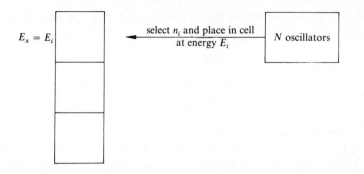

Fig. 8.9 Illustrating the procedure involved in giving n_i oscillators each an energy of E_i.

not produce a new picture; the sequence BCA in a cell of energy E_i says that oscillators B, C, and A have each an energy E_i. The sequence ACB says the same thing.) In selecting the n_j oscillators for another level j of energy E_j we have only $(N - n_i)$ left from which to choose, n_i having just been allocated. This selection may be made in $_{N-n_i}C_{n_j}$ ways. Overall the total number W of pictures corresponding to a particular *type* of arrangement which places n_i oscillators in level i, n_j in level j, etc., is given by

$$W = {_N}C_{n_i} \times {_{N-n_i}}C_{n_j} \times {_{N-n_i-n_j}}C_{n_k} \times \cdots$$

$$W = \frac{N!}{n_i!\,n_j!\,n_k!\dots} \tag{8.18}$$

Since all N oscillators must be placed in one cell or another it follows that

$$N = \sum_i n_i \tag{8.19}$$

In addition the oscillators must be placed so that their *total* energy E is always the same. That is

$$E = \sum_i n_i E_i \tag{8.20}$$

The next problem is to find out what type of arrangement yields the greatest number of pictures. In a large population this one type of arrangement will yield so many pictures that pictures arising from other types of arrangement may be ignored in determining the mean number of oscillators with a particular energy. This is exactly the approach we followed in section 6.6. Indeed eq. (8.18) is formally the same as eq. (6.23) with $g_i = g_j = g_k = \cdots = 1$. Equations (8.19) and (8.20) are also formally identical to eqs. (6.27) and (6.28) respectively. Because of these formal identities we may go straight to the result—eq. (6.33)—

adapting it to the present problem. On average, the number of oscillators, $\overline{N(E_i)}$, with an energy E_i is given by

$$\overline{N(E_i)} = e^{-\alpha} e^{-\beta E_i}$$

where α and β are constants, as yet undetermined. That is

$$N(E_i) = A e^{-\beta E_i} \tag{8.21}$$

where A is a constant. For ease of notation we have dropped the bar over $N(E_i)$. You should satisfy yourself that this expression is compatible with the result we obtained on manually sorting a small population (Fig. 8.8). We are now ready to find the mean energy $\overline{E}_x$ of a Planck oscillator.

Exercise 8.1

Using the data given in Fig. 8.8 (and set out in Table 6.2) work out the mean energy of a Planck oscillator when four such oscillators share out a total of five units of energy.

Just as you did in working through this exercise so we may write down that

$$\overline{E} = \frac{\sum\limits_{i} N(E_i) \times E_i}{\sum\limits_{i} N(E_i)} \tag{8.22}$$

Substituting for E_i from eq. (8.17) and for $N(E_i)$ from eq. (8.21) gives

$$\overline{E} = \frac{A(0\, e^{-\beta 0} + \hbar\omega\, e^{-\beta\hbar\omega} + 2\hbar\omega\, e^{-2\beta\hbar\omega} + 3\hbar\omega\, e^{-3\beta\hbar\omega} + \cdots)}{A(e^{-\beta 0} + e^{-\beta\hbar\omega} + e^{-2\beta\hbar\omega} + e^{-3\beta\hbar\omega} + \cdots)}$$

Because of the standard form

$$\frac{d}{dx}(\ln u) = \frac{1}{u}\frac{du}{dx} \tag{8.23}$$

we may write

$$\overline{E} = -\frac{d}{d\beta}\ln(1 + e^{-\beta\hbar\omega} + e^{-2\beta\hbar\omega} + e^{-3\beta\hbar\omega} + \cdots)$$

Now the expression inside the brackets is a geometrical series whose ratio r of any term to the preceding term has a value $e^{-\beta\hbar\omega}$. When $|r| < 1$, as it is here, the infinite series $1 + r + r^2 + \cdots$ has a value $1/(1 - r)$. Therefore

$$\overline{E} = -\frac{d}{d\beta}\ln\left(\frac{1}{1 - e^{-\beta\hbar\omega}}\right)$$

or, applying eq. (8.23),

$$\bar{E} = \frac{\hbar\omega\, e^{-\beta\hbar\omega}}{1 - e^{-\beta\hbar\omega}}$$

$$\bar{E}_x = \frac{\hbar\omega}{e^{\beta\hbar\omega} - 1} \tag{8.24}$$

where we have reinserted the suffix x to emphasize that we have only considered oscillations in the x-direction. However, similar results hold in the y- and z-directions so the total mean energy $\bar{E}$ of atom in the solid is

$$\bar{E} = \frac{3\hbar\omega}{e^{\beta\hbar\omega} - 1} \tag{8.25}$$

The constant β is as yet undetermined. In the case of a gas $\beta = 1/kT$, where k is Boltzmann's constant (eq. (6.45)). Although there is no reason why β should be the same for a gas as for a Planck oscillator we will tentatively assume it to be so. The justification will come when we find that at high temperatures the predicted value of $C_{V,\mathrm{m}}$ tends towards $3R$, in accord with experiment.

The molar heat capacity predicted
The molar internal energy of a solid element is, from eq. (8.25),

$$U_\mathrm{m} = N_\mathrm{A}\bar{E} = \frac{3N_\mathrm{A}\hbar\omega}{e^{\hbar\omega/kT} - 1}$$

Appealing to eq. (1.3) in the limit of $\delta T \to 0$ gives

$$C_{V,\mathrm{m}} = \frac{\mathrm{d}U_\mathrm{m}}{\mathrm{d}T} = 3N_\mathrm{A}\hbar\omega\,\frac{\mathrm{d}}{\mathrm{d}T}(e^{\hbar\omega kT} - 1)^{-1}$$

$$C_{V,\mathrm{m}} = 3R\left(\frac{\hbar\omega}{kT}\right)^2 \frac{e^{\hbar\omega/kT}}{(e^{\hbar\omega/kT} - 1)^2} \tag{8.26}$$

At high temperatures, where $kT \gg \hbar\omega$, (eq. (8.26)) becomes

$$C_{V,\mathrm{m}} = 3R\left(\frac{\hbar\omega}{kT}\right)^2 \frac{1 + (\hbar\omega/kT) + \cdots}{[1 + (\hbar\omega/kT) + \cdots - 1]^2}$$

The $\hbar\omega/kT$ ($\ll 1$) in the numerator is negligible in comparison with unity. In the denominator the ones cancel leaving $(\hbar\omega/kT)^2$, so

$$C_{V,\mathrm{m}} = 3R$$

at high temperatures. Of more interest is what happens at low temperatures when $\hbar\omega \gg kT$. Under these circumstances the one in the denominator of eq. (8.26) is negligible compared to $\exp(\hbar\omega/kT)$, giving

$$C_{V,\text{m}} = 3R\left(\frac{\hbar\omega}{kT}\right)^2 e^{-\hbar\omega/kT} \qquad (8.27)$$

With decreasing temperature the exponential term decreases more rapidly than does $(\hbar\omega/kT)^2$ increase. As a consequence the predicted heat capacity falls. In fact, as Fig. 8.6 shows, it falls rather too rapidly. We have somehow over-corrected! The curve shown in Fig. 8.6(b) was obtained by assuming $\hbar\omega/k = 240$ K. It is usual to call $\hbar\omega/k$ the *Einstein temperature* θ_E. A value of $\theta_E = 240$ K implies a period $T_v = 2\pi/\omega = h/k\theta_E$ of $2 \cdot 0 \times 10^{-13}$ s. We can see whether such a period is reasonable by comparing it with the period deduced from the speed v of sound in a solid. Sound is transmitted as a compressional wave is passed from atom to atom. The time it takes for atom i in Fig. 8.3 to "pass the message" from atom j to atom k is of order r_0/v. Since this time is equal to half the vibrational period of i

$$T_v \approx \frac{2r_0}{v}$$

In copper $v = 3 \cdot 81 \times 10^3$ m s^{-1} and the nearest-neighbour distance $r_0 = 2 \cdot 56 \times 10^{-10}$ m. This predicts $T_v = 1 \cdot 3 \times 10^{-13}$ s, in gratifying agreement with the value of $2 \cdot 0 \times 10^{-13}$ s which must be assumed to make Einstein's theory roughly fit the experimental data for copper.

If the oscillating atoms are truly independent of one another they will never be able to exchange energy. With no facility to exchange energy a particular picture—which specifies the actual energy of every single atom and which need not be of the type described by eq. (8.21)—will persist forever. Now it is implicit in Einstein's model that the individual oscillating atoms can exchange energy; that they *are* weakly coupled. Yet once we introduce such coupling we also introduce a range of frequencies. This is, of course, inconsistent with Einstein's assumption that there is a single vibrational frequency for all the atoms. As we shall now show, it is this range of vibrational frequencies which provides the key to understanding why Einstein's model fails at very low temperatures.

8.3 The one-dimensional coupled oscillator model

How the atoms behave

When we came up against problems in discussing a real gas we considered a one-dimensional gas. We were then able to guess how a three-dimensional gas might behave. We adopt the same strategy here, considering a one-dimensional line of N identical atoms, each one coupled only to its nearest neighbours. At zero temperature the atoms would occupy sites on a regular one-dimensional

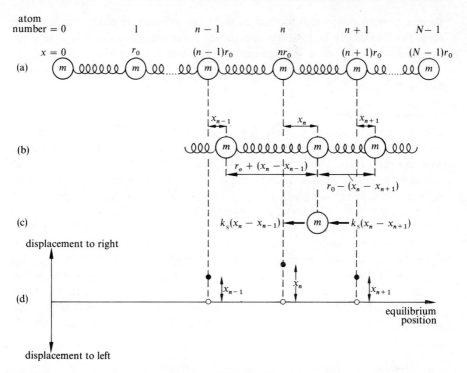

Fig. 8.10 A one-dimensional crystal. (a) At $T = 0$ the N atoms would occupy the lattice sites. (b) At $T > 0$ the atoms will be displaced from their lattice sites. (c) Each displaced atom will experience a restoring force. (d) Showing how the displacements can be represented graphically.

lattice (Fig. 8.10(a)). At a finite temperature the atoms will oscillate about these lattice sites: Fig. 8.10(b) is a snapshot of what the structure might look like at one instant.

If we denote the *displacement* of each atom from its equilibrium position by $x_0, x_1, \ldots, x_{n-1}, x_n, x_{n+1} \ldots$ and denote the interatomic force constant by k_s we have, on applying Newton's second law to atom n (see Fig. 8.10(c)):

$$m \frac{\mathrm{d}^2 x_n}{\mathrm{d}t^2} = -k_s(x_n - x_{n-1}) - k_s(x_n - x_{n+1})$$

$$m \frac{\mathrm{d}^2 x_n}{\mathrm{d}t^2} = k_s(x_{n-1} + x_{n+1} - 2x_n) \tag{8.28}$$

You may find it helpful to compare atom n with atom i of Fig. 8.4. This will remind you that what matters is the *change* in the spring lengths from their equilibrium lengths r_0.

Figure 8.10(d) shows a convenient way of representing the displacements of the atoms of Fig. 8.10(b). Here the longitudinal displacement of an atom from

253

its equilibrium position is plotted as ordinate. When a displacement is to the right (as they are in Fig. 8.10(b)) its value is plotted upwards. When an atom is displaced to the left of its equilibrium position the displacement is plotted downwards. The equilibrium positions of the atoms are indicated by open circles in Fig. 8.10(d).

A simulation study

Our immediate aim is to find the solution of eq. (8.28); by making $n = 0, 1, 2$, etc., we will then be able to deduce how *all* the atoms in Fig. 8.10 behave. We can get clues about the form of the solution by simulating a one-dimensional solid. The simulator consists of "gliders" connected together by springs on a linear air-track (a frictionless mount). On moving one of the outer gliders back and forth we observe that a compressional wave travels down the row of gliders and springs to the far end where it is reflected back. We find that *provided* the vibrational period T_v (or, equivalently, the circular frequency $2\pi/T_v$) is correctly chosen, standing wave patterns are set up. Figure 8.11(a) shows one such standing wave pattern, in which two of the gliders remain permanently at rest. The nature of the standing wave pattern is more clearly brought out in Fig. 8.11(b) which shows the displacement of each glider at times $t = 0, \frac{1}{4}T_v, \frac{1}{2}T_v, \frac{3}{4}T_v$, and T_v. Since it is a bit of a bore to have to

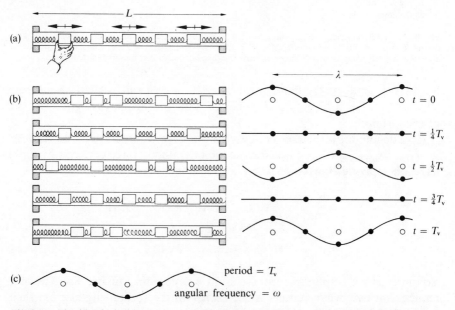

Fig. 8.11 Five identical gliders are connected together by identical springs. (a) Showing one of the standing wave patterns which can be set up. (b) The standing wave pattern examined in detail. The equilibrium positions of the gliders are indicated by open circles. The ordinates show the displacement of each glider. (c) A shorthand description of the standing wave pattern.

keep drawing out such a sequence of graphs of displacements at various times we introduce the shorthand representation shown in Fig. 8.11(c). To obtain the "envelope" which indicates the limits to the displacement of each"glider" this curve must be reflected about the horizontal. To complete the specification of the pattern we must note the vibrational period T_v, or the circular frequency $\omega = 2\pi/T_v$, alongside the figure.

In the course of playing about with the simulator shown in Fig. 8.11(a) we soon discover that several more standing wave patterns can be set up on our glider-and-spring system. Figure 8.12 shows the standing wave patterns which are set up by the five gliders. This figure also gives the wavelengths (see Fig. 8.11) of each of the various vibrational patterns—or *modes* for short—which can be set up. Instead of specifying the wavelength λ we can instead specify the *circular wavenumber* q defined by $q = 2\pi/\lambda$. If we disregard the spring's motion—which we may since we are only interested in how the gliders, and hence the atoms, behave—we see that there are five distinct modes; equal to the number of gliders. (In the last mode shown in Fig. 8.12 all the gliders are at rest and only the springs move.) If you carry out this type of experiment you will discover what, at first sight, appears to be additional modes. One such mode is shown in Fig. 8.13. However, forget what the springs are doing and you will discover that this mode is the same as that labelled $\lambda = \frac{2}{3}L$ (i.e.,

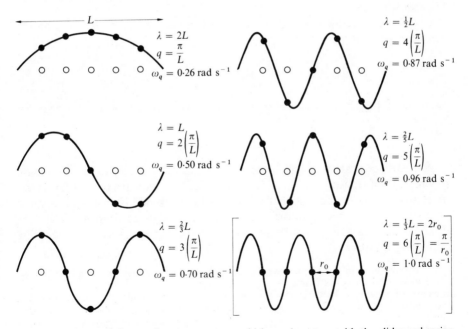

Fig. 8.12 Shows all the standing wave patterns which can be set up with the glider-and-spring apparatus of Fig. 8.11(a).

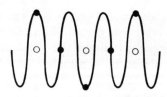

Fig. 8.13 So far as the gliders are concerned this mode is the same as that labelled $q = 3(\pi/L)$ in Fig. 8.12.

$q = 3\pi/L$) in Fig. 8.12. It is a general rule, one that still holds true with very many gliders, that the number of distinct modes is equal to the number of gliders.*

In setting up all the modes shown in Fig. 8.12 we will have observed that in any *one* mode (for example, that with $\lambda = 2L/5$) all the atoms vibrate with the *same frequency* but that the vibrational frequency is different in each mode. In other words, the frequency of vibration of the atoms in a mode depends on the wavelength of the mode—or, if you prefer, the circular frequency ω of the atoms depends on the circular wavenumber q. Figure 8.12 lists the values of ω_q for each mode (the suffix q reminding us that ω depends on q) in the particular case where each glider had a mass of 0·2 kg and each spring a force constant of $5 \times 10^{-2}\ \mathrm{N\ m^{-1}}$.

The problem solved

We shall therefore look for standing wave solutions to eq. (8.28). A standing wave can be written as

$$x = A \cos 2\pi \frac{X}{\lambda} \cos 2\pi \frac{t}{T_v} = A \cos qX \cos \omega t$$

Atom n in Fig. 8.10 is at $X = nr_0$ so its displacement at time t may be written

$$x_n = A \cos qnr_0 \cos \omega_q t \tag{8.29}$$

You can see that eq. (8.29) correctly expresses the fact that the amplitude of vibration of an atom ($= A \cos qnr_0$) depends on which atom it is (that is, on n). It also expresses the fact that in any particular mode (that is q) the value of ω_q is the same for all atoms (it is independent of n). If you are in any doubt sketch eq. (8.29) at various times and see if it behaves like a standing wave (Fig. 8.11(b)).

---

* You may—justifiably—feel that the simulation of Fig. 8.11(a) does not accurately mirror Fig. 8.10(a), in which atoms 0 and $(N - 1)$ are connected to only one "spring". Some authors circumvent this problem by fixing the two outer atoms; this again leads to the conclusion that the number of modes is equal to the number of atoms which are *free to move*. (If you like, you too can have fixed gliders attached to the outer ends of the air track in Fig. 8.11(a)!) We elect to have the outer atoms free to move—and in the manner simulated in Fig. 8.11 since the surface of the solid is under continuous bombardment by the surrounding gas (Fig. 8.1).

Substituting eq. (8.29) into eq. (8.28) gives

$$mA \cos qnr_0 \frac{d^2}{dt^2}(\cos \omega_q t)$$

$$= k_s A[\cos q(n-1)r_0 + \cos q(n+1)r_0 - 2 \cos qnr_0] \cos \omega_q t$$

which becomes

$$-m\omega_q^2 \cos qnr_0 = k_s(2 \cos qnr_0 \cos qr_0 - 2 \cos qnr_0)$$

$$-m\omega_q^2 = 2k_s(\cos qr_0 - 1)$$

or, since $\cos \theta = 1 - 2 \sin^2 (\theta/2)$,

$$m\omega_q^2 = 4k_s \sin^2 \tfrac{1}{2}qr_0 \tag{8.30}$$

Therefore

$$\omega_q = 2\left(\frac{k_s}{m}\right)^{1/2} |\sin \tfrac{1}{2}qr_0| \tag{8.31}$$

Because the negative root of eq. (8.30) implies a negative frequency, which is without physical significance, we only take the positive root into account. Equation (8.31) tells us *how the frequency of a standing wave is related to the wavelength* ($= 2\pi/q$) *in a regular one-dimensional structure* composed of atoms of mass m, which have an equilibrium separation r_0, and for which the force constant is k_s in an isolated pair of atoms.

We have yet to feed into eq. (8.31) the information that our one-dimensional crystal (Fig. 8.10) has a finite length L ($= Nr_0$) with an antinode (a maximum amplitude of vibration) at each end, that is at $X = 0$ and $X = L$. As Fig. 8.12 demonstrates, the only wavelengths which allow such standing waves to exist are those satisfying the condition

$$L = \frac{\lambda}{2}, \lambda, \frac{3\lambda}{2}, 2\lambda, \ldots$$

or, in terms of the circular wavenumber q ($= 2\pi/\lambda$),

$$q = \left(\frac{\pi}{L}\right), 2\left(\frac{\pi}{L}\right), 3\left(\frac{\pi}{L}\right), \ldots$$

Figures 8.12 (and 8.13) remind us that beyond $N(\pi/L) = \pi/r_0$ the standing wave patterns merely repeat earlier ones (ignoring what the springs are doing); so q satisfies the relation

$$q = \left(\frac{\pi}{L}\right), 2\left(\frac{\pi}{L}\right), 3\left(\frac{\pi}{L}\right), \ldots, N\left(\frac{\pi}{L}\right) \tag{8.32}$$

257

To be absolutely precise, since there are N free atoms in Fig. 8.10(a) we should —compare Figs. 8.10(a) and 8.11(a)—write $L = (N + 1)r_0$, giving the maximum value of q (cf. the mode $q = 5\pi/L$ in Fig. 8.12) as $N(\pi/L) = N\pi/(N + 1)r_0$. In practice (remember $N_A = 6{\cdot}0 \times 10^{23} \text{ mol}^{-1}$) it introduces little error to assume, as we do in eq. (8.32) and in the discussion which follows, that the maximum value of $q = N\pi/(\text{length of crystal}) = \pi/(\text{interatomic separation})$.

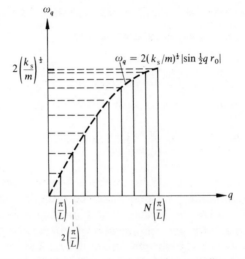

Fig. 8.14 The abscissa records the values of q that produce standing wave patterns in a one-dimensional structure. Each of these modes has a unique circular frequency, indicated by the height of the vertical lines. The top of these lines fit a smooth curve given by eq. (8.31).

Figure 8.14 shows how to represent the information contained in eqs. (8.31) and (8.32). Along the abscissa we mark off all the permitted values of q as given by eq. (8.32). To find the values of ω_q—the circular frequency of the atoms in the mode of circular wavenumber q—we merely substitute each permitted value of q into eq. (8.31) and plot the result.

Exercise 8.2

Five gliders, each of mass $0{\cdot}2$ kg, are connected together by springs as shown in Fig. 8.11(a) on a track of total length $1{\cdot}8$ m. The force constant of each spring is $5 \times 10^{-2} \text{ N m}^{-1}$. Without looking back at Fig. 8.12 draw out all the physically distinct vibrational patterns. Even try and find a few extra ones! If you find extra ones see to which of the modes in Fig. 8.12 they are equivalent. Calculate the circular frequency of each mode and check your answers against the values given in Fig. 8.12.

So instead of picturing a solid as consisting of a regular arrangement of atoms which vibrate independently of one another we must picture many different standing wave patterns, in *each* of which *all the atoms* of the solid participate. The analogue of an open organ pipe comes readily to mind. In such a pipe many different modes will be present; however the actual vibrational pattern of an individual air molecule will be the resultant of the motions associated with all the *modes* present in the pipe. As a result the motion of an individual air molecule will appear to be highly complex. Likewise in a crystal the motion of an individual atom will be the resultant of the motions which it executes in sustaining all possible vibrational patterns in the crystal. A casual observer would see each atom behaving in a highly complex, seemingly chaotic, manner. Such a vibrational pattern could well be established by the erratic bombardment of the surface of the solid by gas molecules. In other words the surrounding gas could well set up many different vibrational modes in the crystal.

To find the total energy of the air molecules in an organ pipe one can proceed by finding the energy associated with each mode and then sum over all the modes which are present. To find the total internal energy of our solid we first evaluate the energy of a single mode; of a single vibrational pattern in which *all* the atoms participate. We will then sum the energies for all the *modes* that are present. So we know what we have to do. It is very important that you keep in mind throughout the ongoing discussion that a mode involves *all* the atoms in the structure. It is also very important that you keep in mind that in looking at a *single mode* we are only looking at a *part* of the motions of these atoms; it takes the other modes to complete the picture.

The energy of a single mode

In evaluating the total energy associated with a vibrational mode of circular frequency ω_q we will consider first the kinetic energy of all the atoms in the structure when this mode is present. Since

$$\text{K.E.} = \tfrac{1}{2}m \sum_{\text{atoms}} \left(\frac{dx_n}{dt}\right)^2$$

we have on substituting for x_n from eq. (8.29),

$$\text{K.E.} = \tfrac{1}{2}m \sum_{n=0}^{N} (-A\omega_q \sin \omega_q t \cos qnr_0)^2$$

$$\text{K.E.} = \tfrac{1}{2}mA^2\omega_q^2 \sin^2 \omega_q t \sum_{n=0}^{N} \cos^2 qnr_0 \qquad (8.33)$$

Strictly speaking the summation is only to $N-1$ since the last lattice site is at $(N-1)r_0$ (see Fig. 8.10(a)) but we can safely ignore this nicety since N is very large in practice.

We must now find the total potential energy associated with this particular vibrational mode of circular wavenumber q. We first consider the energy V_n required to displace atom n from its lattice site nr_0. If, as shown in Fig. 8.15,

259

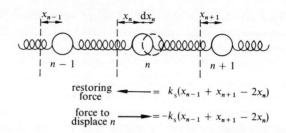

restoring force $\longleftarrow\ = k_s(x_{n-1} + x_{n+1} - 2x_n)$

force to displace n $\longrightarrow = -k_s(x_{n-1} + x_{n+1} - 2x_n)$

Fig. 8.15 As atom n is displaced through dx_n its potential energy increases.

this atom is displaced an amount x_n from its lattice site it will, according to eq. (8.28), experience a (restoring) force of value $k_s(x_{n-1} + x_{n+1} - 2x_n)$. In displacing atom n through a further distance dx_n energy of amount $-k_s(x_{n-1} + x_{n+1} - 2x_n)\,dx_n = k_s(2x_n - x_{n-1} - x_{n+1})\,dx_n$ is fed into the structure, where it is stored as potential energy. The potential energy V_n of atom n, when at some displacement x_n, is therefore given by

$$V_n = \int_0^{x_n} k_s(2x_n - x_{n-1} - x_{n+1})\,dx_n$$

$$V_n = k_s(x_n^2 - x_{n-1}x_n - x_{n+1}x_n)$$

In performing this calculation we have taken the potential energy of atom n as zero when it is on its lattice site nr_0. An exactly similar calculation can be carried out for each and every atom in the structure, giving the total potential energy of the disturbed structure as

$$\text{P.E.} = k_s \sum_{n=0}^{N} x_n^2 - \tfrac{1}{2}k_s \sum_{n=0}^{N} (x_{n-1}x_n + x_{n+1}x_n) \qquad (8.34)$$

where the summation is over all atoms. Notice the factor of $1/2$ which has been introduced into the summation involving the mixed terms. This is necessary to prevent each term making two appearances. When atom 5, say, is displaced from atom 4 then atom 4 is automatically displaced from atom 5, so we must not add in another energy term. Without this $1/2$ in eq. (8.34) both these energies would be counted. Substituting eq. (8.29) for x_n into eq. (8.34) we obtain, after some manipulation,

$$\text{P.E.} = 2A^2 k_s \cos^2 \omega_q t \sin^2 \tfrac{1}{2}qr_0 \sum_{n=0}^{N} \cos^2 qnr_0$$

Making use of eq. (8.30), which relates the circular frequency ω_q and the circular wavenumber q of the mode, to eliminate k_s gives

$$\text{P.E.} = \tfrac{1}{2}mA^2\omega_q^2 \cos^2 \omega_q t \sum_{n=0}^{N} \cos^2 qnr_0 \qquad (8.35)$$

To find the *total* energy E_q associated with this *one* mode of circular wave-number q we add eqs. (8.33) and (8.35):

$$E_q = \text{K.E.} + \text{P.E.}$$

$$= \tfrac{1}{2}mA^2\omega_q^2(\sin^2 \omega_q t + \cos^2 \omega_q t) \sum_{n=0}^{N} \cos^2 qnr_0$$

$$= \tfrac{1}{2}mA^2\omega_q^2 \sum_{n=0}^{N} \cos^2 qnr_0$$

That is:

$$E_q = \tfrac{1}{2}mA_1^2\omega_q^2 \tag{8.36}$$

where

$$A_1 = A\left(\sum_{n=0}^{N} \cos^2 qnr_0 \right)^{1/2} \tag{8.37}$$

If you compare eq. (8.36) with eq. (8.11) you will see that they both have the same form. So the total energy associated with *one particular mode*—with one particular standing wave pattern of wavelength $2\pi/q$ in which *all* the atoms of the structure are involved—is equal to the energy of a harmonic oscillator. (The word *harmonic* is used when the restoring force on the oscillating mass is proportional to its displacement.) To be exact, the energy of the mode is equal to that of a harmonic oscillator whose oscillating mass m is equal to that of an atom of the structure, whose circular frequency is equal to that of the mode and whose amplitude of oscillation A_1 is related to the amplitude of oscillation A of the mode by eq. (8.37).

So, energy-wise, each *mode* may be replaced by a harmonic oscillator. However, we will never explain the temperature dependence of $C_{V,m}$ if we assume that the oscillator behaves like the one we discussed in section 8.1. It is therefore tempting to regard each replacement oscillator as a Planck oscillator whose mean energy $\bar{E}_q$ is given by eq. (8.24) with $\beta = 1/kT$:

$$\bar{E}_q = \frac{\hbar\omega_q}{e^{\hbar\omega_q/kT} - 1} \tag{8.38}$$

This temptation can be justified, but not here! Figure 8.16 summarizes the position we have reached so far, taking the linear chain of five atoms (Fig. 8.12) as our example. In words: (1) Each standing wave pattern—each mode—is characterized by a particular circular wavenumber $q(= 2\pi/\lambda)$. (2) The circular frequency is uniquely related to q by the so-called *dispersion relation*, eq. (8.31). (3) The total energy of each mode, in which all the atoms participate, is that of a harmonic oscillator of circular frequency ω_q. (4) We assume that each mode-replacement behaves as a Planck oscillator.

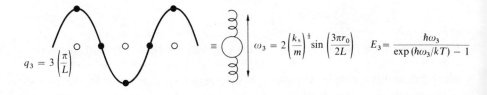

$$q_1 = \frac{\pi}{L} \qquad \omega_1 = 2\left(\frac{k_s}{m}\right)^{\frac{1}{2}} \sin\left(\frac{\pi r_0}{2L}\right) \qquad E_1 = \frac{\hbar\omega_1}{\exp\left(\hbar\omega_1/kT\right) - 1}$$

$$q_2 = 2\left(\frac{\pi}{L}\right) \qquad \omega_2 = 2\left(\frac{k_s}{m}\right)^{\frac{1}{2}} \sin\left(\frac{2\pi r_0}{2L}\right) \qquad E_2 = \frac{\hbar\omega_2}{\exp\left(\hbar\omega_2/kT\right) - 1}$$

$$q_3 = 3\left(\frac{\pi}{L}\right) \qquad \omega_3 = 2\left(\frac{k_s}{m}\right)^{\frac{1}{2}} \sin\left(\frac{3\pi r_0}{2L}\right) \qquad E_3 = \frac{\hbar\omega_3}{\exp\left(\hbar\omega_3/kT\right) - 1}$$

$$q_4 = 4\left(\frac{\pi}{L}\right) \qquad \omega_4 = 2\left(\frac{k_s}{m}\right)^{\frac{1}{2}} \sin\left(\frac{4\pi r_0}{2L}\right) \qquad E_4 = \frac{\hbar\omega_4}{\exp\left(\hbar\omega_4/kT\right) - 1}$$

$$q_5 = 5\left(\frac{\pi}{L}\right) \qquad \omega_5 = 2\left(\frac{k_s}{m}\right)^{\frac{1}{2}} \sin\left(\frac{5\pi r_0}{2L}\right) \qquad E_5 = \frac{\hbar\omega_5}{\exp\left(\hbar\omega_5/kT\right) - 1}$$

Fig. 8.16 Each mode of Fig. 8.12 has the same energy as Planck oscillator vibrating with the same circular frequency as the mode.

The total internal energy

To obtain the molar internal energy U_{m1} of our one-dimensional crystal we must sum the energies of all the distinct modes which the crystal can sustain; if you like, we must sum the entries in the last column of Fig. 8.16. You will remember that the number of distinct modes is equal to the number of atoms present (cf. Fig. 8.12). Since we are dealing with one mole the number of distinct modes is therefore N_A and so

$$U_{m1} = \sum_{q=(\pi/L)}^{N_A(\pi/L)} \bar{E}_q$$

or, substituting from eq. (8.38),

$$U_{m1} = \sum_{q=\pi/L}^{N_A(\pi/L)} \frac{\hbar\omega_q}{e^{\hbar\omega_q/kT} - 1} \qquad (8.39)$$

Since each mode is separated in circular wavenumber by π/L (see eq. (8.32) and Fig. 8.14) it follows that there are L/π modes per unit range of q. (Go unit distance along the abscissa of Fig. 8.14 and you will pass L/π points denoting modes.) In a range dq there are therefore $(L/\pi)\,dq$ modes. Equation (8.39) therefore becomes

$$U_{m1} = \frac{L}{\pi} \int_0^{\pi/r_0} \frac{\hbar\omega_q}{e^{\hbar\omega_q/kT} - 1} dq \qquad (8.40)$$

where

$$\omega_q = 2\left(\frac{k_s}{m}\right)^{1/2} \sin \tfrac{1}{2}qr_0 \qquad (8.41)$$

You will notice that we have taken the lower limit of the integral to be zero in eq. (8.40) rather than giving it the correct value of π/L (eq. (8.39)). Since $L\,(= N_A r_0)$ is very large, π/L will be very close to zero. In writing the upper limit of the integral as π/r_0 we have used the fact that $L = N_A r_0$, making $N_A(\pi/L) = \pi/r_0$.

Differentiating eq. (8.40) with respect to T gives

$$C_{V,m} = \frac{L}{\pi kT^2} \int_0^{\pi/r_0} \frac{(\hbar\omega_q)^2\, e^{\hbar\omega_q/kT}}{(e^{\hbar\omega_q/kT} - 1)^2} dq \qquad (8.42)$$

with ω_q determined by the dispersion relation, eq. (8.41), as the molar heat capacity at constant volume of a one-dimensional crystal. You should be able to show that $C_{V,m}$ tends to a constant value at high temperatures and falls towards zero as $T \to 0$. At least we are on the right track!

To recap the main lines of the arguments: we calculated the number of modes which could be sustained by the one-dimensional crystal. We showed that the mean energy of each mode (in which all the atoms participate) was equal to the mean energy of a harmonic oscillator. We took the oscillator to be one of Planck's. Summing this energy over the total number of modes (which number is equal to N_A) gave the total internal energy of the crystal.

263

Differentiating U_{m1} with respect to T gave $C_{V,m}$ for our one-dimensional crystal.

8.4 The three-dimensional coupled oscillator model

For simplicity we will only consider the vibrational patterns which can be set up in a simple cubic structure when the sample is in the form of a rectangular block with (100), (010), (001), ($\overline{1}$00), (0$\overline{1}$0), and (00$\overline{1}$) faces. Figure 8.17 illustrates how whole planes of atoms can vibrate so as to set up standing wave patterns characterized by circular wavenumbers which are integral multiples of π/L_x,

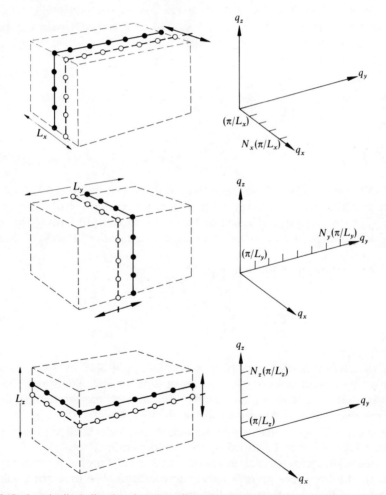

Fig. 8.17 Longitudinal vibrations in a three-dimensional crystal produce standing wave patterns which are characterized by their circular wavenumbers.

π/L_y, and π/L_z where L_x, L_y, and L_z are the lengths of the block's edges. The values of q_x range from π/L_x to $N_x(\pi/L_x)$, where N_x is the number of atoms along the x-edge; q_y ranges from π/L_y to $N_y(\pi/L_y)$; q_z from π/L_z to $N_z(\pi/L_z)$. In general, any permitted value of q_x may be present with any permitted values of q_y and q_z; a mode may therefore be characterized by giving the coordinates (q_x, q_y, q_z) of a point in q_x–q_y–q_z space. Figure 8.18 shows all the permitted points—all the permitted modes—which have a common value of q_z. It is clear that the total number of permitted modes is $N_x \times N_y \times N_z$. Since N_x is the number of atoms along the x-edge, N_y the number along the y-edge, and N_z the number along the z-edge, $N_x N_y N_z$ is equal to the total number N of atoms present in the crystal.

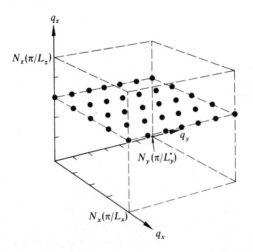

Fig. 8.18 The modes in a three-dimensional crystal are characterized by the triplet (q_x, q_y, q_z). For clarity only those modes having $q_z = 3(\pi/L_z)$ are shown.

So far we have only considered longitudinal vibrations in the crystal. Figure 8.19 shows how transverse vibrations can occur. Each of these types of transverse vibrations will also lead to standing wave patterns in which q_x, q_y, and q_z are, respectively, integral multiples of π/L_x, π/L_y, and π/L_z. So in our crystal containing N_A atoms there are a total of $3N_A$ possible modes; N_A due to longitudinal vibrations and $2N_A$ due to transverse vibrations. We may therefore write down that the molar internal energy of our three-dimensional crystal is (cf. eq. (8.39))

$$U_{m3} = \sum_q \frac{\hbar\omega_q}{e^{\hbar\omega_q/kT} - 1} \tag{8.43}$$

where the summation is over all $3N_A$ modes.

Without the dispersion relations—the relations between ω_q and q—to

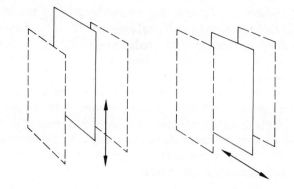

Fig. 8.19   Transverse vibrations are possible in a three-dimensional crystal.

accompany it, eq. (8.43) will not tell us U_{m3} and so $C_{V,m}$. As you might expect, these relations depend on the form of the crystal and on the nature of the interatomic forces. However, they are much more tedious to derive than was the one-dimensional relation (eq. (8.31)) and we shall not attempt to do so!

8.5   The Debye approximation

Having arrived at the procedure for evaluating the heat capacity of a real crystal we have been forced to abandon the calculation because of the problems likely to be encountered in deriving the dispersion relations. But all is not lost. Now is the time to introduce a number of approximations—to be judiciously chosen with a view to making the calculation tractable. As in section 8.4 we shall assume that the crystal, in the form of a rectangular block of sides L_x, L_y, and L_z, has a simple cubic structure with a nearest neighbour separation of a. If these are N_x atoms along the side of length L_x then $a = L_x/N_x$. Likewise $a = L_y/N_y$ and $a = L_z/N_z$.

The approximations

The first approximation we shall make is to replace the three-dimensional array of points which is bounded by planes at $q_x = N_x\pi/L_x = \pi/a$, at $q_y = \pi/a$ and at $q_z = \pi/a$ by the same array of points but now bounded by an octant of the same volume in q_x–q_y–q_z space. This replacement is shown in Fig. 8.20. For the cube and the octant to have the same volume we must have

$$\left(\frac{\pi}{a}\right)^3 = \frac{1}{8}\left(\frac{4}{3}\pi q_D^3\right)$$

$$q_D = \left(\frac{6\pi^2}{a^3}\right)^{1/3} = 1 \cdot 2\left(\frac{\pi}{a}\right) \tag{8.44}$$

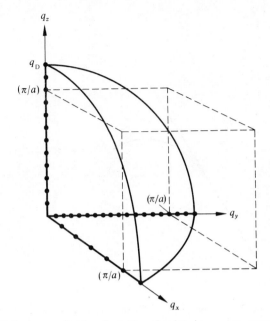

Fig. 8.20 In the Debye approximation the lattice of points in q_x-q_y-q_z space is bounded by an octant of radius q_D such that the total number of points within the octant equals the number within the cube of side π/a.

where q_D is the radius of the replacement octant, and is often called the Debye circular wavenumber. We shall shortly see that this approximation helps to simplify the mathematics. It should raise a few eyebrows since the octant includes certain modes twice but excludes others. We have already seen (in section 8.3) that modes for which q_x, q_y, and q_z exceed π/a are not distinguishable physically from other modes of lower q. You can see from eq. (8.44) and from Fig. 8.20 that in approximating the cube by an octant we are including certain modes near three cube corners twice but are excluding certain modes near other cube corners. Since q_D only exceeds π/a by 20 per cent this approximation is unlikely to have any very harmful effects.

We have seen that the major problem in calculating heat capacities is how to obtain the dispersion relation. Here an approximation introduced by Debye in 1912 is of considerable help. He assumed that the velocity v of longitudinal sound waves in a solid is constant, independent of frequency. Since $v = \lambda/T_v = 2\pi\lambda/2\pi T_v = \omega/q$, this implies

$$\omega = qv \tag{8.45}$$

Figure 8.21 shows the nature of this approximation. Only at high q, where $\lambda(= 2\pi/q)$ is small—at $q = \pi/a$ (i.e., $\lambda = 2a$) for example—does the true dispersion curve differ significantly from that assumed by Debye. Since our first

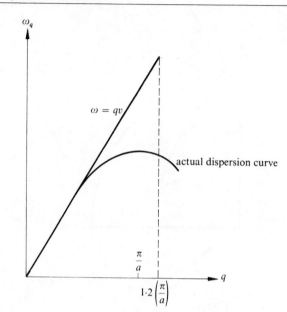

Fig. 8.21 The Debye approximation assumes the linear dispersion relation; $\omega = qv$.

approximation also interfered with this region we should not shed too many tears over it now!

The heat capacity

Armed with both these approximations we are now in a position to calculate the molar internal energy of the crystal, that is, to evaluate eq. (8.43)

$$U_{m3} = \sum_q \frac{\hbar\omega_q}{e^{\hbar\omega_q/kT} - 1} \tag{8.43}$$

where the summation is over all $3N_A$ modes (of which N_A are longitudinal and $2N_A$ are transverse). First though we introduce a couple more—but minor—approximations. We shall assume that the longitudinal and transverse vibrations propagate through the crystal with a common velocity v. This will enable us to use the single dispersion relation, eq. (8.45). We shall also assume that the crystal is in the form of a cubical block with sides $L_x = L_y = L_z = L$ say. This enables us to say that the points in q-space describing the various standing wave patterns which can exist are separated by π/L measured along the q_x-, q_y-, and q_z-axes. In other words each point occupies a volume of $(\pi/L)^3$, as can be seen from Fig. 8.22(a).

The first step in evaluating eq. (8.43) is to replace the summation by an integral. The number of points which lie within the shell of radius q and thickness dq shown in Fig. 8.22(b) is the volume of the shell divided by the

268

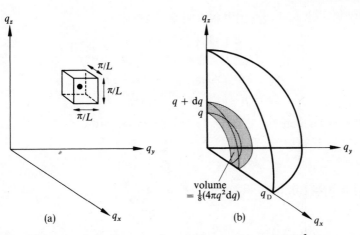

Fig. 8.22 (a) Each point, indicating a mode, occupies a volume of $(\pi/L)^3$ in q_x-q_y-q_z space. (b) The points show those modes whose circular wavenumbers lie between q and $q + dq$.

volume occupied by each point, that is $\frac{1}{8}(4\pi q^2 \, dq)/(\pi/L)^3$. Equation (8.43) therefore becomes

$$U_{m3} = \frac{3}{8}\left(\frac{L}{\pi}\right)^3 \int_0^{q_D} \frac{\hbar\omega_q}{e^{\hbar\omega_q/kT} - 1} 4\pi q^2 \, dq \qquad (8.46)$$

where we have multiplied by three to take account of the one longitudinal and the two transverse modes at each value of (q_x, q_y, q_z).

The next step is to introduce Debye's dispersion relation (eq. (8.45))

$$q = \frac{\omega}{v}$$

$$dq = \frac{1}{v} d\omega$$

Substituting these expressions for q and dq into eq. (8.46) gives

$$U_{m3} = \frac{3}{8}\left(\frac{L}{\pi}\right)^3 \frac{1}{v^3} \int_0^{\omega_D} \frac{\hbar\omega}{e^{\hbar\omega/kT} - 1} 4\pi\omega^2 \, d\omega \qquad (8.47)$$

where the upper limit of integration is

$$\omega_D = q_D v = \left(\frac{6\pi^2}{a^3}\right)^{1/3} v \qquad (8.48)$$

as follows from eq. (8.44).

Differentiating eq. (8.47) with respect to T gives

$$C_{V,m} = \frac{3}{8}\left(\frac{L}{\pi}\right)^3 \frac{1}{v^3} \int_0^{\omega_D} \frac{\hbar\omega(\hbar\omega/kT^2)}{(e^{\hbar\omega/kT}-1)^2} 4\pi\omega^2 \, d\omega$$

$$C_{V,m} = \frac{3V_m k^4 T^3}{2\pi^2 v^3 \hbar^3} \int_0^{\omega_D} \frac{(\hbar\omega/kT)^2 \, e^{\hbar\omega/kT}}{(e^{\hbar\omega/kT}-1)^2} \left(\frac{\hbar\omega}{kT}\right)^2 d\left(\frac{\hbar\omega}{kT}\right) \tag{8.49}$$

where the molar volume $V_m = L^3$. For neatness we write

$$x = \frac{\hbar\omega}{kT}$$

so that the upper limit of integration becomes

$$x_D = \frac{\hbar\omega_D}{kT} = \frac{\theta_D}{T}$$

where θ_D, known as the *Debye temperature,* is given by

$$\theta_D = \frac{\hbar\omega_D}{k} = \frac{\hbar}{k}\left(\frac{6\pi^2}{a^3}\right)^{1/3} v \tag{8.50}$$

On making these substitutions, along with $R = N_A k = (V_m/a^3)k$, eq. (8.49) becomes

$$C_{V,m} = 9R\left(\frac{T}{\theta_D}\right)^3 \int_0^{\theta_D/T} \frac{x^4 \, e^x}{(e^x-1)^2} \, dx \tag{8.51}$$

At high temperatures θ_D/T is small so that the values of x which the integrand take are small. We may therefore approximate e^x in the numerator by unity and write $e^x = 1 + x$ in the denominator. Equation (8.51) then approximates to

$$C_{V,m} = 9R\left(\frac{T}{\theta_D}\right)^3 \int_0^{\theta_D/T} \frac{x^4}{(1+x-1)^2} \, dx$$

$$= 9R\left(\frac{T}{\theta_D}\right)^3 \frac{1}{3}\left(\frac{\theta_D}{T}\right)^3$$

$$C_{V,m} = 3R \quad \text{at} \quad T \gg \theta_D$$

which is just as well!

At low temperatures the upper limit of integration in eq. (8.51) may be taken as infinity for all practical purposes. This being so, the integral tends to a constant value $(4\pi^4/15)$. Therefore

$$C_{V,m} = \frac{12\pi^4}{5} R\left(\frac{T}{\theta_D}\right)^3 \quad \text{at} \quad T \ll \theta_D \tag{8.52}$$

This T^3 variation in heat capacity is very closely obeyed by a wide variety of substances.

Although the integral in eq. (8.51) can only be expressed analytically at the extremes of high and low temperatures it can be evaluated numerically at any temperature. Figure 8.23 shows the sort of fit which is achieved between the Debye theory and experiment. If you compare Fig. 8.23 with Fig. 8.6 you will see that Debye's theory more closely fits the facts than does Einstein's. To improve on Debye's theory—and improvements are necessary in view of the simplifying assumptions made in the theory—one must work with eq. (8.43) and the calculated dispersion relations.

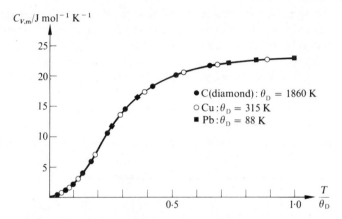

Fig. 8.23 The curve indicates the molar heat capacity of diamond, copper, and lead calculated from Debye's relation (eq. (8.51)) assuming $\theta_D = 1860$ K for diamond, $\theta_D = 315$ K for copper, and $\theta_D = 88$ K for lead. These values of θ_D compare favourably with those given by eq. (8.50).

8.6 Heat capacity of metals

To explain the high electrical conductivity of a metal it is necessary to postulate that at least some of the electrons present in the metal are free to move. The observed electrical conductivity of a monovalent metal, such as copper, can be fairly adequately explained on the assumptions that each atom in the metal gives up one electron—in doing so the atom will, of course, become an ion—and that these electrons constitute an electron gas. A mole of copper will therefore contain N_A free electrons. According to classical physics each of these electrons will (as a result of collisions with the metal ions) come into thermal equilibrium with the structure. Consequently each electron will have a kinetic energy $\frac{1}{2}m\overline{u^2} = \frac{3}{2}kT$. The total kinetic energy of the electrons in one mole of copper should therefore be $N_A(\frac{3}{2}kT) = \frac{3}{2}RT$. Since the ions have an internal energy of $3RT$ (at high temperatures) the total internal energy of one mole of copper should be $4.5RT$. So the heat capacity $C_{V,m}$ of copper should be $4.5R$. It is not—it does not exceed $3R$ (Fig. 8.6(b)).

271

By now you may just be able to diagnose troubles with heat capacity theories! The trouble—as you may have guessed—is that the energies of the electrons are quantized. Although we have just discredited the relation $\frac{1}{2}m\overline{u^2} = \frac{3}{2}kT$ or $m\bar{u} \approx (3mkT)^{1/2}$ so far as electrons are concerned, de Broglie's relation $(\lambda = h/mu = h/(3mkT)^{1/2})$ nevertheless predicts that at 300 K the de Broglie wavelength of an electron is 6×10^{-9} m. This is approximately thirty atomic diameters. So, even on the basis of this dubious calculation, it looks as if the electron's behaviour should be described in wave rather than in particle language.

A free electron in a metal

Before we bring in some wave-mechanical ideas it is worth examining how classical mechanics would describe the motion of a free electron residing in an isolated rectangular block of copper (Fig. 8.24). According to Newton's second law, if the electron (mass m) is given a constant velocity u_x directed, say, along the x-axis (which is drawn perpendicular to one of the faces of the block) the electron will proceed with a *constant* momentum mu_x—*provided* that there are no forces acting on the electron. It is surely most unlikely that there should be no forces! Recall that the electron gas—of which our electron is but one member—is created by each atom giving up an electron to the common pool.

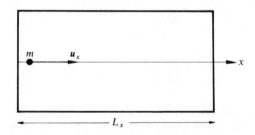

Fig. 8.24 A free electron in a rectangular block of metal as described by classical mechanics.

So our block of copper really consists of Cu^+ ions arranged on a regular lattice, and an equal number of electrons which must somehow "float around" in between the ions. But how can our electron—any electron—possibly avoid being tugged hither and thither by the lattice of Cu^+ ions? Surely each ion will exert the familiar electrostatic force $(e^2/4\pi\varepsilon_0 r^2)$ on our electron?

Let us pretend the ions are not there! Or, rather, let us smear them out to form a fixed uniform background of positive charge—a kind of jelly—within which the electron gas can move freely. Our justification for taking what appears to be an extreme liberty is that—as we shall presently discover—many predictions made on the basis of this *free electron model* are in close agreement with experiment.

So our electron in Fig. 8.24 can proceed to move along the x-axis with a constant momentum mu_x. But what happens when it reaches the far side of the block, a distance L_x away? Maybe it will just keep on going and escape! Wait, if it does leave the block, the metal will acquire a net positive charge e (block plus electron are electrically neutral) and this positive charge may well pull the electron back into the block. Should this happen, the electron will have its motion reversed and it will proceed back towards the left-hand face with momentum $-mu_x$, where the same frustrated attempt at escape will recur. The picture we end up with therefore is of an electron bouncing back and forth between opposite faces of the metal block with a constant momentum mu_x. Only if the speed of the electron is such that $\frac{1}{2}mu_x^2$ exceeds the energy required to remove the electron to infinity (the magnitude of the electrostatic potential energy of the electron in the metal) can the electron escape. Provided u_x is less than the speed required for escape we can give it any value we choose; in other words, the momentum of the electron can have any value we choose.

However, according to the ideas of wave mechanics (here it might be a good idea for you to read section 2.4 again) a free electron with a specified momentum mu must be thought of not as a particle but rather as a group, or packet, of waves whose wavelength is $\lambda = h/mu$ (where h is Planck's constant) and whose group velocity is u (see Fig. 2.5). How might such a group of waves behave in our isolated block of metal? What, in other words, is to replace our classical picture of a particle bouncing back and forth between opposite faces of the block?

We may get clues by looking at how transverse waves behave on a rope (or a piece of rubber tubing). There is nothing like actually doing the experiment! Take a long length L (say 5 m) of rope or tube and lay it out straight, along a smooth floor. Clamp both ends of the rope. Now, using your wrist, give the rope a smart sideways (lateral) flick near one of its ends. You will observe that a pulse, like that shown in Fig. 8.25(a), travels down the rope and is reflected inverted (shown dashed). If we are—as indeed we are—using the lateral displacement of the rope to give us clues as to the form of $\psi(x)$ for a free electron in a metal then, according to Fig. 2.5, we must be sending down the rope not a single pulse but a very long train or group of waves. Indeed according to wave mechanics—we state this without proof—if a "particle" (it would be better to call it a "wavicle") has a precisely defined momentum mu, the wave train (of wavelength $\lambda = h/mu$) is infinitely long. There is no problem about sending out a short train of waves on the rope—you flick your wrist back and forth a few times with a constant period. However, if you try to send out a very long train, waves reflected back from the far end of the rope will "interfere" with waves which you are still transmitting. You will find that, unless you choose the right to and fro period for your hand, your efforts produce very little effect—the rope remains essentially at rest. If you do choose the right period for the motion of your hand you will set up standing

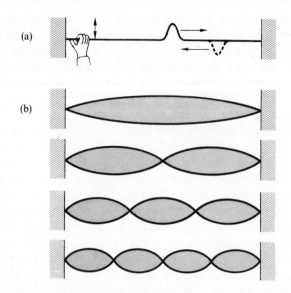

Fig. 8.25 (a) A single pulse sent down a rope is reflected, inverted, at the clamped end. (b) Standing wave patterns on a rope clamped at both ends.

wave patterns in which the rope oscillates to and fro but in which the pattern does not travel along. Figure 8.25(b) shows some of the standing wave patterns which can be generated.

It would be very unwise to claim that waves on a rope simulate the waves introduced by de Broglie. All they can do is provide a clue or two as to the form of $\psi(x)$—the form of the wave function. By clamping the rope at both ends we have certainly simulated the requirement that $\psi(x) = 0$ when $0 \gg x \gg L_x$. This is necessary to ensure that $|\psi(x)|^2$, which measures the probability of the electron within unit volume (in one dimension within unit length) at point x, is zero outside our isolated block of metal (which is what classical mechanics suggests it ought to be). By demanding that the wave train on the rope be infinitely long we have found that either the rope does not budge or that certain standing wave patterns are produced. So let us hazard the guess that the wave functions have the form shown in Fig. 8.26(a). [We are *not* saying that $\psi(x)$ has the same time-dependence as standing waves on a rope (Fig. 8.25(b)). If it did, $\psi(x, t)$ would be zero at certain times (when the rope is straight). At such times $|\psi(x, t)|^2$ would vanish everywhere—the electron would disappear! In fact $\psi(x, t) = \psi(x)[\cos(Et/\hbar) - i \sin(Et/\hbar)]$, where $i = (-1)^{1/2}$ and E is the energy of our free electron. (This assumes that an infinite energy is required to remove the electron from the metal; that is, the (constant) potential energy of the electron in the metal is $-\infty$.) All we are doing in Fig. 8.26(a) is to sketch the form of $\psi(x)$. Although $\psi(x, t)$ is complex, $|\psi(x, t)|^2$ is always real. In the present problem $|\psi(x, t)|^2 = |\psi(x)|^2$. Figure 8.26(b) shows

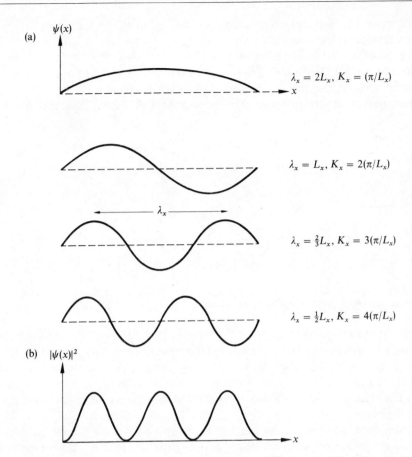

Fig. 8.26 (a) Some wave functions of a free electron confined as in Fig. 8.24. (b) How $|\psi(x)|^2$ varies along the x-axis.

$|\psi(x)|^2$ when $\lambda_x = 2L/3$.] As you can see, the wave functions of Fig. 8.26(a) are characterized by

$$L_x = \frac{\lambda_x}{2}, \lambda_x, \frac{3\lambda_x}{2}, 2\lambda_x, \ldots$$

or, in terms of the circular wavenumber $K_x (= 2\pi/\lambda_x)$

$$K_x = \left(\frac{\pi}{L_x}\right), 2\left(\frac{\pi}{L_x}\right), 3\left(\frac{\pi}{L_x}\right), 4\left(\frac{\pi}{L_x}\right), \ldots \tag{8.53}$$

So far we have only considered an essentially one-dimensional problem— an electron confined between $x = 0$ and $x = L_x$ (Fig. 8.24). To get clues as to the form of the wave-function in a two-dimensional metal we might look

275

at the various wave patterns which can be sustained on a rectangular piece of stretched rubber firmly clamped along all four edges. Figure 8.27 shows one possible standing wave pattern. (This is a view looking down on the sheet at a particular instant; the + indicates movement upwards, out of the plane of the paper; the − denotes downward movement of the rubber; the lines, regions where the rubber is at rest.) As Fig. 8.27 shows, this standing

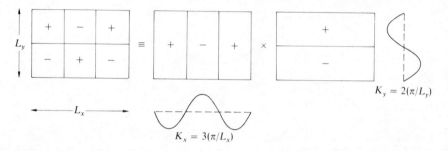

Fig. 8.27 Showing how a standing wave pattern on a two-dimensional sheet can be thought of as the product of two separate standing wave patterns.

wave pattern can be thought of as the *product* of two separate standing wave patterns (of the same vibrational frequency), one characterized by $K_x = 3(\pi/L_x)$, $K_y = 0$, the other by $K_x = 0$, $K_y = 2(\pi/L_y)$. (You can check this out in a rough sort of way by multiplying the displacement at a particular point on the plate with $K_x = 3(\pi/L_x)$, $K_y = 0$ by the displacement at the same point on the plate with $K_x = 0$, $K_y = 2(\pi/L_y)$. Call the displacements $+1$, 0, or -1 as appropriate.) In general, any value of K_x from the list given below can coexist with any value of K_y given below (except that K_x and K_y cannot both be zero; this means the plate is at rest)

$$\left. \begin{aligned} K_x &= 0, (\pi/L_x), 2(\pi/L_x), 3(\pi/L_x), \ldots \\ K_y &= 0, (\pi/L_y), 2(\pi/L_y), 3(\pi/L_y), \ldots \end{aligned} \right\} \tag{8.54}$$

(In a one-dimensional system we exclude $K_x = 0$ since this implies that $\lambda_x = \infty$; that the rope is not vibrating.) Once the values of K_x and K_y are specified, the standing wave pattern on a rubber sheet of length L_x and width L_y is determined. So we shall hazard the guess that the wave function of a free electron in a two-dimensional metal of length L_x and width L_y is characterized by quoting the values of (K_x, K_y), where K_x and K_y are to be chosen from the list, eq. (8.54) (except for $K_x = K_y = 0$). Once the values of K_x and K_y are specified the (time-independent part of the) wave function may be found using the technique illustrated in Fig. 8.27.

It scarcely requires genius to now suggest that the wave function of a free electron in a rectangular block of metal of length L_x, width L_y, and depth

L_z is characterized by the values of (K_x, K_y, K_z), where K_x, K_y, and K_z must be chosen from the following list. (We cannot choose $K_x = K_y = K_z = 0$, i.e., $\lambda_x = \lambda_y = \lambda_z = \infty$, since this says the electron is not in the metal.)

$$
\left.
\begin{aligned}
K_x &= 0, (\pi/L_x), 2(\pi/L_x), 3(\pi/L_x), \ldots \\
K_y &= 0, (\pi/L_y), 2(\pi/L_y), 3(\pi/L_y), \ldots \\
K_z &= 0, (\pi/L_z), 2(\pi/L_z), 3(\pi/L_z), \ldots
\end{aligned}
\right\}
\qquad (8.55)
$$

From now on it will suit our purposes best to take the block of metal to be a cube of side $L = L_x = L_y = L_z$. It will also help us to have a graphical method of recording the (K_x, K_y, K_z) value of an electron's wave function. Figure 8.28 shows the method we shall adopt. What we do is to construct a simple cubic lattice of points in K_x–K_y–K_z space in which the nearest neighbour separation is (π/L). Because of the form of eq. (8.55) (with $L = L_x = L_y = L_z$) it follows that each point may be used to characterize the wave function of an electron. (For clarity only a few lattice points are shown in Fig. 8.28.) Suppose an electron has a wave function with $K_x = 2(\pi/L)$, $K_y = (\pi/L)$, $K_z = 4(\pi/L)$.

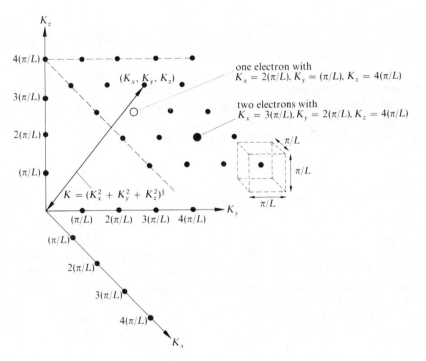

Fig. 8.28 A convenient way of recording the quantum numbers of the free electrons in a metal (which is in the form of a cube of length L). For clarity, only a few lattice points are shown.

To denote this we may draw in an open circle around this lattice point as in Fig. 8.28. If a second electron has the same value of (K_x, K_y, K_z) we may fill in the circle. You can see from Fig. 8.28 that two electrons have $K_x = 3(\pi/L)$, $K_y = 2(\pi/L)$, $K_z = 4(\pi/L)$. Indeed there is a limit to the number of electrons which can have the same values of (K_x, K_y, K_z)—according to wave mechanics the limit is two. (We will take this as gospel. In fact if two electrons do have the same values of (K_x, K_y, K_z) they must have opposite "spin". In classical language, we would picture the electron as a spinning sphere whose axis may point in two different directions—often called "up" and "down".) The values of (K_x, K_y, K_z) and a statement of whether the electron is "spin up" or "spin down"—all four pieces of information—may be said to constitute the *quantum numbers* of our free electron.

There is a real danger in Fig. 8.28; certain people think it shows how electrons are arranged in *space* within the metal! It shows nothing of the kind. It is only a convenient way of tabulating information about the quantum numbers of the free electrons in a metal. Another possible source of confusion arises because it looks much the same as Fig. 8.18. All Fig. 8.18 does is to tabulate the wave numbers of permitted standing wave patterns of atoms in a solid. Likewise, it is not a sketch of the crystal structure of the solid!

The energy of a free electron gas

Before we can calculate the heat capacity of a metal like copper we must be able to calculate the contribution which the electrons will make to the internal energy of the metal. This involves knowing how the energy of an electron is related to the values of (K_x, K_y, K_z) which characterize its wave function. It also involves knowing how to assign values for (K_x, K_y, K_z) to each electron in the metal.

The kinetic energy of free electron is given by (see eq. (3.12))

$$\text{K.E.} = \tfrac{1}{2}mu^2 = \tfrac{1}{2}m(u_x^2 + u_y^2 + u_z^2)$$

$$\text{K.E.} = \frac{1}{2m}\left[(mu_x)^2 + (mu_y)^2 + (mu_z)^2\right]$$

where m is the mass of an electron.

We have argued on p. 272 that the potential energy of a free electron is constant inside a metal. For convenience we will take this constant value to be zero. (You can give it any value you wish. When we come to differentiate our expression for the internal energy with respect to T to obtain the heat capacity, the potential energy term will vanish.) The total energy E of a free electron in a metal is therefore given by

$$E = \frac{1}{2m}\left[(mu_x)^2 + (mu_y)^2 + (mu_z)^2\right]$$

Since $K_x = 2\pi/\lambda_x$ and $\lambda_x = h/mu_x$, that is $K_x = mu_x/h$, with similar expressions for K_y and K_z, it follows that

$$E = \frac{\hbar^2}{2m}(K_x^2 + K_y^2 + K_z^2) = \frac{\hbar^2 K^2}{2m} \tag{8.56}$$

where K is the distance of the point (K_x, K_y, K_z) from the origin in Fig. 8.28. In other words, a sphere, or rather an octant, drawn in K_x–K_y–K_z space with the origin as centre and of radius $K = (K_x^2 + K_y^2 + K_z^2)^{1/2}$ is a surface of constant energy on which $E = \hbar^2 K^2/2m$.

The rule for assigning quantum numbers is that only two electrons (of opposite spin) can have the same triplet (K_x, K_y, K_z). If the metal is supposed to be at $T = 0$, then the quantum numbers must be assigned in such a way as to minimize the mean energy of an electron. In view of eq. (8.56) we must assign quantum numbers starting from the origin of K_x–K_y–K_z space (excluding $K_x = K_y = K_z = 0$) and move outwards in spherical fashion as shown in Fig. 8.29. If there are N free electrons to be assigned quantum numbers the sphere at which we call it quits must have a radius K_F which is such as to include $\frac{1}{2}N$ points within it. (The factor of $1/2$ arises, of course, because each point can describe two electrons; one spin up; the other spin down.) Since a point in K_x–K_y–K_z space occupies a volume $(\pi/L)^3$ (see Fig. 8.28) it follows that the number of points within an octant of radius K_F is $\frac{1}{8}(\frac{4}{3}\pi K_F^3)/(\pi/L)^3$, and so;

$$\frac{1}{2}N = \frac{\frac{1}{8}(\frac{4}{3}\pi K_F^3)}{(\pi/L)^3}$$

$$K_F = \left(\frac{3N\pi^2}{L^3}\right)^{1/3}$$

or

$$K_F = (3\pi^2 n)^{1/3} \tag{8.57}$$

where $n = N/L^3 = N/V$ is the number of free electrons per unit volume of the metal. The energy E_F of those electrons with $K = K_F$ is, from eqs. (8.56) and (8.57), given by

$$E_F = \frac{\hbar^2 K_F^2}{2m} = \frac{\hbar^2}{2m}(3\pi^2 n)^{2/3} \tag{8.58}$$

and this energy is referred to as the *Fermi energy*.

The picture of points in K_x–K_y–K_z space being assigned to electrons may be a helpful image but it still leaves us with the task of finding the energy distribution function for a free electron gas, that is of finding the number of electrons per unit range of energy at a particular energy.

279

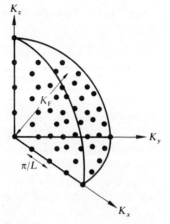

Fig. 8.29 The heavy dots indicate those values of (K_x, K_y, K_z) which have each been assigned to two electrons in the metal.

The Fermi–Dirac energy distribution function

Since each point in K_x–K_y–K_z space occupies a volume $(\pi/L)^3$ it follows that the number of points lying within an octant-shaped shell of radii K and $K + \mathrm{d}K$ (cf. Fig. 8.21(b)) is $\frac{1}{8}(4\pi K^2\,\mathrm{d}K)/(\pi/L)^3 = VK^2\,\mathrm{d}K/2\pi^2$. Because each of these points can describe the values of (K_x, K_y, K_z) of two electrons (with opposite spins) it follows that the number $\mathrm{d}N$ of electrons whose circular wavenumbers lie between K and $K + \mathrm{d}K$ is twice the number of points within the octant-shaped cell, and so

$$\mathrm{d}N = \frac{V}{\pi^2} K^2\,\mathrm{d}K \qquad \text{(for } K < K_\mathrm{F} \text{ at } T = 0\text{)}$$

From eq. (8.56), $K^2 = 2mE/\hbar^2$, that is

$$\mathrm{d}K = \frac{m\,\mathrm{d}E}{\hbar^2 K}$$

$$\mathrm{d}K = \frac{m\,\mathrm{d}E}{\hbar(2mE)^{1/2}}$$

and so

$$\mathrm{d}N = \frac{V}{2\pi^2}\left(\frac{2m}{\hbar^2}\right)^{3/2} E^{1/2}\,\mathrm{d}E$$

The energy distribution function of a free electron gas—usually called the *Fermi–Dirac energy distribution* function—is therefore

$$\frac{\mathrm{d}N}{\mathrm{d}E} = \frac{V}{2\pi^2}\left(\frac{2m}{\hbar^2}\right)^{3/2} E^{1/2} \qquad \text{at } T = 0 \qquad (8.59)$$

but this only holds up to $E = E_F$. All points with $K > K_F$ are (by definition of K_F) unassigned at $T = 0$. Therefore there are no electrons with $E > E_F$ at $T = 0$. So $dN/dE = 0$ when $E > E_F$, at $T = 0$.

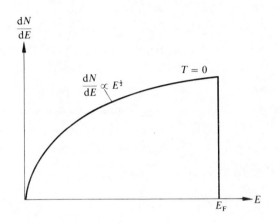

Fig. 8.30 The energy distribution function for a free-electron gas at $T = 0$.

The electronic heat capacity

In thinking about the heat capacity of the electron gas we are, of course, interested in the energy distribution function at a finite temperature, and in how the distribution function changes with temperature. If we heat the metal from absolute zero to a temperature T only those electrons within an energy range of about kT of E_F can be thermally excited; kT is the sort of energy that is available from a vibrating atom of the metal. Electrons whose energy is lower than about $(E_F - kT)$ cannot accept extra energy, for the states to which they would be excited (meaning the new values of (K_x, K_y, K_z) to which they would have to move) are already filled. The energy distribution function is therefore unaltered up to an energy of about $(E_F - kT)$. We might well expect (drawing on what we know of a monatomic gas) that those electrons which can be excited will have their energy *increased* by about $\frac{3}{2}kT$ as the temperature of the metal is raised from near absolute zero to a value T. In calculating the heat capacity of a free electron gas we need therefore only consider those electrons with energies in the range $(E_F - kT)$ to $(E_F + kT)$. The number of such electrons is equal to the area shown shaded in Fig. 8.31 (remember that dN/dE tells us the number per unit range of energy) or, since the area of a triangle is $\frac{1}{2}$ base × height;

$$\int_{E_F - kT}^{E_F + kT} \frac{dN}{dE} \, dE \approx \frac{1}{2}(2kT)\left(\frac{dN}{dE}\right)_{E_F} = \left(\frac{3}{\pi^4}\right)^{1/3} \frac{Vmn^{1/3}}{h^2} kT \quad (8.60)$$

281

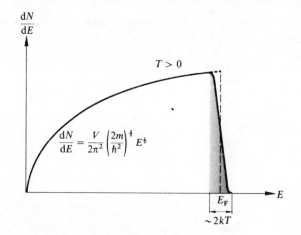

Fig. 8.31 The energy distribution function for a free-electron gas at a finite temperature T. The area shown shaded is equal to the number of excited electrons.

where we have substituted for dN/dE from eq. (8.59) with E_F given by eq. (8.58).

The extra energy acquired by each of these electrons in being thermally excited is $\frac{3}{2}kT$ so the *increase* in energy of the electron gas on raising its temperature from absolute zero to a temperature T is the product of the number given by eq. (8.60) and $\frac{3}{2}kT$. Differentiating this product with respect to T gives

$$C_e = \left(\frac{3}{\pi^4}\right)^{1/3} \frac{Vmn^{1/3}}{h^2} \frac{d}{dT}(kT \times \tfrac{3}{2}kT)$$

If we assume that there is one mole of metal present and that each atom contributes one free electron then $V = V_m$ and $n = N_A/V_m$, so

$$C_{e,m} = \gamma T \qquad \text{where } \gamma = \left(\frac{3}{\pi}\right)^{4/3} \frac{V_m^{2/3} N_A^{1/3} mk^2}{h^2} \qquad (8.61)$$

Substituting for the known values of the constants in eq. (8.61) predicts an electronic heat capacity for copper at 300 K of 0·15 J mol^{-1} K^{-1} which is less than 1 per cent of the atomic heat capacity at this temperature. This then is the reason why the heat capacity of a metallic and of a non-metallic element are practically equal at high temperatures (Fig. 8.6).

At low temperatures, where the heat capacity of the structure is proportional to T^3 (eq. (8.52)), we may also write total molar heat capacity of the metal as

$$C_{V,m} = \beta T^3 + \gamma T$$

$$\frac{C_{V,m}}{T} = \beta T^2 + \gamma$$

A graph of $C_{V,\mathrm{m}}/T$ plotted against T^2 should therefore be linear with a slope β and an intercept γ. Figure 8.32 shows such a plot for copper. The linearity provides striking confirmation of the T^3 dependence of the atomic heat capacity. The intercept gives a value of γ in fair agreement with that predicted from eq. (8.61) $(7.0 \times 10^{-4}\,\mathrm{J\,mol^{-1}\,K^{-2}}$ as against a predicted value of $4.9 \times 10^{-4}\,\mathrm{J\,mol^{-1}\,K^{-2}})$. The discrepancy could be due to — indeed is due to — the electrons not being as "free" as we supposed.

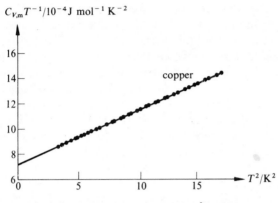

Fig. 8.32 A plot of $C_{V,\mathrm{m}}/T$ against T^2 for copper.

8.7 Thermal defects

How far an atom can roam from its lattice site—meaning its amplitude of vibration—depends on its thermal energy. If this should exceed the energy required to remove the atom from its lattice site then the atom can leave home. As a result a number of *point defects* will be formed in the structure. The word point is used to denote the localized nature of the defects. In the next chapter we will look at defects which extend over large regions of the crystal.

Several possible types of defect come to mind. An atom may simply migrate a short distance from the *vacancy* it created on leaving (Fig. 8.33(a)). This localized *interstitial-vacancy* pair is called a *Frenkel defect*. Or it may migrate to the surface leaving an isolated vacancy; a *Schottky defect* (Fig. 8.33(b)). Another possibility is for an atom to diffuse in from the surface of the crystal

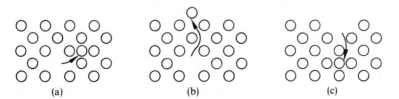

(a) (b) (c)

Fig. 8.33 Illustrating the formation of (a) a vacancy-interstitial pair (a Frenkel defect), (b) an isolated vacancy (a Schottky defect), and (c) an isolated interstitial.

283

to form an isolated interstitial (Fig. 8.33(c)). The energy required to form a particular type of point defect will naturally depend on the crystal structure. In a tightly packed structure such as an hcp or fcc metal (Figs. 7.12 and 7.13) crystal the energy required to introduce an interstitial atom of the element is so large as to make their occurrence extremely unlikely. (To squeeze the atom in, the structure must be deformed for quite some distance around, and this calls for a lot of energy.) In more open structures, such as that of diamond (Fig. 7.18) interstitials are much more easy to accommodate.

We will consider the energy required to form an isolated vacancy; a defect which can, and indeed does, occur in all crystals. The energy required, E_v, to remove an atom from the interior of a crystal to the surface is equal to the energy required to remove an atom from the interior to infinity minus the energy released when an atom is condensed on the surface from an infinite distance away. If the atom is surrounded by p nearest neighbours in the interior of the solid and the dissociation energy of an isolated pair of atoms is ΔE, it requires an energy of approximately $p\Delta E$ to remove the atom to infinity. In condensing the atom back onto the surface an energy of about $(p/2)\Delta E$ is released—on the surface an atom is surrounded by only half as many neighbours as in the interior—giving the net energy E_v required for an atom to leave its lattice site and migrate to the surface as $(p - \tfrac{1}{2}p)\Delta E = \tfrac{1}{2}p\Delta E$. As an example, solid argon has a fcc structure in which each atom is surrounded by twelve equidistant nearest neighbours. For argon $\Delta E = 1{\cdot}7 \times 10^{-21}$ J, so the energy required to form an isolated vacancy is $E_v = \tfrac{1}{2} \times 12 \times 1{\cdot}7 \times 10^{-21}$ J $= 1{\cdot}0 \times 10^{-20}$ J.

The number of vacancies existing in a crystal should be roughly equal to the number of atoms whose vibrational energy E exceeds E_v, that is, the number whose energy lies between $E = E_v$ and $E = \infty$. To find this number we will adopt an Einstein model of the crystal. According to this model (eq. (8.21)

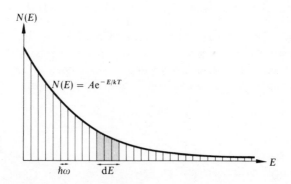

Fig. 8.34 The number of atoms with a particular energy E according to Einstein's model. The vertical lines emphasize that the energy is quantized in multiples of $\hbar\omega$. In the energy interval dE at E there will be $dE/\hbar\omega$ more atoms than there are at energy E. (The number $N(E)$ is effectively constant within the interval dE.)

with $\beta = 1/kT$) the number of atoms with *one particular energy E* (one which is quantized in integral multiples of $\hbar\omega$) is given by

$$N(E) = A\,e^{-E/kT} \tag{8.62}$$

and this is shown graphically in Fig. 8.34, where the vertical lines indicate that only discrete energies are permitted. If we now look at the energy range dE (Fig. 8.34) we see that the number of atoms whose energies lie within this range is given by $A\exp(-E/kT)$ multiplied by the number of vertical lines (more formally, the number of permitted values of E) within dE, that is $A\exp(-E/kT)(dE/\hbar\omega)$. Integrating from $E = E_v$ to $E = \infty$ gives the number n of atoms with an energy in excess of E_v as

$$n = B\int_{E_v}^{\infty} e^{-E/kT}\,dE \tag{8.63}$$

where $B = A/\hbar\omega$ is a constant. We can find B by noting that the total number of atoms N is given by

$$N = B\int_{0}^{\infty} e^{-E/kT}\,dE \tag{8.64}$$

Substituting for B from eq. (8.64) into eq. (8.63) gives

$$n = N\frac{\displaystyle\int_{E_v}^{\infty} e^{-E/kT}\,dE}{\displaystyle\int_{0}^{\infty} e^{-E/kT}\,dE} = N\frac{\left[-e^{-E/kT}\right]_{E_v}^{\infty}}{\left[-e^{-E/kT}\right]_{0}^{\infty}}$$

$$n = N\,e^{-E_v/kT} \tag{8.65}$$

as the number of vacancies, each of which requires an energy E_v to be formed, in a crystal at temperature T. To take the example of solid argon the fraction n/N of sites which are vacant at $T = 50$ K is $e^{-14.5} = 5 \times 10^{-7}$, assuming $E_v = 1 \times 10^{-20}$ J. Even at the triple point temperature (83·8 K) only 0·02 per cent of the lattice sites are vacant.

One way to measure the vacancy concentration is to study how the overall volume of a crystal increases with increasing temperature. Most of this increase in volume is due to thermal expansion of the lattice—but this can be allowed for by using X-ray diffraction techniques to measure how the lattice spacing changes with temperature. The remaining increase must be due to the formation of vacancies with (we assume) the displaced atoms going to the surface of the crystal. By studying the temperature dependence of this excess volume (which is proportional to n)—the results fit eq. (8.65)—one obtains $E_v = 3 \times 10^{-20}$ J for argon. This compares favourably with our rough and ready calculated value ($\frac{1}{2}p\Delta E$) of $1·0 \times 10^{-20}$ J.

8.8. Thermal expansion

Up to now we have assumed that the only effect of raising the temperature of a crystal from near $T = 0$ is to increase the amplitude of vibration of the atoms, with the atoms continuing to vibrate about the sites they would (according to classical mechanics) occupy at $T = 0$. If this were really so a solid could never expand as its temperature is raised. In general, the *linear expansivity* α of a solid (defined as the fractional change in length per unit change of temperature) is small but it is finite. For metals α is of order $10^{-5} \, \mathrm{K}^{-1}$ at room temperature.

To try to discover why solids expand let us consider how an isolated pair of atoms behave. If we find that their mean separation increases with

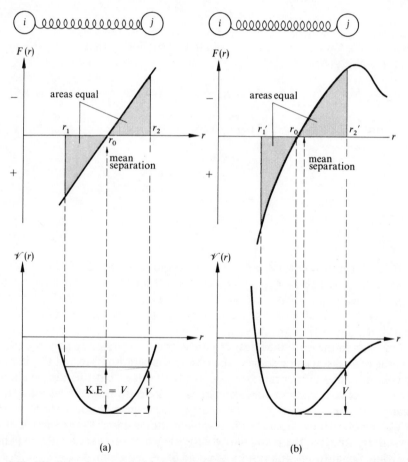

(a)   (b)

Fig. 8.35 The linear interatomic force characteristic of (a) leads to no change in the mean separation of atoms i and j as the energy of j is increased. In (b) the mean separation of i and j does increase.

286

increasing temperature we can be pretty certain that a collection of atoms in which each atom strongly interacts with its nearest neighbours—a solid—will expand. Figure 8.35 shows an isolated pair of atoms in which atom i is held fixed. Beneath is shown the force–separation curve. In Fig. 8.35(a) it has been assumed that $F(r)$ is linear about the static equilibrium separation r_0 of the pair. A linear force curve implies a symmetrical (parabolic) potential energy well. To represent a finite temperature, atom j must be given kinetic energy. This we may do by pulling out j to a separation r_2 and letting it go. It will of course accelerate inwards, overshoot r_0, and continue on inwards until it comes to a momentary rest at a separation r_1, before returning to separation r_2. It will then continue to vibrate between r_1 and r_2. In pulling atom j out to separation r_2 one increases its potential energy by an amount V equal to the area under the force curve between r_0 and r_2. As j speeds back this energy is exclusively kinetic at r_0, and is again all potential at r_1. Throughout the vibration the *total* energy remains constant—the pair is isolated—but the energy changes from one form to another. The mean separation of the pair is the mean of r_1 and r_2. Because the force curve is linear, this mean separation is r_0; in other words a solid will not expand if the force–separation curve is strictly linear. You can, of course, reach the same conclusion by arguing in terms of the potential energy curve. A linear $F(r)$ implies a parabolic $\mathscr{V}(r)$ (the lower curve in Fig. 8.35(a)).

Figure 8.35(b) shows a more realistic force curve with its rapidly increasing repulsive force as the atoms approach closer than r_0. (This may be simulated by mounting a compression spring inside a weaker extension spring.) Once again we move atom j out to some position r_2', so giving it an energy V equal to the area under the force curve between r_0 and r_2'. On releasing it, atom j will move in to some position r_1' such that the area under the force curve between r_1' and r_0 is equal to that between r_0 and r_2'. Because of the non-linear nature of the force curve (or, equivalently, because of the asymmetrical potential well) the mean of r_1' and r_2' is greater than r_0. We have thermal expansion.

8.9 Lindemann's theory of fusion

Building on the idea that the amplitude of vibration of the atoms in a solid increases as the temperature is increased, Lindemann in 1910 proposed that when this amplitude of vibration reaches a certain critical fraction of the mean interatomic spacing the vibrations will interfere to such an extent that the structure becomes mechanically unstable—it fuses (melts). He further proposed that this critical fraction should be the same for all crystals with the same structure. We need only expect the model to be applicable to structures with a single atom as basis; molecules have a vibrational complexity which rules out such a simple model.

Lindemann adopted the Einstein model of a solid. Here, you will recall, each atom is assumed to vibrate independently of one another but with a common circular frequency ω. The mean energy of an atom at temperature T is therefore given by Planck's relation (eq. (8.24) with $\beta = 1/kT$)

$$\bar{E}_x = \frac{\hbar\omega}{e^{\hbar\omega/kT} - 1} \tag{8.66}$$

Since most solids fuse at a temperature $T \gg \hbar\omega/k \, (= \theta_E)$—that is, at a temperature at which $C_{V,m}$ has plateaued out at $3R$—we may take

$$\bar{E}_x = kT \tag{8.67}$$

this being the value of eq. (8.66) when $kT \gg \hbar\omega$. According to eq. (8.10) the energy $\bar{E}_x$ of a vibrating atom is related to the force constant k_s and the amplitude of vibration A by

$$\bar{E}_x = k_s A^2 \tag{8.68}$$

(Equation (8.10) actually does record the mean, albeit constant, value of E_x.) Setting eq. (8.67) with $T = T_f$, the fusion temperature, equal to eq. (8.68) with $A = cr_0$, where c is the supposedly constant fraction of the mean interatomic spacing r_0 at which A is sufficient for fusion to occur, gives

$$kT_f = k_s c^2 r_0^2$$

Since $\omega^2 = 2k_s/m$, where m is the mass of an atom of the solid (eq. (8.3)) and $\hbar\omega/k = \theta_E$, the Einstein temperature, we obtain

$$c^2 = \left(\frac{2\hbar^2}{k}\right) \frac{T_f}{\theta_E^2 m r_0^2} \tag{8.69}$$

If Lindemann's theory is to be believed c as calculated from eq. (8.69) should be constant for all elements of the same crystal structure and be less than unity. Table 8.1 sets out data for a variety of elements whose structure is fcc. (Here r_0 is taken to be the nearest-neighbour separation in the crystal structure of the element.) We see that even though T_f changes a hundred-fold c remains constant to within 30 per cent.

TABLE 8.1

Element	$r_0/10_m^{-10}$	T_f/K	θ_E/K	$c/10^{-2}$
Ne	3·16	24	50	6·8
Ar	3·76	84	60	6·3
Xe	4·34	161	40	6·3
Pb	3·50	600	58	8·2
Al	2·86	933	326	6·2
Cu	2·56	1356	240	7·4
Pt	2·77	2044	149	7·7

Despite its seeming success, Lindemann's theory fails in the last analysis for it cannot explain why the structure of a solid breaks down so suddenly within a very narrow range of temperature. It fails because it deals only with the mean energy (eq. (8.67)) and proceeds by assuming that each and every atom has energy kT_f at the fusion temperature. Rather, it succeeds because it makes these unjustifiable assumptions.

Summary

1. Classical physics predicts that the heat capacity $C_{V,m}$ of a monatomic solid will be $3R$, independent of temperature. Experiments show that $C_{V,m}$ is proportional to T^3 at low temperatures. Einstein's theory, which treats each atom as a Planck oscillator, predicts a too rapid fall-off in $C_{V,m}$. Coupled-oscillator theories predict that standing wave patterns will be established within a solid and that the associated $\omega_q - q$ dispersion curve is non-linear. Each such standing wave pattern, or mode—in which all the atoms participate—has the same energy as one Planck oscillator. The total number of possible modes is three times the number N of atoms present ($2N$ modes being transverse and N longitudinal). Assuming, after Debye, that $\omega = qv$, where v is the velocity of sound in the solid, and that the three-dimensional cubical array of points in q-space describing the possible modes can be replaced by points confined to an octant, leads to $C_{V,m} \propto T^3$.

2. The heat capacity of a metal is only slightly greater than that of a non-metal. The reason is that only those electrons within a range of about kT of the Fermi energy are free to have their energy increased.

3. Defects whose number density is proportional to $\exp(-E_v/kT)$, where E_v is the energy required to produce the defect, are thermal in origin.

4. Thermal expansion arises because the interatomic force characteristic is non-linear about the equilibrium separation. (There may also be a small contribution arising from the creation of Schottky defects.)

5. Lindemann's theory of fusion supposes the crystal structure to break up when the amplitude of thermal vibration of an atom reaches a certain fraction of the interatomic spacing.

PROBLEMS

8.1 An object of mass 0.2 kg is attached to the end of a vertical spring which extends 5×10^{-2} m as a consequence. The object is removed and replaced by another of mass 4 kg which is then pulled down below its equilibrium position. What is the period and circular frequency of the resulting vibration? Assume $g = 10$ m s^{-2}.

8.2 An atom i lies between two atoms j and k as shown in Fig. 8.3. Assuming that j and k can be regarded as fixed (their average position is on a lattice site), show that the amplitude A of vibration of i is related to the temperature T of the (one-dimensional) solid by $A = (kT/k_s)^{1/2}$, where k_s is the force constant in an isolated pair of atoms. What percentage of the mean interatomic separation (2.86×10^{-10} m) is A in aluminium at 300 K? Assume $k_s = 20$ N m^{-1}.

8.3 Show that in an isolated pair of atoms which interact according to the Mie potential model (eq. (2.14)) the restoring force k_s per unit displacement from equilibrium is $m(n - m)Ar_0^{-(m+2)}$. In an isolated NaCl molecule $r_0 = 2.5 \times 10^{-10}$ m, $A = e^2/4\pi\varepsilon_0$, $m = 1$, and $n = 9$. Calculate k_s and the period of vibration of the molecule (assuming the chlorine ion to be held fixed). ($A_r(\text{Na}) = 23$.)

8.4 What, according to Einstein's theory, is the heat capacity of a monatomic solid at the Einstein temperature?

8.5 The molar heat capacity of copper at 1 K is only about 10^{-5} of its value at room temperature (see Fig. 8.6(b)). If a piece of copper at 1 K falls through a distance of 10^{-5} m and the energy is dissipated as heat, what will be the percentage rise in the temperature of the block? (This can be an important consideration in the design of equipment to operate at very low temperatures.) Assume $g = 10$ m s^{-2}, $A_r(\text{Cu}) = 63.5$.

8.6 Four gliders of the same mass are connected together by identical springs as shown in Fig. 8.11(a). Draw out all the possible distinct vibrational modes. In deciding if two modes differ look at what the gliders are doing—disregard the springs. Assuming that each glider has a mass of 0·4 kg and each spring a force constant of 8×10^{-2} N m^{-1}, calculate the circular frequency of each mode on a track of total length 1·8 m.

8.7 Starting with the dispersion relation for a one-dimensional monatomic structure, eq. (8.31), calculate the velocity at which longitudinal vibrations of large wavelength ($q \approx 0$) travel down the structure. You should compare your answer with the rough estimate for the velocity of sound ($2r_0/T_v$) which we arrived at in section 8.2. Are the two velocities roughly equal? (A more exact calculation shows that as $q \to 0$ eq. (8.31) goes over to precisely the form which applies to a continuum.)

8.8 Assuming that the period of vibration of atoms in a brass rod is 10^{-13} s and that the average interatomic separation is 2.5×10^{-10} m, calculate the speed of sound in brass. You can estimate the speed of sound by hitting one end of a brass rod held at its centre. Using tuning forks to provide reference frequencies one can guess the frequency of the sound emitted by the vibrating brass rod. Assuming that a particular longitudinal mode exists on the rod—you should know which— derive an expression relating the velocity of sound in the rod to the frequency of the emitted sound. Since this velocity is simply related to the period of vibration of atoms in the solid we can estimate the vibrational periods of atoms by tapping large objects!

8.9 Show that in a one-dimensional monatomic crystal of length L and interatomic separation a the number of standing wave patterns within a range $d\omega$ at a circular frequency ω is $2L\, d\omega/a\pi(\omega_m^2 - \omega^2)^{1/2}$, where ω_m is the maximum circular frequency which the structure can sustain.

8.10 Consider a circularly shaped chain of atoms of length L containing N identical atoms with an interatomic separation a. Compressional waves may run around the ring in either sense. A wave travelling in one sense is described by the equation $x = A \cos(\omega t - qX)$ and a wave travelling in the other sense by $x = A \cos(\omega t + qX)$. Here X is the distance around the ring. The, so-called, *periodic boundary conditions* demand that the displacement at X and at $X + L$ be equal (X and $X + L$ are the same point). Show that only those waves satisfying the condition

$$q = \pm \left(\frac{2\pi}{L}\right), \pm 2\left(\frac{2\pi}{L}\right), \pm 3\left(\frac{2\pi}{L}\right), + \cdots, \pm \frac{N}{2}\left(\frac{2\pi}{L}\right)$$

are permissible. (All the arguments which we based on standing waves could equally well have been based on travelling waves. The conclusions which we reached would have been unaltered.)

8.11 Adopting a free electron model, calculate the Fermi energy E_F and the Fermi velocity u_F in copper, taking the number density of free electrons to be $8{\cdot}5 \times 10^{28}$ m^{-3}. At what temperature would a classical gas have a mean thermal energy of E_F?

8.12 Show that the de Broglie wavelength of a free electron at the Fermi level is $(8\pi/3zN)^{1/3}$, where z is the number of free electrons contributed by each atom in the metal, of which there are N per unit volume. What is the value of this wavelength in silver? Take $z = 1$. (Density of silver $= 1{\cdot}0 \times 10^4$ kg m^{-3}. $A_r(\text{Ag}) = 108$.)

8.13 Show that the mean energy of an electron in a free electron gas at absolute zero is $3E_F/5$.

8.14 Using the data given in Fig. 8.6(b) and adopting Debye's T^3 expression for the molar heat capacity of a solid, estimate the Debye temperature for copper.

9. Mechanical Properties of Solids

There are three distinct ways of deforming a solid. We may "squeeze it evenly all over"—that is, subject it to a constant (hydrostatic) pressure. Its behaviour under these conditions is summed up in the "solid" face of the p–V–T surface. We may also stretch a solid, perhaps to the point where we "pull it apart"—that is, we may apply a tensile stress. Or we may shear it, as we might splay out a deck of cards.

We shall try to account for the behaviour of a solid under these three different stress conditions. In doing so we shall discover that most solids fail to live up to their theoretical expectations. Small structural imperfections in a solid can be the weak link which limit their strength. Contrast this with what happens in a gas. Unless the state of the system lies on the region of the p–V–T surface in which a "gas" and a "liquid" are indistinguishable, imperfections (in the form of a finite ΔE and a non-zero atomic diameter) only slightly perturb the properties of an otherwise perfect gas.

9.1 The bulk modulus

A definition

If we wish to study how the volume of a solid changes with changing hydrostatic pressure we must clearly immerse the solid in a fluid whose pressure can be changed. What characterizes a hydrostatic pressure is its constancy in all directions at any point in the fluid. Figure 9.1(a) shows the type of experiment we wish to perform. If the pressure is increased from p to $p + \mathrm{d}p$ we can expect that the volume of the solid to change by $\mathrm{d}V$ (which will, of course, have a negative value). Assuming the experiment to be performed at constant temperature, we define the *isothermal bulk modulus K_T* by

$$K_T = \frac{\mathrm{d}p}{(-\mathrm{d}V/V)} = -V\frac{\mathrm{d}p}{\mathrm{d}V} \tag{9.1}$$

The minus sign is incorporated to make the value of K_T positive. The bulk modulus may also be written as the inverse of the *compressibility,* defined as the fractional change in volume per unit change of pressure, $(-\mathrm{d}V/V)/\mathrm{d}p$. A gas, which is normally highly compressible, therefore has a low bulk modulus. A solid, on the other hand, has a low compressibility and so has a high

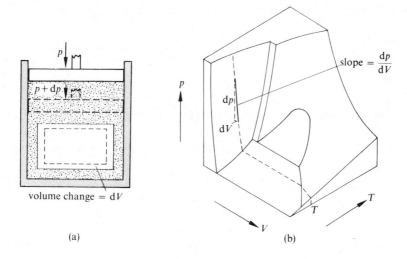

Fig. 9.1 (a) If the hydrostatic pressure is raised by dp the volume of the solid changes by dV. (b) The isothermal bulk modulus is the magnitude of the slope of the isothermal line multiplied by the volume of the solid at the point where the slope is measured.

bulk modulus. Figure 9.1(b) shows that the bulk modulus measures the magnitude of the slope of a slice of the p–V–T surface at constant temperature multiplied by the volume at the point in question.

Experimental techniques

As it stands the apparatus of Fig. 9.1(a) is of little practical value. To withstand high pressures the cylinder has to be made of steel, which precludes us from directly observing how the volume of the solid changes with increasing pressure. One solution might be to measure the total change in the volume of liquid plus solid (this could be found from the position of the piston and the overall dimensions of the cylinder when under compression) and to subtract from this the change in volume of the liquid (this could be found in a separate experiment with only the liquid present). Unfortunately the correction term — the volume change in the liquid — has a much greater magnitude than the volume change in the solid. So we must devise a method of measuring the change in the volume of the solid directly.

The leading physicist of this century in the field of high pressure physics was P. W. Bridgman, who won a Nobel prize (in 1946) for his work. Measurements of bulk moduli were just one of his contributions. What Bridgman did was to measure the fractional change in the length of a rod of the substance under hydrostatic pressure. Assuming the substance is isotropic (has the same properties in all directions), as it is in polycrystalline samples, the fractional change in volume is three times the fractional change in length. This can easily be shown by considering a cube of side l, that is of volume $V = l^3$. So

$$dV = 3l^2\,dl$$

$$\frac{dV}{V} = \frac{dV}{l^3} = \frac{3\,dl}{l}$$

To measure the fractional change in length of the specimen Bridgman used a sliding electrical contact, so dispensing with the need to see the specimen.

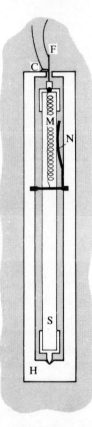

Fig. 9.2 Bridgman's apparatus for measuring the relative linear compressibility of substances available in the form of long rods.

Figure 9.2 shows the arrangement, all of which is immersed in a high pressure liquid contained in a compression cylinder—but more of this presently. The specimen S, in the form of a long rod, is kept pressed against the bottom of an iron holder H by a spring M which pulls on the top of the specimen. A high-resistance wire is attached to the upper end of the specimen and this slides over a contact C which is attached to H but insulated from it. (Spring

N keeps the resistance wire pressed against the contact.) By measuring the electrical resistance between C and a terminal F fixed to the wire one can deduce the change in the length of the specimen (this is proportional to the change in electrical resistance). As described, the experiment naturally only gives the compressibility of the specimen relative to that of the holder. One absolute measurement is therefore required. This may be found by dispensing with the iron holder H, using the compression cylinder itself as the mount. The specimen now presses directly against the end of the compression cylinder (not shown) and contact C is attached to the cylinder wall. The change in length of the mount—now the cylinder—is found by measuring, with a travelling microscope, the change in the separation of marks on the outside of the cylinder. As you can imagine, an absolute measurement is a lot more tedious to make than a relative measurement.

Bridgman's greatest contribution to experimental techniques was probably his invention of a leak-proof piston. Earlier work was hampered by the fact that the high pressure liquid tended to leak out between the piston and the cylinder to the low pressure surroundings. Figure 9.3 shows how Bridgman overcame this problem. The kernel is the mushroom-shaped plug M. The stem of the mushroom projects freely into a hollow in the end of the plunger P, made of hardened steel. Pressure is transmitted to the head of the mushroom through a soft rubber ring. At equilibrium the force acting down on the upper

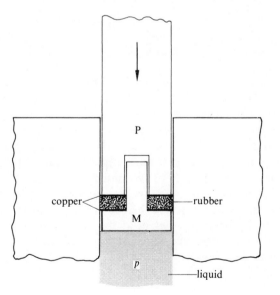

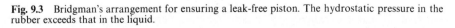

Fig. 9.3 Bridgman's arrangement for ensuring a leak-free piston. The hydrostatic pressure in the rubber exceeds that in the liquid.

face of the head (which is the pressure in the rubber multiplied by the area of the ring) must equal the force acting upon the head (the pressure in the liquid multiplied by the entire area of the head). Since the area of the rubber ring is less than that of the area in contact with the liquid it follows that the hydrostatic pressure in the rubber exceeds that in the liquid. The tendency is for the rubber to leak into the liquid and not vice versa! Copper discs prevent the rubber from leaking (Fig. 9.3).

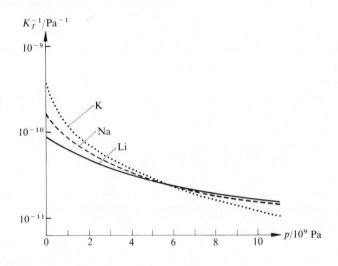

Fig. 9.4 The compressibility $(1/K_T)$ of lithium, sodium, and potassium as a function of pressure. The measurements were made at room temperature.

Figure 9.4 shows the results of one of Bridgman's studies in which he measured the compressibility $(1/K_T)$ of sodium, potassium, and lithium at pressures up to 10^{10} Pa $(10^5$ times atmospheric pressure). This decrease in compressibility with increasing pressure—or, correspondingly, an increase in the bulk modulus—is hardly unexpected when we reflect that the repulsive force between atoms increases ever more rapidly as the atoms approach each other ever more closely (Fig. 2.8b). We must now try to make explicit the connection between the bulk modulus of a solid and the interatomic force, or potential energy, characteristic of the constituent atoms. Our line of attack will be to calculate the energy fed in at the macroscopic level and then to equate this to the energy change which occurs as a result of the atoms being squeezed together more closely.

Predicting K_T

If a face of the solid has an area A then the total hydrostatic force acting on that face is pA, where p is the hydrostatic pressure in the surrounding liquid. This force is directed inwards along a normal to the face. If, on increasing the pressure slightly, the face moves in through a distance δx the energy transferred to the solid is $p(A\,\delta x)$. The same argument applies over all other faces of the solid, so the total energy δU acquired by the solid is $-p\,\delta V$. The negative sign is required to make δU positive; remember that, since the solid shrinks, δV is negative. Therefore the gain in internal energy of the solid is

$$\delta U = -p\,\delta V$$

or, in the limit,

$$p = -\frac{\mathrm{d}U}{\mathrm{d}V} \qquad (9.2)$$

Substituting eq. (9.2) into the defining relation for the bulk modulus, eq. (9.1), gives

$$K_T = V\frac{\mathrm{d}^2 U}{\mathrm{d}V^2} \qquad (9.3)$$

Actually we have cheated. Equation (9.1) is the definition of the *isothermal* bulk modulus in which thermal energy can flow between the solid and the compression liquid so as to maintain the solid at a constant temperature. Equation (9.2) on the other hand assumes that all of $-p\,\delta V$ goes into the solid—it assumes that none of it flows back out as heat. In the language of thermodynamics, eq. (9.2) assumes the compression is adiabatic while eq. (9.1) assumes it is isothermal. We will ignore the difference. (The adiabatic and the isothermal bulk moduli approach the same value as the temperature tends to absolute zero. So, strictly speaking, our arguments are only valid at such temperatures.)

Equation (9.3) involves the internal energy and the volume of the entire block of the solid. Somehow, we want to introduce the potential energy $\mathscr{V}(r)$ of a pair of atoms and their interatomic separation r. Here is how we do this. We first relate the volume V of the solid to the interatomic spacing r. If we regard the atoms as cubes of side r, and if there are N atoms present in the volume V, then

$$V = Nr^3$$

$$\frac{\mathrm{d}V}{\mathrm{d}r} = 3Nr^2 \qquad (9.4)$$

The differential in eq. (9.3) involves the volume V. To introduce r we note that

$$\frac{\mathrm{d}U}{\mathrm{d}V} = \frac{\mathrm{d}U}{\mathrm{d}r}\frac{\mathrm{d}r}{\mathrm{d}V}$$

$$\frac{\mathrm{d}^2 U}{\mathrm{d}V^2} = \frac{\mathrm{d}}{\mathrm{d}V}\left(\frac{\mathrm{d}U}{\mathrm{d}r}\frac{\mathrm{d}r}{\mathrm{d}V}\right)$$

297

$$\frac{d^2U}{dV^2} = \frac{dU}{dr}\frac{d^2r}{dV^2} + \frac{dr}{dV}\left[\frac{d}{dV}\left(\frac{dU}{dr}\right)\right]$$

$$\frac{d^2U}{dV^2} = \frac{dU}{dr}\cdot\frac{d^2r}{dV^2} + \frac{dr}{dV}\left[\frac{dr}{dV}\cdot\frac{d}{dr}\left(\frac{dU}{dr}\right)\right]$$

$$\frac{d^2U}{dV^2} = \frac{dU}{dr}\cdot\frac{d^2r}{dV^2} + \left(\frac{dr}{dV}\right)^2\cdot\frac{d^2U}{dr^2} \tag{9.5}$$

All that remains is to relate the internal energy U of our block of solid to the energy of the individual atoms. In a solid at low temperatures, $\frac{1}{2}mu^2 \ll \Delta E$; so the kinetic energy of the atoms can be ignored, leaving only the potential energy of the atoms to be considered. The potential energy will, of course, depend on how the atoms are arranged, that is, on the structure of the crystal. In both the hexagonal close-packed and the face-centred cubic structures— and over 45 per cent of the elements crystallize with one or other of these structures—each atom is surrounded by $n = 12$ nearest neighbours. We will shortly make an exact calculation of the potential energy of an fcc structure. For the time being a rough calculation will suffice.

Imagine a close-packed structure containing a vacant site which we fill by bringing an atom up from infinity. Assuming that only nearest-neighbour interactions count, the energy required to do so is $n\mathscr{V}(r)$. Here r is the nearest-neighbour separation in the solid and $\mathscr{V}(r)$ is the potential energy of an isolated pair of atoms at separation r. If a similar operation is carried out on all N atoms in the crystal (thereby forming the crystal) the energy provided is $\frac{1}{2}N(n\mathscr{V}(r))$. The, by now familiar, half takes care of the fact that in bringing an atom i up from infinity to a distance r from atom j we have brought j up to a distance r from i. By definition, the energy fed in is the change in the internal energy of the system. Therefore

$$U = \tfrac{1}{2}Nn\mathscr{V}(r) \tag{9.6}$$

$$\frac{dU}{dr} = \tfrac{1}{2}Nn\frac{d\mathscr{V}(r)}{dr} \tag{9.7}$$

$$\frac{d^2U}{dr^2} = \tfrac{1}{2}Nn\frac{d^2\mathscr{V}(r)}{dr^2} \tag{9.8}$$

Substituting eqs. (9.7) and (9.8), along with eq. (9.4), into eq. (9.5) gives

$$\frac{d^2U}{dV^2} = \tfrac{1}{2}Nn\frac{d\mathscr{V}(r)}{dr}\cdot\frac{d^2r}{dV^2} + \left(\frac{1}{3Nr^2}\right)^2\cdot\tfrac{1}{2}Nn\frac{d^2\mathscr{V}(r)}{dr^2}$$

If the deformation of the solid is small we may take $r = r_0$. (For the present it is adequate to take r_0 as the equilibrium separation of an isolated pair of atoms.) The term $(d\mathscr{V}(r)/dr)_{r=r_0} = 0$ (Fig. 2.8c), so

$$\frac{d^2 U}{dV^2} = \frac{n}{18Nr_0^4}\left(\frac{d^2 \mathscr{V}(r)}{dr^2}\right)_{r=r_0}$$

Substituting this expression, along with $V = Nr_0^3$, into eq. (9.3) gives the isothermal bulk modulus as

$$K_T = \frac{n}{18r_0}\left(\frac{d^2 \mathscr{V}(r)}{dr^2}\right)_{r=r_0} \tag{9.9}$$

Calculating K_T
Let us attempt to calculate the bulk modulus of a substance whose interatomic potential energy can be represented by the Lennard-Jones 6-12 potential (eq. (2.16))

$$\mathscr{V}(r) = 4\varepsilon\left[-\left(\frac{\sigma}{r}\right)^6 + \left(\frac{\sigma}{r}\right)^{12}\right]$$

As we saw in section 2.6, the constant σ is related to the equilibrium separation r_0 of an isolated pair by $r_0 = 2^{1/6}\sigma$, giving

$$\mathscr{V}(r) = \varepsilon\left[-2\left(\frac{r_0}{r}\right)^6 + \left(\frac{r_0}{r}\right)^{12}\right]$$

Differentiating this twice with respect to r gives

$$\frac{d^2 \mathscr{V}(r)}{dr^2} = \varepsilon\left[-\frac{2 \times 6 \times 7}{r^8}r_0^6 + \frac{12 \times 13}{r^{14}}r_0^{12}\right]$$

At $r = r_0$

$$\frac{d^2 \mathscr{V}(r)}{dr^2} = \frac{72\varepsilon}{r_0^2}$$

Equation (9.9) therefore becomes

$$K_T = \frac{4n\varepsilon}{r_0^3} = \frac{8}{N_A r_0^3}(\tfrac{1}{2}N_A n\varepsilon)$$

You will remember from section 2.6 eq. (2.23) that the constant ε in the Lennard-Jones potential is equal to the energy required to dissociate an isolated pair of atoms. Therefore $\tfrac{1}{2}N_A n\varepsilon$ is the energy required to dissociate one mole of the solid into its N_A constituent atoms an infinite distance apart. This (as near as makes no difference) is the *molar enthalpy of sublimation* $H_{m,s}$ of the solid (often called the latent heat of sublimation)—the energy required to transform one mole of the solid into a gas at the same temperature and pressure. Therefore

$$K_T = \frac{8H_{m,s}}{V_m} \tag{9.10}$$

where we have made the further substitution $V_m = N_A r_0^3$.

It is perhaps a curious result that for solids bound together by van der Waals' forces, for which the Lennard-Jones 6-12 potential applies, the isothermal bulk modulus should be eight times the molar enthalpy of sublimation per unit volume. Perhaps though, the result is not totally unexpected for both $H_{m,s}$ and K_T have to do with changing the interatomic separation of atoms in a solid.

For solid argon $H_{m,s} = 7.7 \times 10^3$ J mol^{-1} and $V_m = 2.27 \times 10^{-5}$ m^3 mol^{-1}. Substituting these values into eq. (9.10) predicts an isothermal bulk modulus of 2.7×10^9 Pa. The experimental value is 2.5×10^9 Pa. As another example, the predicted isothermal bulk modulus of solid nitrogen is 1.4×10^9 Pa; the experimental value is 1.26×10^9 Pa. Considering the many approximations which were introduced in our discussions, this level of agreement is very gratifying.

Exercise 9.1

Using a Mie potential model (eq. (2.24)) for the interaction between a sodium and a chlorine ion, predict the isothermal bulk modulus of solid sodium chloride. Assume that $U = N\mathscr{V}(r)$, where $\mathscr{V}(r)$ is the potential energy of an isolated Na$^+$–Cl$^-$ ion pair. We may picture ourselves forming the NaCl crystal by first forming N *isolated* NaCl molecules. We next put these together to form the crystal: this calls for little extra energy as one NaCl *molecule* exerts little force on another. (A single molecule has zero net charge; it is however a dipole.) Assume $r_0 = 2.8 \times 10^{-10}$ m. The experimental value of $K_T = 2.5 \times 10^{10}$ Pa.

9.2 The internal energy of a crystal

The exact calculation of the internal energy of a crystal poses few problems if the structure of the crystal and the interatomic potential energy $\mathscr{V}(r)$ are both known. As mentioned in section 9.1 we will make the calculation for a fcc structure. The inert gases are among the 20 per cent of all elements which crystallize with this structure, a portion of which is shown in Fig. 9.5. We shall assume that the crystal is at absolute zero, so we do not have to worry about the vibrational energy of the atoms (provided we believe classical physics!).

We start by considering a single atom i of the crystal. Atom i makes contact with 12 others (Fig. 9.5(a)); there are the 4 in the corner $(j, k, l,$ and $m)$,

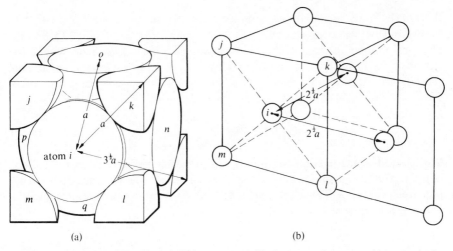

Fig. 9.5 (a) A cell of a face-centred cubic structure with the atoms drawn roughly to scale. In (b) part of a neighbouring cell is shown; here the atoms are not drawn to scale.

another 4 cube-face atoms (n, o, p, and q) and 4 more cube-face atoms out of the plane of the paper. Spheres that touch have, of course, a common distance between their centres which we shall denote by a (Fig. 9.5(a)). Adopting a Lennard-Jones 6-12 potential (eq. (2.16)) the potential energy of i due to these 12 nearest neighbours at $r = a$ is given by

$$12 \times 4\varepsilon \left[-\left(\frac{\sigma}{a}\right)^6 + \left(\frac{\sigma}{a}\right)^{12} \right] \tag{9.11}$$

In addition to these 12 nearest neighbours, atom i has 6 second-nearest neighbours at distance $2^{1/2}a$ between centres (Fig. 9.5(b)). Their contribution to the potential energy of i is

$$6 \times 4\varepsilon \left[-\frac{1}{2^3}\left(\frac{\sigma}{a}\right)^6 + \frac{1}{2^6}\left(\frac{\sigma}{a}\right)^{12} \right] \tag{9.12}$$

where we have substituted $r = 2^{1/2}a$ in the Lennard-Jones potential and multiplied the result by 6. There are 24 third-nearest neighbours at a distance $3^{1/2}a$ from i (Fig. 9.5(a)) and their contribution is

$$24 \times 4\varepsilon \left[-\frac{1}{3^3}\left(\frac{\sigma}{a}\right)^6 + \frac{1}{3^6}\left(\frac{\sigma}{a}\right)^{12} \right] \tag{9.13}$$

The procedure is to be repeated with fourth-nearest neighbours, fifth-nearest neighbours, and so on. Adding together eqs. (9.11), (9.12), (9.13), etc., gives the total potential energy of atom i as

$$4\varepsilon \left\{ -\left[12 + \frac{6}{2^3} + \frac{24}{3^3} + \cdots \right]\left(\frac{\sigma}{a}\right)^6 + \left[12 + \frac{6}{2^6} + \frac{24}{3^6} + \cdots \right]\left(\frac{\sigma}{a}\right)^{12} \right\} \tag{9.14}$$

Both of the series in square brackets converge; the first to a limit of 14·45392; the second (which is more obviously converging) to a limit of 12·13188. To obtain the molar internal energy of a substance which crystallizes with a fcc structure, eq. (9.14) must be multiplied by $\frac{1}{2}N_A$, where that very familiar half prevents us from counting the potential energy contribution of each pair twice. So

$$U_m = \tfrac{1}{2}N_A \times 4\varepsilon\left[-14\cdot45\left(\frac{\sigma}{a}\right)^6 + 12\cdot13\left(\frac{\sigma}{a}\right)^{12} \right] \qquad (9.15)$$

You should note that if 14·45 and 12·13 are each approximated by 12, eq. (9.15) is the same as eq. (9.6) with $\mathscr{V}(r)$ given by the Lennard-Jones 6-12 potential and $r = a$. This goes much of the way towards explaining the success of our calculation of K_T.

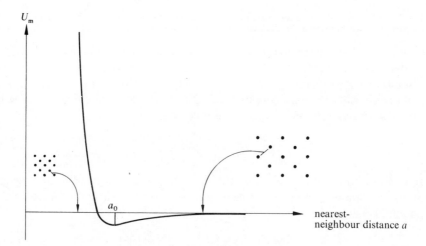

Fig. 9.6 The molar internal energy U_m of a fcc crystal as a function of the nearest-neighbour distance a.

It is worth emphasizing that eq. (9.15) gives the molar internal energy in terms of the nearest-neighbour separation a. As Fig. 9.6 emphasizes, the internal energy is large if a is large. This is because the attractive interatomic forces have yet to give up energy (stored in their fields) which can occur as the structure shrinks. Again the internal energy is large at very small values of a for this would require the structure to be compressed against (majority) repulsive forces. Only at one separation, $a = a_0$ say, is the structure in equilibrium under the combined effect of the interatomic forces arising from all N_A atoms present. At this separation $dU_m/da = 0$. Applying this condition to eq. (9.15) predicts $a_0/\sigma = 1\cdot09$, which should be the same for all inert gas crystals. Experiments give values of 1·14 for neon, 1·11 for argon, 1·10 for krypton, and 1·09 for xenon; in remarkable good agreement with the theoretical value. In conclusion, it is worth pointing out that the equilibrium separation in an *isolated pair* of atoms interacting according to the Lennard-Jones 6-12 potential, namely $1·122\sigma$ (eq. (2.19)), is not all that different from the equilibrium value in a *crystal*, $1·09\sigma$. This is comforting in view of the many times we have assumed that the equilibrium separation in an isolated pair of atoms is the same as the nearest-neighbour separation in a crystal.

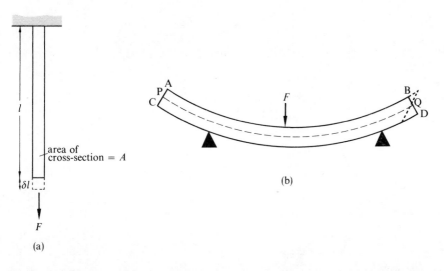

Fig. 9.7   In (a) the length of the solid is increased by an amount δl, the same all across the specimen, when a force F is applied. In (b) the top surface of length AB has contracted, and the bottom surface CD has expanded, relative to the unchanged central region PQ.

9.3   Young's modulus
Few, if indeed any, of us would claim to have sensed the bulk modulus of a solid in our everyday lives. We just do not go about subjecting solids to changing hydrostatic pressures and noting the consequences. Not so the elastic, or Young's, modulus of a solid. We have surely all applied a tension to a piece of rubber and observed that it stretches (Fig. 9.7(a)). We have walked across a wooden floor and felt the planks bend under our weight; when that happens, as Fig. 9.7(b) shows, the upper surface AB of the plank is compressed and the lower surface CD is extended, relative to the length PQ they had before we walked on the plank. Decrease the interatomic separation in a solid to below the equilibrium value and repulsive restoring forces come into play; increase the interatomic separation beyond the equilibrium value and attractive restoring forces come into play. If it were not for these forces we would fall through the floor.

Young's modulus defined

One can in fact study the elastic properties of a solid by observing how a beam bends under various loads. It is much more usual however to apply a force F along the axis of a specimen of constant cross-sectional area A and to observe the change δl in its length l. In such an experiment the solid is said to be subjected to a *tensile stress,* defined as F/A, with the result that it is *strained* by amount $\delta l/l$. You will notice that stress is measured in units of N m^{-2} (i.e., Pa) and that strain, being a ratio, is a pure number.

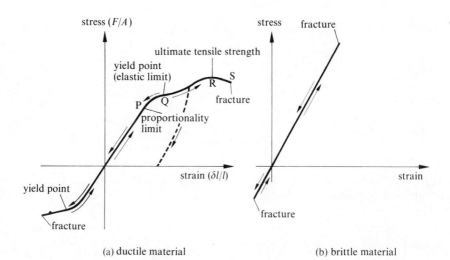

Fig. 9.8 The stress–strain curve of (a) a ductile material and (b) a brittle material. The exact form of the curves depends, of course, on the material in question. These curves are purely a qualitative indication of how these two classes of material behave.

Figure 9.8(a) shows the general form of a stress–strain curve for a poly-crystalline metal (such as steel). Up to point P, the *proportionality limit,* the strain is proportional (or very nearly proportional) to the applied stress and the strain disappears on removing the stress. This reversible behaviour continues to a point Q known as the *yield point* which represents the limit of the *elastic* behaviour of the specimen. If the stress is removed at a point beyond Q a permanent strain results; a material behaving in this way is said to be *ductile.* Notice that the word *elastic* is used to denote reversibility and does *not* necessarily imply that stress is proportional to strain. It may be—or it may not be. With a further increase in stress the material continues to flow plastically. At a point R, the maximum on the curve, a local constriction ("necking") occurs and at a point S fracture occurs. The behaviour of the solid under compression is also shown. As in tension, an initial elastic region extending to the yield point is followed by a region of flow and finally fracture.

Figure 9.8(b) shows the behaviour of a brittle material like cast iron or glass. The elastic region is abruptly terminated when the specimen suddenly snaps.

Our goal is clear enough. We must ask ourselves how a perfect crystal would behave under a tensile and compressive stress and then see how our predictions tie in with experiment. In particular, we will try to predict the slope of the stress–strain curve in the linear (proportional) region and to predict the stress at which fracture occurs. The slope of the linear portion of the curve is known as the *elastic,* or *Young's, modulus* E of the material; that is, it is defined by

$$E = \frac{\text{stress}}{\text{strain}} = \frac{F/A}{\delta l/l} \qquad (9.16)$$

Young's modulus derived

It is a fair bet that E is going to reflect the interatomic force characteristic within the solid under investigation. This hunch becomes even stronger on learning that the bulk modulus—which we know strongly reflects the interatomic force characteristic—and Young's modulus are almost equal in a wide variety of materials (for example, in steel $K_T = 1.8 \times 10^{11}$ Pa and $E = 2.0 \times 10^{11}$ Pa). For this reason we should, at least to begin with, consider a solid with a known structure and with an interatomic force characteristic which can be represented analytically. Sodium chloride is such a solid.

Figure 9.9(a) shows a section through a crystal of sodium chloride which is being subjected to a force F. If there are n rows of atoms the force acting along each now is, of course, F/n. Denoting the row spacing by r_0 (which we will assume to be constant, independent of F) and the cross-sectional area by A, we have $n = A/r_0^2$ and so the force acting along each row is Fr_0^2/A. This force is the same at all points; it does not "evaporate" on route in moving from one end of the row to the other! By way of analogy, if you pull on a (static) rope the pull a friend feels at your end is the same as at the other end. For the crystal to be at rest the support must provide an equal upward force F, that is, an upward force Fr_0^2/A along each row of atoms (Fig. 9.9(a)). We will now isolate a single pair of atoms (Fig. 9.9(b)) and ask how their separation varies with Fr_0^2/A, that is, with F. In so doing we are deliberately ignoring forces from atoms on neighbouring rows. We are also considering only nearest-neighbour forces along the row. The unstrained length of the crystal is, of course, $l = Nr_0$ where N (or rather $N + 1$) is the number of atoms along the row. If the interatomic separation changes by δr under the influence of the force Fr_0^2/A—and it *will* change until the restoring force between the atoms reaches Fr_0^2/A (Fig. 9.9(b))—the length of the crystal will increase by $\delta l = N \delta r$. Therefore

$$\text{strain} = \frac{\delta l}{l} = \frac{N \delta r}{Nr_0} = \frac{\delta r}{r_0}$$

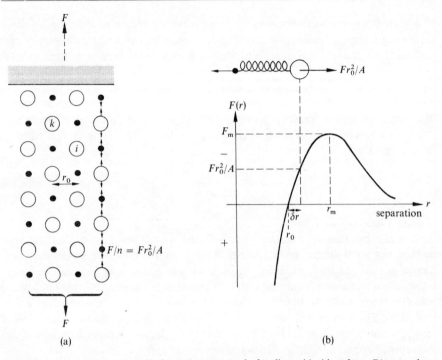

Fig. 9.9 (a) On applying a tensile force F to a crystal of sodium chloride a force F/n acts along each row of ions, where n is the number of rows of ions across the crystal. (b) At equilibrium this force will equal the restoring force between a pair of ions.

For small strains $\delta r \approx (-dr/dF(r))\,\delta F$. The minus sign is necessary since the applied force acts in the opposite direction to the interatomic force $F(r)$. Here $\delta F = Fr_0^2/A$, so

$$\text{strain} = -\frac{Fr_0}{A}\left(\frac{dr}{dF(r)}\right)_{r=r_0}$$

Substituting this expression for strain along with that for the applied stress (F/A) into eq. (9.16) gives

$$E = -\frac{1}{r_0}\left(\frac{dF(r)}{dr}\right)_{r=r_0}$$

or, since $F(r) = -d\mathscr{V}(r)/dr$

$$E = \frac{1}{r_0}\left(\frac{d^2\mathscr{V}(r)}{dr^2}\right)_{r=r_0} \tag{9.17}$$

This equation is uncannily like that for the bulk modulus (eq. (9.9)).

Adopting a Mie potential model for the interaction between a sodium and

306

a chlorine ion leads, as you will have found in Exercise 9.1, to the result $(d^2 \mathcal{V}(r)/dr^2)_{r=r_0} = 8e^2/4\pi\varepsilon_0 r_0^3$. Therefore $E = 8e^2/4\pi\varepsilon_0 r_0^4$. Since $r_0 = 2\cdot82 \times 10^{-10}$ m in sodium chloride this predicts a Young's modulus of $29\cdot2 \times 10^{10}$ Pa. The experimental value is $4\cdot0 \times 10^{10}$ Pa; a factor of seven down. Although such a level of disagreement between the predicted and the actual results could spell disaster in other fields, in certain areas of physics it is often cause for congratulations. It suggests that the theory is probably on the right lines and that we may only need to refine it a little, rather than to start afresh with a totally new model. Here the refinement is to look at the cross-links which, up to now, we have ignored. As the crystal of Fig. 9.9(a) extends the separation of an ion like i from its next nearest neighbours, such as k, will alter. The restoring force on i will therefore change as the crystal extends. Whatever justification we can invent for ignoring cross-linking in an unstrained crystal it becomes quite untenable in a strained crystal! You can often ignore a term which is constant: You can seldom ignore a term which changes. When these improvements are made the theoretical and the experimental values of E usually agree to within a factor of two. Had we chosen to draw, say, a fcc or hcp structure in Fig. 9.9(a) the need to consider cross-links would have been obvious from the start.

Exercise 9.2

In section 8.1 we showed that the circular frequency of vibration of an atom in a solid is $(2k_s/M)^{1/2}$ where k_s is the restoring force per unit displacement in an isolated pair of atoms and M is the mass of an atom. Show that $k_s = Er_0$. Calculate the Einstein frequency ω and the Einstein temperature θ_E in copper, taking $E = 13\cdot0 \times 10^{10}$ Pa and $r_0 = 2\cdot6 \times 10^{-10}$ m. $A_r(\text{Cu}) = 63\cdot5$.

9.4 The tensile strength of a solid

The theory

In view of the success we have had in predicting the values of the bulk modulus and Young's modulus we might anticipate that our estimates of the strength of a solid would be equally successful. A crystal should only break under tension when the force Fr_0^2/A along a row of atoms exceeds F_m, the maximum restoring force which can be provided by a pair of atoms (Fig. 9.9(b)). The breaking stress F/A—the force per unit area—of a crystal under tension should therefore be $-F_m/r_0^2$ (as follows on equating Fr_0^2/A and $-F_m$).

Exercise 9.3

Predict the breaking stress under tension of sodium chloride. Adopt a Mie potential model for the interaction between a sodium and a chlorine ion, taking $r_0 = 2 \cdot 8 \times 10^{-10}$ m. What is the strain at which the crystal breaks? Do tackle this exercise before reading on.

The facts!

The sort of crystal you are likely to find in a bottle in a chemistry laboratory will break at a tensile stress which is about a hundredth or thousandth of its theoretical value. The breaking strain will be correspondingly down on the value of $0 \cdot 1$ to $0 \cdot 3$ which is predicted from a Mie or Lennard-Jones potential model. Magnesium oxide, for example, fractures in brittle fashion at a strain of $0 \cdot 002$. This discrepancy between theory and experiment would seem to suggest that something is *drastically* wrong with our model; yet the level of agreement between the theoretical and the experimental values of E would argue otherwise. Figure 9.10 highlights the problem; the experimental and the theoretical slopes more or less agree, but the experimental and the theoretical breaking stress wildly disagree. This disagreement exists irrespective of whether the material is brittle or ductile. The irreversible behaviour of ductile materials provides an additional headache, but more of that later.

9.5 Whiskers

Under appropriate conditions it is possible to grow whisker-like crystals. These are long filamentary single crystals of uniform cross-section whose length to diameter ratio may be a thousand or more. Sodium chloride, for example, normally crystallizes as small imperfect cubes; the familiar table salt. Slowly cooling the solution will produce a few whiskers. Adding a few per cent of polyvinyl alcohol (a large organic molecule) prior to crystallization induces the salt to crystallize exclusively as whiskers. Lengths of a centimetre or more are easily obtained.

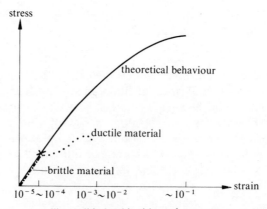

Fig. 9.10 In theory a crystalline solid should withstand a tensile strain of about 10^{-1} before fracture occurs. In practice a brittle solid will fracture at a strain of about 10^{-5} to 10^{-4}; a ductile material at a strain of about 10^{-3} to 10^{-2}.

Experimental techniques

It was found by Gordon and others in the 1950s that whiskers could be bent into very tight circles before they snapped. As Fig. 9.7(b) reminds us, this implies a large breaking strain. Although Gordon was able to measure the strain by manipulating the whiskers under the microscope with a dissecting needle he was unable to measure the stress.* This problem was overcome

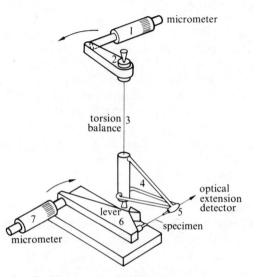

Fig. 9.11 A micro-tensile testing machine.

by Marsh who built a micro-tensile testing machine which enabled the stress–strain curve of a whisker to be measured directly. Figure 9.11 shows the basic principles of the machine. A torsion head arm 2 transmits a torque via torsion wire 3 to the support 4, so applying a tensile force to the specimen. The tensile stress depends on the setting of the head arm 2 and this is accurately controlled by means of micrometer 1. As the specimen strains the position of the specimen end-mount 5 will, of course, shift. Rather than attempt to measure the extension directly the mount 5 is restored to its original position by means of the lever 6 which is rotated by micrometer 7. An optical detector is used to ascertain that the mount is in its original position. There are several advantages in using a null method (the name arises because the loaded end of the specimen is maintained at a fixed position). Firstly, the applied stress is always strictly proportional to the torsion head setting. Secondly, large strains can be easily accommodated. Thirdly, since the optical system purely functions as a null detector no demands are placed on it behaving

* You will find a quite delightful account of this work in J. E. Gordon *The New Science of Strong Materials*, Penguin, 1968.

in a linear fashion. It is for this type of reason that null methods are popular among experimental scientists. Such is the versatility and the precision of the micro-tensile testing machine that it can apply loads of from 10^{-5} N to about 4 N to specimens having cross-sections from 10^{-13} m² to 10^{-8} m², and lengths from 5×10^{-4} m to 1×10^{-2} m. It can measure extensions of from 5×10^{-10} m to $1{\cdot}5 \times 10^{-2}$ m.

The properties of whiskers

With such a device at hand it became possible to determine the stress–strain characteristic of whiskers. Figure 9.12 shows this characteristic for a 2×10^{-6} m diameter whisker of silicon. You will notice that although the crystal is elastic, Hooke's law is not obeyed. This non-linear behaviour is to be expected when we recall that, except for small displacements from the equilibrium separation, the interatomic force characteristic is non-linear (Fig. 9.9(b)). You will also notice that fracture occurs at a strain of close to 0·03, which is gratifyingly close to the theoretical value of around 0·15. (The predicted value depends, as you know from Exercise 9.3, on the assumed form of the interatomic potential.) Further evidence that, at fracture, the interatomic separation approaches the value r_m at which the interatomic force has its maximum value F_m (Fig. 9.9(b)) comes from the observation that, when a strong whisker fractures, it frequently does so explosively, disappearing into a cloud of fine dust. As another example of their strength, a whisker of sodium chloride may withstand a tensile stress of up to one-third of the theoretical fracture stress.

Steps and cracks

The strength of most whiskers depends on their diameter, decreasing from near theoretical values at diameters of less than about 10^{-6} m to the characteristic bulk value at diameters of about 10^{-4} m. Gordon and Marsh have

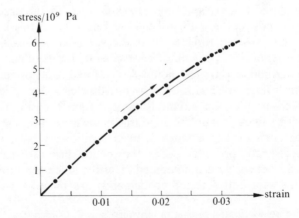

Fig. 9.12 The stress–strain characteristic of a silicon whisker. (Data: J. E. Gordon.)

explained this dependence in terms of stress concentrations which arise at steps on the surface of these near-perfect crystals. The first stage in the growth of a whisker is the formation of a fine smooth filament which then thickens as new sleeve-like layers of material spread down the filament. Different layers, each of which may be a single layer of atoms thick, will advance at different rates; the exact rate of advance of a layer depends on how fast it is fed with atoms from the surrounding liquid or vapour. Those layers which are fed faster may catch up on more slowly moving lower layers, resulting in the formation of steps on the surface of the whisker. You might think that these steps would only lead to an increase in stress by virtue of a reduction in the cross-sectional area of the whisker. However, as Fig. 9.13(a) shows, the situation in which atoms throughout region ABCD are unstrained is inadmissible since it leads to mismatch between atoms in planes BC and EF. Such a mismatch would in fact lead to interatomic forces between atoms in planes BC and EF which would attempt to align the atoms in these planes. It is clear that much of the stress which is necessary to maintain region ABCD in a strained condition must be provided by those atoms near the root B of the step. This is illustrated very schematically in Fig. 9.13(b). Only in the vicinity of A is the stress relieved, with interatomic separations close to their unstrained value. Because of the stress concentration which occurs near the root B of the step, the stress in this region will attain the value at which fracture occurs long before

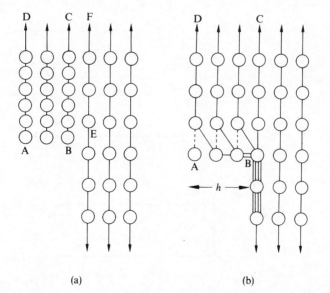

(a)   (b)

Fig. 9.13 (a) The presence of a step AB cannot lead to the complete removal of strain throughout region ABCD since this would introduce a shear strain between BC and EF (the atoms in the two planes would be out of phase). (b) In practice the stress necessary to maintain much of ABCD in a state of strain is provided by a relatively few atoms at the root B of the step.

the average stress throughout the whisker reaches this value. So steps can lead to premature failure of a whisker during a tensile test. It is also plausible that the greater the step height h (Fig. 9.13(b)) the greater will be the stress concentration at the tip; as h increases the stress in more and more rows of atoms in region ABCD must be fed through a few atoms in the root. Marsh found that, in the case of silicon whiskers, the step height h was a constant fraction (1/40) of the whisker diameter. Using these ideas he was able to account for the observation that the thicker the whisker the lower its strength.

Surface steps and cracks—a crack is also effective in concentrating stress— are not unique to whiskers. Most brittle fracture, as for example happens when a glass is dropped on the floor, can be traced to the spreading of such cracks. On a larger scale, many a ship has broken in two because the designer was unaware of the stress concentrating nature of such small apertures as hatchways.

9.6 The shear modulus

The definition

We have looked at the consequences of subjecting a solid to a uniform hydro-static stress and to an axial tension. The other distinctive way to deform a solid is to shear it by subjecting it to a force F which acts parallel to a face

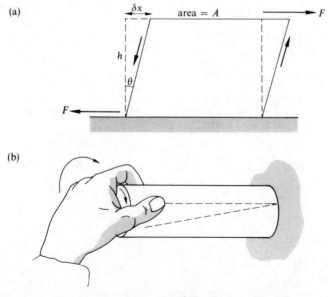

Fig. 9.14 (a) On applying a shear stress F/A the solid is strained by an amount $\delta x/h$. (b) In twisting a wire one attempts to slide a plane of atoms over an adjacent plane.

(Fig. 9.14(a)). If the solid is not to move the mount must exert a force equal and opposite to F. However if these were the only two forces acting on the solid it would rotate. To prevent this an equal and opposite couple must be applied. The shear stress is defined as F/A, where A is the area of the face parallel to which F acts. The shear strain is defined as $\delta x/h$ (Fig. 9.14(a)); for small deformations this is approximately equal to the angle θ. The ratio of stress to strain, so defined, is called the *shear modulus G*;

$$G = \frac{\text{stress}}{\text{strain}} = \frac{F/A}{\delta x/h} \tag{9.18}$$

Usually the shear modulus of a solid is a factor of two or three smaller than the bulk or Young's modulus (which, you will recall, are almost equal in magnitude).

The shear modulus is directly relevant whenever one attempts to twist a piece of wire about its axis (Fig. 9.14(b)). In such a "torsion wire" one is attempting to slide one plane of atoms over an adjacent plane.

Shear stresses can arise in rather unexpected ways. If we subject a solid to a tensile stress we necessarily alter the separation between cross-linked atoms (such as i and k in Fig. 9.9(a)). This, of course, introduces new stresses. At the macroscopic level we may resolve a tensile force F into a normal and a tangential component as shown in Fig. 9.15. We see that the slice, which has a cross-sectional area of $A/\sin\phi$, where A is the cross-sectional area of the

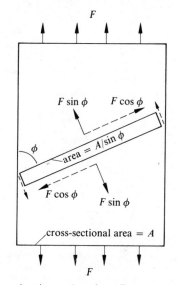

Fig. 9.15 A tensile force F resolves into a shear force $F\cos\phi$ acting parallel to the surface of the slice and into a normal tensile force $F\sin\phi$.

solid, is subject to shearing force of $F \cos \phi$. The slice is therefore subject to a shear stress of magnitude

$$\text{shear stress} = \frac{F \cos \phi}{A/\sin \phi} = \frac{F}{A} \cos \phi \sin \phi = \frac{F}{2A} \sin 2\phi \qquad (9.19)$$

which has a maximum when $\phi = 45°$. In fact whiskers of isotropic substances like glass do tend to fail along planes at $45°$ to the tensile stress. More generally, we can expect a single crystal subjected to an increasing axial tensile stress to fail along whichever plane the resolved shear stress first reaches the critical shear stress appropriate to that plane—provided the crystal does not first fail by cleaving along a plane perpendicular to the axial tensile stress, as discussed in section 9.4. Most large metal whiskers fail in shear; whiskers of normally brittle materials (such as silicon) undergo tensile failure.

Calculating the critical shear stress

In shearing a crystal we move, or rather we attempt to move, two planes of atoms past one another. If we assume that the planes remain individually undistorted the discussion becomes essentially that of how an atom (i in Fig. 9.16(a)) moves from one equilibrium position A to an adjacent equilibrium position B. Clearly the net restoring force F in the shear plane is zero at A and B since these are equilibrium positions. It is also clear, by symmetry,

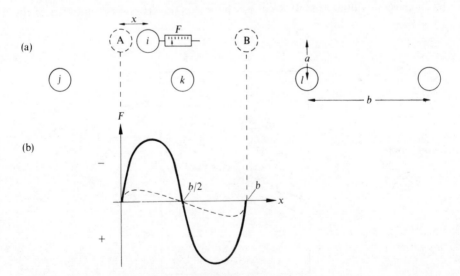

Fig. 9.16 (a) In shearing a solid we must displace a plane of atoms (of which only one atom i is shown) by an amount x relative to the underlying plane of atoms (j, h, l, etc.). (b) A thought experiment in which we displace atom i from one equilibrium site A to an adjacent equilibrium site B, recording the restoring force on i as we shift it. The full curve is a sinusoidal approximation. The dotted curve is a more realistic approximation.

that F will be zero at the midpoint between A and B. (At this point the component of the force which j exerts on i in the shear plane will be equal and opposite to that of l on i.) Symmetry also demands that whatever be the form of F from $x = 0$ to $x = b/2$ the form from $x = b/2$ to $x = b$ will be equal in magnitude but opposite in direction. Here b is the interatomic separation in the shear direction. So the restoring force must be a periodic function of x with period b. It is, of course, quite possible to deduce the function when the interatomic force characteristic is known. However, following Frenkel, we shall assume it to be sinusoidal (Fig. 9.16(b)), this being the simplest function with the desired properties:

$$F \propto - \sin\left(\frac{2\pi x}{b}\right)$$

The negative sign expresses the fact that F is directed to the left from $x = 0$ to $x = b/2$. The shearing force necessary to maintain equilibrium will be equal and opposite to this, so (since the shear plane containing atom i is supposed to have a constant area, A)

$$\text{shear stress} = \frac{-F}{A} = C \sin\left(\frac{2\pi x}{b}\right) \tag{9.20}$$

where C is a constant. The value of C may be determined by using eq. (9.20) to predict the value of stress/strain at low strains (which can then be set equal to the experimental value of G). Of course, once we inject the experimentally determined value of G into the proceedings we cannot then turn round and use the theory to predict G! All we can hope to predict is the shear strength of a solid. For small strains, $\sin(2\pi x/b) \approx 2\pi x/b$, so eq. (9.20) becomes

$$\text{shear stress} = \frac{C2\pi x}{b}$$

But the shear strain is x/a, where a is the separation of adjacent planes (Fig. 9.16). Therefore

$$\frac{\text{shear stress}}{\text{shear strain}} = \frac{C2\pi a}{b}$$

Equating this ratio to G gives $C = Gb/2\pi a$. The critical shear stress at which the structure becomes mechanically unstable with one plane of atoms slipping over its adjacent plane is given by the maximum value of eq. (9.20), which is C. So

$$\text{critical shear stress} = \frac{Gb}{2\pi a}$$

Since $a \approx b$ in most crystals, a crystal should fracture when the shear stress reaches $G/2\pi$ where G is the shear modulus measured at small stresses. Since shear strain = shear stress/G we may equally well conclude that a solid should fracture when the shear strain reaches $(G/2\pi)/G = 1/2\pi = 0.16$. This is several orders of magnitude greater than the strain at which most ordinary materials fail.

Could the discrepancy between theory and experiment simply be due to our assuming a sinusoidal force characteristic? If we know the form of the interatomic potential it should surely be possible to obtain a more reliable estimate of the shear strain. It is; a Lennard-Jones 6-12 potential, for example, predicts a critical shear strain of 0.03, which implies that the interatomic shear stress curve should be drawn as suggested by the dashed line in Fig. 9.16. Although a step in the right direction—the sinusoidal curve predicted a critical shear strain of 0.16—it is still orders of magnitude greater than the actual critical shear strain of most solids. Only certain whiskers live fully up to expectations.

Slip

We have seen (Fig. 9.8(a)) that a ductile material subjected to a tensile stress undergoes an irreversible increase in length before it fractures. We have also seen that an axial tensile stress—such as is applied in Fig. 9.8(a)—has a shear component (Fig. 9.15). These two observations are closely related.

When a ductile material (such as a large single crystal of cadmium) is subjected to a tensile stress that exceeds the elastic limit it is observed that the material divides itself up into bands which have slipped with respect to one another (Fig. 9.17). The slip (or glide) surface is often a densely packed crystal plane; this is hardly surprising since the denser the packing the further apart will adjacent planes be. Face-centred cubic metals, for example, slip on $\{1\,1\,1\}$ planes. Sodium chloride slips on $\{1\,1\,0\}$ planes. When all planes are equally densely packed, as they are in isotropic materials, slip occurs in a plane at an angle of 45° to the tensile stress.

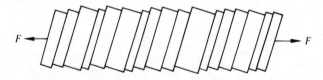

Fig. 9.17 On stretching a single crystal rod of a ductile material it divides itself up into bands which have slipped with respect to one another.

In view of the argument summarized in Fig. 9.15, slip *per se* is not unexpected. What is unexpected is that (whiskers apart) it occurs at strains many times lower than the predicted value. More worrying, perhaps, when slip does occur the cadmium crystal flows plastically; it does not suddenly fracture—

as it should on our model—where the restoring force is the same for all atoms in the slip plane (see Fig. 9.16). Continued slip, which leads eventually to failure of the solid, requires the continued application of a force (Fig. 9.8(a)).

We could explain the discrepancy between the theoretical and the experimental shear strength of a solid if we could find a mechanism which raised the local stress in the crystal to the yield value. It is worth considering thermal fluctuations. Only on average is $\frac{1}{2}m\overline{u^2} = \frac{3}{2}kT$. At some one point in the crystal the value of $\frac{1}{2}m\overline{u^2}$ might momentarily be sufficient to rearrange the atoms so that, with help from the externally applied stress, the local shear stress exceeds the yield value. If E is the energy required to create the necessary atomic rearrangement then the probability of this happening (cf. eq. (8.65)) is $\exp(-E/kT)$. Putting numbers to E gives such a low probability that the mechanism must be ruled out. It is also ruled out since the strength of a crystal does not decrease exponentially with the inverse of the temperature as this mechanism would predict. The critical shear strength of cadmium for example only decreases by a factor of two on raising the temperature from 70 K to 300 K.

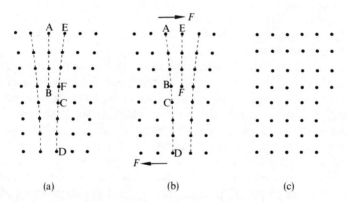

(a)   (b)   (c)

Fig. 9.18   The edge dislocation. (a) AB shows an end-on view of an extra half plane of atoms. (b) On applying a shearing force F the continuous plane ABCD forms and EF becomes the extra half plane. (c) By such means the half plane is displaced to the surface.

Dislocations

We are forced to conclude that sources of mechanical weakness must exist in a crystal which allows slip to occur at very low applied stresses. The simplest such weakness is the *edge dislocation*. This arises from the presence of an extra half-plane of atoms; AB in Fig. 9.18(a). It takes only a small stress to cause AB to line up with CD, making EF the extra half plane (Fig. 9.18(b)). This process continues until the extra half plane arrives at the surface of the

317

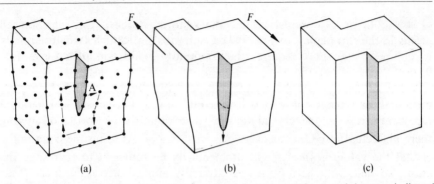

Fig. 9.19 A screw dislocation. (a) Starting from atom A and travelling around the route indicated by arrows we arrive at the next plane into the crystal. (b) Under stress the dislocation moves as shown, until (c) a step extends the full length of the surface.

crystal (Fig. 9.18(c))—slip has occurred. The motion is akin to the motion of a ruck or wrinkle across a carpet; it takes a lower force to move a ruck than it does the entire carpet.

Another important type of dislocation is the *screw dislocation*. This is illustrated in Fig. 9.19(a). What were once parallel planes of atoms have become distorted in "spiral staircase" fashion. If we start at an atom A and move around from atom to atom as shown by the arrowed path we end up in the plane beneath. Under stress the axis of the dislocation moves as shown in Fig. 9.19(b) producing a step which extends the length of the surface (Fig. 9.19(c))—slip has occurred.

For a solid to be strong there must either be no dislocations present or, if present, they must not move freely. The first of these criteria is satisfied by whiskers. (Actually many whiskers contain a single screw dislocation up their centre but this has no tendency to move under an axial tension.) In other solids such as diamond, tungsten carbide, and aluminium carbide, the dislocations cannot be moved at stresses much below the theoretical shear strength. Materials in which dislocations behave in this manner are called *inherently strong solids*. When prepared with smooth crack free surfaces they show great strength even in large pieces. In most metals the dislocations move at stresses well below the theoretical shear strengths. These materials may be strengthened by cold-drawing them through a die. This procedure introduces so many dislocations that they become entangled and unable to move! Another way to pin dislocations is to introduce impurity atoms. An impurity atom at point B in Fig. 9.18(a) will pin the edge dislocation. Carbon in steel is an example of an impurity which impedes the movement of dislocations.

Summary

1. For solids in which the Lennard-Jones 6-12 interatomic potential model applies the predicted isothermal bulk modulus is eight times the latent

heat of sublimation per unit volume; in good agreement with experiment. This prediction assumes that the internal energy U of the solid is $\frac{1}{2}Nn\mathscr{V}(r)$ where N is the number of atoms present, n is the number of nearest neighbours surrounding an atom, and $\mathscr{V}(r)$ is the interatomic potential energy. A more exact calculation, which considers all the atoms surrounding a given atom, does not materially alter the numerical value of U.

2. Although the experimental value of Young's modulus of a solid is often in satisfactory agreement with the value predicted from the interatomic potential function, the measured fracture stress of a solid is usually several orders of magnitude below the predicted value. The theoretical strength is usually only realized with smooth-surfaced whiskers. Any surface cracks or steps act as stress concentrators, thereby reducing the fracture strength.

3. Adopting a sinusoidal model for the shear stress acting between two planes of atoms predicts that a solid will fail in shear when the applied stress reaches $G/2\pi$, where G is the shear modulus measured at small stresses. If the interatomic potential is introduced explicitly this value is reduced by about an order of magnitude. Only in dislocation-free crystals, or in specimens in which the dislocations cannot move freely, is the theoretical shear strength realized.

PROBLEMS

9.1 What is the isothermal compressibility of a perfect gas?

9.2 Show that the potential energy of an ion in an infinite one-dimensional sodium chloride crystal whose ions interact according to a hard-sphere coulombic model is

$$\mathscr{V}(r) = -\frac{\alpha e^2}{4\pi\varepsilon_0 r}$$

where $\alpha = 2\ln 2$ and r is the interionic spacing. What is the internal energy for a mole of such a hypothetical crystal?

$$\left(\ln(1+x) = x - \frac{x^2}{2} + \frac{x^3}{3} - \frac{x^4}{4} + \cdots\right)$$

9.3 Repeat exercise 2 but for a real sodium chloride structure and deduce the corresponding value of α. (Again take r to be the spacing of an ion from its nearest neighbour of opposite sign charge.)

9.4 Show that in a monatomic hcp structure there are, about any one atom, 12 nearest neighbours (at separation a say), 6 second-nearest neighbours at separation $2^{1/2}a$, and 2 third-nearest neighbours at separation $(8/3)^{1/2}a$.

9.5 Starting with eq. (9.15), show that the equilibrium separation of nearest neighbours in a fcc structure whose atoms interact according to a Lennard-Jones 6-12 potential is $1\cdot09\sigma$.

9.6 What is the shear modulus of a gas? Explain.

9.7 A rectangular slab of material is maintained in equilibrium by a pair of equal and opposite stresses τ_1 acting along the top and bottom surfaces respectively and by another equal and opposite pair of stresses τ_2 acting on both end faces. What is the relation between τ_1 and τ_2?

319

9.8 Show that the energy stored per unit volume in a solid is $\frac{1}{2}$(stress) × (strain) if the stress–strain characteristic is linear.

9.9 It is an experimental fact that Young's modulus of a single crystal falls with increasing temperature. Show that this observation is compatible with the model proposed in section 8.8 for thermal expansion.

9.10 Figure 9.20 show the equilibrium positions of atom i relative to two other atoms j and k; we may take it that r_0 is the equilibrium separation of an isolated pair of atoms. Considering only the interaction of atoms i and j and assuming a Lennard-Jones potential model (eq. (2.15)) show, that the separation r_m at which the restoring force is a maximum is given by $r_m = r_0[(q + 1)/(p + 1)]^{1/(q-p)}$. What is r_m/r_0 assuming a Lennard-Jones 6-12 potential? Since $r_m \approx r_0$, the shear strain when the restoring force is a maximum is approximately $(r \sin \theta - r_0 \sin \theta)/r_0 \cos \theta$. So what is the theoretical critical shear strain on the basis of this simple two-atom model?

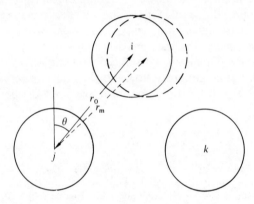

Fig. 9.20 A simple two-atom model of shear.

10. Transport Processes in Solids

As in a gas, diffusion in a solid proceeds by the transport of mass, thermal conduction by the transport of energy and electrical conduction by the transport of charge. But there the similarity ends. For one thing, a gas atom spends most of its time travelling freely through distances which are large compared with an atomic diameter; an atom in a solid is, for the most part, confined by the attractive forces exerted by its neighbours. For another, the transport properties of a (low pressure) gas are virtually the same for all substances; the transport properties of a solid can vary drastically from substance to substance. As an example, the electrical conductivity of copper at room temperature is some 10^{22} times greater than that of sulphur. We shall not attempt to explain why these differences arise—to do so would require a firm grounding in quantum mechanics—but we shall look at a few salient characteristics of transport processes in solids which can be treated classically or with a minimum of quantum mechanics.

10.1 Diffusion

Unlike diffusion in liquids or gases, diffusion in solids is not part of our every-day experience. The layer of silver found on plated steel cutlery seems to remain stable. The chromium layer on a car bumper does not disappear by diffusing into the underlying steel. At room temperature the interdiffusion of the surface and the interior atoms is indeed too slow to produce any notice-able effects. At high temperatures, 1300 K for example, the silver and chro-mium would disappear into the steel in a matter of weeks. Another example of a layered structure is the integrated circuit. In manufacturing these devices a silicon chip is held at a temperature close to its melting point and various impurities are allowed to diffuse into the chip over a period of minutes. Once the device is cooled to room temperature it is essentially stable for all time.

Possible mechanisms
Early theories of diffusion supposed it to proceed by adjacent atoms inter-changing places as, for example, in Fig. 10.1(a). To allow such an interchange to occur the surrounding atoms must be pushed far apart. In a closely packed solid this calls for so much energy as to render the process highly unlikely. A much more plausible explanation is that diffusion in closely packed structures

proceeds by atoms hopping into adjacent vacant lattice sites (Fig. 10.1(b)); indeed it is generally accepted that this is the mechanism operative in fcc metals, in the solidified inert gases (fcc) and in ionic solids such as sodium chloride. The other main mechanism for diffusion arises from the hopping of interstitials (Fig. 10.1(c)); the carbon and hydrogen atoms present in steel are thought to diffuse by this means.

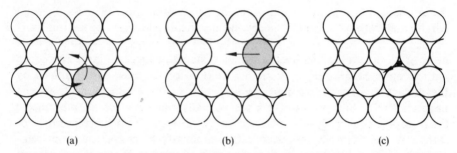

| (a) | (b) | (c) |

Fig. 10.1 Three possible mechanisms for diffusion in a solid. In (a) two atoms interchange places by rotating about a midway point, forcing neighbouring atoms apart. In (b) diffusion proceeds by atoms hopping into adjacent vacant lattice sites. In (c) interstitial atoms hop to adjacent vacant sites.

An experimental study

For simplicity we will only look at the diffusion of a monatomic solid into its radioactive equal (possessing atoms of approximately the same mass and of identical size and charge). In one particular experiment of this type the diffusion of the radioactive isotope ^{64}Cu through ^{63}Cu was established by depositing electrolytically a layer of ^{64}Cu onto a face of a single crystal of ^{63}Cu. To find out how far the ^{64}Cu had diffused into the crystal, the sample was placed in a precision grinding machine and successive layers were ground off the surface. By counting the radioactivity present in each sample—the count rate is proportional to the number of ^{64}Cu atoms present in that sample—the diffusion coefficient D was evaluated. (We shall presently see how D is related to the mean diffusion distance.) To find out how the coefficient varied with temperature it was, of course, necessary to repeat the entire operation at a variety of different temperatures. Figure 10.2 shows the results of such a study. You should contrast this rapid temperature dependence of D—the graph implies that D varies exponentially with T^{-1}—with the weak $T^{3/2}$ dependence found in a gas at constant pressure (eq. (5.21)). Some quite different mechanism is evidently at work in a solid.

Calculating D

Figure 10.3(a) shows the problem facing an atom i as it attempts to diffuse through a closely packed structure. To hop into site j two criteria must be

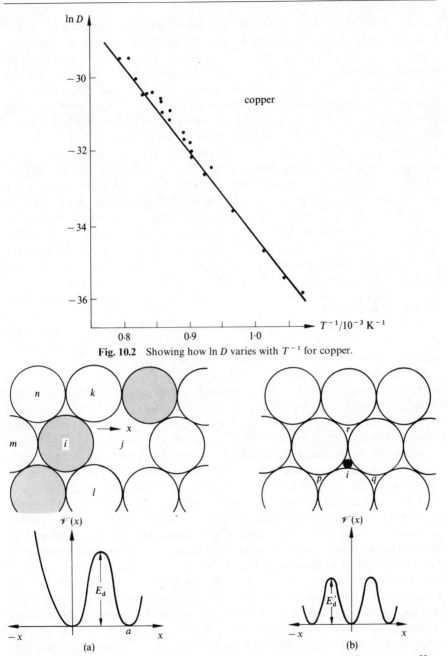

Fig. 10.2 Showing how ln D varies with T^{-1} for copper.

Fig. 10.3 (a) For atom i to hop to the vacant site j it must have an energy E_d or greater. Here $\mathscr{V}(x)$ is the potential energy of i as it is displaced from its lattice site. (b) For an interstitial i to hop to an adjacent site like p it must have an energy E'_d or greater. (Strictly speaking the $+x$-direction is along line iq and the $-x$-direction along ip.)

323

satisfied. First, site j must be vacant. The probability that j is vacant—which is equal to the fraction of vacancies present in the crystal—is given by eq. (8.65), namely $\exp(-E_v/kT)$, where E_v is the energy required to create the vacancy. The second requirement is that i should have the necessary energy to move to site j.

To escape to site j atom i must squeeze atoms k and l apart against their mutual attractive force. It must also escape the backward pull of atoms like m and n. We may represent the net energy required to displace atom i from its lattice site by a potential energy curve as shown in Fig. 10.3(a). You will notice that escape to the left is ruled out; to place i on top of atom m requires an infinite energy (Fig. 2.8 should remind you of this). In this figure the zero of potential energy $\mathscr{V}(x)$ is taken to be at the undisplaced site of atom i. In calculating the probability that atom i has the energy E_d or greater which is necessary for escape we shall adopt the same model of a solid as that adopted by Einstein in discussing the heat capacity of a solid (section 8.2). We shall therefore picture atom i vibrating back and forth along the x-axis with a constant vibrational frequency—in the manner of a Planck oscillator. (Since we are only considering diffusion in the x-direction we may ignore vibrations in the y and z Cartesian directions.) Following through exactly similar arguments as those on p. 285 which lead to eq. (8.65) I conclude that a fraction $\exp(-E_d/kT)$ of the atoms of a solid will have an energy $E_x \geq E_d$. We may take it that this fraction is equal to the probability that an *individual* atom will have a vibrational energy $E_x \geq E_d$.

Taking both requirements for diffusion into account we see that the probability that an atom has an adjacent vacant site *and* that it has the necessary energy to hop into this site is given by $\exp(-E_v/kT) \times \exp(-E_d/kT)$, i.e., $\exp[-(E_v + E_d)/kT]$. Our next task is to calculate the speed at which an atom hops through the crystal.

According to the Einstein model, we may picture atom i vibrating back and forth along the x-axis with a constant vibrational frequency $\omega_E/2\pi$ where ω_E is the circular Einstein frequency. Although the energy of i will alter as it exchanges energy with other atoms of the solid, its *vibrational frequency* $\omega_E/2\pi$ remains constant. So the number of *attempts* which i makes at escape per unit time as it vibrates back and forth will be constant and indeed simply equal to the number of occasions it reaches (say) the right-hand extremity of its vibration (Fig. 10.3(a)) in unit time. This is, of course, the vibrational frequency $\omega_E/2\pi$. For an escape *attempt* to be successful we have seen that an adjacent site must be vacant and that the vibrating atom has the necessary escape energy. Since the probability of both these events occurring simultaneously is $\exp[-(E_v + E_d)/kT]$, it follows that the average number of escape hops per unit time is $(\omega_E/2\pi)\,e^{-(E_v+E_d)/kT}$. Now each hop is of length a, the interatomic spacing, so the (average) hopping speed v_d of i is given by

$$v_d = \frac{a\omega_E}{2\pi}\,e^{-(E_v+E_d)/kT} \tag{10.1}$$

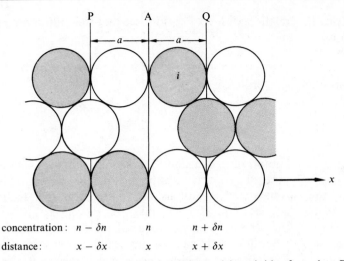

concentration: $n - \delta n$ n $n + \delta n$

distance: $x - \delta x$ x $x + \delta x$

Fig. 10.4 Atoms crossing plane A in a single hop will have originated either from plane P or plane Q, each a distance a away from plane A. The number density n refers to that of the radioactive (shaded) species.

The final task is to calculate the net number of labelled atoms (such as the shaded atoms in Fig. 10.3(a)) which pass through unit area per unit time. To do this we consider a plane A of unit area (Fig. 10.4). Atoms passing through this plane will have hopped there either from a plane P or a plane Q, each a distance a away. If the number density of labelled atoms at $x + \delta x$ is, say, $n + \delta n$ then the actual number of these which cross plane A in unit time is $(n + \delta n)v_d/6$; the factor of 1/6 is included to take account of the fact that an atom also vibrates in the $\pm y$- and $\pm z$-directions. It may therefore hop in any of these directions rather than in the $-x$-direction. (Only one hop in six will be in the direction which interests us.) The number of labelled atoms which cross plane A per unit time moving to the right is likewise $(n - \delta n)v_d/6$ where $n - \delta n$ is the number density of these atoms at $x - \delta x$ (Fig. 10.4). The net number crossing unit area per unit time, the flux j, is therefore

$$j = -\left[\tfrac{1}{6}(n + \delta n)v_d - \tfrac{1}{6}(n - \delta n)v_d\right]$$

where we have inserted a minus sign to denote the fact that the radioactive species diffuse to the left (see section 5.4). So

$$j = -\tfrac{1}{3}v_d\,\delta n$$

Multiplying the right-hand side by a/a, and remembering that the concentration gradient is $\delta n/\delta x = \delta n/a$, gives

$$j = -\tfrac{1}{3}v_d a \frac{\delta n}{\delta x}$$

325

Comparing this relation with eq. (5.17) we see that the diffusion coefficient D is given by

$$D = \tfrac{1}{3}v_d a \qquad (10.2)$$

or, substituting for v_d from eq. (10.1), by

$$D = \frac{a^2 \omega_E}{6\pi} e^{-(E_v + E_d)/kT} \qquad (10.3)$$

In other words a graph of $\ln D$ against $1/T$ should be linear with a gradient $-(E_v + E_d)/k$. Figure 10.2 confirms this prediction. However, if diffusion proceeds by the movement of interstitials, as illustrated in Fig. 10.3(c), a very similar analysis applies. Essentially, E_v disappears from eq. (10.3) and E_d is replaced by E_d', the activation energy required for the interstitial to hop to an adjacent site. Because both mechanisms lead to the same temperature dependence of D it is not possible to decide which mechanism is involved on the basis of this dependence alone. Indeed a graph of $\ln D$ plotted against $1/T$ is linear for most solids. Other evidence is required, such as that provided by a study of how the volume of a solid changes with temperature (section 8.7).

Exercise 10.1

Using the data given in Fig. 10.2 compute the number of successful hops per second made by an atom in copper at 1300 K (the melting temperature is 1358 K) and at 300 K. Assume that the Einstein temperature θ_E (defined as the temperature at which $\hbar\omega_E = k\theta_E$) is 240 K. This temperature can, of course, be estimated from heat capacity measurements (section 8.2).

It is important to realize that any *particular* atom, such as i in Fig. 10.4, is just as likely to hop in the $+x$-direction as in the $-x$-direction. Diffusion occurs because of the concentration gradient; because there are more radioactive atoms at Q than at P there are more radioactive atoms to hop to the left through plane A than there are to hop to the right through this plane.

The random walk

You might conclude that because an atom is just as likely to hop in one direction as another it cannot stray far from home. A simple game shows this conclusion to be wrong. Figure 10.5 represents a two-dimensional square lattice. To decide whether atom i is going to jump left, right, up or down from its present site we may spin a four-sided top whose edges are labelled L, R, U, and D. (You can easily construct one out of a match and a piece of card.) After every hop the top is spun afresh. The path marked out in Fig. 10.5 was obtained by playing the game.

326

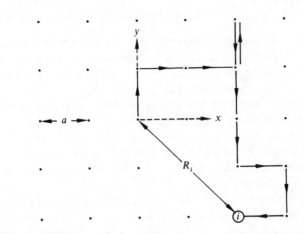

Fig. 10.5 Illustrating the random-walk nature of diffusion in a two-dimensional structure. Each dot represents a lattice site. Whether atom i hops left, right, up or down by one lattice spacing a is decided by a random process.

If we denote the individual displacements of i as it hops by $x_1, x_2, x_3, \ldots, x_p$ and $y_1, y_2, y_3, \ldots, y_q$ we see from Fig. 10.5 that the overall distance R_i gone in this so-called *random walk* is given by

$$R_i^2 = (x_1 + x_2 + x_3 + \cdots + x_p)^2 + (y_1 + y_2 + y_3 + \cdots + y_q)^2$$

$$R_i^2 = (x_1^2 + x_2^2 + x_3^2 + \cdots + x_p^2) + (y_1^2 + y_2^2 + y_3^2 + \cdots + y_q^2)$$

$$+ 2x_1 x_2 + \cdots + 2y_1 y_2 + \cdots \qquad (10.4)$$

A similar expression can be written down for any other atom, say j, as it too executes a random walk of $n = p + q$ steps. Our interest is the mean square distance $\overline{R^2}$ gone by the average atom as it takes a random walk of n steps. If there are N atoms on the lattice we have

$$\overline{R^2} = \frac{\sum\limits_{i=1}^{N} R_i^2}{N} \qquad (10.5)$$

where R_i^2, etc., are given by expressions like eq. (10.4). Now each of $x_1, x_2, \ldots, y_1, y_2, \ldots$ are of magnitude a, the lattice spacing, so that $x_1^2 = x_2^2 \cdots = y_1^2 = y_2^2 = \cdots = a^2$. Averaged over the motion of all N atoms, terms like $2x_1 x_2$ will all equal zero because each of x_1, x_2, etc., has an equal chance of being $+a$ or $-a$. So eq. (10.5) becomes

$$\overline{R^2} = \frac{\sum\limits_{1}^{N} [(pa^2) + (qa^2)]}{N} + 0 = \frac{\sum\limits_{1}^{N} [(p + q)a^2]}{N} = \frac{N(na^2)}{N} \qquad (10.6)$$

327

$$(\overline{R^2})^{1/2} = an^{1/2} \tag{10.7}$$

—the root mean square distance travelled by an atom making a random walk of n steps, each of length a, in a two-dimensional structure. It is left as an exercise for you to show that a similar result holds in a three-dimensional structure, on the assumption that an atom gets places by "tossing a dice" a total of n times—with each toss telling the atom whether to go "left", or "right", or "up", or "down", or "in", or "out" through a distance a.

We can now return to our original problem of the chromium coating on the steel bumper. If the chromium is to diffuse on average 1 mm $[\approx (\overline{R^2})^{1/2}]$ into the steel (in which $a \approx 2 \cdot 5 \times 10^{-10}$ m) each atom will according to eq. (10.7) need to make about $n = 10^{-6}$ m$^2/6 \cdot 25 \times 10^{-20}$ m$^2 = 1 \cdot 6 \times 10^{13}$ jumps. Except at temperatures very close to the melting point, the number of successful hops per second is well below unity (Exercise 10.1) so we need never worry about chromium disappearing by diffusion into the steel. To treat the problem a bit more formally, the time t it takes to make n jumps is

$$t = \frac{n}{\text{number of jumps per unit time}} = \frac{n}{(\omega_E/2\pi)\exp\left[-(E_v + E_d)/kT\right]}$$

Substituting for $(\omega_E/2\pi)\exp\left[-(E_v + E_d)/kT\right]$ from eq. (10.3) and for n from eq. (10.7) gives

$$(\overline{R^2})^{1/2} = (3Dt)^{1/2} \tag{10.8}$$

In many situations we are only interested in the net diffusion in one particular direction—such as into the bumper. Since, by symmetry, $\overline{X^2} = \overline{Y^2} = \overline{Z^2}$, so that $\overline{R^2} = \overline{X^2} + \overline{Y^2} + \overline{Z^2} = 3\overline{X^2}$, the r.m.s. displacement in the x-direction is given by

$$(\overline{X^2})^{1/2} = \left(\frac{\overline{R^2}}{3}\right)^{1/2}$$

or, substituting from eq. (10.8),

$$(\overline{X^2})^{1/2} = (Dt)^{1/2} \tag{10.9}$$

So by studying the variation of $(\overline{X^2})^{1/2}$ with $t^{1/2}$ the diffusion coefficient can be found. This is one of the techniques employed in analysing the results from radioisotope diffusion studies, such as the diffusion of ^{64}Cu through ^{63}Cu.

10.2 Creep

In describing how a material responds to an applied stress (chapter 9) we made no mention of any time dependence of the resulting strain. In fact, when a material other than a perfect whisker is stressed the strain does not remain

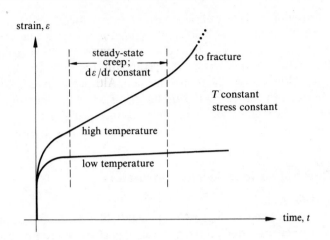

Fig. 10.6 When a material is subjected to a constant stress the strain does not remain constant, although at low temperatures the creep rate $d\varepsilon/dt$ is often negligible. At high temperatures the steady-state region (where $d\varepsilon/dt$ is constant) may eventually give way to a region in which the creep rate accelerates, leading to fracture.

constant but increases with time—the material *creeps*. A familiar example of creep is lead on an old church roof; over the centuries it flows down under the stress provided by gravity. This creep is akin to viscous flow in a fluid where a steady stress produces a continuous flow. Figure 10.6 shows the nature of creep. When a constant stress is applied a near instantaneous strain ε results. At low temperatures—below about one-third of the melting temperature—the rate of creep $d\varepsilon/dt$ soon decreases to a nearly constant low value. In the region in which $d\varepsilon/dt$ is constant the creep is called steady-state creep. Increasing the temperature T increases the steady-state creep rate; if the stress is constant it is often found that

$$\frac{d\varepsilon}{dt} = \text{constant } e^{-E/kT} \tag{10.10}$$

where E is a constant.

We will learn in chapter 12 that the rate at which a liquid flows under a constant (shear) stress also increases with temperature in the fashion of eq. (10.10). In both cases a thermally-activated process is involved.

At low temperatures creep occurs mainly by the movement of dislocations. As a dislocation moves it will encounter obstacles such as impurity atoms or other dislocations with which it may become "entangled". At least some of these obstacles may be overcome with the aid of thermal fluctuations. Indeed the mechanism is reminiscent of that which leads to diffusion (Fig. 10.3). If a dislocation requires an energy E to hop past the obstacle the probability that it has at least this energy is, as we have seen, $\exp(-E/kT)$. The hopping

329

rate and so the creep rate will, at constant stress, therefore be proportional to $\exp(-E/kT)$. Since several different activation energies may be involved, each with its own value of E, the value of E determined experimentally via eq. (10.10) will be some weighted average attributable to these different mechanisms. Although we have only considered creep at one fixed stress the creep rate can be increased by raising the stress while maintaining a constant temperature. As we shall see in chapter 12, increasing the stress effectively lowers the activation energy and therefore increases the creep rate.

10.3 Thermal conduction in non-metals

Some surprising facts

Our everyday experiences suggest that metals like silver and copper, which are the best electrical conductors, are very good conductors of heat. If you have ever stirred a cup of tea, or eaten an ice cream, with a *solid* silver spoon you will know how rapidly heat is conducted to or from your hand. Such experiences are of course acquired within a rather narrow range of temperatures—probably from about 250 K to 500 K—and what holds true within this range may be quite untrue outside it.

At room temperatures most metallic substances are indeed better conductors of heat than most non-metallic substances. However the thermal conductivity of very perfect crystals can rise to extremely high values as the temperature

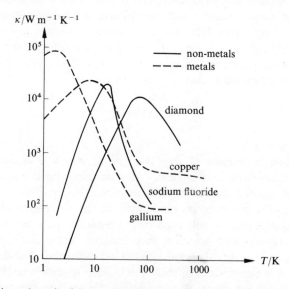

Fig. 10.7 The thermal conductivity κ of metallic and non-metallic substances as a function of temperature. The copper data is for a pure annealed crystal.

is decreased and can easily exceed that of copper. Figure 10.7 shows some examples of how the thermal conductivity of different substances varies with temperature. We see that even at room temperature diamond of gem quality has a higher conductivity than copper. Despite a superficial resemblance in the temperature dependence of the thermal conductivity of metallic and non-metallic substances there is a fundamental difference in the mechanism whereby heat is transported in these two classes of substances. In metals heat is conducted by electrons; in non-metals it is conducted through coupled vibrations of the atoms.

Phonons

If we raise the temperature at one end of a solid bar we will, of course, raise the vibrational energy of the atoms in this region. As a consequence of the coupling which exists between the atoms in a solid the neighbouring atoms will soon be set oscillating more violently; a disturbance travelling with the speed of sound moves outward from the heated region. When this disturbance reaches the cooled end of the bar this extra energy is removed (in practice one end of the bar is often surrounded by a coil of cooling water). Now if this picture of thermal energy entering the specimen at the hot end (temperature T_1) and proceeding *unhindered* to the cold end (temperature T_2) were the whole story, the heat flux Φ would be independent of the length l of the specimen, and so would not be proportional to the temperature gradient $(T_1 - T_2)/l$. It is; eq. (5.44) also applies to a solid. So we must discover a mechanism whereby the disturbance can have its energy scattered as it travels along the specimen. We saw how interatomic collisions could achieve this in a gas; we will, presently look for a similar mechanism in a solid. First though, a reminder of what happens to a solid as thermal energy is fed in.

In chapter 8 we saw that because of the interatomic coupling present in a solid many different vibrational patterns—modes—can be set up. At any given temperature the seemingly chaotic thermal motion of an atom is the resultant of the motions it makes in sustaining all possible modes in the crystal. A mode, you will recall, is characterized by its $q(= 2\pi/\lambda)$ value; in a one-dimensional structure by q; in a three-dimensional structure by q_x, q_y, q_z. We saw that each mode—in which all the atoms participate—has a mean energy $\overline{E}_q$ of

$$\overline{E}_q = \frac{\hbar\omega_q}{e^{\hbar\omega_q/kT} - 1} \tag{10.11}$$

where ω_q is the circular frequency of the mode of circular wavenumber q (eq. (8.38)). You will also recall that the relation between ω_q and q—the so-called dispersion relation—involves the interatomic force constants and the atomic masses. In a one-dimensional structure the relation is eq. (8.31), portrayed graphically in Fig. 8.14.

331

Another way of looking at eq. (10.11) follows when we rewrite it as

$$\bar{E}_q = n_q \hbar \omega_q \tag{10.12}$$

where

$$n_q = \frac{1}{e^{\hbar\omega_q/kT} - 1} \tag{10.13}$$

We see that, so far as the energy of this one particular mode of circular frequency ω_q is concerned, it is equivalent to the energy of $n_q = [\exp(\hbar\omega_q/kT) - 1]^{-1}$ "particles" each of which has an energy $\hbar\omega_q$. In fact we say that the mode of circular frequency ω_q has n_q phonons (each of energy $\hbar\omega_q$) associated with it at temperature T. (Since the left-hand side of eq. (10.12) denotes the average energy we should really say that n_q represents the average number of phonons. For brevity we shall often omit the word average.) The number n_q is also referred to as the *phonon occupancy* of the mode of circular frequency ω_q (at temperature T). Figure 10.8(a) shows the situation graphically. Here each mode is designated by a triplet of values q_x, q_y, and q_z. (We assume that the crystal is a cube of side L and that the crystal lattice is simple cubic of lattice constant a.) The average number of phonons to be

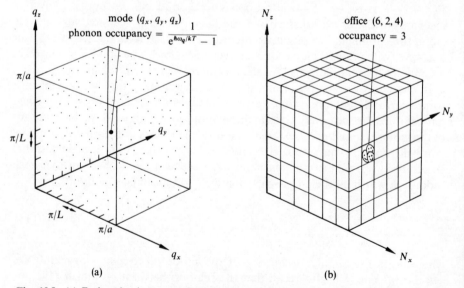

(a)   (b)

Fig. 10.8 (a) Each point in q-space corresponds to a mode and each mode has a circular frequency ω_q, determined by the dispersion relation. The phonon occupancy of each mode is determined by eq. (10.13). (b) An analogous problem. Each room of the office block has a certain occupancy.

associated with each mode—each dot in Fig. 10.8(a)—is given by eq. (10.13). Straightaway we see what looks like a problem in specifying the phonon occupancies; we know the q_x, q_y, and q_z of each dot—but our expression for the phonon occupancy (eq. (10.13)) unfortunately does not seem to be interested in (q_x, q_y, q_z). It is only concerned with ω_q. False alarm! Someone, somewhere, knows the dispersion relation—the relation between ω_q and (q_x, q_y, q_z). We tell him our (q_x, q_y, q_z) and he tells us what ω_q is. We can now calculate the phonon occupancy of each mode via eq. (10.13).

Here is a roughly analogous situation. A developer puts up an office block, Fig. 10.8(b), in which all the rooms are of the same size. The location of each office is specified by the floor level and by two corridor numbers—let us say an office is specified by N_x, N_y, N_z; for example, (6, 2, 4). The entire block is rented by a single organization. It falls to Smith to work out how many people are to occupy each office. His organization lays down a formula which relates the occupancy of an office to its rental. Unfortunately Smith only knows where each office is located (the values of N_x, N_y, N_z); he has no idea of the rental. However Jones knows how the rental is related to the office location. So Smith learns the rental of each office. The rest is plain sailing: he only has to plug the rental of an office into the company's formula to discover how many workers are to occupy that office. Between Smith and Jones—and it does take them both—the problem is solved. At least it is solved for the present. No doubt in a years time the company formula will change and all the calculations will have to be done again. In the same way, if the temperature T of a solid changes, the phonon occupancy of a mode will change (eq. (10.13)) and all the phonon occupancies will have to be recalculated.

The total phonon population
Just as Smith would find the total number of persons in the building by adding together the number of persons occupying each office so we find the total number N_P of phonons in our solid by adding together the phonon occupancy of each mode:

$$N_P = \sum_q n_q = \sum_q \frac{1}{e^{\hbar\omega_q/kT} - 1} \tag{10.14}$$

where the summation is from $q_x = \pi/L$ to $q_x = \pi/a$, from $q_y = \pi/L$ to $q_y = \pi/a$, and from $q_z = \pi/L$ to π/a (Fig. 10.8(a)). As we have seen, this expression by itself is useless without the dispersion equation relating ω_q to q_x, q_y and q_z. Now the dispersion relation is very difficult to derive for anything other than a one-dimensional monatomic crystal: you remember how we were forced to abandon an exact calculation of the heat capacity of a solid just because we did not know this relation. But wait—Debye came to the rescue with a couple of very welcome approximations. He replaced the lattice of points in q_x–q_y–q_z space bounded by planes at $q_x = \pi/a$, $q_y = \pi/a$, and $q_z = \pi/a$ by the same lattice of points but now bounded by an octant of radius q_D occupying the same volume in q_x-q_y-q_z space (Fig. 8.20). He also replaced the actual dispersion curve by the relation $\omega = qv$ where v is the velocity of sound in the solid (Fig. 8.21). Figure 10.9 shows these approximations applied in the present context.

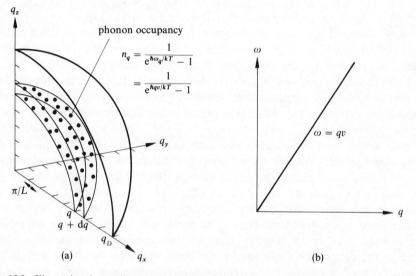

Fig. 10.9 Illustrating the application of Debye's approximations in calculating the total phonon population. (a) How one evaluates the number of modes within the octant of radius q_D. (b) Debye's dispersion relation.

To find the total phonon population we begin by finding the number of phonons associated with modes represented by those points lying within the octant of radii q and $q + dq$. The number of such points—each of which occupies a volume of $(\pi/L)^3$ in q_x-q_y-q_z space—is $\frac{1}{8}(4\pi q^2 dq)/(\pi/L)^3$. Since each point— each mode—has $[\exp(\hbar qv/kT) - 1]^{-1}$ phonons associated with it (eq. (10.13) with $\omega = qv$) it follows that the total phonon population is given by

$$N_P = \frac{1}{8}\left(\frac{L}{\pi}\right)^3 \int_0^{q_D} \frac{4\pi q^2 \, dq}{e^{\hbar qv/kT} - 1} \tag{10.15}$$

Writing

$$x = \frac{\hbar qv}{kT} \tag{10.16}$$

so that the upper limit of integration is

$$x_D = \frac{\hbar q_D v}{kT} = \frac{\hbar \omega_D}{kT} = \frac{\theta_D}{T} \tag{10.17}$$

where $\theta_D = \hbar\omega_D/k$ is the Debye temperature, eq. (10.15) becomes

$$N_P = \frac{4\pi}{8}\left(\frac{L}{\pi}\right)^3\left(\frac{T}{\theta_D}\right)^3 q_D^3 \int_0^{\theta_D/T} \frac{x^2}{e^x - 1}\,dx$$

Substituting for q_D from eq. (8.44) and multiplying the result by three to allow for the fact that there are three types of modes—two transverse and one longitudinal—gives

$$N_P = \frac{9L^3}{a^3}\left(\frac{T}{\theta_D}\right)^3 \int_0^{\theta_D/T} \frac{x^2}{e^x - 1}\,dx \qquad (10.18)$$

At high temperatures $x(= \hbar\omega/kT = \hbar qv/kT)$ and the upper limit of integration are both small, so eq. (10.18) approximates to

$$N_P = \frac{9L^3}{a^3}\left(\frac{T}{\theta_D}\right)^3 \int_0^{\theta_D/T} \frac{x^2}{1 + x - 1}\,dx$$

$$= \frac{9L^3}{a^3}\left(\frac{T}{\theta_D}\right)^3 \frac{1}{2}\left(\frac{\theta_D}{T}\right)^2$$

$$N_P = \left(\frac{9L^3}{2a^3\theta_D}\right)T$$

or, since L^3 is the total volume of the crystal, the number of phonons per unit volume is $n = N_P/L^3$, giving

$$n = \left(\frac{9}{2a^3\theta_D}\right)T$$

As a and θ_D are constant,

$$n \propto T \qquad \text{at } T > \theta_D \qquad (10.19)$$

At low temperatures the upper limit of integration in eq. (10.18) may be taken as infinity for all practical purposes. Under these conditions the integral tends to a constant value $(2\cdot77\ldots)$ giving

$$n \propto T^3 \qquad \text{at } T < \theta_D \qquad (10.20)$$

The mean phonon energy

By definition, the mean energy $\bar{E}$ of a phonon is given by

$$\bar{E} = \frac{\sum_q n_q \times (\text{energy of phonon})}{\sum_q n_q}$$

Since (see p. 332) the energy of a phonon of circular frequency ω_q is $\hbar\omega_q$,

$$\bar{E} = \frac{\sum_q n_q \hbar\omega_q}{\sum_q n_q} \tag{10.21}$$

where n_q is given by eq. (10.13).

Introducing both of Debye's approximations—his octant and his dispersion relation—transforms eq. (10.21) to

$$\bar{E} = \frac{\int_0^{q_D} (e^{\hbar qv/kT} - 1)^{-1} 4\pi q^2 (\hbar qv)\,dq}{\int_0^{q_D} (e^{\hbar qv/kT} - 1)^{-1} 4\pi q^2\,dq}$$

or, writing $x = \hbar qv/kT$, to

$$\bar{E} = kT \frac{\int_0^{\theta_D/T} (e^x - 1)^{-1} x^3\,dx}{\int_0^{\theta_D/T} (e^x - 1)^{-1} x^2\,dx} \tag{10.22}$$

At high temperatures x and θ_D/T are both small, so eq. (10.22) approximates to

$$\bar{E} = kT \frac{\int_0^{\theta_D/T} x^2\,dx}{\int_0^{\theta_D/T} x\,dx}$$

$$= \frac{2}{3} kT \left(\frac{\theta_D}{T} \right)$$

$$\bar{E} = \tfrac{2}{3} k\theta_D \qquad \text{at } T > \theta_D \tag{10.23}$$

At low temperatures the upper limit of integration in both the numerator and the denominator of eq. (10.22) may be taken as infinity. Under these conditions the numerator tends to $6\cdot49\dots$, the denominator* to $2\cdot77\dots$ giving

$$\bar{E} = 2\cdot34\,kT \qquad \text{at } T < \theta_D \qquad (10.24)$$

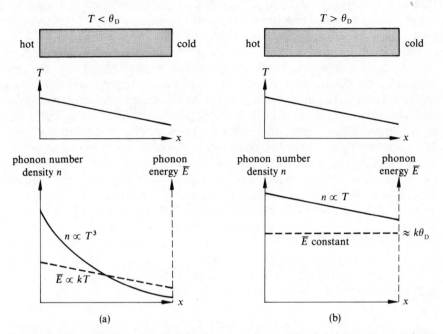

Fig. 10.10 Shows how the number of phonons per unit volume and their mean energy change as one moves along a bar, down which a constant temperature gradient exists. In (a) the (mean) temperature of the bar is well below the Debye temperature. In (b) the (mean) temperature is well above the Debye temperature.

The mechanism of thermal conduction

We may now return to our solid bar, one end of which is heated, the other cooled. Instead of merely being able to assert that the atoms at the hot end are vibrating more rapidly than those at the cold end we can now state that the number of phonons and their mean energy is different at each end of the bar.

---

*It is not hard to show that this is a plausible value. Ignoring the one in $(e^x - 1)^{-1}$—which we can more or less do at low temperatures when $x(= \hbar q v / kT) \gg 1$—the integral in the denominator becomes

$$\int_0^\infty x^2\,e^{-x}\,dx = -[x^2\,e^{-x}]_0^\infty + \int_0^\infty 2x\,e^{-x}\,dx$$

$$= 0 - 2[x\,e^{-x}]_0^\infty + 2\int_0^\infty e^{-x}\,dx$$

$$= 2$$

You can likewise show that when $x \gg 1$ the integral in the numerator of eq. (10.22) has an approximate value of 6. This leads to the result $\bar{E} \approx 3kT$.

337

Figure 10.10 summarizes the situation when the mean temperature of the bar is (a) well below θ_D and (b) well above θ_D. The top graphs show how the temperature changes as one moves along the bar; it is an experimental fact that the temperature gradient dT/dx is constant. The lower graphs show schematically how the number density and the mean energy of the phonons change as a consequence; see eqs. (10.20), (10.24), (10.19), and (10.23).

There is an obvious analogy to be drawn between the phonons in the solid and the atoms in a gas. The analogy cannot be pressed too far. For one reason, in a solid the total number of phonons is a function of temperature (eq. (10.18)), whereas in a gas the total number of atoms is constant. Nevertheless it does suggest that we may be able to apply gas-kinetic arguments to our phonon gas. Figure 10.11 shows a plane A of unit area in the solid. Phonons passing through this plane will have come either from plane P or plane Q, each a distance λ away, equal to the phonon mean free path. The total number of phonons which pass through A moving to the right per unit time is $(n + \delta n)v/6$, where $(n + \delta n)$ is the number density of phonons at P and v is their speed (which, following Debye, we take as constant and equal to the speed of sound). Since each phonon has a mean energy $\bar{E} + \delta\bar{E}$ at P it follows that their contribution to the heat current is $(n + \delta n)(\bar{E} + \delta\bar{E})v/6$. Likewise phonons leaving Q will contribute an amount $(n - \delta n)(\bar{E} - \delta\bar{E})v/6$ to the heat current and this will be directed to the left through A. The net heat current Φ flowing to the right through A is therefore

$$\Phi = \frac{v}{6}\left[(n + \delta n)(\bar{E} + \delta\bar{E}) - (n - \delta n)(\bar{E} - \delta\bar{E})\right] \qquad (10.25)$$

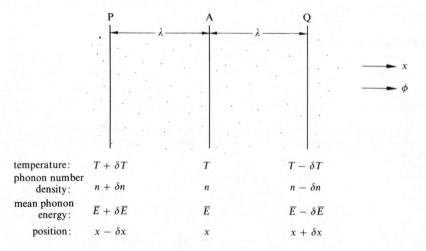

	P	A	Q
temperature:	$T + \delta T$	T	$T - \delta T$
phonon number density:	$n + \delta n$	n	$n - \delta n$
mean phonon energy:	$\bar{E} + \delta\bar{E}$	$\bar{E}$	$\bar{E} - \delta\bar{E}$
position:	$x - \delta x$	x	$x + \delta x$

Fig. 10.11 Phonons flowing to the right through A will have originated at P; those flowing to the left through A will have originated at Q.

Ignoring the second-order term $2\delta n \, \delta \bar{E}$ this becomes

$$\Phi = \frac{v}{3}(\bar{E}\,\delta n + n\,\delta\bar{E}) \qquad (10.26)$$

$$\Phi = \frac{v}{3}\delta(n\bar{E})$$

Multiplying the right-hand side by $\delta x/\delta x$, where $\delta x = \lambda$ is the distance within which the phonon density changes by δn and the mean phonon energy changes by $\delta\bar{E}$ (Fig. 10.11), gives

$$\Phi = \frac{v\lambda}{3}\frac{\mathrm{d}}{\mathrm{d}x}(n\bar{E})$$

$$\Phi = \frac{v\lambda}{3}\frac{\mathrm{d}}{\mathrm{d}T}(n\bar{E})\frac{\mathrm{d}T}{\mathrm{d}x}$$

If a heat current flowing to the right in Fig. 10.11 is to have a positive value we must insert a minus sign since the temperature gradient $\mathrm{d}T/\mathrm{d}x$ has a negative value:

$$\Phi = -\left[\frac{v\lambda}{3}\frac{\mathrm{d}}{\mathrm{d}T}(n\bar{E})\right]\frac{\mathrm{d}T}{\mathrm{d}x}$$

Comparing this with the definition of thermal conductivity κ (eq. (5.44) with $A = 1$) shows that

$$\kappa = \frac{v\lambda}{3}\frac{\mathrm{d}}{\mathrm{d}T}(n\bar{E}) \qquad (10.27)$$

Since v is (essentially) independent of temperature—Debye's dispersion relation $v = \omega/q$ assumes to be so—the reason for the temperature dependence of the thermal conductivity of non-metals, which is so evident in Fig. 10.7, must be sought in λ, n, and $\bar{E}$.

Phonon scattering at high temperature
We start by examining the high temperature region. Here (see eqs. (10.19) and (10.23)) the number density of phonons $n \propto T$ and the mean phonon energy $\bar{E}$ is constant. According to gas kinetic theory (eq. (5.4))

$$\lambda = \frac{1}{\pi d^2 n} \qquad (10.28)$$

and so, since $n \propto T$, we would expect $\lambda \propto 1/T$. Making these substitutions into eq. (10.27) gives

$$\kappa \propto \frac{1}{T} \frac{dT}{dT}$$

$$\kappa \propto \frac{1}{T} \text{ at } T > \theta_D \tag{10.29}$$

This behaviour is indeed observed in solids. A convenient way to test it is to plot $\log \kappa$ against $\log T$. Figure 10.12 shows how, for solid argon, krypton, and neon, such plots are linear at high temperature with gradients, as predicted by eq. (10.29), of -1. Further examples are provided by the plots for sodium fluoride and diamond (see Fig. 10.7).

Because we have been able to account for the high temperature behaviour of κ by assuming, in gas-kinetic fashion, that the mean free path is inversely proportional to the number density of phonons present this does not *prove* that phonons collide with one another as do gas atoms. It is salutary to return to our earlier language of a lattice disturbance travelling from the hot to the cold end of a bar to see what extent we can avoid using language that originated in gas-kinetic theory. It may help to picture this disturbance as a compressional pulse travelling down a long stretched spring. If such a pulse

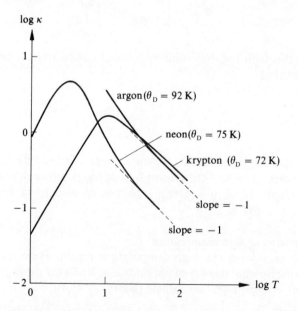

Fig. 10.12 The temperature dependence of the thermal conductivity κ of solidified neon, argon, and krypton. The thermal conductivity measurements were in units of W m^{-1} K^{-1} and T was measured in K.

meets another pulse travelling in the opposite direction both pulses will emerge unscathed and continue as before. They will only interact with one another—be scattered—if the spring's restoring force is not proportional to its extension, that is, if the force–extension characteristic is non-linear. It follows that if a solid were accurately to obey Hooke's law the phonons could not interact with one another. In fact we know from the observation that all solids expand on heating that the interatomic force characteristic is never truly linear (section 8.8). So we do have a mechanism whereby phonon–phonon scattering can occur.

If the phonon–phonon interaction was of a "hit or miss" nature, as between two billiard balls, the mean free path would be inversely proportional solely to the number density of the phonons (eq. (10.28) with d constant). However the evidence shows that as T is reduced to just below the region in which $\kappa \propto T^{-1}$ then κ rises more rapidly than T^{-1} (see Fig. 10.12). We met a somewhat similar problem in discussing thermal conduction in a gas, where we found a more rapid variation of κ with T than simple theory predicted (section 5.6). These we were able to ascribe the discrepancy to a temperature dependent collision cross-section (πd^2). We may likewise ascribe the too-rapid temperature dependence of κ to a collision cross-section which is temperature sensitive; it follows from eqs. (10.27) and (10.28) that the phonon–phonon collision cross-section ("πd^2") must decrease as T is reduced. (The actual mechanism whereby this occurs is extremely complex. Only certain types of interaction give rise to thermal resistance.)

Phonon scattering at low temperature

We see from Fig. 10.12 that as the temperature is further reduced below θ_D the conductivity passes through a maximum and decreases towards zero. The reason is not hard to find. As we have just seen, the mean free path increases with decreasing temperature; eventually it must become comparable to the specimen diameter D. When this happens eq. (10.27) tells us

$$\kappa = \frac{vD}{3}\frac{\mathrm{d}}{\mathrm{d}T}(n\bar{E}) \tag{10.30}$$

leaving n and $\bar{E}$ responsible for the temperature dependence of κ. You will remember that at high temperatures $n\bar{E}$ is proportional to T, making $\mathrm{d}(n\bar{E})/\mathrm{d}T$ independent of T. At low temperatures ($T < \theta_D$) we have from eq. (10.20) and (10.24) that $n \propto T^3$ and $\bar{E} \propto T$, giving

$$\kappa \propto D\frac{\mathrm{d}}{\mathrm{d}T}(T^4)$$

$$\kappa \propto DT^3 \qquad \text{at } T < \theta_D \tag{10.31}$$

Figure 10.13 shows the results of a detailed study aimed at testing this relation

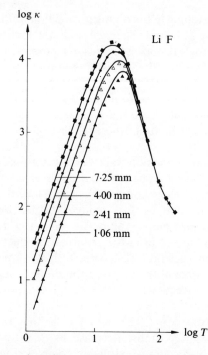

Fig. 10.13 The temperature dependence of the thermal conductivity κ of (isotopically pure) LiF crystals in the form of rods of square cross-sections. The numbers refer to the rod widths. All the specimens were sandblasted. The thermal conductivity measurements were in units of W m^{-1} K^{-1} and T was measured in K. (Data from P. D. Thacher, *Phys. Rev.*, **156**, 975 (1967).)

in LiF. Each of the specimens was in the form of rods of square cross-section. You can verify for yourself that at any fixed temperature below 10 K, $\kappa \propto D$. You can also verify that $\kappa \propto T^3$ for each and every specimen. All these specimens had their surfaces roughened by sandblasting. Figure 10.14 shows that the thermal conductivity of a specimen—this time a sapphire crystal—is greater when the specimen has a smooth finish. This is hardly surprising for we might well expect some of the phonons to be scattered from the smooth surface with no loss of energy. In other words, their mean free path exceeds D and so κ is increased. All this is very reminiscent of what happens at a solid interface during gaseous thermal conduction, and the problem may be analysed in much the same way. The calculations show that at 2 K roughly 30% of the phonons are scattered off the smooth sapphire surface with no loss of energy. At 5 K the fraction falls to about 20%. Once again we see how a technique developed to deal with a particular problem in one field can be taken over and used in quite a different field of study.

Exercise 10.2
Another way of expressing eq. (10.27) follows on noting that since n is

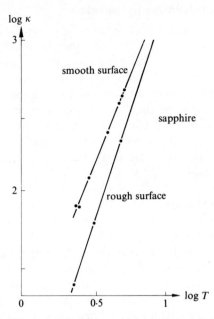

Fig. 10.14 Shows how the thermal conductivity κ of a sapphire crystal depends on the surface finish. The thermal conductivity measurements were in units of W m^{-1} K^{-1} and T was measured in K. (Data from R. Berman, E. L. Foster, and J. M. Ziman, *Proc. Roy. Soc.*, **A231**, 130 (1955).)

the number of phonons per unit volume of the crystal and since $\bar{E}$ is their mean energy, the product $n\bar{E}$ is the internal energy U *per unit volume* of the crystal. Therefore

$$\kappa = \frac{v\lambda}{3}\frac{\mathrm{d}U}{\mathrm{d}T}$$

$$\kappa = \tfrac{1}{3}v\lambda C \tag{10.32}$$

where C is the heat capacity *per unit volume* of the crystal. What was the approximate diameter of the diamond specimen employed in the experiments whose results are shown in Fig. 10.7? You will recall that at $T < \theta_{\mathrm{D}}$ the heat capacity of a non-metal closely approximates to (eq. (8.52))

$$C_{V,\mathrm{m}} = \frac{12\pi^4 R}{5}\left(\frac{T}{\theta_{\mathrm{D}}}\right)^3$$

The Debye temperature of diamond is about 2000 K and its density is 3.5×10^3 kg m^{-3}. Take the velocity of sound to be 5×10^3 m s^{-1} in diamond.

343

10.4 Thermal conduction in metals

The thermal conductivity of a pure metal at first increases as the temperature is reduced, then passes through a maximum and decreases (Fig. 10.7). Any resemblance to the behaviour of non-metals is, however, entirely coincidental. Heat is conducted solely by phonons in a non-metal and (almost) exclusively by electrons in a metal. (The phonon contribution to the thermal conductivity of a pure metal is usually so small that it can safely be ignored.) Moreover, the detailed shapes of the κ–T curves are quite different in the two cases. In a metal $\kappa \propto T$ at temperatures well below the maximum, while above the maximum $\kappa \propto T^{-2}$. In a non-metal we have seen that the corresponding relations are $\kappa \propto T^3$ and $\kappa \propto T^{-1}$.

The mechanism of conduction

Just as we took over some of the techniques of gas-kinetic theory and applied them to the phonon gas in a non-metal so we shall attempt to apply these same techniques to a free electron gas in a metal. You will recall from section 8.6 that the only electrons which are free to have their energy increased, and therefore to participate in thermal conduction, are those within an energy range kT at the Fermi energy E_F (Fig. 8.31). We saw that the number density n of such electrons if proportional to T (eq. (8.60)). Each of these electrons have a speed close to the Fermi speed u_F defined by

$$\tfrac{1}{2}mu_F^2 = E_F$$

$$u_F = (2E_F/m)^{1/2} \qquad (10.33)$$

We further saw that the mean thermal energy $\bar{E}$ of those electrons which are excited is $\tfrac{3}{2}kT$. Figure 10.15 summarizes how n and $\bar{E}$ will vary along a metal bar down which a constant temperature gradient exists. Because of the formal similarities between Fig. 10.15 and Fig. 10.10(a)—namely that n and $\bar{E}$ both vary along the bar—we can take over results derived for a phonon gas and apply them to a free-electron gas. (If you are unhappy about doing so you should derive the relations afresh for the electron gas, starting with Fig. 10.11 and eq. (10.25).) In particular let us take over eq. (10.27):

$$\kappa = \frac{u\lambda}{3} \frac{\mathrm{d}}{\mathrm{d}T}(n\bar{E})$$

For an electron gas (see Fig. 10.15) $n \propto T$ and $\bar{E} = \tfrac{3}{2}kT$. Also $u = u_F$, which is constant, independent of T (eq. (10.33)). Therefore

$$\kappa \propto \lambda \frac{\mathrm{d}}{\mathrm{d}T}(T^2)$$

$$\kappa \propto \lambda T \qquad (10.34)$$

We can obtain a more explicit expression on noting (see exercise 10.2) that

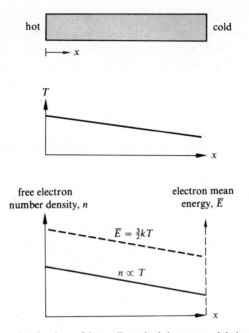

Fig. 10.15 How the number density n of thermally excited electrons and their mean energy $\overline{E}$ change as one moves along a metal bar down which a constant temperature gradient exists (shown in the top plot).

$n\overline{E}$ is the internal energy per unit volume of the electron gas. So $\mathrm{d}(n\overline{E})/\mathrm{d}T$ is the *electronic* heat capacity C_e per unit volume. That is,

$$\kappa = \tfrac{1}{3}u_F \lambda C_e \tag{10.35}$$

All that remains is to determine the mean free path of an electron. In general we can expect that the free path of an electron will be terminated when it collides with either an impurity atom present in the otherwise pure metal or with a phonon. This poses the problem of how to take two such independent scattering processes into account.

In discussing the behaviour of atoms in a gas (section 5.2) we expressed the probability that a gas atom will suffer a collision with another gas atom in travelling a distance $\mathrm{d}l$ as $\alpha\,\mathrm{d}l$. We then showed that $\alpha = 1/\lambda_g$ where λ_g is the mean free path arising from such collisions. In other words, the probability of a gas atom colliding with a like atom in travelling a distance $\mathrm{d}l$ is $\mathrm{d}l/\lambda_g$. If we now suppose that there are impurity atoms—that is atoms of a different atomic species—present, the probability that a gas atom will collide with one such impurity atom in travelling a distance $\mathrm{d}l$ is $\mathrm{d}l/\lambda_i$ where λ_i is the mean value of the free paths which are terminated by collisions with impurity atoms. Overall, the probability that a gas atom collides with *either* a like atom *or* with an impurity atom in travelling a distance $\mathrm{d}l$ is $(\mathrm{d}l/\lambda_g + \mathrm{d}l/\lambda_i) = (1/\lambda_g + 1/\lambda_i)\,\mathrm{d}l = \gamma\,\mathrm{d}l$,

345

say. (You can see why the probabilities add by considering a die. The probability that *either* a 2 *or* a 5 is thrown is $1/3 = 1/6 + 1/6$.) To evaluate the mean free path λ with both these scattering processes present we follow exactly the same procedure as that adopted in section 5.2 except that γ replaces α. This gives $\lambda = 1/\gamma$, that is

$$\frac{1}{\lambda} = \frac{1}{\lambda_g} + \frac{1}{\lambda_i}$$

In the present context we may therefore write the electronic mean free path λ as

$$\frac{1}{\lambda} = \frac{1}{\lambda_T} + \frac{1}{\lambda_i} \tag{10.36}$$

where λ_T is the mean free path of the electron due to phonon scattering and λ_i is the mean free path due to impurity scattering. Multiplying eq. (10.36) through by $3/C_e u_F$ gives the following expression for the overall thermal conductivity κ

$$\frac{1}{\kappa} = \frac{1}{\kappa_T} + \frac{1}{\kappa_i} \tag{10.37}$$

where

$$\kappa_T = \tfrac{1}{3} u_F \lambda_T C_e \tag{10.38}$$

$$\kappa_i = \tfrac{1}{3} u_F \lambda_i C_e \tag{10.39}$$

The temperature variation of κ may now be sought in κ_T and κ_i. Once we can predict how κ_T and κ_i vary with temperature (if at all) eq. (10.37) will tell us how the overall thermal conductivity should depend on T.

Scattering electrons

We have seen that at temperatures below θ_D the number of phonons present is proportional to T^3 (eq. (10.20)). Since λ_T—the mean free path of the electron due to phonon scattering—is inversely proportional to the number of phonons present (assuming a constant scattering-cross section) it follows that $\lambda_T \propto 1/T^3$. As $C_e \propto T$ (see eq. (8.61)) and u_F is constant, eq. (10.38) predicts

$$\kappa_T \propto 1/T^2 \qquad \text{at } T < \theta_D \tag{10.40}$$

With impurity scattering λ_i should be independent of temperature so eq. (10.39) predicts

$$\kappa_i \propto T \tag{10.41}$$

Testing the theory

Substituting eqs. (10.40) and (10.41) into eq. (10.37) gives

$$\frac{1}{\kappa} = \alpha T^2 + \frac{\beta}{T} \qquad \text{at } T < \theta_D \qquad (10.42)$$

where α and β are constants. At very low temperatures the second term—arising from impurity scattering—predominates; predicting $\kappa \propto T$. At higher temperatures, but below θ_D (remember we assumed the number of phonons to be proportional to T^3) the first term—arising from phonon scattering—predominates; predicting $\kappa \propto 1/T^2$. Figure 10.7 shows that these predictions are borne out for copper and gallium. (At even higher temperatures, at $T > \theta_D$, the thermal conductivity becomes constant. At such temperatures the number of phonons ceases to be proportional to T^3, becoming instead proportional to T (eq. (10.19)) so that $\lambda_T \propto 1/T$. Therefore $\kappa_T (= \frac{1}{3} u_F \lambda_T C_e)$ is constant once $T > \theta_D$.)

It always makes for easier experimental verification of a theoretical expression relating two quantities, here κ and T, if the expression can be rearranged to predict a linear relationship. Multiplying eq. (10.42) through by T gives

$$\frac{T}{\kappa} = \alpha T^3 + \beta \qquad \text{at } T < \theta_D \qquad (10.43)$$

Figure 10.16(a) shows how the thermal conductivity of two lithium samples of different purity varies with temperature. Figure 10.16(b) shows that graphs of T/κ plotted against T^3 are indeed linear as predicted by eq. (10.43). We also see that the slope α of these lines is, as expected, independent of the impurity level. It is worth re-emphasizing that eq. (10.43) only applies for $T < \theta_D$. The Debye temperature for lithium is 344 K.

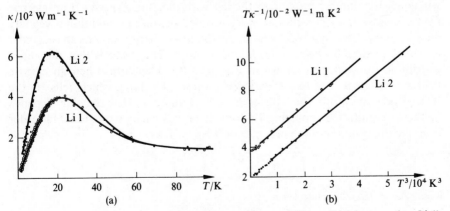

Fig. 10.16 (a) The thermal conductivity κ of two specimens of lithium (Li 2 is purer than Li 1) as a function of temperature T. (b) The same information plotted as T/κ against T^3. The Debye temperature of Li is 344 K. (Data from H. M. Rosenberg, *Phil. Mag.*, **1**, 738 (1956).)

10.5 Electrical conduction

Adapting gas-kinetic theory

In view of the considerable success which we have had in adapting gas-kinetic theory to describe at least some aspects of thermal conduction in a metal we might expect that our discussion of electrical conduction in a gas can likewise be applied to metals. And indeed it can. However, a free electron model is powerless to explain why these electrons are free to move in metals yet are unable to do so in non-metals.

You will recall how we pictured a gaseous ion drifting under the influence of an electric field and how the drift velocity acquired from the field is removed in collisions between the ion and neutral atoms (section 5.7). Throughout this discussion we paid no attention to the fact that the thermal speeds of the ions are distributed according to the Maxwell-Boltzmann distribution function. We ought to check up on the role of the velocity distribution function for this will be important when we seek to apply the results to an electron gas which, we know, obeys the Fermi–Dirac, and not the Maxwell–Boltzmann distribution function. This little exercise will also show us how to build the actual velocity distribution into the calculation of one transport coefficient; something we have not done up to now.

A formal calculation

For simplicity, let us think about a one-dimensional ion gas in which the ions *all* have the same charge q. (This is, of course, the classical analogue of a free electron gas.) Figure 6.31 shows the *speed* distribution of such a gas assuming it to obey Maxwell–Boltzmann rules. This figure is redrawn in Fig. 10.17(a) as a *velocity* distribution function. (Symmetry demands that the number of ions per unit range of speed, dN/du, moving to the right with a particular speed u will equal the number moving to the left with that same speed.) If an electric field E is now applied each and every ion will acquire an additional velocity $\delta u = v_d = qE\tau/2m$ (eq. (5.62)) where q is the ion's charge, m is its mass, and τ is the mean time between collisions of the ions. The result is that the entire distribution is shifted as shown in Fig. 10.17(b). Therefore, when an electric field E is present it is the shifted distribution $(dN/du)_{E,\tau}$ which tells us the steady-state situation. The suffixes E and τ remind us that the shift depends on these quantities. By applying Taylor's theorem we may write, to a first order in E, the distribution in the presence of the field E as

$$\left(\frac{dN}{du}\right)_{E,\tau} = \frac{dN}{du} - \delta u \frac{d}{du}\left(\frac{dN}{du}\right)$$

where $\delta u = qE\tau/2m$. Therefore

$$\left(\frac{dN}{du}\right)_{E,\tau} = \frac{dN}{du} - \left(\frac{qE\tau}{2m}\right)\frac{d^2N}{du^2} \tag{10.44}$$

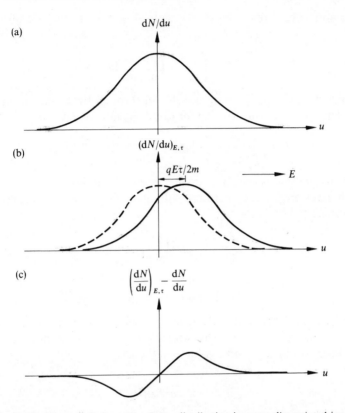

(a)

dN/du

u

(b)

$(dN/du)_{E,\tau}$

$qE\tau/2m$

E

u

(c)

$\left(\dfrac{dN}{du}\right)_{E,\tau} - \dfrac{dN}{du}$

u

Fig. 10.17 (a) The Maxwell–Boltzmann *velocity* distribution in a one-dimensional ion gas in the absence of an electric field. (b) The velocity distribution in the presence of a field E. Notice how the shape of the distribution is unaltered; it is merely shifted to the right by an amount $qE\tau/2m$. (c) The difference between the two distributions as given by eq. (10.45).

$$\left(\frac{dN}{du}\right)_{E,\tau} - \frac{dN}{du} = -\frac{d^2N}{du^2}\left(\frac{qE\tau}{2m}\right) \qquad (10.45)$$

This difference between the steady-state distribution in the presence and the absence of the field—as given by eq. (10.45)—is shown in Fig. 10.17(c). To a first order this graph is the same as that obtained directly by subtracting the ordinate values in Fig. 10.17(b) from those in Fig. 10.17(a).

What interests us is the ion current in the gas. Let us work out the total charge flowing through a plane of unit area, perpendicular to the field direction, per unit time—the so-called *current density J*. To do this we construct a cylinder of unit cross-sectional area and of length u. The total number of ions within this cylinder with velocities between u and $u + du$ is the product of the volume of the cylinder ($1 \times u$) and the number of ions per unit volume with velocities between u and $u + du$, namely $(dn/du)_{E,\tau}\, du$. Multiplying by the charge q on

349

each ion and integrating from $u = -\infty$ to $u = +\infty$ (to include all the ions) gives

$$J = \int_{-\infty}^{+\infty} qu \left(\frac{dn}{du}\right)_{E,\tau} du \qquad (10.46)$$

We obtain $(dn/du)_{E,\tau}$ by dividing eq. (10.44) through by V, the volume of the ion gas. This gives, on substituting for $(dn/du)_{E,\tau}$ into eq. (10.46),

$$J = q \int_{-\infty}^{+\infty} u \left(\frac{dn}{du}\right) du - \frac{q^2 E\tau}{2m} \int_{-\infty}^{+\infty} u \frac{d^2 n}{du^2} du \qquad (10.47)$$

The first integral vanishes since, in the absence of a field, there are as many ions with a velocity $+u$ as there are with a velocity $-u$. The second integral may be integrated by parts:

$$J = -\frac{q^2 E\tau}{2m} \int_{-\infty}^{+\infty} u\, d\left(\frac{dn}{du}\right)$$

$$J = -\frac{q^2 E\tau}{2m} \left[u \frac{dn}{du}\right]_{-\infty}^{+\infty} + \frac{q^2 E\tau}{2m} \int_{-\infty}^{+\infty} \frac{dn}{du} du \qquad (10.48)$$

The first term on the right-hand side of this equation vanishes since $dn/du = 0$ at $u = +\infty$ and at $u = -\infty$. The integral in the second term represents the total number n of ions per unit volume in the gas, so

$$J = \frac{q^2 E\tau n}{2m} \qquad (10.49)$$

Surprisingly, surely, this expression is independent of the form of the velocity distribution of the ions. It almost seems too good to be true. Can eq. (10.49) really apply to an electron gas which obeys the Fermi–Dirac, and not the Maxwell–Boltzmann, velocity distribution function?

It is not too difficult to predict the Fermi–Dirac velocity distribution function for a free electron gas. We shall do so first for a one-dimensional gas. As a preliminary, refresh your memory about how we dealt with a one-dimensional *classical* gas by studying the answer to exercise 6.8. There we carved up one-dimensional *velocity* space into modules of constant length (shown dotted in Fig. E6.8). In allocating vector tips to each module we had no "ground rules" which put an upper limit to the number of tips which could land in each module. The only real restriction was that the total energy of the gas was constant. This allowed us to consider arrangements which placed many tips in one module (cf. Fig. 6.15). However in an electron gas there is one very severe restriction: only *two* electrons (of opposite spin) can have the same momentum and, therefore, the same velocity $\boldsymbol{u}$. Furthermore there are, as we

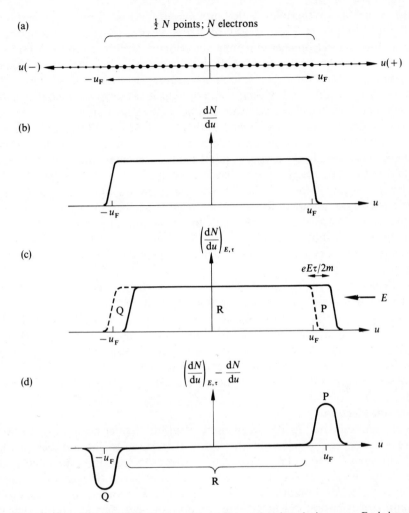

Fig. 10.18 (a) Showing how electrons are allocated to points in velocity space. Each large dot denotes the fact that the velocity vectors of two electrons (of opposite spin) end here. (b) The Fermi–Dirac velocity distribution function in a one-dimensional free electron gas in the absence of an electric field. (c) The velocity distribution with an electric field E present. (d) The difference between the two distributions.

have seen in section 8.6, restrictions on what u may be. In terms of Fig. 10.18(a) each module houses a single point on which a vector tip (or, at most, two vector tips) may land; they cannot land anywhere else. Now let us imagine ourselves allocating electrons to these modules. (We should, of course, speak of allocating velocity-vector tips to these modules.) If there are N electrons to be fitted into the modules then at $T = 0$, where we do our best to minimize the (mean) electron energy, our best choice is to allocate two electrons (of opposite

351

spin) to each of $\frac{1}{2}N$ modules. Filled modules are indicated by large solid dots in Fig. 10.18(a). So at $T = 0$ the Fermi–Dirac velocity distribution function—the number of electrons per unit range of velocity—will be constant from $-u_F$ to $+u_F$, where the span $-u_F$ to $+u_F$ in velocity space is sufficient to include $\frac{1}{2}N$ points (Fig. 10.18(a)). At a finite temperature, electrons whose energies lie within a range of about kT of $\frac{1}{2}mu_F^2$—and only such electrons—can be thermally excited. These excited electrons produce a tail to the distribution (Fig. 10.18(b)).

When an electric field E is applied to this one-dimensional free-electron gas *every* electron in the distribution undergoes the same velocity change $eE\tau/2m$. There is therefore always a vacant point ready to accommodate the velocity-vector tips of two electrons whose velocities have been so changed by the electric field; this vacancy is, of course, created by the simultaneous change in the velocity of another electron pair. (If an *entire* battalion takes one step to the right everyone has somewhere to move to.) The result is that the steady-state distribution shown in Fig. 10.18(c) is realized. Figure 10.18(d) shows the difference between the distributions with and without an electric field present.

The calculation of the current density J in an electron gas subjected to an electric field follows exactly similar lines to that in an ion gas. The only difference is that dn/du, in eq. (10.47) for example, is understood to be the Fermi–Dirac, and not the Maxwell–Boltzmann function. Equation (10.48) therefore also applies to our electron gas. Since $dn/du\,[=(dN/du)/V] = 0$ at $u = -\infty$ and at $u = +\infty$ in the Fermi–Dirac distribution (Fig. 10.18(b)), it follows that eq. (10.49) likewise applies to our electron gas.

Scattering electrons

Once again, compare Fig. 10.18(c) with Fig. 10.18(b). Notice how in Fig. 10.18(c) there are an excess of electrons in region P (relative to the number in Fig. 10.18(b) when $E = 0$) and a deficiency of electrons in region Q. These facts are, of course, presented in Fig. 10.18(d). Some mechanism must exist which takes the excess electron in region P back to region Q. Without such a mechanism the entire distribution in Fig. 10.18(c) would move ever further and further to the right with passing time and (contrary to the experimental facts) the current density J would cease to be proportional to the electric field E. In the language of eq. (10.49), we are looking for a mechanism that makes τ finite.

Whatever mechanism, or mechanisms, it is that send electrons of our one-dimensional gas back from region P to region Q it must operate in one fell swoop. There is no point in dreaming up some mechanism that will gradually, "put on the brakes" to bring electron in region P first to rest and to send it gently on its way again so that it ends up in region Q. Such a mechanism would mean that the velocity-vector tip of our electron has to occupy, in turn, every point in velocity space from $u = u_F + (eE\tau/2m)$ to $u = 0$ through to $u = -u_F + (eE\tau/2m)$. But all these points are occupied—each contains two electrons. It is "house full" throughout region R in Fig. 10.18. So we must find a scattering process that is able, in a twinkling, to change the velocity of an electron from $u = u_F$ to $u = -u_F$, that is, a process which is able to change the momentum of the electron by $2mu_F$. It is worth noting in passing that this "one fell swoop" restriction does not apply to a gas obeying the Maxwell–Boltzmann rules. Because there is no limit to the number of vector tips which may occupy any module in velocity space, a velocity vector can shrink from a value u to zero, and slowly grow to a value $-u$. Unlike the situation in an electron gas, there are no excluded modules into which a gas atom cannot be scattered. This, of course, shows up as a non-vanishing difference function; Fig. 10.17(c) has no region like R in Fig. 10.18(d).

Although the foregoing arguments have assumed a *one-dimensional* free electron gas we shall now show that much the same conclusions follow in a three-dimensional free electron gas. First, though, you might like to skim through sections 6.3 and 6.4 in which we discussed the velocity distribution function in a classical two-dimensional gas. You will recall how we divided two-dimensional *velocity* space (Fig. 6.12) up into cells of equal area and how we examined all the ways that velocity-vector tips could be assigned to these modules (using the bookshelf technique of Fig. 6.13) so that the total energy of all the gas atoms is constant. In so sorting the vector tips, no restrictions were placed on the number of tips which could occupy a given module; that is, any number of atoms of a classical Maxwell–Boltzmann gas may have the same velocity. Not so in an electron gas: only two electrons (of opposite spin) can have the same momentum and, therefore, the same velocity u. Furthermore, as in the one-dimensional electron gas, restrictions are placed on the values permitted for u. These restrictions are tantamount to saying that each module in velocity space contains a single point* on which one (or, at most, two) velocity-vector tips may land. This lattice of points is shown in Fig. 10.19(a). We must now allocate two vector tips to each point starting at the centre and moving out. If there are N electrons in our Fermi–Dirac gas and the gas is at $T = 0$, we will stop at a radius u_F such that the circle has $N/2$ lattice points within it (Fig. 10.19(b)). At a finite temperature T some of the lattice points in the immediate vicinity of the circle of radius u_F will be unfilled or will contain the vector tip of only one electron.

In following through the same arguments in three dimensions we find—you have almost certainly anticipated this—that the permitted values of u_x, u_y, and u_z form a lattice in three-dimensional velocity space and that at $T = 0$ all

---

* You may feel like employing eq. (8.54) to calculate the separation between these points. In fact you cannot! Equation (8.54) was based on a standing wave representation of the electron wave function. If you must calculate the distance between points in velocity space you should use travelling waves and "periodic boundary conditions" as in problem 8.10. This leads to the conclusion that the points are separated by $\Delta K_x = \Delta K_y = 2\pi/L$ (that is, since $K = 2\pi/\lambda$ and $\lambda = h/mu$, by $\Delta u_x = \Delta u_y = h/mL$). The actual value of the separation between permitted points in velocity space is of no real consequence here.

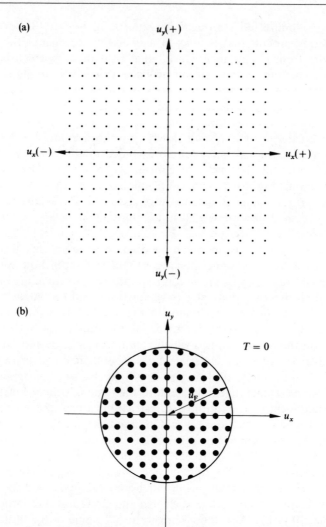

Fig. 10.19 (a) Showing a lattice of points in velocity space. In a two-dimensional electron gas the tips of the velocity vectors must terminate on these points. Each point may accommodate two tips at most (corresponding to electrons of opposite spin). (b) Showing how to allocate electrons to the points in (a). All those points within the circle of radius u_F are occupied by the vector tips of two electrons.

points within a sphere of radius u_F are filled and all points outside this sphere are empty (Fig. 10.20(a)). We shall call the surface of this sphere the *Fermi surface* of our free electron gas. (Strictly speaking the name Fermi surface is usually reserved for the surface drawn in K_x–K_y–K_z space rather than in u_x–u_y–u_z space.) When an electric field E is applied the entire surface and its contents shifts an amount $eE\tau/2m$, as shown in Fig. 10.20(b) (looking in along

(a)

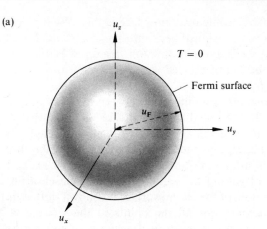

(b)

(c)

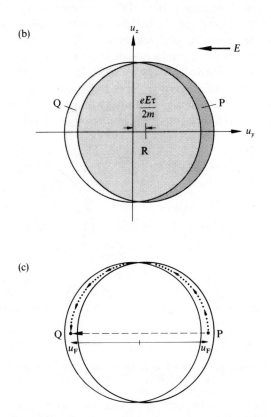

Fig. 10.20 (a) All points within the sphere (which are not shown for clarity) are filled; each is occupied by the velocity vector tips of two electrons of opposite spin. (b) An electric field E shifts the entire sphere an amount $Ee\tau/2m$. (c) Two ways of changing the momentum of an electron by $2mu_F$.

the u_x-axis). The problem we now face is this: What mechanism can herd the excess electrons in region P back into the electron deficient region Q, without sending them through the "house full" region R. Without some such scattering mechanism the Fermi surface would move off into the far beyond; τ in eq. (10.49) must be finite.

There is an important difference between the one- and the three-dimensional electron gas. In the one-dimensional case the *only* way to get electrons back from region P to region Q is to give them an almighty boot which, in one fell swoop, changes their momentum by $2mu_F$. In the three-dimensional case that option is still open (shown dashed in Fig. 10.20(c)). However, there is a gentler way of getting the same end result; the electron can be nudged all round the outside of the Fermi surface (as shown dotted in Fig. 10.20(c)). This is possible because not all the points in the vicinity of the Fermi surface contain their fill of two electrons (meaning, of course, that these points may contain one or zero vector tip). It really is necessary to send an electron all the way back to Q to produce a substantial effect on the electron current. A change like that shown in Fig. 10.21(a) makes little impact on the current—the contribution which this one electron makes to the total current is only changed from eu_F to $eu_F \cos\theta$, that is by $eu_F(1 - \cos\theta)$. It is only when θ is large—let us say of order 180° (where $\cos\theta = -1$)—that scattering severely limits the current (Fig. 10.21(b)). So whether we do it by one almighty kick, or by gentler means, we must get those electrons back all the way around the Fermi surface!

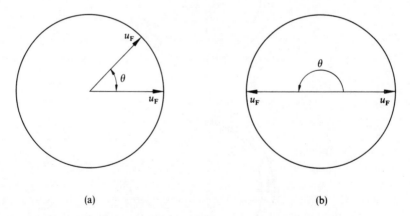

(a)   (b)

Fig. 10.21 When an electron is scattered as in (a) the contribution which it makes to the total current is but little changed. Only when θ approaches 180°, as in (b), is the effect serious.

Before we look at possible scattering mechanisms it is worth rewriting eq. (10.49) in a slightly different form. Remembering that the only electrons which are able to be scattered are those at the Fermi surface (which all have a *speed* close to u_F) we define the electron mean free path to be $\lambda = u_F\tau$. Substituting

$\tau = \lambda/u_F$, along with $q = -e$, into eq. (10.49) gives

$$J = \frac{ne^2\lambda}{2mu_F} E$$

or

$$J = \sigma E \tag{10.50}$$

where

$$\sigma = \frac{ne^2\lambda}{2mu_F} \tag{10.51}$$

is known as the *electrical conductivity* of the metal. Since the current density J is measured in units of $A\,m^{-2}$, that is $C\,s^{-1}\,m^{-2}$, and E is measured in $N\,C^{-1}$ the conductivity is measured in $C^2\,s\,m^{-3}\,kg^{-1}$ which agrees, as it must, with the units on the right-hand side of eq. (10.51). The name *ohm* is given to $V\,A^{-1}$, that is, to $J\,C^{-1}/C\,s^{-1}$, so the conductivity can be expressed in units of $ohm^{-1}\,m^{-1}$. Instead of talking of the conductivity of a metal we may talk instead of its *electrical resistivity* ρ defined by

$$\rho = \frac{1}{\sigma}$$

Equation (10.51) may therefore be written as

$$\rho = \frac{2mu_F}{ne^2\lambda} \tag{10.52}$$

The advantage of introducing the resistivity is that the mean free path λ appears in the denominator. In view of eq. (10.36) the resistivities attributable to different scattering processes may be added.

Exercise 10.3

Copper at 295 K has an electrical conductivity of $5\cdot9 \times 10^7\ ohm^{-1}\,m^{-1}$ and (with a pure enough sample) a conductivity of some 10^5 times greater at 4 K. On the assumption that there are as many free electrons as there are copper atoms, calculate the electronic mean free path at these two temperatures. Compare these values with the mean free path as calculated classically assuming the copper atoms to be hard spheres and the electron to have zero diameter. For simplicity, suppose copper to have a simple cubic lattice (it is fcc). The density of copper is $8\cdot9 \times 10^3\ kg\,m^{-3}$ and $A_r(Cu) = 63\cdot5$. Take $u_F = 1\cdot6 \times 10^6\ m\ s^{-1}$ (you calculated it in problem 8.11).

As this exercise has demonstrated, the mean free path of an electron in a metal is considerably greater than can be accounted for by classical arguments; an electron in a metal is seemingly not scattered by a regular atomic structure. We must therefore look elsewhere for scattering processes that can bring about the desired change in the velocity of an electron (Fig. 10.21(b)).

Impurity scattering; the big kick

The first obvious candidate for study is an imperfection in the structure, such as an impurity atom or a dislocation. Just as a ping-pong ball rebounds with little loss of speed in a collision with a billiard ball so we can expect an electron in a metal to behave similarly when it strikes a massive imperfection in the lattice, and therefore to produce the type of scattering we are seeking. The mean free path λ_i associated with such a scattering mechanism should be temperature independent when it is caused by impurity scattering. It should be almost independent of temperature when dislocations are responsible for the scattering (except close to the melting temperature, where the number density of dislocations will depend on T). We therefore have a temperature independent contribution to the resistivity given by, (see eq. (10.52))

$$\rho_i = \frac{2mu_F}{ne^2\lambda_i} \tag{10.53}$$

Phonon scattering; the gentle nudge

It is an experimental fact that the resistivity of all pure metals increases with increasing temperature. This can be extremely useful—if the resistivity of tungsten were to decrease with increasing temperature an electric light bulb would have a rather short life! This temperature dependence must clearly be sought in the temperature dependence of the lattice vibrations, that is, in the interactions of electrons with phonons.

Instead of saying that the scattering mechanism must be such as to lead to a change in velocity of an electron from u_F to $-u_F$ (Fig. 10.20(c)) we can say that the mechanism must be such as to change the momentum of the electron from mu_F to $-mu_F$. If phonons are indeed the culprit we must calculate the mean momentum of a phonon without further ado.

By definition:

$$\text{mean phonon momentum} = \frac{\sum_q n_q \times \text{momentum of a phonon}}{\sum_q n_q} \tag{10.54}$$

where n_q is the number of phonons associated with mode q. Assuming that we can apply de Broglie's relation $\lambda = h/mv$ to a phonon, we see that

$$\text{momentum of a phonon} = \frac{h}{\lambda} = \left(\frac{h}{2\pi}\right)\left(\frac{2\pi}{\lambda}\right) = \hbar q$$

Appealing once again to our old friend Debye's dispersion relation $\omega_q = qv$, i.e., $q = \omega_q/v$, gives

$$\text{momentum of a phonon} = \frac{\hbar\omega_q}{v}$$

Substituting this into eq. (10.54) we obtain

$$\text{mean phonon momentum} = \frac{1}{v} \frac{\sum\limits_q n_q \hbar\omega_q}{\sum\limits_q n_q}$$

Apart from the constant multiplier $1/v$ this is identical to eq. (10.21). We may therefore take over the results which were obtained on evaluating eq. (10.21); in particular eqs. (10.23) and (10.24). Multiplying the right-hand sides of these equations by $1/v$ and approximating the numerical factors of $2/3$ and 2.34 by unity tells us that

$$\text{mean phonon momentum} = \frac{k\theta_D}{v} \qquad \text{at } T > \theta_D \qquad (10.55)$$

$$\text{mean phonon momentum} = \frac{kT}{v} \qquad \text{at } T < \theta_D \qquad (10.56)$$

Now that we know the momentum of a phonon we must ask how it interacts with an electron.

At low temperatures the phonon momentum kT/v is insufficient to change the momentum of an electron from mu_F to $-mu_F$ in one go; the scattering process shown dashed in Fig. 10.20(c) cannot take place. The only way that a phonon in a metal at a low temperature can reverse the momentum of an electron is to nudge it around the Fermi surface, along the dotted route in Fig. 10.20(c). Figure 10.22(a) shows a single electron–phonon interaction; Figure 10.22(b) shows the sequence of collisions which is required to reverse the momentum of the electron. Waltzing round the Fermi surface might be a better description of what happens. An electron–phonon collision can result in the removal of momentum from the electron. (Swap the labels "initial" and "final" in Fig. 10.22(a) and reverse the momentum of the phonon.) So in going round the surface it may be two steps forward, then one back. This is essentially the random walk problem of section 10.1 in a new guise.

It is clear from Fig. 10.22(b) that, in momentum space, the total distance to be travelled by the tip of the vector representing the electron's momentum is one half the circumference of a circle of radius mu_F, that is πmu_F. We know from eq. (10.7) that

359

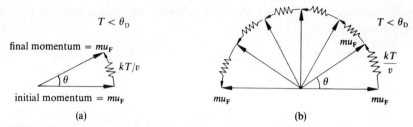

Fig. 10.22 (a) In a single encounter with a phonon the momentum of the electron is but little changed. (b) It takes many such encounters to change the electron's momentum from mu_F to $-mu_F$.

$$\text{distance gone} = \text{hop length} \times (\text{number of hops required})^{1/2}$$

Since the hop length (if one may mix "hopping" with "waltzing"!) is here kT/v, and since the distance gone is πmu_F, it follows that

$$\text{number of hops required} = \frac{(\pi mu_F)^2}{(kT/v)^2}$$

Now u_F and v are independent of temperature, so

$$\text{number of hops required} \propto \frac{1}{T^2} \qquad \text{at } T < \theta_D \qquad (10.57)$$

As it takes this number of encounters with phonons for the momentum of a particular electron to be reversed it follows that, at any moment, the number of phonons which are effective in scattering electrons is the total number of phonons present divided by the number of hops required to "do the necessary". (By way of analogy: it takes 6 throws of a die, on average, to secure a desired result, say a 4. If 100 dice are thrown together the number producing the desired result (4) is about 100/6.) At $T < \theta_D$ the total number of phonons present is proportional to T^3 (eq. (10.20)). Therefore

$$\text{effective number of phonons} = \frac{\text{total number of phonons}}{\text{number of hops required to reverse an electron}}$$

Substituting from eqs. (10.20) and (10.57) gives

$$\text{effective number of phonons} \propto \frac{T^3}{1/T^2} \propto T^5 \qquad (10.58)$$

Since the mean free path λ_T of an electron is inversely proportional to the number of phonons which can cause the momentum reversal we are interested in, we have, from eq. (10.58) that $\lambda_T \propto 1/T^5$. Therefore, from eq. (10.52), $\rho_T \propto 1/\lambda_T$ and so

$$\rho_T \propto T^5 \qquad \text{at } T < \theta_D \qquad (10.59)$$

At $T > \theta_D$ the mean phonon momentum $k\theta_D/v$ (eq. (10.55)) *is* sufficient to reverse the momentum of an electron in a single encounter. *All* phonons are therefore effective in scattering electrons through 180° when $T > \theta_D$. Since the number of phonons at $T > \theta_D$ is proportional to T (eq. (10.19)) this tells us that $\lambda_T \propto 1/T$ at such temperatures. Therefore, from eq. (10.52)

$$\rho_T \propto T \qquad \text{at } T > \theta_D \tag{10.60}$$

The test

Multiplying eq. (10.36) through by $2mu_F/ne^2$ (see eq. (10.52)) predicts that the overall resistivity of a metal $\rho(T)$ at temperature T should be the sum of the resistivity ρ_T due to phonon scattering of the conduction electrons and the resistivity ρ_i due to impurity scattering of the electrons:

$$\rho(T) = \rho_i + \rho_T \tag{10.61}$$

Substituting from eqs. (10.53) and (10.59) gives

$$\rho(T) = \rho_0 + AT^5 \qquad \text{at } T < \theta_D \tag{10.62}$$

where ρ_0 and A are constants.

Figure 10.23 shows how the resistance of three samples of sodium, each of different purity, vary with temperature. Clearly, as $T \to 0$ the resistance of each sample does tend to a constant value, in accordance with eq. (10.62). Equation (10.62) also predicts that $\rho(T) - \rho_0$ plotted against T should be the same for all specimens. This is so; all three curves in Fig. 10.23 do superimpose if we

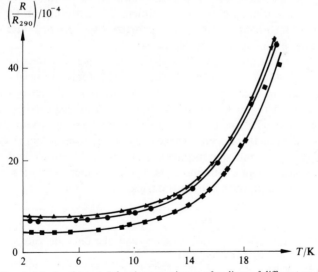

Fig. 10.23 The electrical resistance R for three specimens of sodium of different purity, expressed as a fraction of the specimen resistance at $T = 290$ K. (Data from D. K. C. MacDonald and K. Mendelssohn, *Proc. Roy. Soc.*, **A202**, 103 (1950).)

subtract from each curve the constant resistance at $T \approx 0$. In addition the temperature dependence at temperatures well below θ_D does conform to the T^5 dependence predicted by eq. (10.62). Finally, at $T > \theta_D$ (for sodium $\theta_D = 158$ K), $\rho(T) - \rho_0$ is proportional to T as is predicted when eq. (10.60) is substituted into eq. (10.61).

Summary

1. The main mechanism for diffusion in closely packed structures is by hopping of an atom into an adjacent vacant lattice site. The hopping of interstitials in impure structures is the other important mechanism. Both predict $\ln D \propto -E/T$, where E is the sum of the energy required to create a vacancy *and* the energy required for an adjacent atom to hop into the site in the first mechanism, and is the activation energy required for an interstitial to change sites in the second mechanism. At the atomic level diffusion proceeds by an atom executing a random walk; characterized by the fact that after n hops, each of length a, an atom will have travelled an r.m.s. distance of $an^{1/2}$.

2. An imperfect material may creep when subjected to a constant stress.

3. Thermal conduction in non-metals may be described in terms of a phonon "gas" in which the number density of the phonons and their mean energy is a function of temperature (the function being different at high and at low temperatures). The conductivity is limited by scattering of the phonons by other phonons and, at low temperatures, where the phonon mean free path approaches the diameter of the specimen, by scattering at the specimen boundaries. In metals heat is transported by electrons and these are scattered by impurities and by phonons.

4. Electrical conduction in metals is the result of electrons acquiring a drift velocity by virtue of the applied electric field. Only those electrons with speeds close to u_F are free to be scattered although *all* electrons contribute to the electric current (eq. (10.49)). To have much impact on the conductivity the momentum of a free electron must be changed by about $2mu_F$. Such scattering around the Fermi surface may result from a single collision of the electron with a massive impurity atom (or dislocation) or it may result from multiple collisions with phonons. At high temperatures ($T > \theta_D$) a single encounter with a phonon can do the trick.

PROBLEMS

10.1 Show that in a one-dimensional random walk the r.m.s. distance travelled after n hops, each of length a, is $an^{1/2}$.

10.2 In a process called *carburizing* low-carbon steels are given a thin skin of high-carbon steel. Many parts of a car engine, for example, need to have a hard surface without being brittle (which low carbon steel is, in bulk). This is achieved by packing carbon (and other substances) around the low-carbon steel part and heating them both to around 1170 K. The carbon diffuses into the steel forming the high-carbon layer. If it takes 25 hours to produce a "case" $\frac{1}{8}''$ (3·2 mm) thick at 1140 K, how long will it take to produce the same thickness case at 1230 K? Assume that the activation energy required for the interstitial carbon to hop from site to site is $1·4 \times 10^{-19}$ J.

10.3 Consider a thin slice of material of unit area and thickness δx. If the concentration gradient at the left-hand end of the slice is dn/dx and that at the right-hand end is $dn/dx + (d^2n/dx^2)\,\delta x$, as follows from Taylor's theorem, then the flux j_i of labelled atoms entering will, from Fick's law (eq. (5.17)), be different from the flux j_o leaving the slice. Show, by equating the difference between these two fluxes to the time rate of change of the number of labelled atoms within the slice, that

$$\frac{\partial n}{\partial t} = D\frac{\partial^2 n}{\partial x^2}$$

This expression is often called the *diffusion equation*.

10.4 A thin layer of N atoms is deposited on a surface of area A on a thick solid. After a certain time t some of the surface atoms will have diffused into the solid. Show (by substitution into the expression derived in problem 10.3) that the concentration $n(x)$ of surface atoms as a function of distance x into the solid is, at time t, given by

$$n(x) = \frac{N}{A(\pi Dt)^{1/2}}\exp\left(-x^2/4Dt\right)$$

Make a rough sketch of this relation at time $t = 1/4D$, $t = 1/2D$, and $t = 1/D$. Find the value of x at the point of inflexion, and compare your value with the r.m.s. distance travelled (eq. (10.9)).

10.5 The activation energy involved in creep of a pure aluminium single crystal is $1·95 \times 10^{-19}$ J (within the temperature range of 600 K to 800 K). What temperature change is necessary to double the steady-state creep rate in such a crystal if its present temperature is 700 K?

10.6 Sodium chloride at 83 K—which is above the temperature of the maximum in κ—has a thermal conductivity κ of 27 W m^{-1} K^{-1} and a heat capacity of $1·0 \times 10^6$ J m^{-3} K^{-1}. Assuming the speed of sound is 5×10^3 m s^{-1} in NaCl, what is the phonon mean free path at 83 K?

10.7 Using the information contained in Fig. 10.16 calculate the ratio of the impurity concentration in Li 1 to that in Li 2. Explain your reasoning.

10.8 Aluminium at 300 K has a resistivity of $2·7 \times 10^{-8}$ ohm m. Calculate the drift velocity of an electron in a 0·1 m length of aluminium which is connected across a 250 V direct current supply. If the aluminium is connected instead to a 250 V, 50 Hz supply, roughly how far will the electron travel before the current reverses? Assume $u_F = 2 \times 10^6$ m s^{-1} and $n = 1·8 \times 10^{29}$ m^{-3}.

10.9 In large samples the electrical resistivity of a certain material is ρ_b and the electron mean free path is λ_b. Show that the resistivity ρ_D of the material when prepared as a cylinder of diameter D is given by

$$\frac{\rho_D}{\rho_b} = 1 + \frac{\lambda_b}{D}$$

Assume that the momentum of an electron may be changed by $2mu_F$ in each and every collision which it makes with the surface of the cylinder. (In other words disregard any effects which may, and indeed do, arise from incomplete momentum

363

accommodation at the surface.) The resistivity of a metal prepared in a very thin sample, of thickness less than λ_b, *is* greater than the resistivity of the metal in a large sample. Assume that the temperature of the material is close to 0 K.

11. The Liquid Phase

In this chapter we shall attempt to discover what a liquid is like at the atomic level. We shall find however that, unlike the situation in a gas or solid, it requires the language of mathematics to fully describe the structure of even a simple liquid. Furthermore there is not just one such model—there are many. Part of the reason for the many models is that in attempting to predict the structure we come up against a mathematically intractable equation. To solve this equation requires various and often sophisticated approximations, each of which corresponds to a slightly different physical picture. So no neat picture of a liquid will emerge, one that can be described so succinctly as that for a perfect gas or a perfect solid. In fact we shall not follow through the mathematical analysis. Instead we shall appeal to simulation studies which do give us some feel for what a liquid may be like at the atomic level.

Of course, a liquid may also be studied at the macroscopic level. One might, for example, measure its heat capacity at constant pressure or its compressibility at constant temperature. The natural next step would be to try to account for these measurements starting each time from a microscopic picture of the liquid. In fact one does not need to keep returning to a microscopic picture. The laws of thermodynamics assure us that provided we know the equation of state of a substance—the relationships between the pressure, volume, and temperature of a fixed mass of the substance—and an "energy equation", such as the internal energy of the substance, all the *equilibrium* properties of the substance can be categorized. (Transport processes are, of course, excluded since they are non-equilibrium in nature.) So we shall devote some time to attempting to determine the equation of state and the internal energy of a liquid. We did not adopt this tactic in discussing solids and gases because it is relatively easy to predict their equilibrium properties from a microscopic picture. Since the atoms are arranged in a regular fashion in a perfect solid it is quite straight-forward to predict the compressibility directly. Again, because the atoms are entirely free in a perfect gas, it is straightforward to predict its compressibility directly. In a liquid where the atoms are part-free, part-bound, such direct calculations are never easy.

Throughout this chapter we will focus on the properties of simple liquids—which we may define loosely as liquids whose molecules are roughly spherical and which interact according to a Mie or Lennard-Jones type of potential model. This definition encompasses liquids like carbon tetrachloride and the liquified inert gases. It excludes liquids composed of long-chain molecules. Although excluded from prime consideration it will nevertheless be interesting, from time to time, to see whether such liquids do possess the properties predicted for a simple liquid.

11.1   Liquids vis-à-vis gases and solids

How should we begin our discussion? Even if it should prove applicable to the liquid phase, the rough equality which we argued for in section 3.1;

$$\tfrac{1}{2}m\overline{u^2} \approx \Delta E \qquad (11.1)$$

is not going to tell us how the atoms are arranged in a liquid! Perhaps we should begin by questioning whether it really is necessary to "go the whole hog" of equating $\tfrac{1}{2}m\overline{u^2}$ and ΔE. Could we not simply regard a liquid as a very imperfect gas—one where the dissociation energy ΔE is a significant fraction (say $\tfrac{2}{3}$) of the mean atomic kinetic energy $\tfrac{1}{2}m\overline{u^2}$? Or perhaps a truer model would be of a thermally "imperfect" solid—one where the kinetic energy is a significant fraction of the dissociation energy? So we should first ask whether the liquid phase is a "close relative" of either the gaseous or the solid phases, or whether it is indeed "in the middle" as is implied by eq. (11.1). We shall seek an answer to this question by contrasting the mechanical and thermal properties of liquids with the corresponding properties of gases and solids. We will also look for evidence to the, so-called, radial density curves.

The p–V–T surface

You may remember the confusion over whether to label the region shown shaded in Fig. 1.11 "liquid" or a "gas". The confusion arose because, starting from a point where liquid and gas are undoubtedly both present (point i in Fig. 1.10) we could proceed to a point f within the region in question by two distinct routes. Following one route (that is full line) we would see the volume of liquid expand as the temperature is increased until the substance appeared to be wholly "liquid". Following another route (that in dashed line) we would see the volume of liquid diminish until the substance appeared to be wholly "gaseous". So sometimes we would be inclined to dub a substance a "gas" and sometimes a "liquid" when it is present as a single phase. We resolved this problem of nomenclature by agreeing to use the word liquid to denote the single phase present when its state is represented by points lying on the portion of the p–V_m–T surface shown shaded in Fig. 1.11. Figures 11.1(a) and (b) show how the surface projects onto the p–T and p–V_m planes. When we consider that the scales of p, V_m, and T extend to near infinity, we can see just how tenuous is the liquid phase. In terms of the p–T projection it extends from the triple point temperature T_{tr} to the critical temperature T_c. In terms

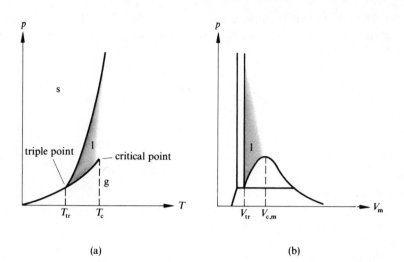

Fig. 11.1 Showing how the $p-V_m-T$ surface projects onto (a) the $p-T$ plane, and (b) the $p-V_m$ plane.

of the $p-V_m$ projection it extends from $V_{tr,m}$ to $V_{c,m}$. Both of the ratios T_c/T_{tr} and $V_{c,m}/V_{tr,m}$ are usually in the range 1–5 (see Table 1.1), so there really is very little latitude possible in assigning values to the independent variables T and V_m if the substance is to be in the liquid phase.

There is no critical point associated with the liquid-to-solid transaction; one cannot pass unknowingly from the gaseous or liquid phase to the solid phase. At some stage during the process two phases will be present—either the solid and the gaseous, or the solid and the liquid—and at the conclusion one will have no doubt that it is a solid which is present. (You should convince yourself that this is so by tracing out various paths over the $p-V-T$ surface of Fig. 1.11.)

The evidence gleaned from the $p-V-T$ surface clearly suggests that a liquid more closely resembles a gas than a solid; particularly so in the vicinity of the critical point where the two phases become indistinguishable. However this is only a tentative conclusion based on restrictive evidence. It could still be that, at the atomic level, a liquid more closely resembles a solid at temperatures close to the triple point.

Exercise 11.1

If the arguments based on competing binding and kinetic energy are correct then the relation $\frac{1}{2}m\overline{u^2} \approx \Delta E$ must hold true *somewhere* in the liquid range. Since $\frac{1}{2}m\overline{u^2} = \frac{3}{2}kT$ this relation may be written as $\frac{3}{2}kT \approx \Delta E$. Using the data set out in Table 11.1 investigate whether this relation does hold true for the inert gases anywhere in their liquid range T_{tr} to

T_c. If it does hold even approximately correct, does it do so at temperatures closer to T_{tr} or T_c? Notice that, for convenience, ΔE is shown already divided by k.

TABLE 11.1

Substance	$(\Delta E/k)/K$	T_{tr}/K	T_c/K
Ne	35·6	24·5	44·4
Ar	120	84	151
Kr	171	116	209
Xe	221	161	290

Thermal properties

(a) *The internal energy*   To melt (fuse) one mole of a solid at a constant pressure p requires energy $H_{m,f}$—the molar enthalpy of fusion (at pressure p). To evaporate one mole of a liquid at constant pressure p requires energy $H_{m,e}$—the molar enthalpy of evaporation (at pressure p).

Experiments show that at pressures close to p_{tr} the value of $H_{m,e}$ always exceeds $H_{m,f}$. As examples, $H_{m,e}/H_{m,f}$ is 5·5 for argon, 3·0 for carbon dioxide, 7·0 for water, and 25 for mercury. To turn a liquid into a gas (at a fixed pressure close to p_{tr}) thus requires an energy roughly ten times that needed to melt the solid. At such pressures the molar internal energy of a liquid is therefore closer to that of a solid than to that of a gas. However, as one repeats the measurements at higher pressures one discovers that $H_{m,e}$ falls towards zero as p approaches p_c but that $H_{m,f}$ remains (virtually) constant. Near the critical point the situation is therefore reversed: the molar internal energy of a liquid is closer to that of a gas than to that of a solid. You will find these conclusions presented more formally in Fig. 1.19; study it!

(b) *The molar heat capacity*   Another way of probing the internal energy is to study how the molar heat capacity at constant volume $C_{V,m} = (\delta U_m/\delta T)_V$ (eq. (1.3)) changes when a substance undergoes a phase transition. You will recall that the atoms of a perfect gas possess only kinetic energy $\frac{1}{2}mu^2 = \frac{3}{2}kT$, giving $U_m = \frac{3}{2}kN_AT = \frac{3}{2}RT$, and therefore $C_{V,m} = \frac{3}{2}R$. You will also recall that the atoms of a perfect solid possess both kinetic and potential energy, each of amount $\frac{3}{2}kT$ (at $T > \theta_D$) giving $U_m = 3RT$, and therefore $C_{V,m} = 3R$. So if a solid melts to form a liquid which is essentially solid-like there should be no change in $C_{V,m}$. If, on the other hand, it melts to form a perfect gas-like liquid there should be a substantial reduction in $C_{V,m}$. In practice the value of $C_{V,m}$ changes but little when most solids melt. As an example, it decreases by about 15 per cent when solid argon melts.

(c) *Heats of solution*   Although we shall subsequently exclude solutions from further consideration, there is a simple experiment which might be able to tell us the degree to which atoms do cluster together in a liquid. Here is the idea behind the experiment.

Consider any solid known to dissolve in a given liquid. In imagination dissolve the solute (the solid) in the solvent (the liquid). If the solute atoms are all widely dispersed in the solution so formed—and by widely dispersed we mean several atomic diameters or more—this will require energy. It is not difficult to calculate the energy required to disperse the N atoms of the solid; as we saw in section 9.1 it is roughly equal to $\frac{1}{2}Nn\,\Delta E$, where ΔE is the dissociation energy of a pair of solute atoms and where n is the number of nearest neighbours to an atom of the solid. If the liquid is contained within adiabatic walls this energy can *only* come from the kinetic energy of the atoms of the solution. According to these arguments the temperature of any liquid should drop when a solid is dissolved in it. Should the temperature of the liquid not change a reasonable inference would be that the atoms of the solid had not dispersed significantly —they might for example exist as large clusters invisible to the eye.

When one carries out this simple experiment one discovers that, depending on one's choice of solute, the liquid may indeed cool—or it may heat up—or no change in temperature may occur!

Our simple arguments offer no explanation as to why the solution might heat up. Actually what happens here is that the solute atoms bond to the solvent atoms and the energy released in this process is more than the energy required to disperse the solid into separate atoms (or ions). So measuring heats of solution gives little information about the nature of the solvent *per se*. Not all simple ideas work out as expected!

Taken overall, the thermal evidence suggests that, near the triple point, the liquid phase is closer to the solid than the gaseous phase, but that the opposite is true near the critical point.

Mechanical properties

(a) *Tensile strength* Because of the way we can splash about in water and thereby separate one mass of water from another you might infer that there is little cohesion between water molecules—so little that water is unable to resist any tensile stress. But liquids *can* withstand tensile stresses (often called negative pressures). This can be demonstrated by taking a thick-walled tube, fitted with a valve, and filling it almost full of liquid (Fig. 11.2(a)) leaving only a small bubble of vapour. (All other gases, such as air, must be excluded.) If the tube is heated slightly (Fig. 11.2(b)) the liquid will expand to fill the entire tube and the bubble will disappear. On cooling the tube the vapour bubble does not reappear at the expected temperature—the liquid is now in a state of tension, being "stretched" to fill the tube (Fig. 11.2(c)). On further cooling, the liquid suddenly ruptures with the appearance of many tiny vapour bubbles (Fig. 11.2(d)). These then rise to reform the vapour bubble. Negative pressures corresponding to stresses of, for example, about 10^6 Pa for liquid argon and about 10^7 Pa for mercury are observed by this method. By comparison, steel has a tensile strength of around 10^9 Pa.

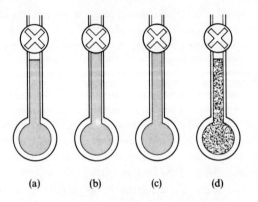

Fig. 11.2 In (a) the sealed tube contains the liquid and a small amount of vapour (all other gases are rigorously excluded). (b) The tube is heated, the liquid expands, and the vapour bubble disappears. (c) When the liquid is cooled it contracts but the bubble fails to reappear at the expected temperature. (d) With further cooling the liquid suddenly ruptures.

(b) *Compressibility* Our everyday experiences might suggest that liquids are about as incompressible as solids (any child who has even played with a water pistol will tell us that if the jet is blocked the piston cannot be pushed in!). The fact that liquids are pretty incompressible is, of course, recorded in the $p–V–T$ surface; the rapidly rising shaded region of Fig. 1.11 tells us that it takes a large increase in pressure to bring about a small reduction in volume. But the even more rapidly rising solid region of the surface tells us that an even larger increase is required to bring about the same fractional change in the volume of a solid.

We know from our discussions in section 9.1 that there is relatively little free volume in a solid and that the compressibility reflects the repulsive forces between closely-packed atoms. Now when a solid melts to form a liquid there is a small change in the volume of the substance; typically around 10–15 per cent. Perhaps then a liquid is more compressible than a solid because this *free volume,* so-called, can be relatively easily squeezed out. We might even feel like proposing that a liquid is only a thermally very-imperfect solid with 10–15 per cent of its lattice sites vacant!

The radial density
In section 7.3 we saw that much could be learnt about the way atoms are arranged in a material by studying how a beam of X-rays is scattered. Such diffraction techniques tell us how many atoms there are on average at a distance r from any one atom. Since the diffraction photograph collects information from all over the sample the average is spatial. But it is also time-averaged, since a diffraction photograph requires a time exposure—usually minutes— which is very much greater than the vibrational period of the atoms. Figure

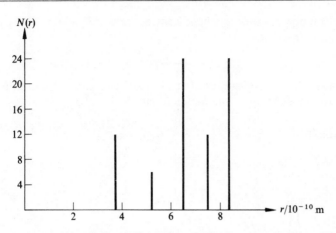

Fig. 11.3 The number of atoms $N(r)$ at a distance r from any one atom in solid argon.

11.3 shows the sort of information that one can obtain about solid argon (here at a temperature approaching absolute zero). The value of $N(r)$ records the number of atoms which are to be found at any specified distance r from an arbitrarily chosen central atom. If you like, this is another way of presenting the information that solid argon has an fcc structure.

Figure 11.4 shows what a snapshot of a liquid might look like. If the mean number of atoms per unit volume at radius r is $\rho(r)$, the total number of atoms whose centres lie within a shell of radii r and $r + \delta r$ is given by

$$\text{number in the shell} = (\text{volume of shell})(\text{atomic number-density in shell})$$
$$= 4\pi r^2 \, \delta r \, \rho(r) \qquad (11.2)$$

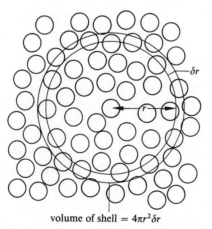

volume of shell $= 4\pi r^2 \delta r$

Fig. 11.4 A hypothetical "snapshot" of conditions in a liquid showing the disposition of neighbours about an arbitrarily chosen central atom. Although illustrated in two dimensions we consider the liquid to be three-dimensional.

371

This total number of atoms whose centres lie within the shell may also be written as $g(r)\,\delta r$ so that

$$g(r) = 4\pi r^2 \rho(r) \tag{11.3}$$

We shall call $\rho(r)$—the mean number of atoms per unit volume at a distance r from our reference atom—*the radial density.**

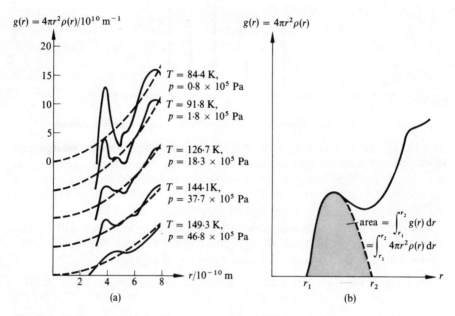

$g(r) = 4\pi r^2 \rho(r)/10^{10}\,\mathrm{m^{-1}}$

$g(r) = 4\pi r^2 \rho(r)$

$T = 84.4\,\mathrm{K},$
$p = 0.8 \times 10^5\,\mathrm{Pa}$

$T = 91.8\,\mathrm{K},$
$p = 1.8 \times 10^5\,\mathrm{Pa}$

$T = 126.7\,\mathrm{K},$
$p = 18.3 \times 10^5\,\mathrm{Pa}$

$T = 144.1\,\mathrm{K},$
$p = 37.7 \times 10^5\,\mathrm{Pa}$

$T = 149.3\,\mathrm{K},$
$p = 46.8 \times 10^5\,\mathrm{Pa}$

$r/10^{-10}\,\mathrm{m}$

$$\text{area} = \int_{r_1}^{r_2} g(r)\,dr$$
$$= \int_{r_1}^{r_2} 4\pi r^2 \rho(r)\,dr$$

(a)

(b)

Fig. 11.5 (a) Shows $g(r)$ for liquid argon at various points along the saturated liquid line. For clarity the ordinate values of successive curves are displaced by $5 \times 10^{10}\,\mathrm{m^{-1}}$. (b) Shows how the first coordination number may be estimated. (Data from A. Eisenstein and N. S. Ginrich, *Phys. Rev.*, **62**, 261 (1942).)

X-ray diffraction studies give the value of $g(r)$ and therefore the value of $\rho(r)$ (see eq. (11.3)). Figure 11.5(a) shows $g(r)$ for argon at six points along the saturated liquid line (line ac of Fig. 1.4). Since $T_{tr} = 83.8$ K we see that even at 0.6 K above the triple point the long-range order which is characteristic of the solid phase (Fig. 11.3) has all but disappeared although short-range order persists. As the temperature of the liquid is raised what peaks there are become less pronounced: the curves approximate more and more closely to the value to be expected for a perfect gas where $\rho(r)$ is constant at all r,

---

* Many and varied are the names given to $\rho(r)$ and $g(r)$. The name *radial distribution function* is commonly given to $\rho(r)$. We use the words radial density since $\rho(r)$ is indeed a number density (number per unit volume) and the description is shorter! Other authors call our $g(r)$ (eq. (11.3)) the radial distribution function. Yet other authors interchange the symbols $\rho(r)$ and $g(r)$ in eqs. (11.2) and (11.3). Our usage of $\rho(r)$ and $g(r)$ is the same as that to be found, for example, in *The Liquid State*, by J. A. Pryde (Hutchinson, 1966).

causing $g(r)$ to be proportional to r^2 (indicated by dotted line in Fig. 11.5(a)).

We can obtain the number of nearest neighbours to the atom at the origin by estimating the area under the first peak as shown in Fig. 11.5(b). This follows since the area is

$$\int_{r_1}^{r_2} g(r)\,dr = \int_{r_1}^{r_2} 4\pi r^2 \rho(r)\,dr = \text{number of atoms within shell of radii } r_1 \text{ and } r_2$$

(see eq. (11.2)). This number is called the *first coordination number*. Applying this technique to argon (Fig. 11.5(a)) shows that the first coordination number decreases from 12 in the solid (Fig. 11.3) to about 10 in the liquid near the triple point, to about 4 near the critical point. It is worth noting that the nearest-neighbour separation, given by the value of r at the maximum of the first peak, does not change significantly in going from the solid phase right through to the liquid phase close to the critical point ($T_c = 150\cdot7$ K).

We may eliminate the "gas" effect ($4\pi r^2$) inherent in plots of $g(r)$ by plotting instead $g(r)/4\pi r^2$, that is $\rho(r)$ (eq. (11.3)). In the limit as $r \to \infty$ the value of $\rho(r)$ will tend to $\rho_0 (= N_A/V_m)$, the average number density of the liquid as a whole. Figure 11.6 shows $\rho(r)/\rho_0$ for liquid argon. The peaks now show up a little more clearly than they did in Fig. 11.5(a). It is also perhaps more evident

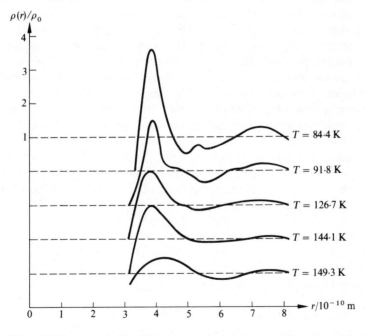

Fig. 11.6 The radial density $\rho(r)$ of liquid argon at various points along the saturated liquid line; the same points as in Fig. 11.5. Here ρ_0 is the mean number density in the liquid.

that their position does not alter significantly as we move along the saturated liquid line from near the triple point to near the critical point.

These X-ray studies confirm our suspicions—suspicions based on the thermal and mechanical properties of liquids—that close to the triple point a liquid possesses features reminiscent of a solid and that close to the critical point the features are reminiscent of a gas. So we know where a liquid, or to be precise a monatomic liquid, stands with respect to its solid and gaseous counterparts. But we have other aims. We would like to know something more of the structure of a liquid. We would also like to know its equation of state and its internal energy for, knowing these two, the equilibrium properties of the liquid could be deduced. In fact, structure cannot be fully considered in isolation. We shall shortly discover that to elucidate the equation of state, or the internal energy, we must know the structure of the liquid. We are about to unearth a fundamental problem inherent in predicting the structure of any liquid.

11.2 Clausius virial theorem: the equation of state

Deriving the equation of state of a perfect gas was a relatively simple task. It was made easy because we chose to define a perfect gas as one in which the atoms have effectively zero size and in which the interatomic force is zero. When we found that real gases failed to conform to the equation of state derived on the basis of these assumptions—namely $pV_m = RT$—we set about refining the model. We gave the atoms a finite size. We allowed them to interact. Introducing these refinements led to van der Waals' equation; an equation which is astonishingly successful in describing the behaviour of gases in their critical region—or, if you like, the behaviour of a liquid close to its critical point. The success was astonishing because normally when one modifies a theory by introducing "correction terms" the theory only works in regions where the correction terms are indeed small, and this is not true at the critical point. It would clearly be pushing our luck too far to hope that van der Waals' equation of state might apply close to the triple point where, as we have seen, a liquid more closely resembles a solid in some of its properties than a gas. (In problem 11.1 you will attempt to predict the tensile strength of a liquid at temperatures well below T_c via van der Waals' equation.) What we need to do is to derive the equation of state afresh, this time with the interatomic force characteristic built in *ab initio* rather than put it in as an afterthought. Although the derivation may *look* formidable you should be able to understand each step of the arguments. The final result (eq. (11.24)) is not too complex; nor is it too difficult to apply.

How a single atom behaves

We will consider a vessel in the form of a cube of side l (Fig. 11.7) containing N_A atoms of a monatomic fluid, each atom having a mass m. As the atoms

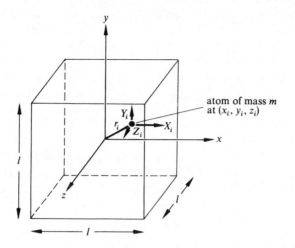

Fig. 11.7 The atom of mass m at point (x_i, y_i, z_i) is acted on by forces X_i, Y_i, Z_i.

move about in the fluid each will be subjected to a rapidly fluctuating force. At any one instant the force on atom i located at point (x_i, y_i, z_i)—we take the coordinate origin to be at the centre of the cube—may be resolved into its Cartesian components X_i, Y_i, Z_i. The response of the atom to this force is, of course, determined by Newton's second law:

$$X_i = m \frac{d^2 x_i}{dt^2} \tag{11.4}$$

or, multiplying both sides by x_i,

$$X_i x_i = m x_i \frac{d^2 x_i}{dt^2} \tag{11.5}$$

Similar equations apply for the other two force components along the y- and z-directions. We now make use of the following identity (the identity is nothing more than the rule for differentiating a product):

$$\frac{d}{dt}\left(m x_i \frac{dx_i}{dt} \right) = m x_i \frac{d^2 x_i}{dt^2} + m \left(\frac{dx_i}{dt} \right)^2$$

$$m x_i \frac{d^2 x_i}{dt^2} = - m \left(\frac{dx_i}{dt} \right)^2 + \frac{d}{dt}\left(m x_i \frac{dx_i}{dt} \right) \tag{11.6}$$

Substituting eq. (11.6) for the right-hand side of eq. (11.5) gives

$$X_i x_i = - m \left(\frac{dx_i}{dt} \right)^2 + m \frac{d}{dt}\left(x_i \frac{dx_i}{dt} \right) \tag{11.7}$$

375

Now

$$\frac{1}{2}\frac{d}{dt}\left[\frac{d(x_i^2)}{dt}\right] = \frac{d}{dt}\left(x_i\frac{dx_i}{dt}\right)$$

so that eq. (11.7) may be written as

$$X_i x_i + m\left(\frac{dx_i}{dt}\right)^2 = \frac{m}{2}\frac{d}{dt}\left[\frac{d(x_i^2)}{dt}\right] \tag{11.8}$$

Similar equations to (11.8) apply to the y- and the z-components;

$$Y_i y_i + m\left(\frac{dy_i}{dt}\right)^2 = \frac{m}{2}\frac{d}{dt}\left[\frac{d(y_i^2)}{dt}\right] \tag{11.9}$$

$$Z_i z_i + m\left(\frac{dz_i}{dt}\right)^2 = \frac{m}{2}\frac{d}{dt}\left[\frac{d(z_i^2)}{dt}\right] \tag{11.10}$$

Adding together eqs. (11.8), (11.9), and (11.10) gives

$$\frac{m}{2}\frac{d}{dt}\left[\frac{d}{dt}(x_i^2 + y_i^2 + z_i^2)\right] = X_i x_i + Y_i y_i + Z_i z_i +$$

$$m\left[\left(\frac{dx_i}{dt}\right)^2 + \left(\frac{dy_i}{dt}\right)^2 + \left(\frac{dz_i}{dt}\right)^2\right] \tag{11.11}$$

But $x_i^2 + y_i^2 + z_i^2 = r_i^2$ (Pythagoras's theorem in three dimensions) where r_i is the distance of atom i from the centre of the box (Fig. 11.7). Also $(dx_i/dt)^2 = u_{xi}^2$ where u_{xi} is the x-component of the velocity of i. Similar expressions apply along the y- and the z-directions. Therefore eq. (11.11) may be written as

$$\frac{m}{2}\frac{d}{dt}\left[\frac{d}{dt}(r_i^2)\right] = X_i x_i + Y_i y_i + Z_i z_i + m(u_{xi}^2 + u_{yi}^2 + u_{zi}^2)$$

But the speed u_i of atom i is related to the component speeds u_{xi}, u_{yi}, and u_{zi} by $u_i^2 = u_{xi}^2 + u_{yi}^2 + u_{zi}^2$ (eq. (3.12)) so we may write

$$\frac{m}{2}\frac{d}{dt}\left(\frac{d}{dt}r_i^2\right) = X_i x_i + Y_i y_i + Z_i z_i + mu_i^2 \tag{11.12}$$

How an atom behaves on average
Although we have considered only a single atom of the fluid, exactly the same analysis applies to each and every atom of the fluid. So writing down similar expressions to eq. (11.12) for all N_A atoms present we obtain, on adding all these expressions together,

$$\sum_i \frac{m}{2}\frac{d}{dt}\left(\frac{d}{dt}r_i^2\right) = \sum_i (X_i x_i + Y_i y_i + Z_i z_i) + \sum_i mu_i^2 \tag{11.13}$$

This represents what is happening at one instant of time in the fluid. As time goes by the distances r_i will vary as an atom changes position in the box; as it executes a random walk, in fact. However r_i cannot increase without limit for each atom is contained within the box. When a time-average is taken the left-hand side of eq. (11.13) vanishes,* giving

$$0 = \left\langle \sum_i (X_i x_i + Y_i y_i + Z_i z_i) \right\rangle + \left\langle \sum_i m_i u_i^2 \right\rangle \tag{11.14}$$

where we use $\langle \ \rangle$ to indicate averaging. This notation is more convenient here than the bar-notation which we used in earlier chapters.

Bringing in the forces acting on an atom

So far we have said nothing of the origin of the force on atom i. This force is made up of two contributions. Firstly, there will be the forces acting on it due to all other atoms in the fluid. Secondly, there will be forces acting on it due to all the atoms of the solid which make up the walls of the box. We may therefore write the component force X_i as

$$X_i = X_i' + X_i'' \tag{11.16}$$

where X_i' is the x-component of the resultant force acting on atom i attributable to all other atoms of the fluid, and X_i'' is the x-component of the resultant

---

* It is not difficult to prove this result. We rewrite each term inside the summation on the left-hand side of eq. (11.13) (ignoring the constant term m) as follows

$$\frac{1}{2} \frac{d}{dt} \left(\frac{d}{dt} r_i^2 \right) = \frac{d}{dt} \left(r_i \frac{dr_i}{dt} \right)$$

We now sum this over all atoms and then take the time-average of our summed expression. We have, by definition of time-average (over some time τ),

$$\left\langle \sum_i \frac{d}{dt} \left(r_i \frac{dr_i}{dt} \right) \right\rangle = \frac{1}{\tau} \int_0^\tau \sum_i \frac{d}{dt} \left(r_i \frac{dr_i}{dt} \right) dt$$

$$= \frac{1}{\tau} \int_0^\tau \sum_i d \left(r_i \frac{dr_i}{dt} \right)$$

$$= \frac{1}{\tau} \sum_i \left[\left(r_i \frac{dr_i}{dt} \right)_{t=\tau} - \left(r_i \frac{dr_i}{dt} \right)_{t=0} \right] \tag{11.15}$$

assuming $\sum$ and $\int$ commute (i.e., that their order can be "swapped"). It is not difficult to accept that provided τ is sufficiently large there will be no correlation between what happens at time 0 and at time τ, that is

$$\sum_i \left(r_i \frac{dr_i}{dt} \right)_{t=0} = \sum_i \left(r_i \frac{dr_i}{dt} \right)_{t=\tau} \qquad \text{as } \tau \to \infty$$

Even if the term in square brackets in eq. (11.15) is not identically zero for a particular atom i, it is equally likely to be positive or negative for any atom; the sum over all atoms will therefore more nearly vanish. Even if this suspicion is unjustified the presence of $1/\tau$ multiplying the right-hand side of eq. (11.15) should cause it to vanish as $\tau \to \infty$.

force attributable to all the atoms of the box. We may likewise write

$$Y_i = Y_i' + Y_i'' \tag{11.17}$$

and

$$Z_i = Z_i' + Z_i'' \tag{11.18}$$

Substituting eqs. (11.16), (11.17), and (11.18) into eq. (11.14) gives

$$\left\langle \sum_i (x_i X_i' + x_i X_i'' + y_i Y_i' + y_i Y_i'' + z_i Z_i'' + z_i Z_i'') \right\rangle = -\left\langle \sum_i mu_i^2 \right\rangle \tag{11.19}$$

where the summation is made over all N_A atoms in the box, and then this sum is time-averaged. We would expect X_i'', Y_i'', and Z_i'' only to be significant when atoms come to within a few atomic diameters of the wall. Therefore terms like $\sum_i x_i X_i''$ will make an essentially zero contribution except when $x = -\frac{1}{2}l$ and when $x = +\frac{1}{2}l$, and similarly for the y and z terms. We shall write the value of X_i'', for example, at $x = \frac{1}{2}l$ as $X_i''(\frac{1}{2}l)$. Equation (11.19) may therefore be written, with negligible error, as

$$\left\langle \left[\sum_i (x_i X_i' + y_i Y_i' + z_i Z_i') + \sum_i \tfrac{1}{2}l X_i''(\tfrac{1}{2}l) - \sum_i \tfrac{1}{2}l X_i''(-\tfrac{1}{2}l) + \sum_i \tfrac{1}{2}l Y_i''(\tfrac{1}{2}l) \right. \right.$$
$$\left. \left. - \sum_i \tfrac{1}{2}l Y_i''(-\tfrac{1}{2}l) + \sum_i \tfrac{1}{2}l Z_i''(\tfrac{1}{2}l) - \sum_i \tfrac{1}{2}l Z_i''(-\tfrac{1}{2}l) \right] \right\rangle = -\left\langle \sum_i mu_i^2 \right\rangle$$

or, since $\frac{1}{2}l$ is constant, as

$$\left\langle \left[\sum_i (x_i X_i' + y_i Y_i' + z_i Z_i') + \tfrac{1}{2}l \sum_i X_i''(\tfrac{1}{2}l) + \tfrac{1}{2}l \sum_i Y_i''(\tfrac{1}{2}l) + \tfrac{1}{2}l \sum_i Z_i''(\tfrac{1}{2}l) \right. \right.$$
$$\left. \left. - \tfrac{1}{2}l \sum_i X_i''(-\tfrac{1}{2}l) - \tfrac{1}{2}l \sum_i Y_i''(-\tfrac{1}{2}l) - \tfrac{1}{2}l \sum_i Z_i''(-\tfrac{1}{2}l) \right] \right\rangle = -\left\langle \sum_i mu_i^2 \right\rangle \tag{11.20}$$

The summations in the last six terms on the left-hand side of eq. (11.20) represent the *total* force between each face (such as that at $x = \frac{1}{2}l$) and the adjacent layer of atoms (those within a few atomic diameters of the face). Evaluating $\sum_i X_i''(\frac{1}{2}l)$, etc., might seem a daunting proposition. Fortunately we may appeal to Newton's third law, from which we deduce that the force exerted by the wall on the fluid will be equal in magnitude but opposite in direction to the force exerted by the fluid on the wall. We know that the force exerted by the fluid on, say, the yz face of area l^2 at $x = \frac{1}{2}l$, is $+pl^2$ where p is the pressure in the liquid. It therefore follows that $\sum_i X_i''(\frac{1}{2}l) = -pl^2$.

Writing down similar expressions, with due regard to sign, at each of the other five faces and substituting these expressions into eq. (11.20) gives

$$\left\langle \sum_i (x_i X_i' + y_i Y_i' + z_i Z_i') \right\rangle + 3[\tfrac{1}{2}l(-pl^2) - \tfrac{1}{2}l(pl^2)] = -\left\langle \sum_i mu_i^2 \right\rangle$$

where we have dispensed with $\langle \; \rangle$ around the terms involving p, since p is already time averaged (as measured experimentally). Remembering that V_{m},' the volume of the liquid, is l^3 gives

$$\left\langle \sum_i (x_i X_i' + y_i Y_i' + z_i Z_i') \right\rangle - 3pV_{\mathrm{m}} = - \left\langle \sum_i mu_i^2 \right\rangle \qquad (11.21)$$

Introducing the interatomic force

You might guess that the summation terms on the left-hand side of eq. (11.21) will vanish when summed over all atoms and then time-averaged. In fact, they fail to vanish because the atoms of the liquid are not independent.

Consider a pair of atoms i and j separated by distance r_{ji} (Fig. 11.8). Let X_{ij}' denote the *part* of the net force X_i' acting on i (the first suffix in X_{ij}') which is due to atom j (the second suffix). We may likewise write X_{ji}' to denote that *part* of the net force X_j' acting on j which is due to i. By Newton's third law, $X_{ji}' = - X_{ij}'$. The contribution which X_{ij}' and X_{ji}' make to the first term in eq. (11.21) is

$$x_i X_{ij}' + x_j X_{ji}' = X_{ji}'(x_j - x_i) \qquad (11.22)$$

In the liquid inert gases the force between two atoms is directed along the line joining their centres. With such a, so-called, *central* force present we write for X_{ji}' (which, remember, means that part of the force on j due to i):

$$X_{ji}' = F(r_{ji}) \cos \theta$$

where θ is the angle r_{ji} makes with the x-axis and $F(r_{ji})$ is the central force at interatomic separation r_{ji}. But $\cos \theta = (x_j - x_i)/r_{ji}$ (you can see this immediately if your shift the axes without changing their direction so that the origin is at atom i in Fig. 11.8). Therefore

$$X_{ji}' = F(r_{ji}) \left(\frac{x_j - x_i}{r_{ji}} \right)$$

Substituting this expression for X_{ji}' into eq. (11.22) gives

$$x_i X_{ij}' + x_j X_{ji}' = F(r_{ji}) \frac{(x_j - x_i)^2}{r_{ji}}$$

and likewise for the y and z contributions. Feeding all three such relations into eq. (11.21) gives

$$\left\langle \sum_{\mathrm{pairs}} \frac{F(r_{ji})}{r_{ji}} [(x_j - x_i)^2 + (y_j - y_i)^2 + (z_j - z_i)^2] \right\rangle - 3pV_{\mathrm{m}} = - \left\langle \sum_i mu_i^2 \right\rangle$$

379

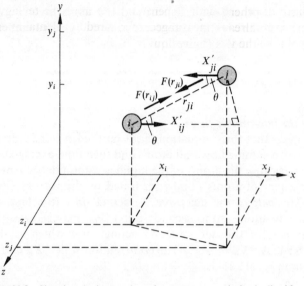

Fig. 11.8 Showing the interaction of two atoms i and j in the liquid.

But the expression inside the square brackets is none other than the expression for r_{ji}^2 (Fig. 11.8) so

$$\left\langle \sum_{\text{pairs}} F(r_{ji})r_{ji} \right\rangle - 3pV_{\text{m}} = -\left\langle \sum_i mu_i^2 \right\rangle$$

or, reverting to our bar notation for averages,

$$\overline{\sum_{\text{pairs}} F(r_{ji})r_{ji}} - 3pV_{\text{m}} = -\sum_i \overline{mu_i^2} = -2\sum_i \overline{\tfrac{1}{2}mu_i^2} \tag{11.23}$$

Introducing the temperature

Since $\tfrac{1}{2}\overline{mu_i^2} = \tfrac{3}{2}kT$, eq. (11.23) becomes

$$\overline{\sum_{\text{pairs}} F(r_{ji})r_{ji}} - 3pV_{\text{m}} = -3\sum_i kT$$

where the right-hand side is summed over all N_A atoms. Therefore, since $3N_A kT = 3RT$,

$$pV_{\text{m}} = RT + \tfrac{1}{3}\overline{\sum_{\text{pairs}} F(r_{ji})r_{ji}} \tag{11.24}$$

This is the *Clausius virial theorem* for atoms with central forces. It says that to find the equation of state of a fluid all one needs to do is multiply the central force $F(r_{ji})$ between a pair of atoms by their distance r_{ji} apart between centres, sum these products over *all* pairs in the fluid, take the average of this result as measured at different times and then substitute the result into eq. (11.24). It makes no difference whether the fluid be a liquid or a gas for no specific atomic model was assumed. In a fluid composed of atoms of effectively zero size in which $F(r) = 0$ for all r, eq. (11.24) reduces to the equation of state of a perfect gas, $pV_m = RT$, as it must if the analysis is correct.

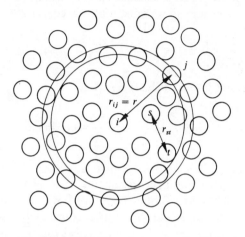

Fig. 11.9 Showing the spatial distribution of atoms in a liquid about a central atom i.

Introducing the interatomic potential

Although eq. (11.24) can be used as it stands, it is much more useful to have the radial density $\rho(r)$ in the result as this is the quantity that is determined experimentally from X-ray studies. If we choose i as the reference atom as shown in Fig. 11.9 and j as one of the atoms in the spherical shell of radius $r = r_{ji}$, then $F(r_{ji}) = -d\mathscr{V}(r)/dr$ where $\mathscr{V}(r)$ is the interatomic pair potential. The form of this potential will, of course, depend on the nature of the atoms in the fluid and it may be possible to represent it by a Mie or Lennard-Jones model. In any event $\mathscr{V}(r)$ will have the general form shown in Fig. 2.8(c). The atoms whose centres lie within the shell of radius r and thickness δr make a contribution of

$$\overline{\sum_{\text{shell}} r_{ji} F(r_{ji})} = r\left(-\frac{d\mathscr{V}(r)}{dr}\right)(4\pi r^2 \, dr \, \rho(r)) \tag{11.25}$$

for the particular atom i. The term $4\pi r^2 \rho(r)$ represents the number of atoms whose centres lie within the shell, each of which is at a distance r from i (eq. (11.2)). To find the contribution to atom i of all other atoms eq. (11.25) must be integrated from $r = 0$ to $r = \infty$:

$$\overline{\sum_j r_{ji} F(r_{ji})} = -\int_0^\infty \frac{d\mathscr{V}(r)}{dr}\rho(r)4\pi r^3 \, dr \tag{11.26}$$

However this only includes some of the pairs; the interaction between i and the other atoms. Equation (11.24) affirms that *all* pairs must be included. We must include the interaction of atom s, say, with all other atoms (Fig. 11.9). You might think that this could be taken care of by multiplying eq. (11.26) by N_A. In fact, to multiply by N_A would include each pair twice; atom s at distance r_{st} from atom t *and* atom t at a distance $r_{ts} = r_{st}$ from atom s. We only want each pair to occur once and so we must multiply eq. (11.26) by $N_A/2$:

$$\overline{\sum_{\text{pairs}} r_{ji} F(r_{ji})} = - \frac{N_A}{2} \int_0^\infty \frac{d\mathscr{V}(r)}{dr} \rho(r) 4\pi r^3 \, dr$$

Substituting this result into eq. (11.24) gives

$$pV_m = RT - \frac{N_A}{6} \int_0^\infty \frac{d\mathscr{V}(r)}{dr} \rho(r) 4\pi r^3 \, dr \qquad (11.27)$$

as the more immediately useful form of the Clausius virial theorem. It is worth reminding ourselves that $\rho(r)$ depends on the state of the liquid, that is on say, p and T (Fig. 11.6). We should therefore have written $\rho(r, p, T)$ rather than $\rho(r)$ in eq. (11.27); for economy we shall continue to use $\rho(r)$.

So, knowing $\rho(r)$—sorry, $\rho(r, p, T)$—and $\mathscr{V}(r)$ we may predict the equation of state of any fluid. We would appear to have reached one of our goals.

Exercise 11.2

This exercise will allow you to predict the pressure of a liquid at a stated volume and temperature. By repeating the procedure at other volumes and temperatures you could arrive at the (empirical) form of the equation of state.

Using the Clausius virial theorem predict the pressure of liquid argon at a (mass) density of 0.98×10^3 kg m^{-3} at 143 K. Figure 11.10(a) shows the form of $\rho(r)$ at this density—which is nearly the density of water—and temperature. The radial density $\rho(r)$ is expressed in units of ρ_0, the mean number density of the liquid as a whole. (The data comes from X-ray studies by P. G. Mikolaj and C. J. Pings, *J. Chem. Phys.*, **46**, 1401 (1967).) Also shown in Fig. 11.10(a) is a plot of r^3 and the derivative with respect to r of the Lennard-Jones potential $\mathscr{V}(r)$ for the interaction between two argon atoms, namely

$$\mathscr{V}(r) = 4\varepsilon \left[\left(\frac{\sigma}{r} \right)^{12} - \left(\frac{\sigma}{r} \right)^6 \right] \qquad (11.28)$$

In argon $\varepsilon/k = 120$ K and $\sigma = 3.4 \times 10^{-10}$ m. To help you, the product $d\mathscr{V}(r)/dr [\rho(r)/\rho_0] r^3$ is shown in Fig. 11.10(b). In evaluating the integral term in eq. (11.27) you can do so graphically ("counting squares") or by

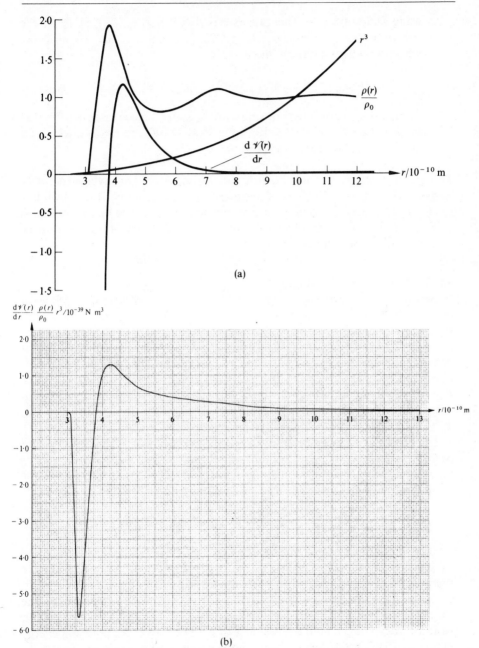

Fig. 11.10 (a) Shows the dependence of $d\mathscr{V}'(r)/dr$, $\rho(r)/\rho_0$, and r^3 on r for liquid argon at a temperature of 143 K and a density of 0.98×10^3 kg m^{-3}. Each scale division of the ordinate corresponds to $d\mathscr{V}'(r)/dr = 1 \times 10^{-11}$ N, $\rho(r)/\rho_0 = 1$, and $r^3 = 1.0 \times 10^{-27}$ m^3. (b) The dependence of $d\mathscr{V}'(r)/dr\,[\rho(r)/\rho_0]r^3$ on r.

383

using Simpson's rule. This rule asserts that if $f_0, f_1, f_2, \ldots, f_{n-1}, f_n$ are the values of $f(x)$ at $x = a, a+h, a+2h, \ldots, a+(n-1)h, a+nh \ (=b)$, where n is an even integer, then

$$\int_a^b f(x)\,dx \approx \frac{h}{3}\left[f_0 + f_n + 4(f_1 + f_3 + \cdots + f_{n-1}) + 2(f_2 + f_4 + \cdots + f_{n-2})\right]$$

Compare your predicted pressure with the experimental value of $6 \cdot 7 \times 10^6$ Pa at the density of $0 \cdot 98 \times 10^3$ kg m^{-3} at 143 K and try to track down any discrepancy. Take $A_r(\text{Ar}) = 40$.

This exercise will have brought home to you the importance of having accurately known values of $\rho(r)$. The sort of accuracy which is required if worthwhile p (or V_m or T) values are to be predicted exceeds the accuracy that is realizable in X-ray studies. A major objective of the structural theory of liquids must be to obtain this information.

11.3   The internal energy

In section 1.5 we introduced the molar internal energy U_m; the difference between the value of which at two states f and i is the change in the energy of the system in going from i to f. This was a thermodynamic definition which involved no knowledge of the microscopic nature of the system. However it does seem reasonable to assume that U_m represents the sum of the atoms' kinetic and potential energies. We shall assume it to be so. We will also take $U_m = 0$ when the atoms are an infinite distance apart and at rest. Macroscopically this is equivalent to taking $U_m = 0$ at $V_m = \infty$, $T = 0$; at this V_m and T the atoms will be an infinite distance apart and at rest.

The potential energy stored (in the field) between atom i in Fig. 11.9 and each atom such as j, lying within the shell of radius r and thickness dr is $\mathscr{V}(r)$. Since there are $4\pi r^2\,dr\rho(r)$ atoms within the shell the potential energy of i due to all these atoms is $4\pi r^2 \rho(r)\mathscr{V}(r)\,dr$. Integrating from $r = 0$ to $r = \infty$ gives

$$\text{potential energy of } i = \int_0^\infty \mathscr{V}(r)\rho(r)4\pi r^2\,dr \tag{11.29}$$

To find the total potential energy Φ of the N_A atoms in one mole of liquid we must multiply this expression by $N_A/2$. To multiply by N_A would include the potential energy contribution between each pair of atoms twice over. (In evaluating the integral, eq. (11.29), about i in Fig. 11.9, one includes the contribution $\mathscr{V}(r_{ij})$ due to the presence of j. In evaluating the integral about j one includes $\mathscr{V}(r_{ji})$ due to the presence of i. Since $\mathscr{V}(r)$ is the potential energy of a *pair* of atoms only one of these contributions must be counted.) So

$$\Phi_m = \frac{N_A}{2}\int_0^\infty \mathscr{V}(r)\rho(r)4\pi r^2\,dr \tag{11.30}$$

The average kinetic energy of an atom is $\frac{1}{2}m\overline{u^2} = \frac{3}{2}kT$ so the total kinetic energy of all N_A atoms is $N_A(\frac{3}{2}kT) = \frac{3}{2}RT$. The total energy of the N_A atoms is therefore given by:

$$U_m = \tfrac{3}{2}RT + \frac{N_A}{2}\int_0^\infty \mathscr{V}(r)\rho(r)4\pi r^2\,dr \tag{11.31}$$

This may, of course, also be written as

$$U_m = \tfrac{3}{2}RT + \tfrac{1}{2}\sum_{\text{pairs}} V(r_{ji}) \tag{11.32}$$

So, once again, if $\mathscr{V}(r)$ and $\rho(r)$ are known the integral can be evaluated. Assuming that the internal energy of the fluid is indeed the sum of the kinetic and the potential energies of the constituent atoms, the techniques of thermodynamics could now be applied to elucidate the equilibrium properties of the fluid starting from U_m and the equation of state.

Exercise 11.3

Predict the molar internal energy of liquid argon at a mass density of 0.98×10^3 kg m^{-3} at a temperature of 143 K. Figure 11.11(a) shows the variation of $\rho(r)/\rho_0$ with r at this density and temperature, where ρ_0 is the average number density of the liquid as a whole. Also shown is a plot of r^2 and the Lennard-Jones potential $\mathscr{V}(r)$ for the interaction between two argon atoms, namely eq. (11.28) with $\varepsilon/k = 120$ K and $\sigma = 3.4 \times 10^{-10}$ m. To help you, the product $\mathscr{V}(r)[\rho(r)/\rho_0]r^2$ is plotted in Fig. 11.11(b). Compare your predicted value for U_m with the experimental value of -1.7×10^3 J mol^{-1}.

In working through this exercise you will have discovered, as in predicting the pressure in the liquid, that the value calculated for U_m depends crucially on the form of $\rho(r)$. X-ray studies are incapable of providing sufficiently accurate information on $\rho(r)$ to make the predicted values of U_m worth adopting in practice.

11.4 The structure of simple liquids

Theoretical approach

We have seen the importance of having accurate information on the radial density, and how very small changes in $\rho(r)$ can cause extremely large changes in the equation of state and in the internal energy. The form of $\mathscr{V}(r)$ seldom causes serious problems.

So far we have treated $\rho(r)$ and $\mathscr{V}(r)$ as if they are independent of one another, yet a moment's thought will show that this is very unlikely to be the case. Consider the two hypothetical forms of $\mathscr{V}(r)$ shown in Fig. 11.12. If

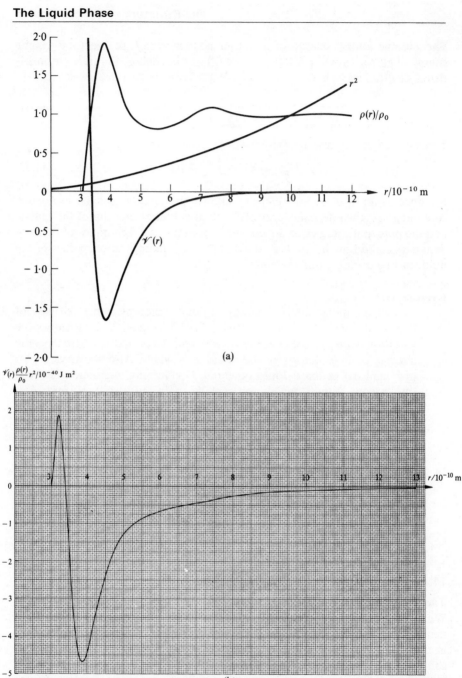

Fig. 11.11 (a) Shows the dependence of $\mathscr{V}(r)$, $\rho(r)/\rho_0$, and r^2 on r for liquid argon at a density of 0.98×10^3 kg m^{-3} and a temperature of 143 K. Each scale division of the ordinate corresponds to $\mathscr{V}(r) = 1 \times 10^{-21}$ J, $\rho(r)/\rho_0 = 1$, and $r^2 = 1 \times 10^{-18}$ m^2. (b) The dependence of $\mathscr{V}(r)[\rho(r)/\rho_0]r^2$ on r.

$\mathscr{V}(r)$ has the form shown in Fig. 11.12(a) then atoms farther apart than the atomic diameter r_0 will have no affinity for one another. If it has the form shown in Fig. 11.12(b), atoms whose separations lie within the range r_0 to r_1 will have a strong affinity for one another. It would be very surprising if the radial density arising out of these interactions were the same in both cases. We might well expect much more closely knit groups of atoms to exist in a fluid in which $\mathscr{V}(r)$ has the form shown in Fig. 11.12(b) than in a fluid in which $\mathscr{V}(r)$ has the form shown in Fig. 11.12(a).

The connection between $\rho(r)$ and $\mathscr{V}(r)$ is, however, not as simple as these arguments might suggest. You will remember that $\rho(r)$ is the number density of atoms which are present *on average* at a radial distance r from a particular (reference) atom. To find $\rho(r)$ we would therefore have to elucidate all possible atomic configurations consistent with the external constraints (p, T) and, from this, calculate the mean configuration. Now the probability that a collection of N_A interacting atoms has a particular configuration—and by configuration we mean that the position and momentum of all N_A atoms are specified—depends on the total energy of that configuration. This energy is the sum of the kinetic and potential energies of all N_A atoms. The mutual potential energy of all the atoms depends of course on how the atoms are arranged in that configuration! There are several techniques available for breaking this "radial density depends on the potential energy which depends on how the atoms are arranged" loop, but none of these techniques can be easily described in words. Each one of these methods involves making approximations which necessarily

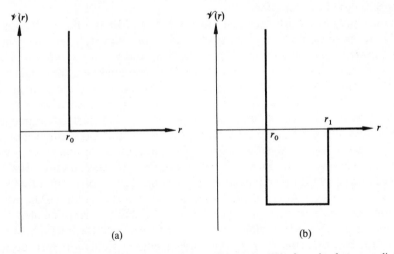

Fig. 11.12 Two (hypothetical) models for the potential energy $\mathscr{V}(r)$ of a pair of atoms a distance r apart. In (a) there is no attractive force between the atoms; only a hard-sphere repulsion at $r \leq r_0$. In (b) there is an attractive force when $r_0 < r < r_1$ and a hard-sphere repulsion at $r \leq r_0$.

limit the range of application of the results. No one analytic theory can describe how the properties of a liquid change as one moves throughout the liquid region (the area shown shaded in Fig. 11.1).

Mechanical simulations

Faced with a knotty theoretical problem we once again turn to simulation techniques. If we can make visible the motion of the "atoms" we will be able to determine the value of $\rho(r)$ directly and therefore to find the equation of state and the internal energy via eqs. (11.27) and (11.31). As an added bonus, a simulator should give us some feel for what a liquid is like at the atomic level. We will be able to see individual "atoms" move about and to form an overall impression of what the liquid is like at any instant in time. Furthermore we will be able to see how this picture changes with time. Contrast this with the rather more limited objectives of analytic theories. The only structural information which can be gleaned from these studies is the average radial density $\rho(r)$; a quantity which is spatially-averaged (throughout the body of the fluid) and time-averaged.

The first serious attempts at simulating a monatomic liquid were those made by J. D. Bernal in the 1950s. He argued that a liquid consists of a *heap* of atoms, unlike a solid which consists of a *pile* of atoms. A pile is produced when spheres, such as marbles, are carefully poured into a box; the "atoms" crystallize into a regular structure. A heap results when the spheres are tossed into the box. However, if one uses an ordinary box some "crystallization" of the balls will occur at the faces of the box. To prevent this, Bernal "dimpled" the inner surfaces of the container.

In one study Scott, who worked independently of Bernal but who adopted similar techniques, poured 4,000 steel balls ($\frac{1}{8}$ in. diameter) into a cylinder whose inner surface was dimpled. After shaking them down molten wax was poured in and allowed to set. One side of the container was next taken off and the outside layers of balls and wax were removed to produce a caviar-like cluster of balls. The top surface of each ball in turn was cleared of wax and polished. Each ball then acted as a spherical mirror which formed an image of the filament of a small lamp. Measuring the x-, y-, and z-coordinates of this point image, using a travelling microscope, gave the coordinates of a ball. After the measurements on a ball were complete the surrounding wax was scraped away and the ball removed. In all, the coordinates of about a thousand balls were measured. An arbitrarily selected ball near the middle of the cluster was used as origin and the distances to all other balls were calculated from the coordinate data. The radial density was then deduced for intervals of one-fifth of the ball diameter (via eq. (11.2)). The entire calculation was repeated using 25 different balls as origin. The average radial density (and the standard deviation in it) was then found from these 25 radial density calculations. Figure 11.13(a) shows the resulting average radial density $\rho(r)$ expressed in units

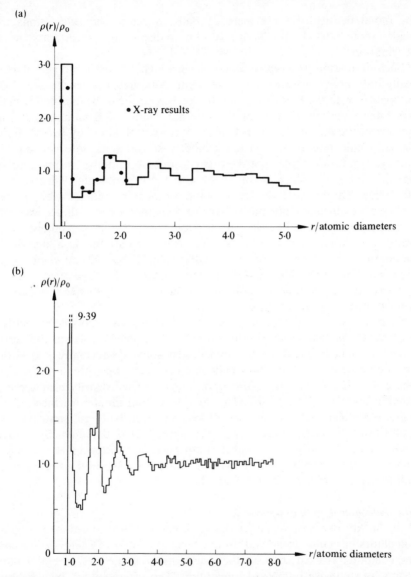

Fig. 11.13 (a) The radial density $\rho(r)$ of random close-packed spheres. (G. D. Scott, *Nature*, **194,** 956 (1962).) Here ρ_0 is the mean number density in the heap of balls. Also shown is the radial density in liquid argon close to its triple point (determined from X-ray diffraction data). (b) Scott's data reanalysed to take account of the distribution about 268 balls. Here the intervals in r are one-twentieth of a ball diameter (compared to one-fifth in (a)). (Data from G. Mason, *Nature,* **217,** 734 (1968).)

of the mean density ρ_0. Also shown in Fig. 11.13(a) are the experimental values for $\rho(r)/\rho_0$ for argon close to the triple point. Figure 11.13(b) shows the result of a more recent analysis of Scott's 1962 data. Here, instead of determining

389

the radial density about a mere 25 balls as centre the calculations were made about 268 balls. Naturally this reduces the uncertainty in the distribution.

Such simulations reproduce conditions in a high density liquid and therefore really only apply close to the triple point. Although the results are closely compatible with the X-ray data they are too inaccurate to be used in predicting either the equation of state or the internal energy of a monatomic liquid. Results very similar to those of Fig. 11.13(a) were obtained by Bernal. Indeed Bernal's main interest was in the geometry of "random close packing". He worked out, for example, that the first coordination number in his simulated liquid is 9.3 ± 0.8, which is consistent with the experimental value of about 10 in liquid argon near the triple point. From our point of view, perhaps his most worthwhile contribution was to demonstrate, in a direct way, what a monatomic liquid is like close to its triple point. Put at its simplest: If you want an instantaneous snapshot of what conditions are like in a high density liquid, throw some balls into an (irregular shaped) box. If you want another snapshot of what the liquid is like at a later instant, repeat the operation!

There are a number of criticisms which we might make of Bernal's simulator. Firstly, it but poorly reproduces the interatomic forces present between real atoms; the force between two balls is only hard-sphere repulsive. (Because the balls have weight there is however an effective downward vertical force between a ball and the one immediately above it.) Secondly, it is static—and we know that the atoms' kinetic energy cannot be ignored in the liquid phase. Thirdly, it only simulates conditions at a fixed density near the triple point. In section 3.2 we described a two-dimensional simulator which is free of these particular defects. It uses oil-coated steel balls to simulate more realistically the interatomic forces. Furthermore it is dynamic. By studying such a simulator in action—and it is not hard to construct the simulator— you can learn something of the dynamic nature of a liquid. Figure 3.2(b) is a still from a cine film made of this simulator.

The molecular dynamics approach

With the advent of large capacity electronic computers the need for mechanical simulators has come to an end. In one technique, that of *molecular dynamics,* the computer is used to solve the equations of motion of several hundred atoms by step-wise numerical integration. The principle can be very easily described: Allow a fixed number of particles to interact with one another according to the appropriate interatomic force characteristic, and see what happens. In this technique the total energy of all the atoms (kinetic plus potential) is constant in a particular "experiment"; the temperature of the system is found from the average kinetic energy of the atoms. Were one to attempt to solve the problem *analytically* one would find that even with as few as three atoms the problem cannot be solved exactly. The peculiar strength of the computer lies in its ability to *numerically* integrate the equations of motion of the atoms. The technique of molecular dynamics is at present the most powerful tool for deriving the macroscopic and microscopic properties of large assemblies of classical particles which interact according to a specified interparticle potential. Such is its success that it is really only limited by the accuracy to which the interatomic potential is known.

The computational steps

Let us look at the main steps involved in such a computer simulation; the details vary from author to author. First one allocates coordinates to all N atoms—the value of N depends on the computer's capacity, but is typically several hundred—so as to locate them at random somewhere inside a fixed volume V, usually in the form of a cube. These coordinates are, of course, stored in the computer. Knowing the position of each atom it is a simple matter to work out the forces $F(r_1)$, $F(r_2)$, $F(r_3)$, etc., which an atom will experience due to the other atoms of the liquid. Figure 11.14(a) shows how these forces are calculated from the interatomic potential $\mathscr{V}(r)$ via $F(r) = -\,\mathrm{d}\mathscr{V}(r)/\mathrm{d}r$. So we know the forces which act on an atom. The next step is to find the resultant force $F = F(r_1) + F(r_2) + F(r_3) + \cdots$ acting on an atom. This is done using the familiar "head to tail" rule as shown in Fig. 11.14(b). Exactly the same procedure is carried out on each and every atom in the system; we therefore know the resultant force which acts on each and every atom in the system. These forces are shown in heavy line in Fig. 11.14(b).

Next one allocates a random velocity to each atom; the dotted lines in Fig. 11.14(c) denote these velocity vectors. In practice one usually gives each atom the same speed but in a randomly chosen direction. This obvious bias—that all the atoms of the system have the same speed—will quickly be eliminated as the "experiment" proceeds. (The same is true of any bias made in allocating starting positions to each atom. Even if the atoms are located on a regular lattice the structure will soon melt—provided $\frac{1}{2}mu^2$ is large enough for this to happen.) So we now have, as in Fig. 11.14(c), the initial configuration at time $t = 0$. We know the starting velocity of each atom; we know the starting position of each atom.

What we want to know is what the atoms are up to at a later time δt. In the technique of molecular dynamics the time interval δt is deliberately chosen small enough that the resultant force which acts on each atom remains sensibly constant, or as nearly constant that it can be taken *as* constant, during the time interval δt. In other words δt must be sufficiently small that the atoms will not move far enough for the interatomic forces $F(r)$ to change by any appreciable amount. A typical value used is 10^{-14} s; in this time an atom with a speed of 10^3 m s^{-1} will have travelled 10^{-11} m, which is roughly one-tenth of an atomic diameter.

It is a simple problem in Newtonian mechanics to calculate where an atom

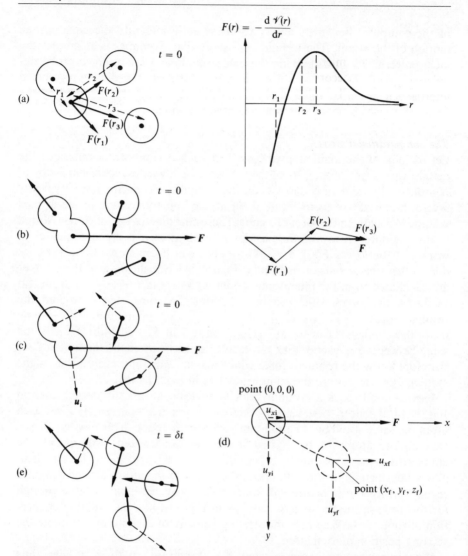

Fig. 11.14 The main steps in a molecular dynamics simulation: (a) The forces experienced by an atom are calculated using $F(r) = -d\mathscr{V}(r)/dr$. (b) The resultant force acting on each atom is found using the head-to-tail rule. (c) The atoms are given random velocities (shown dashed). (d) How an individual atom with velocity components u_{xi} and u_{yi} reacts to a constant force $\textbf{F}$. (e) The situation at a time δt later than in (c).

of mass m with a velocity $\textbf{\textit{u}}_i$ at time $t = 0$ will be at a later time δt, and what its velocity will be at time δt. The calculation only calls for a knowledge of Newton's second law and of two results from elementary kinematics (results you may know as $u_f = u_i + at$ and $s = u_i t + \frac{1}{2}at^2$). What we—or rather the computer—do is to resolve the velocity vector $\textbf{\textit{u}}_i$ of our atom at $t = 0$ into

392

three components; u_{xi} along the x-axis (which is taken for convenience to be along the direction of the resultant force F which acts on our atom) and u_{yi} and u_{zi} along axes perpendicular to each other and to F. If we denote the component speeds of our atom at time δt by u_{xf}, u_{yf} and u_{zf} (Fig. 11.14(d)) then, clearly

$$u_{xf} = u_{xi} + \left(\frac{F}{m}\right)\delta t$$

$$u_{yf} = u_{yi}$$

$$u_{zf} = u_{zi}$$

If we denote the final position of the atom at time δt by x_f, y_f, z_f then, since it started off at time $t = 0$ from the origin of our coordinate system (Fig. 11.14(d)),

$$x_f = u_{xi}\,\delta t + \frac{1}{2}\left(\frac{F}{m}\right)(\delta t)^2$$

$$y_f = u_{yi}\,\delta t$$

$$z_f = u_{zi}\,\delta t$$

Carrying out these calculations on each and every atom in the system tells us where every atom is at time δt and what its velocity is at time δt. What the computer now does is to calculate the *new* (resultant) force which acts on each atom (as in Figs. 11.14(a) and (b)) using the position data at time δt. It then regards these new forces (shown in heavy line in Fig. 11.14(e)) as constant between time δt and $2\delta t$ and proceeds to calculate what such forces will do to atoms whose initial velocities are those existing at time δt (shown dotted in Fig. 11.14(e)). The entire operation is then repeated at times $2\delta t$, $3\delta t$, $4\delta t$, and so on.

As the computation of one configuration after another proceeds a check is made on the speed distribution of the atoms. Once a Maxwell–Boltzmann distribution is realized we may take it that the original contrived configuration has given way to one which truly represents conditions in a system of atoms interacting according to the chosen potential $\mathscr{V}(r)$. The time it takes to reach equilibrium depends on the form of $\mathscr{V}(r)$—hardly surprising since this determines how they interact (or "collide")—but it may be of order $100\delta t$. When equilibrium is reached the average kinetic energy of the atoms, $\frac{1}{2}m\overline{u^2}$, will tell us the temperature of the system (from $\frac{1}{2}m\overline{u^2} = \frac{3}{2}kT$). To explore how the system behaves at, say, a higher temperature the entire "experiment" must be repeated using increased initial velocities for the atoms. To change the density (i.e., V_m) of the system a different number of atoms is introduced into the box and the entire "experiment" is repeated. The time it takes to perform a single "experiment" obviously depends on the computer being used but, to put round figures to it, a large machine may evaluate 1000 configurations every hour in a system of 1000 atoms.

Once the data on each configuration—and a configuration, remember, comprises the position and velocity of every atom in the system—has been stored in the computer the next step is to use this information to compute the $p-V_m-T$ relation and the internal energy U_m of the system by means of eqs. (11.24) and (11.32). In averaging over all configurations we are, of course, taking a time-average, which is what the theory requires. Since the equation of state and the internal energy are, in effect, known the computer can be programmed to predict any other equilibrium properties of the system.

Results of computer studies

Extensive investigations have been carried out using these techniques on the properties of a substance whose interatomic potential can be represented by a Lennard-Jones 6–12 potential. The predicted properties are generally in excellent agreement with experiment throughout the entire liquid range, from the triple to the critical point. Figure 11.15 shows the level of agreement which results between the experimental equation of state of argon and molecular dynamics calculations.

Such is the success of molecular dynamic calculations that small discrepancies between theory and experiment can often be traced to slight departures of the interatomic potential from the assumed model. They can also be used to

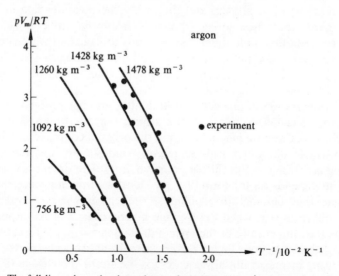

Fig. 11.15 The full lines show the dependence of pV_m/RT on T^{-1} at various densities (that is, at various V_m) as predicted by a molecular dynamics study of argon. (Data from L. Verlet, *Phys. Rev.*, **159**, 98 (1967).) A Lennard-Jones 6–12 potential was assumed with $\varepsilon/k = 119{\cdot}8$ K and $\sigma = 3{\cdot}405 \times 10^{-10}$ m. The experimental results are those of many workers.

predict, with some confidence, the properties of a substance in technically awkward ranges of p, V_m, and T. This is perhaps part of the reason why these simulations are referred to as "experiments".

As another example of the application of computer simulation techniques we will consider a liquid alkali halide, such as liquid potassium chloride. Here there is not just one potential $\mathscr{V}(r)$ but three; $\mathscr{V}(r)^{+-}$ between a K^+ and a Cl^- ion; $\mathscr{V}(r)^{++}$ between two K^+ ions, and $\mathscr{V}(r)^{--}$ between two Cl^- ions.

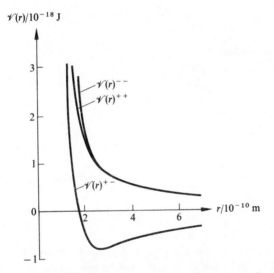

Fig. 11.16 The interatomic potential energy of a K^+–Cl^- ion pair ($\mathscr{V}(r)^{+-}$), a Cl^-–Cl^- pair ($\mathscr{V}(r)^{--}$), and a K^+–K^+ pair ($\mathscr{V}(r)^{++}$) as assumed by L. V. Woodcock and K. Singer (*Trans. Faraday Soc.*, **67**, 12 (1971)) in computing the data presented in Figs. 11.17 and 11.18.

These potentials may be represented as shown in Fig. 11.16, where it is assumed that the potential energy is zero at $r = \infty$. You should be able to work out for yourself why $\mathscr{V}(r)^{--}$ and $\mathscr{V}(r)^{++}$ are always positive and are proportional to r^{-1} at large r. (The reason why $\mathscr{V}(r)^{--}$ and $\mathscr{V}(r)^{++}$ differ at small interatomic separations is that the Cl^- and the K^+ ions have slightly different sizes so that repulsive (overlap) forces come into play at different r in these two interactions.) Figure 11.17 shows how closely the predictions made by computer simulation fit the experimental values of the internal energy. (Actually the computer results were obtained using a somewhat different technique—Monte Carlo—to the one we described.) Analytic techniques have not yet been developed which can discuss a system like liquid potassium chloride with its three different potential energy functions. Because of these three potential energy functions (Fig. 11.16) there are three different radial density curves; namely the radial density $\rho_l(r)$ of ions of like sign to that of the reference ion, the radial density $\rho_u(r)$ of ions of unlike sign, and the mean

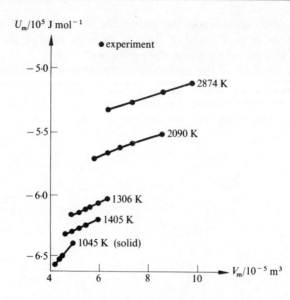

Fig. 11.17 The predicted molar internal energy of KCl as a function of molar volume at five different temperatures. Apart from along the isotherm labelled $T = 1045$ K, the KCl was in the liquid phase. (Data from L. V. Woodcock and K. Singer, *Trans. Faraday Soc.*, **67**, 12 (1971).)

radial density $\rho_m(r)$ ignoring sign. All of these can, of course, be computed from the data stored in the computer. Figure 11.18 shows the values obtained on making this calculation for liquid potassium chloride at 1045 K and at $V_m = 4.88 \times 10^{-5}$ m^3 mol^{-1}. You should be able to explain why each peak in the $\rho_1(r)$ curve occurs at a larger r than does the corresponding peak in the $\rho_u(r)$ curve.

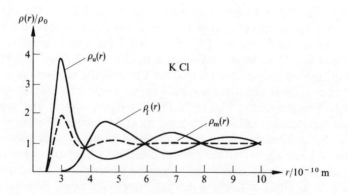

Fig. 11.18 The radial density predicted for ions of like sign, $\rho_1(r)$, of unlike sign, $\rho_u(r)$, and the mean radial density $\rho_m(r)$ ignoring sign in liquid KCl at $T = 1045$ K, $V_m = 4.88 \times 10^{-5}$ m^3 mol^{-1}. (Data from L. V. Woodcock and K. Singer, *Trans. Faraday Soc.*, **67**, 12 (1971).)

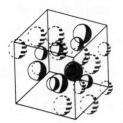
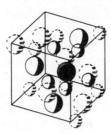
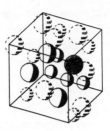
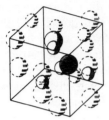
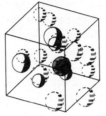
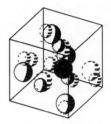
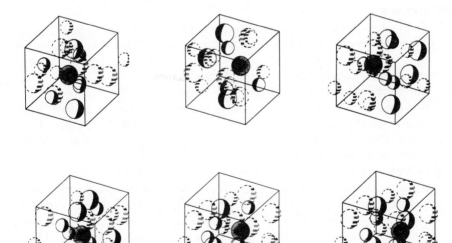

Fig. 11.19 A series of stills (every fifteenth frame) from a film of a molecular dynamics simulation of liquid KCl. The box has been drawn in to aid visualization of the three-dimensional nature of the liquid. When outside the box the ions are given dotted outlines. To appreciate the kinetic nature of the simulation move your eyes from frame to frame in comic-strip fashion. One of the balls has been shaded black—you may find it particularly helpful to concentrate on it. From a molecular dynamics study by J. W. E. Lewis. (Reprinted with permission of the Open University from a television programme available from the university.)

397

Although of no fundamental importance from a quantitative viewpoint, a computer can often be made to display visually the information which it stores. In particular, it can display (on a cathode-ray screen) the positions of the atoms as calculated for each configuration. It can then draw in circles about these points to give the appearance of atoms and add shading to create the illusion of depth. If each configuration is photographed with a cine camera (one frame exposure per configuration) the resulting film will give a remarkably vivid impression of what conditions are like in a liquid, at a known value of (p, V_m, T). What is more relevant is that this picture must be extremely accurate in view of the close agreement between the computer-predicted and the experimental properties of the liquid. Although it takes a cine film to give the true impression you may be able to get some feel for how atoms behave in liquid KCl by studying (Fig. 11.19) the sequence of photographs taken from one such film. (To enable the viewer to see the wood for the trees only a few of the "atoms" stored in the computer are displayed.) Of all the various techniques for describing conditions in a liquid this perhaps is the one which enables us to say, as we look at the screen, "now I *know* what a liquid is like". As a second best, a randomly shaken tray of oil-covered balls is not without merit.

Summary

1. Thermal evidence suggests that, close to the triple point, the liquid phase is a closer relative of the solid than to the gaseous phase. The situation is reversed close to the critical point. Compressibility data and the form of radial density curves tends to confirm this picture.
2. The equation of state of a liquid and its internal energy can be deduced provided the interatomic potential and the radial density are known. X-ray data is usually insufficiently accurate to enable reliable predictions to be made about properties of the liquid based on such experimentally determined radial density curves.
3. Computer simulations provide at present the most powerful method for predicting the properties of a liquid. Their accuracy is usually only limited by the accuracy to which the interatomic potential is known. Bernal's thesis that a "snapshot" of a monatomic liquid close to its triple point can be obtained by forming a heap of balls is worth retaining (if only as a didactic aid!). A cine film showing successive configurations as calculated in a molecular dynamics "experiment" undoubtedly provides the most accurate picture of conditions in a liquid. A dynamic two-dimensional simulator is a fair alternative.

PROBLEMS

11.1   It has been pointed out (Temperley, 1947) that the tensile strength of a liquid can be predicted assuming van der Waals' equation applies. Figure 4.31 shows that at temperatures well below T_c part of the isotherm corresponds to the liquid being at negative pressure, that is under tension. Therefore the pressure at point F must correspond to the tensile strength of the liquid at this temperature. Show that the pressure p at the minimum is given by

$$p = \frac{a(V_m - 2b)}{V_m^3}$$

Now van der Waals' equation (eq. (4.37)) tells us that, at $T = 0$, $V_m = b$. We may therefore write the (limiting) tensile strength of a liquid as

$$p = -\frac{a}{b^2}$$

Drawing on a result from section 4.6 show that this predicts a tensile strength of

$$p = 27p_c$$

Since $p_c = 4\cdot9 \times 10^6$ Pa in argon, for example, this predicts a tensile strength of around $1\cdot3 \times 10^8$ Pa. The experimental value is around 10^6 Pa. Before being too harsh on the theory it is worth remembering how predictions as to the tensile strengths of solids were several orders of magnitude too large in most instances. Indeed, as with solids, the experimentally measured tensile strengths of a liquid depend on the surface conditions—here the nature of the container walls in contact with the liquid. A water–glass system, for example, can withstand tensions of the order 3×10^6 Pa to 5×10^6 Pa, whereas a water–steel system can only withstand tensions of order 1×10^6 Pa to 3×10^6 Pa.

11.2 A possible model of a liquid might be one in which a fraction x of the atoms are assumed to be perfect gas-like and the remainder are assumed to behave like atoms in a classical solid. On the basis of this speculative model relate x to the change $\Delta C_{V,m}$ which occurs in the heat capacity of a solid on melting.

11.3 One way we might attempt to estimate the free space which exists in a liquid is to see how much solid is required to form a saturated solution (one in which no more solute can be dissolved). Try this experiment using, say, salt and water or sugar and water. You may be surprised by the result! (If you have a thermometer you may like to see whether the solvent heats or cools on forming the solution.)

11.4 Using the data given in Fig. 11.5(a) deduce how the first coordination number in liquid argon changes in going from near the triple point ($T_{tr} = 83\cdot8$ K) to near the critical point ($T_c = 150\cdot7$ K) along the saturated liquid line.

11.5 What does the area under the $g(r)$ plot from $r = 0$ to $r = \infty$ represent in a monatomic liquid?

11.6 It is an experimental fact (Troutons' rule) that for many liquids $H_{m,e}$ divided by T_b, the boiling temperature (at a fixed temperature—usually atmospheric) is approximately constant. As examples, $H_{m,e}/T_b$ is 75 J mol^{-1} K^{-1} for Ar, 85 J mol^{-1} K^{-1} for Na, and 93 J mol^{-1} K^{-1} for Hg. Show that this rule is consistent with our first primitive picture of the conditions existing at the atomic level when a substance is in the liquid phase.

11.7 Using the information contained in Fig. 3.2(b) plot a radial density curve for the two-dimensional simulated liquid and compare your plot with that obtained by Scott (Fig. 11.13). You will find it helpful to use a piece of tracing paper on which you have drawn a series of concentric circles of radii d, $1\cdot2d$, $1\cdot4d$, etc., where d is the ball diameter in Fig. 3.2(b). Place the ring system over each ball in turn and count the number of centres lying within each annulus.

399

The Liquid Phase

11.8 Using the data given in Fig. 11.18 calculate the first coordination number for like and unlike ions in liquid potassium chloride at 1045 K and at $V_m = 4\cdot88 \times 10^{-5}$ m^3 mol^{-1}. Compare your answer with the corresponding numbers for solid potassium chloride.

11.9 The following table gives the values of $\rho(r)/\rho_0$ for argon at 148·1 K and at a density of $0\cdot78 \times 10^3$ kg m^{-3}. Using this data and the value of $\mathscr{V}(r)$ given by the Lennard-Jones model (eq. (11.28)) with $\varepsilon/k = 120$ K and $\sigma = 3\cdot4 \times 10^{-10}$ m, predict the pressure of argon at $T = 148\cdot1$ K and at a density of $0\cdot78 \times 10^3$ kg m^{-3}. The experimentally measured value is $4\cdot5 \times 10^6$ Pa. Take $A_r(\text{Ar}) = 40$.

$r/10^{-10}$ m	$\rho(r)/\rho_0$	$r/10^{-10}$ m	$\rho(r)/\rho_0$	$r/10^{-10}$ m	$\rho(r)/\rho_0$
3·0	0	5·6	0·8684	9·4	0·9939
3·1	0·0900	5·7	0·8751	9·6	0·9982
3·2	0·4587	5·8	0·8814	9·8	1·0021
3·3	0·8882	5·9	0·8921	10·0	1·0058
3·4	1·3014	6·0	0·9032	10·2	1·0091
3·5	1·6378	6·1	0·9173	10·4	1·0119
3·6	1·8482	6·2	0·9305	10·6	1·0144
3·7	1·9463	6·3	0·9472	10·8	1·0151
3·8	1·9534	6·4	0·9637	11·0	1·0145
3·9	1·9095	6·5	0·9800	11·2	1·0132
4·0	1·8498	6·6	0·9961	11·4	1·0109
4·1	1·7365	6·7	1·0136	11·6	1·0090
4·2	1·6078	6·8	1·0293	11·8	1·0068
4·3	1·4866	6·9	1·0455	12·0	1·0049
4·4	1·3686	7·0	1·0587	12·4	1·0033
4·5	1·2606	7·2	1·0829	12·8	1·0033
4·6	1·1599	7·4	1·0908	13·2	1·0039
4·7	1·0398	7·6	1·0808	13·6	1·0040
4·8	0·9971	7·8	1·0595	14·0	1·0045
4·9	0·9479	8·0	1·0391		
5·0	0·9148	8·2	1·0201		
5·1	0·8921	8·4	1·0067		
5·2	0·8812	8·6	0·9968		
5·3	0·8724	8·8	0·9913		
5·4	0·8666	9·0	0·9891		
5·5	0·8658	9·2	0·9908		

*Data from Mikolaj, P. G. and Pings, C. J., J. Chem. Phys., **46**, 1401 (1967).*

11.10 Making use of the data given in problem 11.9 calculate the molar internal energy U_m of argon at 148·1 K and at a density of $0\cdot78 \times 10^3$ kg m^{-3}. The experimental value is $U_m = -1\cdot8 \times 10^3$ J mol^{-1}.

11.11 Computer "experiments" have shown that when a molecular dynamics simulation is performed assuming a hard-sphere repulsive-force model devoid of any attractive force there is no liquid phase—only a solid and gaseous phase exist. Does this seem reasonable? Why?

11.12 You might care to have a go at trying to apply the techniques of molecular dynamics to a one-dimensional system of, say, five to ten atoms. To aid computation—and so remove the necessity for a computer—assume that the interatomic force characteristic has the form shown in Fig. 11.20. Decide on appropriate values for F_m, r_0, and r_R. (They should more or less match the maximum interatomic force, the equilibrium separation, and the "range" of the force in whatever substance you have chosen.) Disregard the first few configurations which you calculate—to remove any bias in the starting conditions—and calculate $\rho(r)$ from the next few configurations. To eliminate boundary effects caused by having but few atoms, surround the "cell" which contains the atoms by replicas of itself. An atom near the cell boundary will therefore be subjected to forces both from real and from "ghost" atoms. (This technique is always employed in molecular dynamics calculations unless several hundreds of atoms are present.)

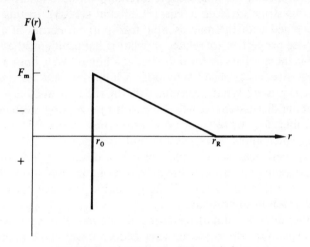

Fig. 11.20 Modelling the interatomic force.

12. Transport Processes in Liquids

In the previous chapter our real concern was with the structure *per se* of a liquid, with its appearance at the microscopic level and with the macroscopic consequences of this structure (seen in eqs. (11.27) and (11.31)). In this chapter we will be concerned with the macroscopic transport properties of a liquid and with how these properties are related to what is happening at the microscopic level. What is the mechanism for diffusion in a liquid? Why does a liquid flow when a shear stress is applied? Why does a liquid become less viscous as its temperature is raised? What determines the thermal conductivity of a liquid? Throughout our discussions we will contrast the underlying mechanisms which are responsible for these transport properties with the corresponding mechanisms which apply in the gaseous and solid phases.

Everyday experiences, such as the party trick of floating a needle on water, or the observation that a free-falling drop of liquid has a spherical shape, remind us of the peculiar nature of the gas-liquid interface. So we shall also look at this region in some detail.

This chapter does not aim at reviewing all the models which have been put forward to explain transport phenomena. Indeed it will make almost exclusive use of just one model—a cell model. Although other models can be employed— sometimes to better effect—they usually require a level of mathematics which is well beyond that assumed in this book.

12.1 The cell model

In the last chapter we saw how a liquid can be simulated by "directing" the component particles to interact in the same way as do the atoms in the substance under investigation. Although it takes a cine-film to represent the dynamic nature of the simulated liquid, individual frames from such a film are not without value. If you count the average number of nearest neighbours to any atom (or ion) in a frame from a molecular dynamics simulation (such as Fig. 11.19) you will find it to be less than the value which applies in the solid phase. If you count the average number of nearest neighbours around any atom in the two-dimensional mechanical simulation of Fig. 3.2(b) you will find that each ball is surrounded by about five nearest neighbours, as opposed to six in a close-packed two-dimensional solid. So an atom has more free space in which to move in a liquid than it has in a solid. An examination of a film of either type of simulation shows that an atom is, for the most, part prevented

402

from wandering too far by the surrounding neighbours. These *seem* to form a *cage* or *cell* about the atom in question, so making it difficult for the atom to "stray" far. If you examine the sequence of frames shown in Fig. 11.19 you can see that any one atom (such as the one which is shaded) does move around but that it is, for the most part, unable to leave its cage or cell. The picture is reminiscent of that of an agitated shopper in a densely packed store—unless she can squeeze her way through, she is confined within a cell or cage formed by her nearest neighbours.

Building on impressions gathered from watching films of simulated liquids

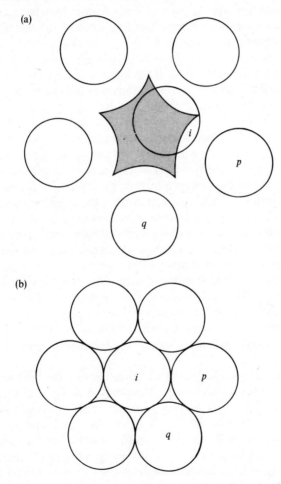

Fig. 12.1 (a) The time-averaged arrangement of atoms in a (two-dimensional) liquid about the "wanderer" *i*. The centre of *i* may move within the region shown shaded. Atoms *p*, *q*, etc., comprise the cell walls. (b) The corresponding situation which prevails in a close-packed solid where atom *i* has little room for movement.

we shall assume that each atom of a liquid may be regarded as confined to a *cell*, the walls of the cell being the nearest neighbours. Figure 12.1(a) shows how the cell walls will appear on average to an individual atom i—here we have averaged the locations of the wall atoms over many frames of the cine film (that is, we have taken a time average of the surroundings of atom i). Atom i is more or less free to wander around within its cell, its centre tracing out the area shown shaded in Fig. 12.1(a). In a solid (Fig. 12.1(b)) the wall atoms p, q, etc., would be close-packed, allowing i but little room for movement. All cell models of a liquid assume that the atoms constituting the wall remain fixed as the "wanderer" moves about inside the cell. It is paradoxical that, depending on one's viewpoint, each individual atom may be regarded either as a "wanderer" or as a "wall" atom, but this facet of the cell model must be tolerated if progress is to be made.

As atom i wanders about inside its cell it will experience forces of attraction and repulsion with the wall atoms. If the forces were not there the atom would not be contained! Expressed differently, the potential energy of the "wanderer" is a function of its position within the cell. It would, of course, be a straightforward matter to write down its potential energy assuming, say, a Lennard-Jones potential model. Fortunately it is often adequate to regard the potential energy as constant while the wanderer moves *within* its cell—energy only being required for the wanderer to *escape from* its cell. This is the model which we shall use in discussing transport processes. By supposing the atom to move freely inside its cell, we are endowing the liquid with some gas-phase attributes. By supposing the bounding cell wall to be fixed—or rather by supposing that the wanderer requires a certain constant energy to escape—we are endowing the liquid with solid-phase attributes. Since the liquid phase is in many ways intermediate in character between that of the gaseous and solid phases, a model combining features of both phases contains, at least, the seeds of future success. We shall see that the model does indeed bear fruit in discussions of most transport processes. However a word of caution must be uttered. The cell model is of only limited value in predicting the equilibrium properties of a liquid; properties such as the equation of state and the internal energy!

In the absence of a single model which can cope with both the equilibrium and the non-equilibrium (transport) properties of a liquid, the best we can do with present knowledge is to employ a small number of models, which, between them, can accomplish all that is required of them. It should also be said that molecular dynamic simulations are providing insight into the various transport processes. Such simulations are very much in the nature of "experiments"—one varies conditions, like the temperature, and sees what happens. If you like, these simulations "blow up" conditions as they exist in a liquid so one can see what is going on. People who develop analytic theories—we shall be, using the cell model—often consider this "cheating"! In truth, if any analytic theory works, it is often easier to handle than the set of numbers provided by a simulation. A single equation is, to many people, more satisfying than a table of numerical values—however accurate those values be.

12.2 Diffusion

We will limit our discussion—as we did in the gaseous and solid phases—to the diffusion of a liquid into its radioactive equal. The self-diffusion coefficient D can be deduced from measurements of how far the radioactive liquid diffuses into the normal liquid at various times. But before we look at experimental details and at the results obtained in such studies, let us attempt to predict the form of D for a monatomic liquid. In particular, how does D depend on the temperature of the liquid?

The mechanism

Figure 12.2(a) shows the time-average environment of an atom i contained within a cell whose wall atoms are $p, q, r, s,$ and t.

For most of the time atom i is confined within its present cell. Occasionally, as a result of fortuitous collisions with the wall atoms, it may acquire enough energy to push the wall atoms apart and so to escape to an adjoining cell. We will suppose that the act of escaping eliminates the cell which formerly surrounded atom i. A new cell will however form around atom i in its new location. By definition, the walls of this cell will be the time-averaged nearest neighbours to i. Some theories suppose that the cell into which i hops is vacant (cf. vacancy diffusion in a solid). Were we to adopt a vacancy model the final expression for D would differ little from the result we shall arrive at on a "reforming" cell model.

The problem which faces i as it attempts to escape from its cell is summarized in a potential energy diagram. This indicates the energy required to displace i from any arbitrarily chosen starting position—say the centre of the cell—where we take the potential energy to be zero. Because a three-dimensional liquid requires four dimensions to display, graphically, how the potential energy varies throughout the cell, we shall confine ourselves to a hypothetical two-dimensional liquid. It is not difficult to see why $\mathscr{V}(x)$ has the form shown in Fig. 12.2(b). Perhaps the best way to derive the form of the potential energy curve is, in imagination, to "freeze" everything and then attach a Newton balance to i. With the aid of a "metre stick" we then evaluate the total energy required to move i from the centre of the cell to some point x; this energy is $\mathscr{V}(x)$. As i is moved out from the centre in, say, the $+x$-direction, energy must be provided by us for atoms $r, s,$ and t will pull back on i as it is displaced. In addition, energy must be provided to separate atoms p and q sufficiently to allow i through the walls of the cell. Once through the "hole in the wall" atoms p and q can close up, restoring energy to us. The rest of the

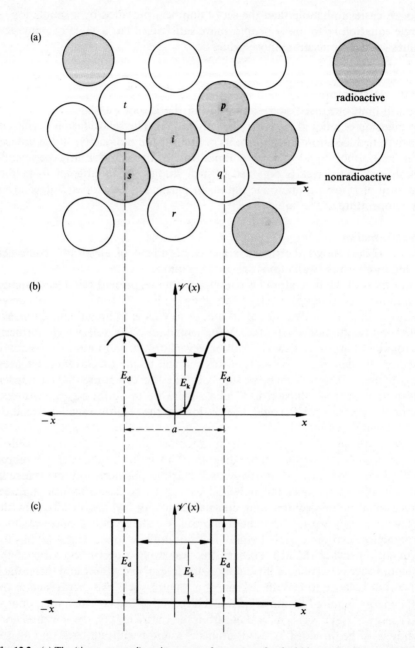

Fig. 12.2 (a) The (time-averaged) environment of atom i confined within a cell whose wall atoms are p, q, r, s, and t. (b) The potential energy $\mathscr{V}(x)$ of atom i as it is displaced along the x-direction from the centre of the cell. (c) A simplified potential model which assumes atom i behaves like a perfect gas atom within its cell.

energy is restored as a new cell forms about i. The potential energy curve will therefore be periodic with a period a, where a is the cell diameter (Fig. 11.2). On average—averaged over many cells—the potential energy will be the same along all diameters.

Once we have established the form of the potential energy curve we "unfreeze" the atoms. Atom i will now be jostled by its neighbours p, q, r, etc. As a result, its kinetic energy E_k will change from one moment to the next. If i is to escape, its kinetic energy must reach a value of at least E_d, the *activation energy for diffusion*. If E_k is less than E_d atom i is trapped within its cell—trapped until such time as it acquires a kinetic energy greater than or equal to the activation energy E_d.

Exercise 12.1

Make an order of magnitude estimate of the activation energy E_d for self-diffusion in liquid argon at a density of $1 \cdot 4 \times 10^3$ kg m^{-3} and a temperature of 84 K (these are the values at the triple point). Assume a hard-sphere repulsive model for the interaction between two argon atoms, with the potential energy due to the (van der Waals) attractive forces given by the Lennard-Jones term

$$\mathscr{V}(r) = -4\varepsilon \left(\frac{\sigma}{r}\right)^6$$

Take $\varepsilon = 1 \cdot 7 \times 10^{-21}$ J and $\sigma = 3 \cdot 4 \times 10^{-10}$ m. What fraction of E_d is the mean thermal energy of an argon atom at 84 K?

The hopping speed of an atom

This exercise will have demonstrated that, at least near the triple point, the average kinetic energy of an atom in a liquid is significantly below the energy required to hop out of its cell. Clearly the number of escape hops f_d per unit time through the cell wall is given by:

$f_d =$ (number of escape attempts per unit time)

$$\times \text{(fraction with } E_k \geq E_d) \qquad (12.1)$$

Since the cell has a diameter a and the "wanderer" a r.m.s. speed of $(\overline{u^2})^{1/2}$, it will collide with the cell wall at time intervals of about $a/(\overline{u^2})^{1/2}$. In other words the number of attempted escapes per unit time is $(\overline{u^2})^{1/2}/a$. But as $\frac{1}{2}m\overline{u^2} = kT$ in a two-dimensional system (see exercise 6.7), where m is the mass of an atom of the liquid and T is the temperature, $(\overline{u^2})^{1/2} = (2kT/m)^{1/2}$ and so

$$\text{number of attempted escapes per unit time} = \frac{1}{a}\left(\frac{2kT}{m}\right)^{1/2}$$

407

However, in the two-dimensional liquid we are considering, only about one jump in four will be in the $+x$-direction. Therefore

number of attempted escapes per unit time in $+x$ direction

$$= \frac{1}{4a}\left(\frac{2kT}{m}\right)^{1/2} \quad (12.2)$$

We must now calculate the second term in eq. (12.1). To simplify the discussion we shall suppose that the wanderer is moving not in a "potential well" like that shown in Fig. 12.2(b) but is moving instead in the well shown in Fig. 12.2(c). In other words we shall suppose the wanderer to behave like a perfect gas atom within its cell. We have already calculated what fraction of the atoms in a two-dimensional gas have an energy lying between E and $E + dE$. We saw in chapter 6 (eq. (6.50)) that

$$\frac{dN}{N} = \frac{1}{kT}e^{-E/kT}\,dE \quad (12.3)$$

We shall assume this fraction is the same as the probability that an individual atom will on (time) average have an energy between E and $E + dE$. This is essentially an axiom, but a not implausible one. To find the probability that the wanderer has an energy $E_k \geq E_d$, the right-hand side of eq. (12.3) must be integrated between $E = E_d$ and $E = \infty$:

$$\int_{E_d}^{\infty} \frac{1}{kT}e^{-E/kT}\,dE = \left[-e^{-E/kT}\right]_{E_d}^{\infty} = e^{-E_d/kT}$$

So the probability that the wanderer will have $E_k \geq E_d$ is $\exp(-E_d/kT)$ and this, therefore, tells us the fraction of escape attempts which will be successful. Substituting this result along with that of eq. (12.2) into eq. (12.1) gives the hopping frequency as

$$f_d = \frac{1}{4a}\left(\frac{2kT}{m}\right)^{1/2} e^{-E_d/kT} \quad (12.4)$$

When the wanderer hops out of its present cell into its new cell it moves a distance a. The speed v_d with which an atom hops is therefore given by

$$v_d = f_d a$$

$$v_d = \frac{1}{4}\left(\frac{2kT}{m}\right)^{1/2} e^{-E_d/kT} \quad (12.5)$$

These arguments should have seemed very familiar—you met broadly similar arguments in discussing diffusion in solids (section 10.1). Had we demanded that the cell adjacent to the one in which the wanderer is located be vacant the right-hand side of eq. (12.5) would have been multiplied by $\exp(-E_v/kT)$, where E_v is the energy necessary to create a vacancy in the liquid. Since $E_v \approx E_d$, including this term would not drastically alter the form of eq. (12.5). In view of the uncertainty inherent in calculating E_d—by a factor of at least two—we could not hope to use experimental data to unequivocally refute either the "vacant adjacent cell" model or the "reforming cell" model.

The diffusion coefficient

As in a solid and a gas, net diffusion of a species in a liquid depends on there being a concentration gradient of that species. In chapter 10 (eq. (10.2)) we saw that the diffusion coefficient D was related to the hopping velocity v_d and the hop distance a by $D = \frac{1}{3}v_d a$. The corresponding relation in two dimensions is

$$D = \tfrac{1}{2}v_d a$$

—assuming that one-quarter of the atoms are at any instant moving along $+x$-, $-x$-, $+y$-, and $-y$-directions. Substituting for v_d from eq. (12.5) gives

$$D = \frac{a}{8}\left(\frac{2kT}{m}\right)^{1/2} e^{-E_d/kT} \tag{12.6}$$

that is

$$D \propto T^{1/2} e^{-E_d/kT} \tag{12.7}$$

Of the two terms $T^{1/2}$ and $\exp(-E_d/kT)$, the first changes so much more slowly with changing T (in the range of T in which the substance is a liquid) than does the second term that we may write, to a good approximation,

$$D \propto e^{-E_d/kT} \tag{12.8}$$

Although our treatment assumed a two-dimensional liquid, the same dominant exponential factor reappears in a full three-dimensional discussion.

How D is measured

Figure 12.3 is a (somewhat simplified) diagram of an apparatus which has been used by Naghizadeh and Rice (1961) to study self-diffusion in the liquid inert gases over a fairly wide range of pressure and temperature. The key item is capillary C which can be opened and closed from both ends by valves V_1 and V_2. In the apparatus used by Naghizadeh and Rice the capillary was formed from a stainless steel block and had an inner diameter of 0·5 mm and a length of 18·5 mm. The experiment involves four basic steps:

(1) Keeping the lower valve V_1 closed, the bath B is filled through F with a suitable mixture of pure and radioactive fluid (cf. the technique used in the experiments of Mifflin and Bennett, section 5.4). The capillary is then filled with pure liquid.

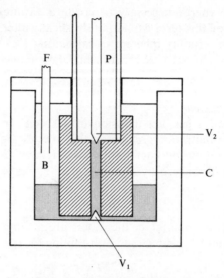

Fig. 12.3 An apparatus for determining the self-diffusion coefficient in the liquid inert gases. On opening valve V_1 radioactive tracers diffuse into the pure liquid contained in the capillary tube C. (Data from J. Naghizadeh and S. A. Rice, *J. Chem. Phys.*, **36**, 2710 (1961).)

(2) The pressure in the capillary and the bath are equalized.

(3) After closing the upper valve V_2, the lower valve V_1 is opened so that diffusion from the isotope-enriched bath into the capillary may proceed.

(4) Once a suitable diffusion time t has elapsed the lower valve is closed. The upper valve is then opened and by pumping through tube P the contents of the capillary are transferred to a sample tube where the level of radio-activity is counted.

Knowing the (mean) level of radioactivity in the capillary and the diffusion time t, the value of D can be readily calculated. (This statement should come as no surprise. You will remember (eq. (10.9)) that the r.m.s. distance travelled by an atom is equal to $(Dt)^{1/2}$. A high radioactive assay implies that the atoms have diffused far into the capillary; that is, the mean concentration is a function of D and t.) To determine D at a different pressure the entire operation is repeated with the liquid in bath B maintained at a new pressure. It is worth noting how the temperature of the system is controlled. The vessel comprising the capillary and the isotope enriched liquid is suspended inside a large dewar flask (not shown) from a long support rod. Another support rod is attached to the underneath surface of the vessel and this dips into liquid nitrogen. Since the upper end of the top support is at room temperature and since the lower end of the bottom support is at liquid nitrogen temperature, the vessel must be at some intermediate temperature.

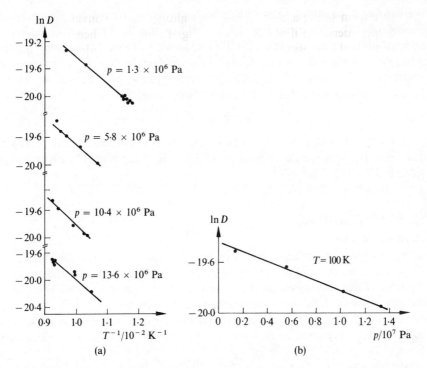

Fig. 12.4 Self-diffusion in liquid argon as a function of temperature and pressure. The data actually refers to the diffusion of ^{41}Ar into natural argon. In (a) the data is presented to show the variation of $\ln D$ with $1/T$ along lines of constant p. In (b) the variation is shown against p along a line of constant T (at $T = 100$ K). The self-diffusion coefficient is measured in units of $m^2\ s^{-1}$. (Data from J. Naghizadeh and S. A. Rice, *J. Chem. Phys.*, **36**, 2710 (1961).)

The pressure and temperature dependence of D

Figure 12.4(a) shows the results of a series of studies of self-diffusion in liquid argon. As predicted by eq. (12.8), graphs of $\ln D$ plotted against $1/T$ are indeed linear. Their gradients $(-E_d/k)$ remain constant, to within 5 per cent, over a ten-fold change in pressure and give a mean value for E_d of 5.0×10^{-21} J. This compares very favourably with the estimate of 10^{-20} J which we arrived at in exercise 12.1. It would perhaps be unwise to recalculate E_d for the cell, knowing the answer! Knowing the answer they are expected to find, theoreticians sometimes have the knack of finding it. (Knowing what they are told to see, experimentalists sometimes have the knack of "seeing" it too!) No doubt, by suitably adjusting the cell geometry the agreement between the theoretical and the experimental values of E_d could be improved.

Instead of plotting how $\ln D$ varies with T^{-1} along lines of constant p, the data contained in Fig. 12.4(a) may be replotted to show how $\ln D$ varies with p along lines of constant T. Figure 12.4(b) shows such a plot at $T = 100$ K. (The plots at other temperatures have the same gradient—to within 5 per cent.)

411

We can see a possible, if not altogether convincing, reason for this pressure dependence if we examine Fig. 12.2(a). When the liquid is subjected to an external pressure, p, extra energy will be required to move atoms p and q apart through a distance of about a so that i can escape. In fact E_d is increased by about $(pa^2) \times a$ (that is, force $\times$ distance) making the activation energy $E_d + pa^3$. Substituting this revised activation energy into eq. (12.8) predicts

$$D \propto e^{-(E_d + pa^3)/kT}$$

or a linear graph of gradient $-a^3/kT$ when $\ln D$ is plotted against p. Taking $a = 3.6 \times 10^{-10}$ m predicts a gradient of 3.4×10^{-8} m^2 N^{-1}. The experimental value is 4.1×10^{-8} m^2 N^{-1}.

12.3   Viscous flow

Possible models

In our discussions of viscous flow in a (perfect) gas we saw that the shear force F applied to the moving plate (Fig. 12.5(a)) feeds momentum into the gas while the shear force F applied to the stationary plate removes momentum from the gas. Let us briefly recall the mechanism. Atoms arriving at the top plate, or rather diffusing to this plate, will have come from a more slowly moving layer of gas. Assuming they stick, at least temporarily, to this plate their

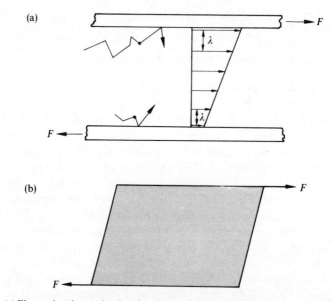

Fig. 12.5   (a) Illustrating the mechanism for viscous flow in a perfect gas. An atom diffusing to the top plate acquires momentum, while one diffusing to the lower plate loses momentum. (b) When a shearing stress is applied to a solid it normally strains elastically but does not flow.

momentum will be increased. This calls for a force. In a similar fashion an atom striking the lower fixed plate will have its drift momentum removed by this plate, or rather, by the force F applied to this plate. There is therefore a continuous transfer of momentum across the body of the gas from the top to the lower plate.

Exercise 12.2

If a similar mechanism to that pertaining to a perfect gas applied in liquids, would the viscosity predicted for a liquid be less than, equal to, or greater than that of a perfect gas at the same density and temperature?

This exercise has demonstrated that some other mechanism must be responsible for the viscosity of a liquid (and of a high density gas). An analogue may help us find the mechanism.

Imagine two persons A and B standing on opposite sides of an "air-table" (a table with a flat frictionless surface). We pose the problem of how to transfer an amount p_x of momentum from A to B. One method would be to send a "puck" from A to B (Fig. 12.6(a)). When B stops the puck he will acquire the requisite (component) momentum p_x. This is, of course, the mechanism which operates in a perfect gas. A quite different method of transferring momentum would be to have many pucks on the table (Fig. 12.6(b)) and to couple them together so that the interatomic forces are simulated. (Weak springs could provide the attractive force component. If the pucks are magnetic their mutual repulsion simulates the repulsive component.) When A gives one puck the momentum p_x this puck will soon "collide" (interact) with another one, and so on across the table—momentum transfer occurs because of the existence of

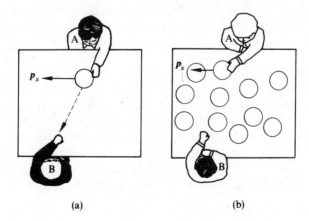

(a)   (b)

Fig. 12.6 A view looking down on an air-table. Momentum may be transferred from person A to person B by either (a) sending a puck across the table or, as in (b), by a sequence of puck "collisions".

413

interpuck forces. You may remember meeting a somewhat similar argument when we discussed the *b*-term in van der Waals' equation of state (section 4.5).

In a low density gas only the first of these mechanisms is significant. In a liquid, both mechanisms are present; momentum transfer by diffusion of the momentum carriers and transfer through interatomic collisions. The first of these contributions is relatively straightforward to calculate. Unfortunately, the second contribution, which is usually the most significant in a liquid, is much more difficult to calculate. If we wished to calculate the rate at which momentum is transferred across the table in Fig. 12.6(b) we would have to know the disposition of the pucks and how they interact with one another. So it is in liquid. In chapter 11 we saw something of the problems encountered in attempts at calculating the structure of a liquid. In predicting the viscosity of a liquid the problem is even more severe for one must know the structure under flow conditions. It hardly needs stating that this is exceptionally difficult to determine!

A quite different way of thinking about viscous flow in a liquid was suggested by the great nineteenth-century British physicist, J. Clerk Maxwell. He pointed out that when a solid is subjected to a (small) shearing stress (Fig. 12.5(b)) it normally deforms elastically but does not flow—unlike a liquid which is incapable of resisting a shearing force for any appreciable period of time. The model of viscous flow which we shall adopt essentially regards a liquid as a solid. Following Maxwell, we shall concentrate on finding a mechanism which allows the strain to relax in our "solid", permitting flow to occur.

The cell model of viscous flow
The velocity gradient present between the plates of Fig. 12.5(a) necessarily implies that one layer of atoms slips relative to the neighbouring layers with slip occurring in the flow direction. Without slip there can be no velocity gradient. Our most pressing task is therefore to find some mechanism whereby the application of a shearing force allows slip to occur.

The slip mechanism
The layer of atoms *i*, *j*, *k*, etc., of the liquid immediately adjacent to the moving plate (atoms *c*, *d*, *e*., etc., in Fig. 12.7(a)) will experience a short ranged attractive force directed towards the upper plate. This attractive force is so short-ranged (if often varies as the inverse eighth power of the separation of an atom from the plate) that the plate will exert no direct force on the second layer of atoms (*q*, *r*, *s*, etc.). Thus, if a shearing force *F* is applied to the top plate (Fig. 12.7(a)) this will in turn exert a tangential force *f* on an atom such as *i* given by

$$f = \frac{F}{\text{number of atoms in liquid layer adjacent to plate}} \tag{12.9}$$

414

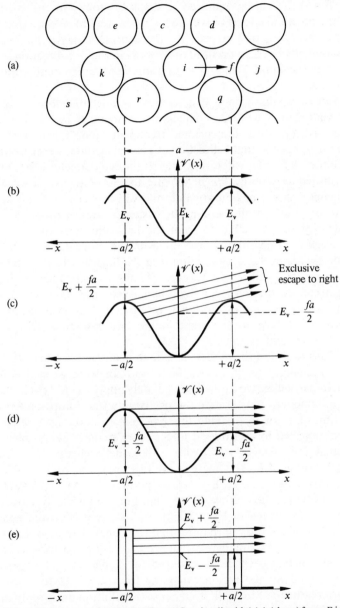

Fig. 12.7 Shows the factors responsible for viscous flow in a liquid. (a) A (shear) force F is applied to the top plate of area A (containing atoms c, d, e, etc.). (b) With no external force the activation energy is the same in the $+x$- and $-x$-directions. (c) The effect of a force f acting on atom i is to increase its kinetic energy by $\frac{1}{2}fa$ when i is at point $\frac{1}{2}a$ and to decrease its kinetic energy by $\frac{1}{2}fa$ when it is at point $-\frac{1}{2}a$. (d) The effect of f is equivalent to reducing the activation energy to $E_v - \frac{1}{2}fa$ at $+\frac{1}{2}a$ and to increasing it to $E_v + \frac{1}{2}fa$ at $-\frac{1}{2}a$. (e) A simplified model in which atom i is considered to behave as a perfect-gas atom between $x \approx -\frac{1}{2}a$ and $x \approx +\frac{1}{2}a$.

415

When $F = 0$ the energy required to displace atom i in the x-direction is given by the potential energy curve shown in Fig. 12.7(b). We see that provided the kinetic energy E_k of i exceeds E_v, *the activation energy for viscous flow*, hopping is equally likely to occur in the $+x$- as in the $-x$-direction, producing no net flow in the liquid. When $E_k < E_v$ hopping occurs in neither the $+x$- nor $-x$-directions.

The effect of having a finite F is to exert a tangential force f on atom i, given by eq. (12.9). This force f changes the kinetic energy of i as it moves back and forth (in a one-dimensional treatment along the x-axis*). When i moves to the right $(+x)$ in the direction of f it will acquire energy from f. When i moves to the left $(-x)$ it will lose energy. If the cell diameter is a (Fig. 12.7(a)) atom i will acquire energy $\frac{1}{2}fa$ in moving to the point $x = +\frac{1}{2}a$, where the potential energy has a maximum value, and will lose energy $\frac{1}{2}fa$ in moving to the point $x = -\frac{1}{2}a$. It will therefore be easier for atom i to escape from the right-hand side of the cell than from the left-hand side. In fact, when the kinetic energy of i (measured at $x = 0$) lies in the range $E_v - \frac{1}{2}fa$ to $E_v + \frac{1}{2}fa$ it can *only* escape in the $+x$-direction (Fig. 12.7(c)). If i has a kinetic energy less than $E_v - \frac{1}{2}fa$ it will remain trapped. If i has a kinetic energy greater than $E_v + \frac{1}{2}fa$ it can escape with equal probability to the right and to the left, producing no net flow parallel to the direction of f. The effect of f is therefore to produce a net flow to the right in the liquid when E_k (at $x = 0$) lies between $E_v - \frac{1}{2}fa$ and $E_v + \frac{1}{2}fa$.

Further discussion of the model is made difficult simply because the kinetic energy of i changes as it moves back and forth between $x = -\frac{1}{2}a$ and $x = +\frac{1}{2}a$. In particular, we cannot immediately apply the Maxwell–Boltzmann distribution function to determine the probability that i hops preferentially in the direction of f, for in deriving this function *we* never considered that the atoms are subjected to an external force. To overcome this problem, we will suppose that the effect of f is to leave the kinetic energy of i alone while reducing the value of E_v, the energy required to escape, to $E_v - \frac{1}{2}fa$ at point $x = \frac{1}{2}a$ and to increase E_v to $E_v + \frac{1}{2}fa$ at point $x = -\frac{1}{2}a$. (This switch in the role of f can be justified although we shall not attempt to do so here.) This assumption is illustrated in Fig. 12.7(d). As before, preferential escape from the right-hand side of the cell requires that the kinetic energy of i lies between $E_v - \frac{1}{2}fa$ and $E_v + \frac{1}{2}fa$. Finally, so that we may use the Maxwell–Boltzmann distribution function—which *we* deduced for a perfect gas—we shall take $\mathscr{V}(x) = 0$ throughout the region extending from $x \approx -\frac{1}{2}a$ to $x \approx +\frac{1}{2}a$ (Fig. 12.7(e)). (Actually, the Maxwell–Boltzmann distribution does apply in a dense classical fluid so the transition from Fig. 12.7(d) to (e) is not really necessary.)

---

* Adopting a one-dimensional model will save us having to resolve forces and from some more tedious integrations. Try a three-dimensional model if you like. Your final answer after much mathematics will still approximate to eq. (12.17).

The hopping speed of an atom

The number, f_v, of escape hops per unit time of an atom like i which lead to a net flow in the direction of f is given by

$f_v =$ (number of escape attempts per unit time)

$$\times \text{ (fraction with } E_v + \tfrac{1}{2}fa > E_k > E_v - \tfrac{1}{2}fa) \qquad (12.10)$$

We will treat the problem one-dimensionally regarding i as constrained to move back and forth along the x-direction. This is not unreasonable since the overall flow is in the $+x$-direction. The number of escape attempts per unit time from the right-hand side of the cell is of order $\overline{(u^2)}^{1/2}/2a$; the atom travels a distance $2a$ between escape attempts. In a one-dimensional gas $\tfrac{1}{2}m\overline{u^2} = \tfrac{1}{2}kT$ (exercise 6.8) so that

$$\text{number of escape attempts per unit time} = \frac{1}{2a}\left(\frac{kT}{m}\right)^{1/2} \qquad (12.11)$$

If you prefer just use $\tfrac{1}{2}m\overline{u^2} = \tfrac{3}{2}kT$: It will not make any significant difference to our final result!

In section 6.8, exercise 6.8, you showed that, in a one-dimensional gas, the fraction of the atoms whose energies lie between E and $E + dE$ is given by

$$\frac{dN}{N} = (\pi kTE)^{-1/2}\,e^{-E/kT}\,dE \qquad (12.12)$$

We shall assume that this fraction is the same as the probability that an individual atom like i will, on average, have an energy between E and $E + dE$. In the present problem $E = E_v$ and $dE = fa$. (We may take it that $fa \ll E_v$; Fig. 12.7(e) is exaggerated.) Equation (12.12) may therefore be rewritten to give

fraction of escape attempts with $E_v + \tfrac{1}{2}fa > E_k > E_v - \tfrac{1}{2}fa$

$$= (\pi kTE_v)^{-1/2}\,e^{-E_v/kT}fa \qquad (12.13)$$

Substituting eqs. (12.11) and (12.13) into eq. (12.10) gives

$$f_v = (4m\pi E_v)^{-1/2}\,e^{-E_v/kT}f$$

Since i hops a distance a as it escapes, preferentially to the right, it follows that the hopping velocity δv of i is given by $f_v a$, that is

$$\delta v = (4m\pi E_v)^{-1/2}\,e^{-E_v/kT}fa \qquad (12.14)$$

The dynamic viscosity

What we have actually calculated is the difference in the velocity of two adjacent layers in the liquid; the one containing i, the other q, r, s, etc. (Fig. 12.7(a)). Since the separation between these layers is about $\tfrac{1}{2}a$ it follows that the velocity gradient in the liquid is given by $\delta v/\frac{1}{2}a = 2\,\delta v/a$ or, substituting for δv, from eq. (12.14)

$$\text{velocity gradient} = (m\pi E_v)^{-1/2}\,e^{-E_v/kT}f \tag{12.15}$$

If the upper plate has an area A then, since an atom like i has a cross-sectional area of approximately $(\frac{1}{2}a)^2 = \frac{1}{4}a^2$, it follows from eq. (12.9) that

$$f = \frac{F}{A/(\frac{1}{4}a^2)} = \frac{Fa^2}{4A}$$

or

$$\frac{F}{A} = \text{shear stress} = \frac{4f}{a^2} \tag{12.16}$$

Now the dynamic viscosity η is related to the shear stress and the velocity gradient by (see eq. (5.27))

$$\eta = \frac{\text{shear stress}}{\text{velocity gradient}}$$

Substituting from eqs. (12.15) and (12.16) gives

$$\eta = \frac{4}{a^2}(\pi m E_v)^{1/2}\,e^{E_v/kT}$$

For any given liquid E_v will (normally) be constant, so that

$$\eta \propto e^{E_v/kT} \tag{12.17}$$

Experimental results

Until recently most studies which have been made of the temperature dependence of η have been made along the saturated liquid line. Such experiments show that $\ln \eta \propto T^{-1}$ as predicted by eq. (12.17) for a wide variety of liquids.

In a study carried out in 1967 de Brock, Grevendonk, and Herreman measured the viscosity of liquid argon at pressures between 10^6 Pa and 2×10^7 Pa and at temperatures between 86 K and 146 K. The experimental technique consisted in comparing the amplitude of vibration of a quartz crystal in a vacuum and when immersed in the liquid. The quartz crystal (length 50 mm and diameter 5 mm) was vibrated at its (transverse) resonant frequency of 3.84×10^4 Hz by applying an alternating voltage between silver electrodes evaporated onto the quartz. The electrical resistance of the quartz provides an (indirect) measure of its amplitude of vibration. You can probably appreciate that the greater the viscosity of the liquid the smaller will be the amplitude of

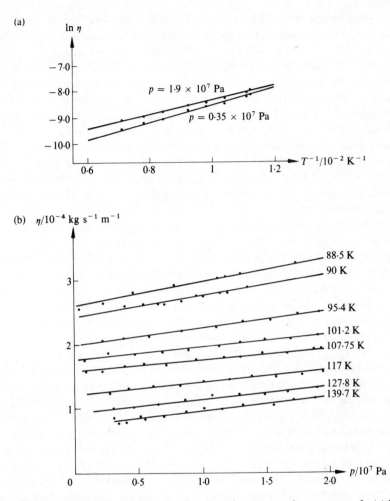

Fig. 12.8 The viscosity of liquid argon as a function of pressure and temperature. In (a) $\ln \eta$ is plotted against T^{-1} at two constant pressures. In (b) η is plotted against p at various constant temperatures. (Data from A. de Bock, W. Grevendonk, and W. Herreman, *Physica,* **37,** 327 (1967).)

vibration, and therefore the smaller the electrical resistance, of the quartz. The crystal was suspended from its leads in a pressure cell not unlike that shown in Fig. 12.3.

Figure 12.8 shows the results obtained in this study. We see (Fig. 12.8(a)) that as predicted from eq. (12.17) graphs of $\ln \eta$ plotted against $1/T$ are linear. The gradients (E/k) give $E_v = 4 \cdot 4 \times 10^{-21}$ J at $p = 0 \cdot 85 \times 10^7$ Pa and $E_v = 3 \cdot 5 \times 10^{-21}$ J at $p = 1 \cdot 9 \times 10^7$ Pa. These values compare favourably with $E_d = 5 \cdot 0 \times 10^{-21}$ J deduced from diffusion measurements (Fig. 12.4(a)). We would expect E_d and E_v to be the same since both measure the activation

419

energy required by an atom to escape from its cell. This rough equality of E_d and E_v holds true in many liquids; in liquid carbon tetrachloride, for example, $E_d = 6\cdot3 \times 10^{-21}$ J and $E_v = 4\cdot1 \times 10^{-21}$ J (both measured along the saturated liquid line). It is also worth noting that E_d is very often about one-quarter to one-third of the enthalpy of evaporation of an atom $(H_{m,e}/N_A)$; a not unexpected result since evaporation involves removing an atom to an infinite distance from its neighbours whereas diffusion and viscous flow only requires the atom to have sufficient energy to escape from its cell. In certain complex liquids—for example, liquids composed of long molecular chains—the molecules may align themselves along the direction of flow once flow begins. This leads to a lowering of E_v and so to a decrease in viscosity (eq. (12.17)). In their unaligned ("jumbled") state E_v, and therefore the viscosity, is high. This lowering of viscosity with increasing stress—a phenomenon known as *thixotropy*—is put to good use in certain nondrip, or thixotropic, paints and adhesives. When the stress is low (such as that resulting from gravity acting on a drop) the viscosity is high. Brushing exerts a large stress and the viscosity falls. Figure 12.8(b) shows that η increases linearly with p over a five-fold change in pressure. In many, more complex, liquids it is $\ln \eta$ rather than η which increases linearly with p. This is a very useful property to have in a lubricant since it prevents it being squeezed out from between the moving surfaces as the load is increased.

Our explanation of viscous flow assumes implicitly that the force f acting on atom i in Fig. 12.7(c) does so for sufficient time to allow atom i to acquire momentum from it. If f acts for a time which is less than the time it takes i to traverse the cell—often called the *relaxation time*—flow cannot occur and the liquid will deform elastically. This effect is not observed in simple liquids where the relaxation times $(\approx a/\bar{u})$ are of order 10^{-10} s to 10^{-12} s, but it is observed in materials of high relative molecular mass. Silicone putty ("bouncing putty") is probably familiar to you. When left on the table a ball of the putty flows to form a pool over a period of minutes. If dropped onto the table from a height it bounces. The relaxation time of a molecule of the putty is presumably greater than the time during which the ball makes contact with the table during a bounce.

It would be unwise to conclude that the success we have had in accounting for the temperature dependence of viscosity is *proof* of the correctness of the underlying model. Many another model also demonstrates that $\ln \eta \propto T^{-1}$.

12.4 Ionic conduction

The facts

The liquid inert gases normally have a near-zero electrical conductivity. If, however, a suitable radioactive source is placed in these liquids they do exhibit a finite conductivity. It is possible to measure the mobility of the charge carriers—that is, their drift velocity per unit electric field—using a time-of-flight

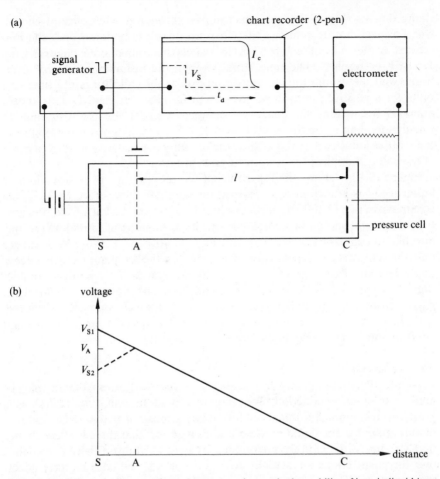

Fig. 12.9 (a) Schematic diagram of an apparatus used to study the mobility of ions in liquid inert gases. The entire grid assembly is mounted in a cell containing the liquid, whose pressure and temperature can be controlled. In addition to the grids shown here there are also intermediate grids between A and C maintained at the appropriate potential so that the field is constant between A and C. (b) The potentials on the various electrodes. By changing the potential on S from V_{S1} to V_{S2} the positive ion current can be switched off. (Data from T. H. Davis, S. A. Rice, and L. Meyer, *J. Chem. Phys.*, **37**, 947 (1962).)

technique very similar to that described in section 2.1. Figure 12.9(a) is a schematic diagram of an apparatus used by Davis, Rice, and Meyer in 1962 to measure ionic mobilities in liquid argon, krypton, and xenon. The ions were created at grid S by a layer of ^{210}Po coated on the source of S. (This is an α-particle source. The particles have such a short range that all the ionization takes place in the plane of S.) When S is at voltage V_{S1} (Fig. 12.9(b)) there is a constant electric field between S and the ion collector C and a constant current will be recorded on the chart recorder. If the voltage on S is now

421

changed to V_{S2} (Fig. 12.9(b)) no ions can pass through A. The collector-current will, however, not drop immediately to zero. It will only do so once the ions created at the end of the "open" cycle—when the voltage on S changes from V_{S1} to V_{S2}—reach C. The time lapse between the instant the "closed" cycle begins and the instant the current disappears at the collector is the time t_d it takes for a positive ion to move from A to C. The drift velocity v_d is simply obtained by dividing the distance l between A and C by the drift time t_d. Finally, dividing v_d by the electric field $E = (V_A - V_C)/l$ gives the mobility of the positive ions (see p. 165). To study the mobility of negative ions the polarities of the voltages applied to the various grids are reversed.

Figure 12.10(a) shows the logarithm of the mobility μ^+ of positive ions in liquid argon as a function of pressure at three different temperatures. This data is redrawn in Fig. 12.10(b) to show how $\ln \mu^+$ varies with T^{-1} at a fixed pressure. Figure 12.10(b) should be compared with Figs. 12.4(a) and 12.8(a). (You may also like to compare Fig. 12.10(a) with Figs. 12.4(b) and 12.8(b).) You will see that the temperature dependence of μ^+ mirrors the temperature dependence of D. The fact that a graph of $\ln \mu^+$ plotted against T^{-1} is linear implies that $\mu^+ \propto \exp(-E_i/kT)$, where E_i is a constant. The gradient $(-E_i/k)$ of the graph shown in Fig. 12.10(b) gives $E_i = 5 \times 10^{-21}$ J, which compares favourably with $E_d = 5 \cdot 0 \times 10^{-21}$ and $E_v = 3 \cdot 9 \times 10^{-21}$ J deduced from diffusion and viscosity measurements in liquid argon.

The mechanism

It is not difficult to adapt our discussion of viscous flow so that it may be applied to ionic conduction. We may regard atom i in Fig. 12.7(a) as a positive ion contained within a cell formed by atoms c, d, q, and r. The number of ions present in the liquid in these studies is so low that there is every chance that an ion will be entirely surrounded by neutral atoms. (There is evidence that the positive ions are actually Ar_2^+ and not Ar^+, but this scarcely affects the arguments. There is also evidence that the negative ions are O_2^-; dissolved oxygen may capture the electrons released when argon is ionized.) If the ion i has a charge q and the electric field is E the force f acting on the ion is Eq. The rest of the analysis, summarized in Figs. 12.7(b) to (e) can be applied with $f = Eq$. Since the activation energy need not be the same as E_d, we shall write it as E_i. In particular, eq. (12.14) gives the drift velocity v_d of the ion:

$$v_d \propto e^{-E_i/kT} Eq$$

The mobility $\mu = v_d/E$ is therefore given by

$$\mu \propto e^{-E_i/kT}$$

which is, as we have seen, in accord with the experimental measurements.

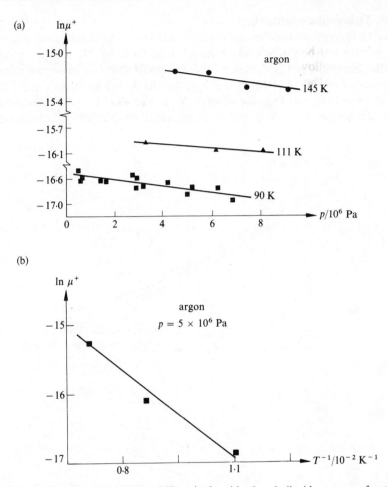

Fig. 12.10 (a) The logarithm of the mobility μ^+ of positive ions in liquid argon as a function of pressure at three different temperatures. (b) $\ln \mu^+$ plotted as a function of T^{-1} at a fixed pressure. All data in (b) was taken from the best straight lines drawn in (a). (Data from T. H. Davis, S. A. Rice, and L. Meyer, *J. Chem. Phys.*, **37**, 947 (1962).)

Exercise 12.3

The solid alkali halides, such as sodium chloride, have a small but measurable electrical conductivity σ. On the assumption that the positive ions have a very much greater mobility than the larger negative ions, show that $\ln \sigma \propto -1/T$. As a clue, draw on eq. (10.1) for the hopping speed of ion in the absence of an electric field. (Diffusion in the alkali halides is mainly by hopping into adjacent vacant lattice sites.) Remember also that the probability that a vibrating atom has an energy greater than or equal to E is $\exp(-E/kT)$ (eq. (8.65)).

423

12.5 Thermal conduction

Figure 12.11(a) shows the thermal conductivity κ of argon measured at various fixed pressures over a temperature range from 90 K to 200 K; the "routes", or paths, along the p–V_m–T surface which were followed in these experiments are indicated in Fig. 12.11(b). You will notice that the ordinate in Fig. 12.11(a) is κ and not $\ln \kappa$, and that the abscissa is T, and not T^{-1}. In other words, unlike the behaviour of D, η, and μ, the thermal conductivity of a liquid does

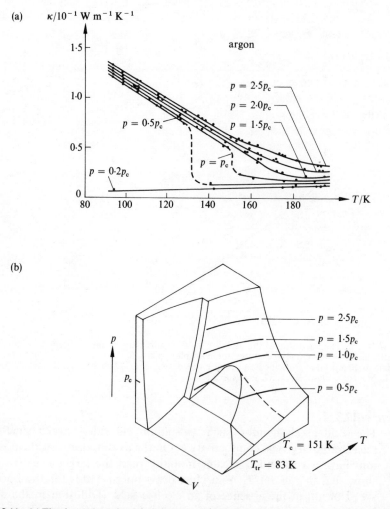

Fig. 12.11 (a) The thermal conductivity of argon as a function of temperature at various pressures (expressed as fractions of the critical pressure $p_c = 4.9 \times 10^6$ Pa). (Data from H. Ziebland and J. T. A. Burton, *Brit. J. Appl. Phys.*, **9**, 52 (1958).) (b) The paths followed along the p–V_m–T surface in the experiments.

not vary exponentially with the inverse temperature. This strongly suggests that a cell model is, to put it mildly, not the most appropriate one with which to discuss thermal conduction.

Possible mechanisms

Let us return to the air-table analogue (Fig. 12.6) and consider how A might transport *energy* to B. (You will remember that thermal conduction involves the transport of energy.) There are two distinct possibilities. First, A might send a puck of mass m and speed v across to B—so transporting an energy $\frac{1}{2}mv^2$ across the table. Alternatively he might fill the table with pucks which could be coupled together (Fig. 12.6(b)) to simulate interatomic forces. On giving energy to one puck, this puck will soon "collide" with another so transferring energy to it. By a succession of collisions energy will be transferred across the table; in each collision kinetic energy is transformed, at least in part, into potential energy before being transformed back into kinetic energy. You will recognize the first of these possible mechanisms for transferring energy as the one which applies in low-density gases; and the second as the one which applies in (non-metallic) solids. We would probably expect energy transfer by collisions to be the dominant mechanism behind thermal conduction in liquids. However we must also bring into the discussion the fact that liquids do have some gas-like attributes—notably they do have some "free-volume" within them.

In our discussions of thermal conduction in gases and in solids we saw that the speed at which energy is transmitted is roughly the speed at which sound travels in these phases. So a sensible starting point might be a consideration of the speed of sound in a liquid. Sound actually travels in liquids at a speed which is about an order of magnitude greater than the mean thermal speed $\bar{u}$ of the liquid's atoms, whereas in a gas the two speeds are practically identical. Is this difference to do with the difference in the number density of atoms in the two phases? An analogue may provide the answer.

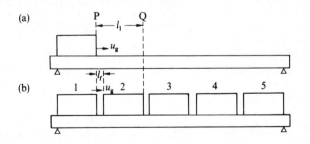

Fig. 12.12 Two possible mechanisms for transmitting energy along a linear air-track. In (a) a single glider is sent bodily from one end to the other. In (b) energy is transmitted via a sequence of inter-glider collisions.

425

A single "glider" on a frictionless air-track (Fig. 12.12(a)) illustrates how sound is transmitted in a (very) low density gas; the message is transmitted with the glider's velocity, u_g say, from one end of the track to the other. Now suppose that instead of a single glider we have several, all of the same mass and all initially at rest (Fig. 12.12(b)). If glider 1 is given the same speed u_g as we gave the single glider in Fig. 12.12(a), the message reaches the far end of the track much more quickly than before. The reason for this is that in a collision between any two gliders, say gliders 2 and 3, the message jumps very quickly from the right-hand side of glider 2 to the right-hand side of glider 3. (You will recall that in an elastic collision between two gliders of equal mass, one of which is initially at rest, the two gliders "change roles"; the one initially moving at speed u_g will stop and the one initially at rest will move off at speed u_g.) So although the speed of the individual gliders is u_g the message gets transmitted more rapidly than this because of the almost instantaneous transmission through the body of a glider.

With a single glider (Fig. 12.12(a)) the message is transmitted from a point P to a point Q, a distance l_1 apart, with a speed u_g. With many gliders, the speed at which the message is transmitted from P to Q is l_1 divided by the time it takes a glider to travel l_f, namely l_f/u_g. Here l_f is the "free space" between two gliders, and l_1 is equal to the distance between the centres of two gliders (see Fig. 12.12(b)). This assumes a very much greater speed of transmission through the gliders than through the "free space". Therefore

$$u_1 = l_1/(l_f/u_g)$$

$$u_1 = \left(\frac{l_1}{l_f}\right)u_g \tag{12.18}$$

If we think of the second experiment as modelling conditions in a liquid we can explain why the speed u_1 of sound in a liquid is some ten times the speed u_g of sound in a gas; the value of l_f is of order one-tenth of l_1 in a liquid. We shall now use this model of a liquid as consisting of hard-sphere repulsive atoms, in an attempt to account for the thermal conductivity measurements of Fig. 12.11(a).

The calculation of κ

In section 5.6 we deduced the following expression (eq. (5.47)) for the thermal conductivity of a gas:

$$\kappa = \tfrac{1}{2}n\bar{u}\lambda k \tag{12.19}$$

Here n is the number density of the gas atoms, λ is their mean free path, and $\bar{u}$ is their mean speed, that is, the speed at which energy is transmitted through a gas. If we are to apply this result to a liquid $\bar{u}$ must become the speed u_1 at which energy is transported through a liquid. This is given by eq. (12.18) with u_g given by $u_g \approx \overline{(u^2)}^{1/2} = (3kT/m)^{1/2}$, where m is the mass of an atom of the liquid. Therefore

$$u_1 = \frac{l_1}{l_f}\left(\frac{3kT}{m}\right)^{1/2}$$

It is not difficult to show that l_1—the mean separation between two atoms of the liquid—and l_f—the "free space" between two atoms—are related to the molar volume $V_{m,1}$ of the liquid and to the change in molar volume ΔV_m when a solid melts to give the liquid by*

$$\frac{l_1}{l_f} = \frac{3V_{m,1}}{\Delta V_m}$$

Therefore

$$u_1 = \left(\frac{3V_{m,1}}{\Delta V_m}\right)\left(\frac{3kT}{m}\right)^{1/2} \tag{12.20}$$

In the case of a gas λ measures the *overall* distance through which energy is transmitted between collisions. In a liquid this distance is l_1, which is (to a good approximation) given by

$$l_1 = \left(\frac{V_{m,1}}{N_A}\right)^{1/3} \tag{12.21}$$

Finally, the number of atoms per unit volume in a liquid is given by

$$n = \frac{N_A}{V_{m,1}} \tag{12.22}$$

Substituting from eqs. (12.22), (12.20), and (12.21) into eq. (12.19) gives

$$\kappa = \frac{3k}{2}\left(\frac{N_A}{V_{m,1}}\right)^{2/3}\left(\frac{V_{m,1}}{\Delta V_m}\right)\left(\frac{3kT}{m}\right)^{1/2} \tag{12.23}$$

for the thermal conductivity of a liquid. Putting in appropriate numbers predicts a thermal conductivity for liquid argon near the triple point which

---

* Since there are N_A atoms in a volume $V_{m,1}$ of liquid the volume occupied by one atom of the liquid is $V_{m,1}/N_A \approx l_1^3$. Likewise in a solid $V_{m,s}/N_A \approx l_s^3$, where l_s is approximately the diameter of an atom. Since $l_f = l_1 - l_s$ it follows that

$$\frac{l_1}{l_f} = \frac{V_{m,1}^{1/3}}{V_{m,1}^{1/3} - V_{m,s}^{1/3}}$$

If ΔV_m is the change in the molar volume when the solid melts, that is $V_{m,s} = V_{m,1} - \Delta V_m$,

$$\frac{l_1}{l_f} = \frac{1}{1 - [(V_{m,1} - \Delta V_m)/V_{m,1}]^{1/3}} \approx \frac{3V_{m,1}}{\Delta V_m}$$

agrees, to within about 30 per cent, with the experimental value. It is, of course, tempting to conclude that this level of agreement vindicates our model. More revealing is the fact that eq. (12.23) predicts an increasing thermal conductivity with increasing temperature; we know that the conductivity actually decreases as the temperature rises (Fig. 12.11(a)). So the model has its little weaknesses! In fact, the weaknesses arose in regarding the atoms as rigid when we calculated the rate at which energy is transmitted (eq. (12.18)). If, instead of making this assumption, we had merely substituted experimental values for the speed of sound in the liquid into eq. (12.19) in place of $\bar{u}$ we would have found that κ decreases with increasing T. In liquid argon, the speed of sound decreases by a factor two on raising the temperature of the liquid from 84 K to 140 K; as does the thermal conductivity (see Fig. 12.11(a)).

12.6 A long-term goal

Much of the success which we have enjoyed in discussing transport processes in liquids has resulted from a judicious choice of models. The cell model seems particularly suited for a discussion of diffusion, viscous flow, and ionic conduction. Yet even it *cannot* be a real winner. Figure 12.13 reminds us that it is possible to take a substance from being a liquid to being a gas without any phase separation occurring. Consider now a series of experiments to measure, say, the self-diffusion coefficient D at various values of T which lie along the isobar AD. Experiments show that in region AB, $D \propto \exp(-E_d/kT)$, where E_d is a constant. Theoreticians get to work and come up with a cell

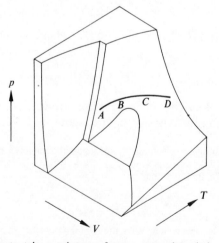

Fig. 12.13 It is possible to take a substance from a state where it is wholly liquid to a state where it is wholly gaseous without phase separation occurring. As illustrated here the path $ABCD$ is one of constant pressure.

model which obligingly yields the right answer! Experiments show that in region CD, $D \propto T^{3/2}$. Theoreticians adopt a perfect gas model and declare that $D \propto T^{3/2}$ is as it should be!

As far as the substance is concerned its properties change gradually as we follow it along AD. There ought surely then to be *one* model which can cope with all regions of path AD. This model cannot be the cell model—the prediction it makes for region AB, namely $\exp(-E_d/kT)$, just does not approximate to $T^{3/2}$ behaviour at large T. Nor, by the same token, can it be a perfect gas model since $T^{3/2}$ does not even approximate to $\exp(-E_d/kT)$ at small T. The goal of transport theories must be to find a single model embracing all regions of the surface—or at least, those regions of the p–V–T surface where the substance is in the liquid or gaseous phases.

12.7 Interfacial phenomena

(a) Surface tension
Childhood experiences will have taught you that it takes some practice to blow a soap bubble. If you blow too gently the soap film will not grow to form a bubble; if you blow too hard the film will break.

The site of the tension
To make a more controlled study of the properties of these thin liquid films one can make use of a U-shaped frame as shown in Fig. 12.14(a). This frame has a loosely fitting slider rod S attached to a suitable force-measuring device, represented here by a Newton balance. When the frame is filled with a soap film, as shown in Fig. 12.14(a) (and in Fig. 12.14(b) in cross-section) a force F must be applied to maintain static equilibrium. All that this proves is that, if we consider a section of film between S and P (Fig. 12.14), there must be a

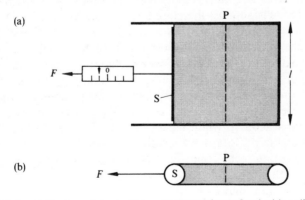

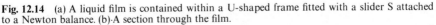

Fig. 12.14 (a) A liquid film is contained within a U-shaped frame fitted with a slider S attached to a Newton balance. (b)·A section through the film.

429

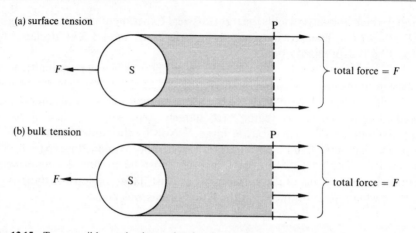

Fig. 12.15 Two possible mechanisms whereby the portion of film SP of Fig. 12.14 might be maintained in equilibrium. In (a) the force F (which must equal the force provided by the Newton balance) originates in the surface regions of the film. In (b) it originates in the bulk.

force to the right of P which, in conjunction with F, keeps the section SP in equilibrium! The film to the right of P must therefore exert a total force F, directed to the right, on the section SP. Figure 12.15 shows two possible ways this force might be provided; in (a) it is provided by having the surfaces in a state of tension; in (b) by having a bulk tension throughout the film. By analogy with stretched solid films, such as thin metal foils, we might well expect the tension to exist throughout the film, as in Fig. 12.15(b). An easy way to distinguish between these two possible hypotheses would be to reduce the thickness of the liquid film by half. If the force F required to maintain equilibrium is halved, then this would argue for a bulk tension. If the force does not change, this would argue for a surface tension. The experiment is very easy to perform; one simply allows the film to evaporate, keeping a record of the force F. What one finds is that, as the film thins by evaporation, F does not change. The tension must therefore lie in the surface regions (Fig. 12.15(a)) and not in the bulk (Fig. 12.15(b)) as it would in a stretched solid sheet. There is a further characteristic which is worth noting. If the force F provided by the spring balance is increased, however slightly, beyond the equilibrium value, the film will expand indefinitely and eventually break. There must, therefore be some mechanism operating in liquids to maintain the surface at this tension irrespective of the surface area. The name *surface tension* (γ) is given to the force acting per unit length of surface. Since the line of the upper surface at P in Fig. 12.15(a) is of length l, the width of the frame, it follows that the force acting to the right of P is γl along the upper line of the film and is γl along the lower line (Fig. 12.16). For the section of film between S and P to be in equilibrium we must have

$$F = 2\gamma l \tag{12.24}$$

Clearly, the surface tension can be found by measuring F.

What causes surface tension?

As we shall presently demonstrate, the tension which exists in the surface of a liquid arises as a consequence of insisting, as insist we must, that as many atoms diffuse from the bulk of a liquid to its surface per unit time as leave

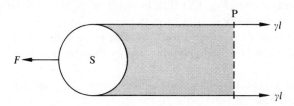

Fig. 12.16 The section of liquid between S and P is maintained in equilibrium by the force F on the rod S and the force $2\gamma l$ acting on the liquid section at P.

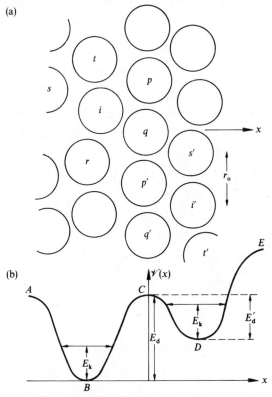

Fig. 12.17 (a) Here the surface layer of the liquid is supposed to have the same (mean) inter-atomic separation as in the bulk. (b) The potential energy of an atom as it is displaced from the bulk to the surface of the liquid. The potential energy is taken as zero when an atom in the bulk is in the centre of its cell.

the surface for the bulk per unit time. If this did not hold, the liquid would not be in an equilibrium state. To see how the surface tension arises we will begin by looking at the consequences of supposing that the interatomic separation in the surface layer of atoms is the same as in the bulk (Fig. 12.17(a)).

The problem which faces atom i as it attempts to diffuse through from the bulk to the surface region of the liquid is summarized in the portion ABC of the potential energy curve; Fig. 12.17(b). In short, it requires an activation energy E_d, the activation energy for diffusion in the bulk liquid. We have already seen (section 12.2) that E_d is made up of the energy required to separate p and q sufficiently to allow i through, plus the energy to separate i from its neighbours r, s, and t.

Now consider the problem which faces atom i' in the surface layer as it attempts to diffuse into the bulk of the liquid. It, like i, also has to squeeze through between atoms, here p' and q'. However, it has fewer surrounding atoms pulling back on it; only t' and s' in the two-dimensional case illustrated in Fig. 12.17(a), as compared to the three atoms r, s, and t which pull back on i. As a consequence, the activation energy E_d' required for i' to diffuse into the bulk is lower than the activation energy E_d required for i to diffuse to the surface. (For i' to escape into the vapour it must escape entirely from the pull of all other atoms. The energy required—the latent heat (or enthalpy) of evaporation per atom—is, as we have seen earlier, typically some four times E_d.) This information is summarized in portion CDE of Fig. 12.17(b).

When atoms like i and i' are given their Maxwell–Boltzmann range of energies E_k, more atoms will leave the surface for the bulk than vice versa.

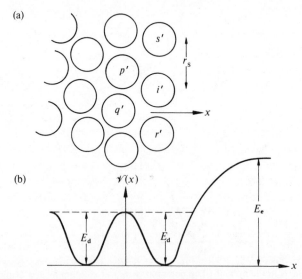

Fig. 12.18 (a) Shows a liquid with a depleted surface layer. (b) The resulting potential energy of an atom as it is displaced from the bulk to the surface of the liquid.

In section 12.2 we saw that the probability of an atom acquiring an energy of at least E was proportional to $\exp(-E/kT)$. Therefore, since E_d' is less than E_d, more atoms will succeed in escaping from the surface into the bulk than vice versa. As a result the surface layer will become depleted. This depleted layer, as we shall presently see, leads to an equality in the two diffusion rates and also to the appearance of a surface tension.

Figure 12.18(a) shows the new condition of the liquid where we have assumed the depletion is confined to the surface layer. (Measurements on the reflection of polarized light from a liquid surface suggest that the decreased density is confined to a few atomic thicknesses.) On this model the value of E_d is essentially unchanged. However the value of E_d' keeps increasing as depletion proceeds, until it equals E_d. When this happens the two escape probabilities, $\exp(-E_d/kT)$ and $\exp(-E_d'/kT)$, become identical and the same number of atoms leave the surface for the bulk per unit time as vice versa. Equality of diffusion rates

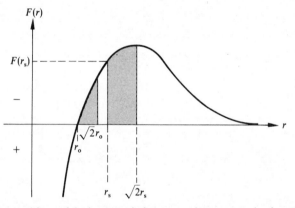

Fig. 12.19 The general form of the interatomic force curve between a pair of atoms. The shaded area under the curve between $r = r_0$ and $r = \sqrt{2}r_0$ is the energy required by atom i' in Fig. 12.17(a) in escaping from atom s'. The shaded area between $r = r_s$ and $r = \sqrt{2}r_s$ is the corresponding energy in Fig. 12.18(a).

means, of course, that the system has reached a state of (dynamic) equilibrium.* To see why E_d' should increase as the surface layer depletes, let us look at atom i' in Fig. 12.18(a). As in the original situation (Fig. 12.17(a)) i' has to squeeze through between p' and q'. But now in escaping from r' and s' it must do so against an increased force, the mean interatomic separation having increased from (approximately) r_0 in Fig. 12.17(a) to, say, r_s in the surface layer shown in Fig. 12.18(a). The force $F(r_s)$ which atoms r' and s' each exert on atom i'

---

* A more careful analysis shows that at equilibrium E_d' and E_d will not be exactly equal. This is because escape jumps out of the surface, in the $+x$-direction, are all but excluded for a surface atom, whereas escape jumps within the bulk are equally likely to occur in $+x$- and $-x$-directions. Analysis shows that dynamic equilibrium is achieved when $E_d' = E_d + kT \ln 2$. For simplicity, we shall ignore the $kT \ln 2$ term. It normally makes only a small correction—in liquid argon at 100 K it only amounts to about 20 per cent of E_d.

while it is in the surface layer can, of course, be calculated from the interatomic force curve $F(r)$ (Fig. 12.19). The contribution which r' and s' each make towards the total activation energy required by i' to diffuse into the bulk may be readily found from Fig. 12.19. When, as in Fig. 12.17(a) i' leaves the surface for the bulk, its separation from s' increases from r_0 to a value of about $\sqrt{2}r_0$ when i' is just squeezing through between p' and q'. The energy required to so escape from s' is the area shown shaded in Fig. 12.19 between $r = r_0$ and $r = \sqrt{2}r_0$. Likewise, in Fig. 12.18(a), when i' escapes from s'—in so doing it moves from $r = r_s$ to about $r = \sqrt{2}r_s$—the energy contribution made by s' is the area shown shaded in Fig. 12.19 from $r = r_s$ to $r = \sqrt{2}r_s$. Clearly more energy is required by i' in escaping from a depleted layer than a full layer. This is a consequence of the fact that in the full layer $F(r_0) \approx 0$, whereas in the depleted surface layer the force $F(r_s)$ on atom i' is non-zero.

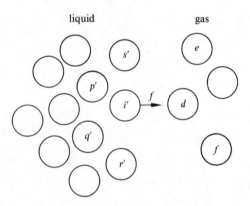

Fig. 12.20 Atoms d, e, f, etc., in the vapour phase contribute a net outward force f on atom i' in the liquid surface so increasing its activation energy for diffusion into the bulk.

Once dynamic equilibrium is achieved atom i' will be acted on by a force $F(r_s)$ from atom s' and a force $F(r_s)$ from atom r' (Fig. 12.18(a)). The tension along a row of atoms in the surface is therefore $F(r_s)$. Because the rows of atoms are separated by a distance r_s it follows that the tension acting per unit length of surface—the surface tension γ—is given by

$$\gamma = \frac{F(r_s)}{r_s} \tag{12.25}$$

The problem of calculating γ therefore resolves into the problem of finding the value of r_s which makes $E_d' = E_d$. The calculations are not difficult but are somewhat tedious. (In general, they require "successive approximation" techniques.) When performed for neon they predict a surface tension of $0.5 \times 10^{-3} \text{ N m}^{-1}$ compared with an experimental value of $5.5 \times 10^{-3} \text{ N m}^{-1}$

close to the triple point.* Now liquid neon is held together by weak van der Waals' forces. At the other extreme comes the molten ionic salts which are held together by strongly ionic forces. An example of such a liquid is molten NaCl (where dissociation into Na^+ and Cl^- ions is effectively complete). Here our model predicts a surface tension of 4 N m^{-1}, compared to an experimental value of 0·11 N m^{-1}. Although the agreement between theory and experiment is not startlingly good it can be improved by allowing the interfacial region to extend into the bulk over a distance of two or three atomic thicknesses.

Some refinements

Throughout this discussion we have ignored the presence of the vapour with which the liquid is in equilibrium. Instead of drawing the interface as we did in Fig. 12.18(a) we should have drawn it as shown in Fig. 12.20. The gas atoms d, e, f, etc., will pull outwards on atom i' with some resultant force f. Because of this force, atom i' will find it more difficult to move into the bulk; E'_d in Fig. 12.17(b) will increase. As a result the surface layer need not be in such a state of tension to ensure dynamic equilibrium between the bulk and surface regions. On raising the temperature of a liquid while keeping it in equilibrium with its vapour the state of the liquid will, of course, move along the saturated liquid line (line ac in Fig. 1.4) while the state of the vapour will move along the saturated vapour line ec. The temperature of the liquid and vapour phases will have a common value in so moving from the triple line to the critical point. Likewise, the pressures of the two phases will be equal. What changes is the density of each phase. At the critical point both phases become indistinguishable and so, according to our model, the surface tension should fall to zero. The measured surface tension of a liquid does indeed fall towards zero as T_c is approached. By a similar argument, if a liquid is contained in an atmosphere of some foreign gas, its surface tension should fall with increasing gas pressure. It does. As a more extreme example, the surface tension of a liquid which is in contact with a solid should be lower than when the liquid is equilibrium with a gas. It usually is. Similar arguments explain the observation that the surface tensions of two immiscible liquids are lowered when they are in contact.

The solid–gas interface

Although we have only examined the liquid–gas interface the same criteria should apply at the solid–gas interface. At *equilibrium* as many atoms must diffuse from the bulk of the solid to the surface per unit time as diffuse in the opposite direction. And this should lead to the surface being in a state of

---

* In making these calculations one often finds that r_s exceeds the maximum on the interatomic force curve, $F(r)$. This does not matter since we never truly *stretch* the surface; only in a solid would this lead to unstable equilibrium. In moving out the slider S in the apparatus of Fig. 12.14(a) we create more surface, in which the interatomic separation is still r_s.

tension. However we would expect that the tension would only be apparent close to the melting point where diffusion can occur at an appreciable rate. In fact, a force must be applied to prevent a metal rod, maintained at a temperature between the fusion temperature T_f and about $0.9T_f$, from contracting. This method for measuring the surface tension of a solid is, of course, the analogue of the frame method for liquids. (The surface tension of most metals, as measured by this technique, turn out to be between about 0.5 N m^{-1} and 2 N m^{-1}.) Because of the rapid dependence of the diffusion coefficient on temperature—D, you will recall, is proportional to $\exp(-E_d/kT)$—surfaces which are formed by fracturing a solid at temperatures well below T_f may not reach equilibrium for centuries. Furthermore the high "viscosity" at these temperatures of even very imperfect solids prevents them from assuming shapes characteristic of liquid drops. Lumps of rock are not spherical! In the case of liquids any time dependence of surface tension is only evident in solutions of high molecular mass solutes, where the times required to establish the bulk and surface solute concentrations appropriate to dynamic equilibrium will be of the order of seconds, or even minutes.

(b) *The saturated vapour pressure*

We have just seen that dynamic equilibrium between the bulk and the surface regions of a liquid demands that as many atoms diffuse from the bulk to the surface per unit time as diffuse in the opposite direction. We have yet to appeal to the fact that dynamic equilibrium must also exist between the surface of the liquid and the surrounding vapour.

For atom i' in the surface of the liquid (Fig. 12.18) to escape into the vapour it must have an energy of E_e or greater, where E_e is the latent heat of evaporation *per atom* of the liquid. The number of successful escape jumps f_e per unit time into the vapour is given by eq. (12.4) with $E_e = E_d$, namely

$$f_e = \frac{1}{4a}\left(\frac{2kT}{m}\right)^{1/2} e^{-E_e/kT}$$

Since there are $1/r_s^2$ atoms per unit area of the surface, in which r_s is the interatomic separation, it follows that the evaporation rate—the number of atoms evaporating per unit area of surface per unit time—is given by

$$\text{evaporation rate} = \frac{1}{4r_s^3}\left(\frac{2kT}{m}\right)^{1/2} e^{-E_e/kT} \tag{12.26}$$

where we have assumed that the cell diameter for i' is equal to r_s.

In a closed system, where the vapour is contained, evaporation will not proceed indefinitely at this rate. As it proceeds the number density n_v of vapour atoms will increase and, as a consequence, the number of atoms available to return to the liquid will increase. Now we know from section 5.3 (eq. (5.15)) that in a gas possessing an atomic number density n_v and a mean atomic speed $\bar{u}$ the number of atoms striking unit area of surface is $\frac{1}{4} n_v \bar{u}$. However condensation requires that the atoms stick and do not simply rebound with no loss of energy from the surface of the liquid. If we denote the probability that a vapour atom will stick on striking the surface of the liquid by θ it follows that the number of vapour atoms condensing per unit area of surface per unit time is given by

$$\text{condensation rate} = \frac{\theta}{4} n_v \bar{u}$$

Since we assumed a two-dimensional liquid in eq. (12.26) we had better now assume a two-dimensional gas! In particular we assume $\frac{1}{2} m u^2 = kT$, giving $\bar{u} \approx \left(\overline{u^2}\right)^{1/2} = (2kT/m)^{1/2}$, and so

$$\text{condensation rate} = \frac{\theta}{4} n_v \left(\frac{2kT}{m}\right)^{1/2} \tag{12.27}$$

Dynamic equilibrium between the liquid and the vapour demands that eqs. (12.26) and (12.27) be equal, that is

$$\frac{\theta n_v}{4} = \frac{1}{4 r_s^3} e^{-E_e/kT}$$

or, since $1/r_s^3$ is the number of atoms per unit volume in the surface regions of the liquid (n_s say),

$$n_v = \frac{n_s}{\theta} e^{-E_e/kT} \tag{12.28}$$

In so far as we may regard the vapour as a perfect gas—this is clearly going to be very risky near the critical point—its pressure p will be related to the number density n_v of the atoms and to the temperature T by $p = n_v kT$ (eq. (4.28)). Therefore, from eq. (12.28)

$$\text{saturated vapour pressure, } p = \frac{n_s}{\theta} kT\, e^{-E_e/kT} \tag{12.29}$$

Since the exponential term will dominate the temperature dependence of p (unless—as seems unlikely at temperatures well below $T_c - n_s$ and θ also vary rapidly with T), eq. (12.29) predicts that a graph of $\ln p$ plotted against T^{-1} should be linear with a gradient $-E_e/k$. Furthermore E_e should equal $H_{m,e}/N_A$. Figure 12.21 shows $\ln p$ plotted against T^{-1} for argon in equilibrium with its vapour at temperatures between 100 and 140 K. The slope gives $E_e = 11 \cdot 0 \times 10^{-21}$ J, which compares very favourably with $H_{m,e}/N_A = 10 \cdot 8 \times 10^{-21}$ J.

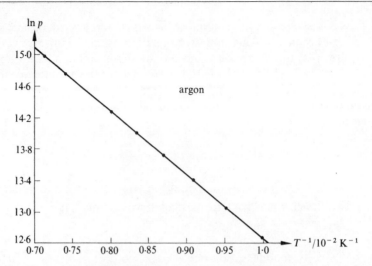

Fig. 12.21 The natural logarithm of the saturated vapour pressure p of liquid argon plotted against T^{-1}. (Data from W. B. Street, and L. A. K. Staveley, *J. Chem. Phys.*, **50**, 2302 (1969).)

In view of the essential correctness of eq. (12.29) it can be used to evaluate θ; the probability that a vapour atom will in fact condense on striking the surface of the liquid. Substituting for the saturated vapour pressure at $T = 100$ K and taking the number density n_s at the surface of the liquid to be equal to the bulk value (which we obtain from the mass density) gives $\theta = 3 \times 10^{-2}$ for argon. For water at 285 K, $\theta = 3.6 \times 10^{-2}$.

(c) *Capillarity*

If one lowers a small-bore glass tube into water, the water will rise up the capillary tube. This is just one particular example of a phenomenon known as *capillary rise*.

Exercise 12.4

Many introductory textbooks explain capillary rise by the following argument. The net force acting *up* on the liquid column (it is argued) is $2\pi r \gamma$ (see Fig. 12.22). The net force acting *down* is its weight $\pi r^2 \rho g h$, where g is the local acceleration due to gravity and ρ is the density of the liquid. At equilibrium the two forces are equal so $2\pi r \gamma = \pi r^2 \rho g h$. Criticize the argument!

Clues

It is important to discover whether capillary rise has anything to do with the inner surface of the tube, or whether some bulk property of the liquid is involved. Evidence arguing for a surface effect comes from the observation that, depending on the cleanliness of the glass, mercury sometimes rises in capillary

438

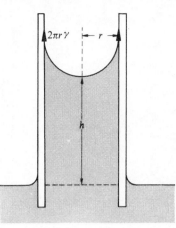

Fig. 12.22 Illustrating a frequently used "explanation" of capillary rise.

tubes and sometimes is depressed below the general level of the liquid. (Mercury rise—or "sticking"—is sometimes seen in vacuum gauges operating under high vacuum conditions.) As another example, the height to which water will rise in a glass capillary depends on the ionic content of the glass, on how the capillary was manufactured, and on the time elapsed since manufacture.

A possible mechanism

Let us examine what is likely to happen, at the atomic level, when a capillary tube is lowered into a liquid. Figure 12.23(a) shows the initial situation. For an atom like i to diffuse up the glass in the $+z$-direction—to "wet the glass"—it must first leave the liquid. This requires an energy E_e, the latent heat of evaporation per atom. On "condensing" on the glass atom i will give up an energy E_a, the *heat of adsorption* (per atom) on the surface. The activation energy required by an atom i to diffuse up the glass is E_e, whereas the activation energy required by an atom i' already on the glass to diffuse back into the liquid is E_a (Fig. 12.23(a)). (Once on the glass an atom may hop from site to site. This process requires an activation energy E_h. Within the body of the liquid the energy required for diffusion is, of course, E_d.) On giving the atoms their Maxwell–Boltzmann range of kinetic energies it is clear that, provided $E_a > E_e$, more atoms will diffuse up the glass out of the liquid than diffuse down the glass into the liquid (*wetting* occurs).

Diffusion of the liquid up the glass does not, however, continue unhindered for as diffusion up the glass proceeds, further diffusion becomes increasingly more difficult. Initially (Fig. (12.23(a)) the downward force acting on i as it attempts to diffuse upwards is the resultant of the interatomic forces between i and the rest of the liquid. However, in the situation pictured in Fig. 12.23(b), atom i is not only pulled downwards by these interatomic forces but there is

439

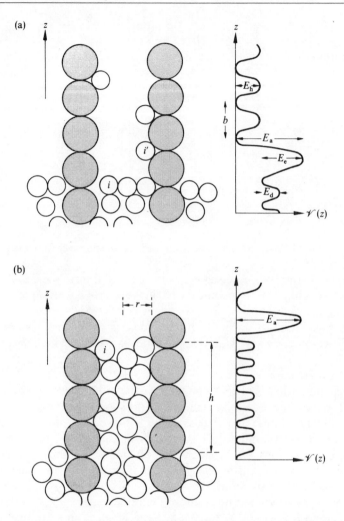

Fig. 12.23 (a) The situation at the moment a capillary is lowered into a liquid. The plot of $\mathscr{V}(z)$ against z denotes the potential energy of an atom i as it moves up the wall in the z-direction. (b) Shows how capillary rise to a height h will ensure dynamic equilibrium between atoms diffusing up and down the inner surface of the tube.

an additional downward pull due to the weight of the liquid column. If a is the lateral spacing of atoms like i around the perimeter of the glass (circumference $2\pi r$), there are $2\pi r/a$ such atoms being pulled downwards by a total force of $\pi r^2 \rho g h$, that is, the additional downward force acting on atom i when the liquid has risen to a height h is $\pi r^2 \rho g h / 2\pi r a^{-1} = \frac{1}{2} r \rho g h a$. If the separation between adsorption sites on the glass is b (see Fig. 12.23(a)) the additional energy required by atom i in escaping this downward force is about $(\frac{1}{2} r \rho g h a)(\frac{1}{2} b)$. A state of dynamic equilibrium such that the number of atoms diffusing up the glass per unit time from the liquid equals the number returning down the glass to the liquid, will be attained when the weight contribution on i is sufficient to increase E_e to E_a (Fig. 12.23(b)), that is when

$$(\tfrac{1}{2}r\rho gha)(\tfrac{1}{2}b) + E_e = E_a$$

or when

$$h = \frac{4(E_a - E_e)}{abr\rho g} \tag{12.30}$$

Equation (12.30) does indeed predict that the height to which a liquid will rise depends on the condition of the glass, through E_a. Should $E_a < E_e$, capillary depression is necessary to ensure dynamic equilibrium. In the usual situation where mercury is depressed to below the general liquid level in a glass capillary, E_a is presumably less than E_e. Only under conditions of great surface cleanliness (such as may occur in a high-vacuum system) is E_a greater than E_e with mercury in glass.

This discussion has focussed on the net force which acts on atom i. But it could equally well have talked of the force which atoms like i exert on the liquid as they diffuse up the glass. These two forces—the force which the liquid exerts on atom i and the force which atom i exerts on the liquid—are equal and opposite (Newton's third law), just as surely as the earth's pull on an air molecule equals the molecule's pull on the earth. In these terms, we may talk of the upward force per unit length of meniscus perimeter, say γ'. At equilibrium

$$2\pi r\gamma' = \pi r^2 \rho gh$$

$$\gamma' = \tfrac{1}{2}r\rho gh$$

Substituting for $r\rho gh$ from eq. (12.30) gives

$$\gamma' = \frac{2(E_a - E_e)}{ab}$$

as the upward force per unit length of meniscus perimeter.

In developing these arguments a number of simplifications have been introduced. We ignored the tension at the interface between the liquid and the solid, from $z = 0$ to $z = h$. (The effect of this will be to lower h somewhat.) We also assumed that the liquid was a solid cylinder of length h in calculating the weight contribution acting on i. Further, we ignored the fact that before the capillary is even lowered into the liquid its surfaces may be covered with a (strongly bound) layer of vapour which has condensed onto the tube from the vapour phase. For this reason, E_a is not to be interpreted as the heat of

441

adsorption onto the virgin glass. Despite all these simplifying assumptions*
eq. (12.30) predicts capillary rises which are in order of magnitude agreement
with experiment. In a silica glass tube of radius 10^{-3} m the predicted rise for
water is 9×10^{-2} m, assuming $a = 3 \times 10^{-10}$ m, $b = 5 \times 10^{-10}$ m,
$E_e(=H_{m,e}/N_A) = 6.8 \times 10^{-20}$ J and $E_a = 10.2 \times 10^{-20}$ J. This value for E_a is
that for a layer of water one molecule thick absorbed onto a virgin silica glass
surface. A somewhat smaller value should therefore be substituted into eq.
(12.30). This would lead to improved agreement with the experimentally
observed rise of 1.2×10^{-2} m. If the layer of water absorbed on the glass is
thick enough to exhibit bulk properties the situation reduces to that shown in
Fig. 12.24 and an analysis based on $2\pi r \gamma = \pi r^2 \rho g h$ will apply!

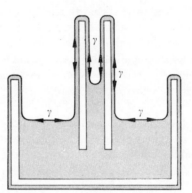

Fig. 12.24   Showing how capillary rise can occur if the glass is covered by a liquid layer thick enough
to exhibit bulk properties.

Summary
1. The cell model employed here seeks to combine properties reminiscent of
   the gaseous and solid phases by allowing an atom within its cell to behave
   in perfect gas fashion but to require an activation energy to escape from
   the cell.
2. Diffusion in liquids is slow because of the small probability that an atom
   will possess the energy necessary to escape from its cell.
3. Viscous flow, on the cell model, arises because the activation energy
   required by an atom to escape in the direction of the applied shear stress
   is lower than in the opposite direction. Ionic conduction may be explained
   in similar terms with the electric field acting on positive ions to lower the
   activation energy in the field direction.

* There were others introduced into the discussion! We assumed the so-called *angle of contact*
to be zero. This is defined as the angle between the tangent plane to the liquid surface, where
it meets the glass, and the glass. Experiments which purport to measure the angle of contact
actually measure some property well removed (at the atomic level) from the glass-liquid junction.
It is hard to ascribe much meaning to a non-zero angle of contact in the immediate
vicinity (within a few atomic diameters) of the glass-liquid junction.

4. The cell model successfully accounts for the linear dependence of D, η, and μ on the exponential of the inverse temperature. It cannot account for the relative insensitivity to temperature of the thermal conductivity of a liquid. A dense gas model is somewhat more successful here.

5. The tension present in the surface layers of a liquid ensures that as many atoms will diffuse per unit time from the bulk regions of the liquid to the surface as diffuse in the opposite direction.

6. Capillary rise can be explained on the assumption that dynamic equilibrium must exist at the inner surface of the tube; that as many atoms diffuse up the surface of the tube from the liquid per unit time as diffuse in the opposite direction.

PROBLEMS

12.1 Calculate the number of escape attempts per second made by an atom of liquid argon from its cell when the liquid is at a temperature of 84 K and has a density of $1 \cdot 4 \times 10^3$ kg m^{-3}. What fraction of these escape attempts are successful? Take $E_d = 5 \times 10^{-21}$ J. $A_r(\text{Ar}) = 40$.

12.2 State, in words, the origin of the $T^{1/2}$ and the $\exp(-E_d/kT)$ term in the final expression for D (eq. (12.7)).

12.3 This easily performed experiment should provide some feel for the temperature dependence of D in a liquid. Although it may not be able to confirm that $D \propto \exp(-\text{constant}/T)$ it should enable you to rule out a perfect gas model of a liquid, which predicts $D \propto T^{3/2}$

Simultaneously drop one lump of sugar into a cup of cold water and another into a cup of hot water. Compare the time taken for the taste of sugar to become apparent at the surface of the cold water with the time taken for the warm water. This may (with a little thought) enable you to deduce the ratio of the diffusion coefficients at two temperatures. Are you sure you are observing diffusion?

12.4 It is an experimental fact that many liquids have roughly the same viscosity, as measured at their melting point. For example, the viscosity of liquid copper at its melting point (under normal atmospheric pressure) of 1356 K is $3 \cdot 4 \times 10^{-3}$ kg m^{-1} s^{-1}; the viscosity of bromine at its melting point (266 K) is $1 \cdot 3 \times 10^{-3}$ kg m^{-1} s^{-1}; the viscosity of lead at its melting point (600 K) is $2 \cdot 6 \times 10^{-3}$ kg m^{-1} s^{-1}. Try to account for this experimental fact. Clues: Think about the exponent term. Also, what happens at the melting point?

12.5 What is the relaxation time of an atom in liquid argon at a temperature of 84 K and at a density of $1 \cdot 4 \times 10^3$ kg m^{-3}? $A_r(\text{Ar}) = 40$.

12.6 State, in words, the origin of the term $fa\exp(-E_v/kT)$ in eq. (12.14).

12.7 In the study made by Davis, Rice, and Meyer, whose results are shown in Fig. 12.10, the ion density in the liquid argon was about 10^{11} m^{-3}. What was the mean separation of the ions in the liquid?

12.8 In the study whose results are shown in Fig. 12.4(a) the self-diffusion coefficient was measured at a series of fixed pressures over a range of temperatures. Sketch in on a p–V_m–T surface the "routes" followed in these experiments. Do the same for the study of the dynamic viscosity whose results are shown in Fig. 12.8(a) and also for the study of the ionic mobility whose results are shown in Fig. 12.10(a). All the experiments relate to argon. Make use of the data on the triple and critical points contained in Table 1.1; these will tell you which experiments were performed

443

on liquid argon and which on gaseous argon. Do D, η, or μ^+ undergo any sudden change as the argon changes from a "liquid" to a "gas"? .

12.9 What is the origin of each of the terms $3V_{m,l}/\Delta V_m$ and $(3kT/m)^{1/2}$ in eq. (12.23). Predict the thermal conductivity of liquid argon near the triple temperature (84 K), at a density of $1 \cdot 41 \times 10^3$ kg m^{-3}. Solid argon has a density of $1 \cdot 64 \times 10^3$ kg m^{-3}. $A_r(\text{Ar}) = 40$.

12.10 It is not hard to accept that if the tension in the soap film forming a soap bubble were to change so would the radius of the bubble. If the tension were to increase, the bubble would shrink. If it were to decrease, the bubble would expand. Once a soap bubble is blown the film thickness will thin by evaporation. By observing a soap bubble over a period of time you should be able to decide whether the tension in the film extends throughout its thickness or is confined to the surface regions. Try the experiment.

Appendix 1. Atomic collisions

Our goal is to derive an expression for the energy transferred from one atom to another in an atomic collision. We will realize this goal by applying the laws of conservation of momentum and energy to the collision process.

Figure A1.1 shows the moment of impact between an atom of mass M and another of mass m. Before impact M has a velocity U; after impact it has a velocity V. Before impact m has a velocity u; after impact a velocity v. Each of these velocities may, of course, be resolved into components along the x-, y-, and z-axes. These components are indicated in parentheses after the velocities. Thus V_x, V_y, and V_z, for example, are the components of V along the three coordinate axes. The x-axis is taken to be along the line of centres of the atoms at the moment of impact. The y-axis lies in the tangent plane between the atoms; here in the plane of the paper. The z-axis (not shown) is directed out of the paper at $90°$ to the x- and y-axes.

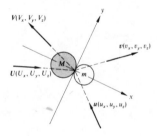

Fig. A1.1   The moment of impact between two atoms.

If we assume that the interatomic force between M and m is directed along the line joining their centres (i.e., along the x-direction) it follows that, since there is no force along the y- and z-directions, there can be no change in momentum along these directions. Therefore:

$$MU_y = MV_y$$

$$MU_z = MV_z$$

$$mu_y = mv_y$$

and

$$mu_z = mv_z$$

or

$$U_y = V_y, U_z = V_z, u_y = v_y, \quad \text{and} \quad u_z = v_z \tag{A1.1}$$

The only direction along which a change in momentum occurs is that of the x-axis (since this is the only direction in which a force acts). The statement that momentum is conserved therefore becomes

$$MU_x + mu_x = MV_x + mv_x$$

$$M(U_x - V_x) = -m(u_x - v_x) \tag{A1.2}$$

When atoms collide they (normally) do so elastically; meaning that none of their translational kinetic energy gets converted into other forms (such as going to increase the potential energy of the atoms' electrons by moving them further from the nucleus). This being so, the equation of conservation of energy takes the simple form

$$\tfrac{1}{2}MU^2 + \tfrac{1}{2}mu^2 = \tfrac{1}{2}MV^2 + \tfrac{1}{2}mv^2 \tag{A1.3}$$

or, since $U^2 = U_x^2 + U_y^2 + U_z^2$, with similar expressions for u, V, and v (see Fig. 3.4),

$$\tfrac{1}{2}M(U_x^2 + U_y^2 + U_z^2) + \tfrac{1}{2}m(u_x^2 + u_y^2 + u_z^2)$$

$$= \tfrac{1}{2}M(V_x^2 + V_y^2 + V_z^2) + \tfrac{1}{2}m(v_x^2 + v_y^2 + v_z^2)$$

Using eq. (A1.1) this simplifies to

$$\tfrac{1}{2}MU_x^2 + \tfrac{1}{2}mu_x^2 = \tfrac{1}{2}MV_x^2 + \tfrac{1}{2}mv_x^2$$

$$M(U_x^2 - V_x^2) = -m(u_x^2 - v_x^2)$$

$$M(U_x - V_x)(U_x + V_x) = -m(u_x - v_x)(u_x + v_x) \tag{A1.4}$$

Dividing eq. (A1.4) by eq. (A1.2) gives

$$U_x + V_x = u_x + v_x \tag{A1.5}$$

(If you are unhappy about dividing one equation by another proceed by rearranging eqs. (A1.4) and (A1.5) so that each equals unity. You can now equate these two expressions.)

What interests us is the energy $\Delta\varepsilon$ transferred from M to m in the collision. Since the energy gained by m must equal the energy lost by M we have

$$\Delta\varepsilon = \tfrac{1}{2}MU^2 - \tfrac{1}{2}MV^2$$

Because $U^2 = U_x^2 + U_y^2 + U_z^2$ and likewise for V^2 this becomes, on applying eq. (A1.1),

$$\Delta\varepsilon = \tfrac{1}{2}MU_x^2 - \tfrac{1}{2}MV_x^2$$

$$\Delta\varepsilon = \tfrac{1}{2}M(U_x - V_x)(U_x + V_x) \tag{A1.6}$$

We will now seek to rewrite this equation so that it involves only the speeds U_x and u_x before impact. We first obtain an expression for V_x in terms of U_x and u_x. We do this by eliminating v_x from eqs. (A1.2) and (A1.5). Substituting for v_x from eq. (A1.5) into eq. (A1.2) gives

$$V_x = U_x\frac{(M - m)}{(M + m)} + \frac{2mu_x}{(M + m)}$$

Substituting this expression for V_x into both terms on the right-hand side of eq. (A1.6) gives

$$\Delta\varepsilon = \frac{2mM}{(m + M)^2}\left[(MU_x^2 - mu_x^2) + (m - M)U_xu_x\right]$$

as the desired expression for the energy transfer from M to m.

Appendix 2. Values of selected physical constants

Quantity	Symbol	Value
Permittivity of a vacuum	ε_0	$8{\cdot}854 \times 10^{-12}\,\text{N}^{-1}\,\text{m}^{-2}\,\text{C}^2$
	$1/4\pi\varepsilon_0$	$8{\cdot}987 \times 10^9\,\text{N}\,\text{m}^2\,\text{C}^{-2}$
Charge of a proton	e	$1{\cdot}602 \times 10^{-19}\,\text{C}$
Planck constant	h	$6{\cdot}626 \times 10^{-34}\,\text{J s}$
	$\hbar = h/2\pi$	$1{\cdot}055 \times 10^{-34}\,\text{J s}$
Avogadro constant	N_A	$6{\cdot}022 \times 10^{23}\,\text{mol}^{-1}$
Rest mass of electron	m_e	$9{\cdot}109 \times 10^{-31}\,\text{kg}$
Rest mass of proton	m_p	$1{\cdot}673 \times 10^{-27}\,\text{kg}$
Gas constant	R	$8{\cdot}314 \text{ J K}^{-1}\,\text{mol}^{-1}$
Boltzmann constant	k	$1{\cdot}381 \times 10^{-23}\,\text{J K}^{-1}$
Gravitational constant	G	$6{\cdot}673 \times 10^{-11}\,\text{N}\,\text{m}^2\,\text{kg}^{-2}$

Conversion factors
1 in $= 2{\cdot}54$ cm
1 lb $= 0{\cdot}453\ 592\ 37$ kg
1 standard atmosphere $= 1{\cdot}013\ 25 \times 10^5$ Pa

These three conversion factors are now defined as exact.

Answers to Exercises

CHAPTER 1

Exercise 1.1
(a) Temperature held constant.

At low pressures the volume of the system is large and the substance is wholly gaseous. As p is increased liquid will start to condense on crossing the saturated gas line. Once this happens p remains constant while the volume of the liquid grows and that of the gas shrinks (as does the total volume of the system). On reaching the saturated liquid line the substance is wholly liquid. Large increases in p are required to reduce the volume of the liquid. Next solid appears in equilibrium with the liquid and the pressure remains constant while the volume of the solid grows at the expense of the liquid. When the substance is wholly solid very large increases in p are required to compress it even slightly—solids are pretty incompressible.
(b) Volume held constant.

Initially solid and gas are in equilibrium—no liquid is present. As T is increased there is one particular value at which solid, liquid, and gas coexist in equilibrium; on the triple line. With further increases in T the pressure rises but only gas and liquid are present until we cross the saturated gas line. Thereafter the substance is wholly gaseous.
(c) Pressure held constant.

Initially only solid is present. Its volume expands (slightly) as T is increased. It then melts; the proportion of liquid to solid increasing as T remains constant. Next the substance is wholly liquid. On crossing the saturated liquid line gas appears which coexists in equilibrium with the liquid. The liquid will have all "evaporated" when the saturated gas line is crossed. The substance is now wholly gaseous and remains so as T is further increased.

Exercise 1.2
In following route 1 where the temperature is held constant the volume of the gas decreases with increasing pressure. On crossing the saturated gas line, drops of liquid are seen to condense out. The pressure remains constant as the condensation proceeds. The eye sees the volume of the liquid grow and the volume of the gas shrink. Once the substance is wholly liquid (as happens when route 1 meets the saturated liquid line) increasing the pressure merely

449

brings about a small reduction in the volume of the liquid. There are no two ways about it—the substance is a liquid at f!

In following route 2 two of p, V, and T must be adjusted so as to stay on the prescribed route. However hard we look we see no phase separation—no drops of liquid forming, no specks of solid materializing—anywhere along the route. The substance started off from point i looking like a gas and ends up at point f looking like a gas. There are no two ways about it—the substance is a gas at f!

CHAPTER 2

Exercise 2.1

A charge of 1 C acquires an energy of 10^3 J on being accelerated through an electrical potential difference of 10^3 V. So a charge of 1.6×10^{-19} C acquires an energy of 1.6×10^{-19} C $\times 10^3$ V $= 1.6 \times 10^{-16}$ J. (Remember that 1 volt means 1 joule coulomb^{-1}.) This energy appears as kinetic energy, $\frac{1}{2}mv^2$. The speed v of an ion is, of course, the length of the drift tube (0·5 m) divided by the flight time (5.46×10^{-6} s), that is 9.16×10^4 m s^{-1}. Equating $\frac{1}{2}mv^2$ to the energy acquired from the electric field gives $m = 3.816 \times 10^{-26}$ kg as the mass of a Na$^+$ ion. To obtain the mass of a sodium atom we should, strictly speaking, add on the mass of the electron which was removed in forming the Na$^+$ ion. Since the electron mass is 9.1×10^{-31} kg, its contribution can be safely forgotten about here. Dividing the mass of the atom by the (nearly equal) mass of a proton or neutron, 1.67×10^{-27} kg, gives 22·85, so the total number of protons plus neutrons in a sodium atom—the mass number—is 23. It would be better physics to have calculated the mass of a sodium *nucleus* before dividing by 1.67×10^{-27} kg. We are told that the atomic number of sodium is 11 so a neutral sodium atom contains 11 electrons. An Na$^+$ ion therefore has 10 electrons. The mass of the sodium nucleus is thus 3.816×10^{-26} kg $- 10(9.1 \times 10^{-31}$ kg$) = 3.815 \times 10^{-26}$ kg, which is substantially the same as our first estimate.

Exercise 2.2

The maximum reading on the detector will be recorded when the de Broglie waves arriving at the detector are in phase; a condition summarized in eq. (2.10). Since n, a, and m remain constant in the series of experiments and since h is a constant we should see whether $v \sin \phi$ is constant from experiment to experiment. This is checked out below in Table E2.2.

The constancy of $v \sin \phi$ is better than 5 per cent, which is within the experimental errors. Incidentally, the reason why the two lower curves of Fig. 2.7 differ from those of Fig. 2.4 is that the curves of Fig. 2.7 incorporate corrections, made to the curves of Fig. 2.4, to allow for systematic errors.

450

TABLE E2.2

$v/\text{m s}^{-1}$	ϕ at maximum detector reading/deg	$v \sin \phi/\text{m s}^{-1}$
920	35	528
1065	31	549
1230	26·5	549
1590	20	544

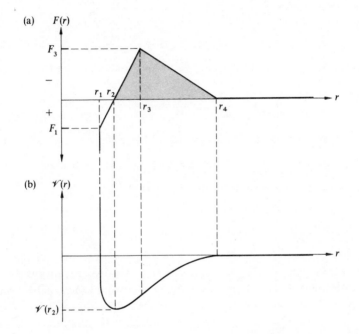

Fig. E2.3 (a) A hypothetical interatomic force characteristic. (b) The corresponding interatomic potential energy.

Exercise 2.3

The potential energy curve of Fig. E2.3(b) may be obtained from Fig. E2.3(a) either by "measuring areas" or—the same thing—by piece-wise integration of $F(r)$ via eq. (2.12). The key features your sketch should have contained—you were only asked to make a rough sketch—are the minimum in the potential curve at separation r_2 where the force is zero and the infinitely rapid rise in $\mathscr{V}(r)$ at $r = r_1$ where the repulsive force becomes infinitely large.

(a) The equilibrium separation is r_2 (and at all separations greater than r_4).
(b) The maximum restoring force is F_3 and occurs at $r = r_3$.

(c) The dissociation energy is either the magnitude of $\mathcal{V}(r_2)$ (the potential energy at $r = r_2$) or, equivalently, the shaded area under the force curve between r_2 and r_4. (The area is zero between r_4 and infinity.)

Exercise 2.4

We first evaluate $F(r)$ as follows:

$$F(r) = -\frac{d\mathcal{V}(r)}{dr} = -\frac{mA}{r^{m+1}} + \frac{nB}{r^{n+1}}$$

Setting $F(r) = 0$ at $r = r_0$ gives

$$\frac{mA}{r_0^{m+1}} = \frac{nB}{r_0^{n+1}}$$

or

$$B = A\frac{m}{n}r_0^{n-m}$$

Substituting this expression back into eq. (2.14) gives the desired expression (eq. (2.24)).

Since $\Delta E = -\mathcal{V}(r_0)$ we obtain the dissociation energy (eq. (2.25)) on letting $r = r_0$ in eq. (2.24) (multiplied through by -1).

CHAPTER 3

Exercise 3.1

We first evaluate $\frac{1}{2}m\overline{u^2}$. The molecular mass m follows, as always, from the relative molecular mass (32) and the Avogadro constant (6.02×10^{23} mol^{-1}):

$$m = \frac{32}{6.02 \times 10^{23} \times 10^3} \text{ kg} = 5.32 \times 10^{-26} \text{ kg}$$

Since $(\overline{u^2})^{1/2} = 600$ m s^{-1} it follows that $\overline{u^2} = 3.6 \times 10^5$ m^2 s^{-2}. Therefore $\frac{1}{2}m\overline{u^2} = 9.6 \times 10^{-21}$ J. (If you are uncertain why units of kg m^2 s^{-2} are the units of joule you should recall that *joule* means *newton metre* and that *newton* means *kilogram metre second*$^{-2}$.) Substituting this value of $\frac{1}{2}m\overline{u^2}$ into eq. (3.20) gives $\theta = 4.8 \times 10^{-20}$ jean when $C = 5$ jean J^{-1}. Remember that no one else but us *defines* temperature by eq. (3.20), and we only do so in passing!

Exercise 3.2

By definition of the mean square speed,

$$\overline{u^2} = \frac{\sum nu^2}{\sum n} = \frac{\sum nu^2}{N} = \left(\frac{n_1}{N}\right)u_1^2 + \left(\frac{n_2}{N}\right)u_2^2 + \cdots$$

Figure 3.7 tells us fractions (n_1/N), (n_2/N), etc., with speeds u_1, u_2, etc., which we may take to be the speeds at the mid-point of each block of the histogram, namely $1\cdot15 \times 10^2$ m s^{-1}, $1\cdot65 \times 10^2$ m s^{-1}, etc. The calculation of $\overline{u^2}$ is set out below in Table E3.2.

TABLE E3.2

n_i/N	$u_i/10^2$ m s^{-1}	$u_i^2/10^4$ m^2 s^{-2}	$(n_i u_i^2/N)/10^4$ m^2 s^{-2}
0·125	1·15	1·32	0·165
0·195	1·65	2·72	0·530
0·235	2·15	4·62	1·086
0·204	2·65	7·02	1·432
0·143	3·15	9·92	1·418
0·098	3·65	13·30	1·303

Adding together the numbers in the last column of the table gives $\overline{u^2} = 5\cdot93 \times 10^4$ m^2 s^{-2}. Since $A_r(Hg) = 200$ it follows that the mass of a mercury atom is $33\cdot2 \times 10^{-26}$ kg. Therefore the mean kinetic energy of a mercury atom within the *beam* is $9\cdot85 \times 10^{-21}$ J. Allowing for the fact that the beam contains a disproportionate number of fast atoms we can deduce that the mean kinetic energy of the mercury atoms within container C of Fig. 3.6 is $\frac{3}{4}(9\cdot85 \times 10^{-21}$ J$) = 7\cdot39 \times 10^{-21}$ J. Because the mercury gas is in thermal equilibrium with the boiling water it follows that the mean kinetic energy of the water molecules is also $7\cdot39 \times 10^{-21}$ J.

Exercise 3.3
Equation (3.20) tells us that

$$\text{temperature} = C(\tfrac{1}{2}m\overline{u^2})$$

Here we suppose that C has a value of $2/3k$, where $k = 1\cdot38 \times 10^{-23}$ J K^{-1}; that is $C = 4\cdot83 \times 10^{22}$ K J^{-1}. On substituting the value of $\frac{1}{2}m\overline{u^2}(=7\cdot39 \times 10^{-21}$ J) calculated in Exercise 3.2 for the mean kinetic energy of the mercury gas atoms within container C of Fig. 3.6 we find that the temperature of the mercury gas is 357 K. Since the gas is in thermal equilibrium with the water it follows that the temperature of boiling water (at normal atmospheric pressure) is 357 K. Now gas thermometry tells us that water boils at 373 K at normal atmospheric pressure. The 5 per cent discrepancy is nothing to worry about. (A look at Fig. 3.7 should tell you why. Note the rather broad range of speeds included in each block of the histogram. Also note that speeds of less than 90 m s^{-1} and greater than 390 m s^{-1} were not measured.)

Exercise 3.4
We know that the water is initially at 300 K (about 27°C). First we translate the requirement that we "raise the temperature of the water from 300 K to

373 K" into a corresponding statement involving the kinetic energies of the water molecules. To do this we use eq. (3.29):

$$T = \frac{2}{3k}\left(\tfrac{1}{2}\overline{mu^2}\right)$$

On writing down two such expressions, one for water at 300 K, the other for water at 373 K, and then dividing the second by the first, we obtain

$$\frac{373}{300} = \frac{\left(\tfrac{1}{2}\overline{mu^2}\right)_{373}}{\left(\tfrac{1}{2}\overline{mu^2}\right)_{300}}$$

where the suffices 300 and 373 remind us that $\tfrac{1}{2}\overline{mu^2}$ depends on T. Since, once thermal equilibrium is attained, the translational kinetic energy of the air molecules surrounding the kettle must equal that of the water molecules inside the kettle, this relation may be written as

$$\frac{373}{300} = \frac{\text{(translational kinetic energy of the air molecules)}_{373}}{\text{(translational kinetic energy of the air molecules)}_{300}}$$

that is,

(translational kinetic energy of the air molecules)$_{373}$

$$= \frac{373}{300}\text{(translational kinetic energy of the air molecules)}_{300}$$

or, cancelling through this expression by the mass of the air molecule,

(m.s. speed of the air molecules)$_{373}$ = 1·24 (m.s. speed of the air molecules)$_{300}$

i.e. (r.m.s. speed of the air molecules)$_{373}$

$$= 1\cdot12 \text{ (r.m.s. speed of the air molecules)}_{300}$$

At 300 K air molecules have an r.m.s. speed of about 500 m s^{-1} (this can be measured using a time-of-flight technique—in chapter 4 we shall see how it can be calculated from pressure and density measurements). An increase in temperature from 300 K to 373 K is therefore equivalent to increasing the speed of the air molecules by a factor of 1·12, or some 12 per cent. Thus the sort of speed which should be given to the air blast is 60 m s^{-1} (which is about 135 m.p.h.).

CHAPTER 4

Exercise 4.1
For the pressure to be due to weight, and to nothing else, the gas molecules must be stacked one on top of the other—like a pile of books—as shown in

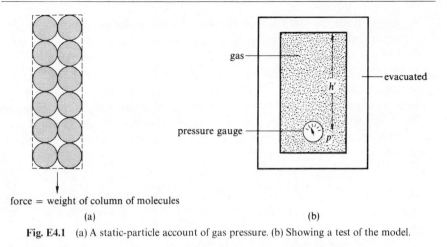

force = weight of column of molecules

         (a)   (b)

Fig. E4.1   (a) A static-particle account of gas pressure. (b) Showing a test of the model.

Fig. E4.1(a). You will remember that the *weight* of an object is defined as the pull of the Earth on the object—operationally, the reading you would get if you hung the stationary object at the end of a Newton balance. According to this assumed model of a gas the gas pressure inside a distant spacecraft, where g is zero, should be zero (eq. (4.2)). It is not! Again, according to this model, if we were to take a pressure gauge, enclose it in an air column of height h' say, and then were to remove the surrounding air (Fig. E4.1(b)) so as to isolate the system from outside pressures, the pressure reading should drop by h'/h. Since h is of order 10^4 m the drop should be quite spectacular. There is none! Gas pressure cannot therefore be *due to* the weight of air overhead. If further proof be required, this model fails to explain Brownian motion.

Exercise 4.2
Knowing the mass m of the helium atom (this follows, of course, from $A_r(\text{He})$ and N_A) and the speed u at which it approaches the piston we can find its momentum mu, and therefore the change in momentum ($2mu$) which it undergoes on striking the piston. This will equal the impulse $F \, \delta t$, where δt is the time during which the (assumed constant) force F acts. The time *must be* the *time during which the force acts.* No other time is of any relevance, be it the time of day or the time that the atom spends in travelling up to the piston.

Exercise 4.3
From eq. (4.24)

$$\overline{u^2} = \frac{3p}{\rho} = \frac{3 \times 10^5}{1\cdot2}\,\text{m}^2\,\text{s}^{-2}$$

$$\overline{u^2} = 25 \times 10^4\,\text{m}^2\,\text{s}^{-2}$$

$$(\overline{u^2})^{1/2} = 500\ \text{m s}^{-1}$$

At some stage of your life you probably "shouted at mountains" and noticed the delay in receiving the echo. A mountain of order 10^2–10^3 m away probably gave a delay of some few seconds, i.e., the speed of sound is of order 10^2–10^3 m s^{-1}. Although the agreement between $(\overline{u^2})^{1/2}$, as predicted from the pressure and density of the gas, and the measured speed of sound in the gas, is only approximate, it does suggest that eq. (4.24) is unlikely to be seriously in error. But this particular experiment was, like the atomic beam studies, only performed at a low gas pressure and density, where the agreement is hardly unexpected!

Exercise 4.4

The key assumptions made were:
1. Newtonian mechanics is applicable.
2. The gas is perfect; that is, $\Delta E = 0$ and the atoms have zero size. The assumption that $\Delta E = 0$ was implicit—we assumed that the atoms do not slow down as they move out of the body of the gas and move up towards the piston. They would slow down if they were "pulled back" by other atoms of the gas (as would happen with a finite ΔE). The assumption of zero size is implicit in the picture that an atom is free to move anywhere in the containing vessel.
3. An atom rebounds immediately after being brought to rest; that is it does not "stick".
4. In each *individual* collision with the piston an atom rebounds with the same kinetic energy, and therefore the same speed, as it had on striking the piston.
5. In each *individual* collision with the piston the angle which the path of an atom makes with the normal to the piston face is the same before and after impact.

CHAPTER 5

Exercise 5.1

Anyone can substitute numbers into an equation! Before doing so you should be satisfied that the equation is at least plausible. Suppose you had been told that $\lambda = \pi d^2 n$—would you have been satisfied? Of course, the equation is obviously wrong since the units of λ are not those of $\pi d^2 n$. But that aside, does your everyday experiences square with $\lambda = \pi d^2 n$? In a crowded store does your "mean free path" increase as the number of people (per unit area) increase? Is your "mean free path" larger among a crowd of broadly-built people than among a crowd of slimly-built people? Of course not! The relation $\lambda = 1/\pi d^2 n$ at least squares with your experiences. You can now substitute numbers into the expression $\lambda = kT/\pi d^2 p$ (which was derived from $\lambda = 1/\pi d^2 n$ by substituting the perfect gas relation $p = nkT$). This gives $\lambda = 1{\cdot}1 \times 10^{-7}$ m at $1{\cdot}0 \times 10^5$ Pa and 300 K. The mean free path reaches 10^{-1} m at a pressure of $1{\cdot}1 \times 10^{-1}$ Pa (about a millionth of normal atmospheric pressure).

Exercise 5.2
If the area of a postage stamp is A the number of molecules striking its surface in unit time is, from eq. (5.15), $\frac{1}{4}n\bar{u}A$. Now $\bar{u} \approx (\overline{u^2})^{1/2} = (3kT/m)^{1/2}$—this follows from $\frac{1}{2}m\overline{u^2} = \frac{3}{2}kT$ (eq. (3.29))—and $n = p/kT$ (eq. (4.28)), so

$$\text{number of gas atoms striking } A \text{ per unit time} = \frac{Ap}{4}\left(\frac{3}{mkT}\right)^{1/2}$$

Substituting $A = 4 \times 10^{-4}$ m^2 (i.e., 2 cm $\times$ 2 cm), $p = 1{\cdot}0 \times 10^5$ Pa, $T = 300$ K and assuming a (mean) relative molecular mass of 29 (which tells us that $m = 29/(6 \times 10^{26})$ kg $= 4{\cdot}8 \times 10^{-26}$ kg) gives the number of gas atoms striking the stamp as $1{\cdot}2 \times 10^{24}$ s^{-1}. It is not surprising therefore that a gas at atmospheric pressure seems to exert a constant pressure on surfaces! If the areas are sufficiently small (as they are in certain torsion-wire instrument suspensions), and if the pressures are low enough, it is possible to detect the pressure fluctuations arising from discrete collisions of gas molecules.

Exercise 5.3
The fast train must pull harder because every time a lump of coal arrives that lump of coal must be speeded up by (50-45) m s^{-1} = 5 m s^{-1} and this calls for an impulse of magnitude $5m$ Pa s, where m is the mass of the lump of coal in kg. Overall this train provides a series of impulses like those shown for train A in Fig. 5.12(b). We know that over a period of 3 s a mass of 10^3 kg of coal arrives on the fast train and that its speed is increased by 5 m s^{-1}. Therefore the total impulse provided by the train in 3 s is 5×10^3 kg m s^{-1} = 5×10^3 Pa s. Equating this to $\bar{F}t$, where $\bar{F}$ is the seemingly constant force provided by the train and $t = 3$ s, gives $\bar{F} = 1{\cdot}67 \times 10^3$ N. The driver of the outer slow train must slow down the coal arriving on his train by 5 m s^{-1}. While his train actually provides a series of impulses like those provided by train D in Fig. 5.12(b) the braking force appears to be constant and of magnitude $1{\cdot}67 \times 10^3$ N. The middle train receives coal from both the faster and the slower train; on average this train requires no net force to maintain speed. It is important to note that the coal which leaves each train does not effect the motion of that train; it is speeded up or slowed down on arriving at a *different* train. (This will only be true if the persons who shovel the coal make sure it leaves their train at 90° to the track, *or* if for every lump which leaves at an angle $+\theta$ an equal mass lump leaves at an angle $-\theta$.)

CHAPTER 6

Exercise 6.1

Your graph may look something like that shown in Fig. E6.1(a). There will only be one student at each height. At most, only one student will have a height of 5·973 059 2...ft *exactly*. Each student will have a height different from all the others! All Fig. E6.1(a) tells us is that there seems to be a fair number of students with heights between 5 ft and 6 ft. To enable the information to be more readily assessed we may count the number of students with heights falling within, say, 3 in. intervals and then plot the results as a histogram. Figure E6.1(b) shows such a histogram. We can now see immediately how the students' heights are distributed.

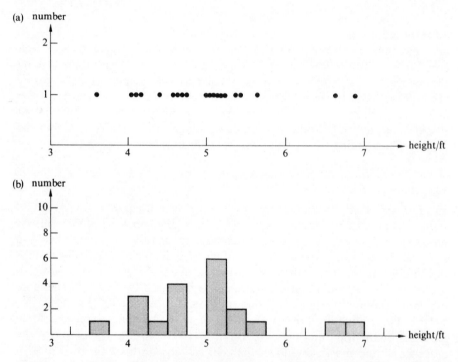

Fig. E6.1 (a) A graph showing the number of students in a class with a particular height. (b) A histogram showing the number of students with heights falling within 3 in. intervals.

Exercise 6.2

A randomly shaken box of elastic spheres (such as marbles or steel balls) could simulate the gas. To measure the speeds, and therefore the energies, of the spheres we would have to illuminate the simulated gas with stroboscopic illumination and then take a stereoscopic picture. One might then use this picture to construct a model showing the position of each sphere every time the light flashed. The velocity of each sphere could then be determined.

Gravity makes the simulation very difficult to achieve; quite apart from the technical problems of stereoscopic photography. If the box has a height h then a sphere of mass m will lose energy mgh in climbing through height h. This loss must clearly be much less than $\frac{1}{2}mu^2$—the average kinetic energy of a sphere. To ensure that $\frac{1}{2}mu^2 \gg mgh$ the box must be shaken violently (or its size kept small).

Exercise 6.3

There is no way of knowing what your vector diagrams look like! Do check that the total energy of ABC and D is indeed 5 in each arrangement. Did you remember to label all the vector tips in each case? You must because each atom is distinct.

Exercise 6.4

This exercise calls for little more than the ability to count correctly and to distinguish one arrangement from another. If you have arrived at all the possible distinct arrangements you should have 56 pictures in all. If you found less, keep going! If you found more, you have duplicated some, or cannot count! (Remember that changing the order of books within a module does not produce a new picture.)

Exercise 6.5

If you found all 18 pictures by "trial and error" you should group them so that pictures of a single type come together. You should have found 6 pictures in all of (3, 0) type. In three of the pictures A is in level 3 (in one of the three modules at this level) while B is fixed in level 0 (one module here). In the other three, A and B swap places. You should also have found 12 pictures, in all, of the (2, 1) type. In six of these A is in level 2 (where it can be in one of three modules) and B is in level 1 (in one of two modules). In the other six the role of A and B are reversed. No other types of picture are permitted when the energy totals to three. Counting up the total number of atoms in each level gives the results shown in Table E6.5, column 2, below. Dividing by the number of pictures (18) gives the mean number of atoms at each level. You should check that the figures in the last column do add to 2—the number of atoms present.

TABLE E6.5

E	Total number of atom appearances $N(E)$	mean number per picture $\overline{N(E)} = N(E)/18$
3	6	0·333
2	12	0·667
1	12	0·667
0	6	0·333

You should be able to picture what this histogram of $\overline{N(E)}$ plotted against E looks like but, if not, do draw it out.

Exercise 6.6

No further calculations are necessary. With only one type of picture present, *all* the pictures (say q) used in computing the mean energy distribution have the same number of atoms in each level. Thus for any given level at energy E_i which contains n_i atoms in a single picture, the average number of atoms at this level—averaged over all q pictures—is

$$\overline{N(E_i)} = \frac{qn_i}{q} = n_i$$

which is just the number in a single picture. So *provided there is only one type of picture present* the type of picture gives the mean energy distribution directly.

Exercise 6.7

As in three dimensions, we write down and evaluate an expression for the total number of atoms present.

$$N = \int dN$$

$$N = \int_0^\infty \frac{dN}{du} du$$

Substituting for dN/du from eq. (6.38) and writing the constant as B gives

$$N = B \int_0^\infty u\, e^{-\beta(\frac{1}{2}mu^2)}\, du$$

$$= -\frac{B}{m\beta} \int_0^\infty d(e^{-\beta(\frac{1}{2}mu^2)})$$

$$N = \frac{B}{m\beta} \tag{1}$$

We next write down and evaluate an expression for the average translational kinetic energy of the atoms.

$$kT = \frac{1}{2}\overline{mu^2} = \frac{\int (\frac{1}{2}mu^2)\, dN}{\int dN}$$

$$= \frac{1}{N} \int_0^\infty (\frac{1}{2}mu^2) \frac{dN}{du}\, du$$

or, substituting for dN/du from eq. (6.38),

$$kT = \frac{B}{N} \int_0^\infty \tfrac{1}{2}mu^3 \, e^{-\beta(\frac{1}{2}mu^2)} \, du$$

To evaluate the integral we use the standard form I_3 given in Table 6.4 with $\lambda = \beta m/2$. This gives

$$kT = \frac{B}{N\beta^2 m} \qquad (2)$$

Solving eqs. (1) and (2) for B and β gives

$$\beta = 1/kT$$

$$B = \frac{mN}{kT}$$

Substituting these values for B and β into eq. (6.38) gives

$$\frac{1}{N}\frac{dN}{du} = \left(\frac{m}{kT}\right) u \, e^{-mu^2/2kT}$$

Exercise 6.8
With a one-dimensional gas the velocity vectors are, of course, all parallel. Figure E6.8 below shows a hypothetical arrangement of such vectors; for clarity these have been displaced somewhat. To find the number within any specified range of energy, say δE about energy E, we mark in two segments on either side of the zero in one-dimensional velocity space; segments of length $\delta u = \delta E/mu = \delta E/(2mE)^{1/2}$ at distances of $u = (2E/m)^{1/2}$ from the zero. (This follows from the relation $E = \tfrac{1}{2}mu^2$.) In one dimension the "cells of constant size"—the modules—are segments of constant length (shown marked

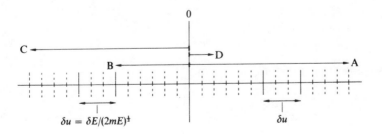

Fig. E6.8 Velocity vectors for a one-dimensional gas.

off by dotted lines in Fig. E6.8). The number of such segments, each of length l_0, contained within an energy range dE at E is therefore given by

$$\mathcal{N}_1(E, l_0) = \frac{1}{l_0} \frac{1}{(2m)^{1/2}} E^{-1/2} dE \tag{1}$$

as follows from dividing $du = dE/(2mE)^{1/2}$ by l_0. Substituting eq. (1) for g_i in eq. (6.33) and writing dN for n_i gives

$$dN = \frac{1}{l_0(2m)^{1/2}} e^{-\alpha} E^{-1/2} e^{-\beta E} dE$$

$$dN = \text{constant } E^{-1/2} e^{-\beta E} dE = C e^{-\beta(\frac{1}{2}mu^2)} du$$

where C is a constant. To find the values of C and β we, as in two and three dimensions, write down expressions for the total number of atoms N and for the average translational kinetic energy (kT). This gives

$$N = \int dN = \int_0^\infty \frac{dN}{du} du$$

$$N = C \int_0^\infty e^{-\beta(\frac{1}{2}mu^2)} du$$

which becomes, on using the standard form I_0 in Table 6.4 with $\lambda = \beta m/2$,

$$N = \frac{C}{2} \left(\frac{2\pi}{\beta m} \right)^{1/2} \tag{2}$$

Also

$$\tfrac{1}{2}kT = \tfrac{1}{2}\overline{mu^2} = \frac{1}{N} \int_0^\infty \tfrac{1}{2}mu^2 \left(\frac{dN}{du} \right) du$$

$$= \frac{Cm}{N2} \int_0^\infty u^2 e^{-\beta(\frac{1}{2}mu^2)} du$$

or, using the standard form I_2 in Table 6.4 with $\lambda = \beta m/2$

$$\tfrac{1}{2}kT = \frac{Cm}{4N} \left(\frac{2\pi}{\beta^3 m^3} \right)^{1/2} \tag{3}$$

Solving eqs. (2) and (3) for C and β gives

$$\beta = 1/kT$$

$$C = N \left(\frac{2}{\pi} \right)^{1/2} \left(\frac{m}{kT} \right)^{1/2}$$

Therefore

$$\frac{1}{N}\frac{\mathrm{d}N}{\mathrm{d}u} = \left(\frac{2}{\pi}\right)^{1/2}\left(\frac{m}{kT}\right)^{1/2} \mathrm{e}^{-mu^2/2kT}$$

or, since $\frac{1}{2}mu^2 = E$ (that is, $\mathrm{d}u = \mathrm{d}E/(2mE)^{1/2}$)

$$\frac{1}{N}\frac{\mathrm{d}N}{\mathrm{d}E} = \frac{1}{\pi^{1/2}}\left(\frac{1}{kT}\right)^{1/2} E^{-1/2}\, \mathrm{e}^{-E/kT}$$

CHAPTER 7

Exercise 7.1

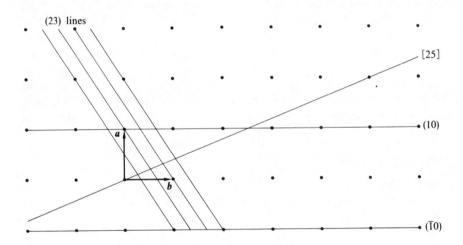

Fig. E7.1 The (23), (10), and ($\bar{1}0$) lines and the [25] direction in a two-dimensional square lattice.

You may have had problems with the (23) lines. As instructed by eq. (7.1) we obtain the orientation of the line by dividing a by 2 and b by 3. We then join the points $a/2$ and $b/3$. Because of the form of eq. (7.1) parallel lines will also be given by the same indices; several (23) lines are shown. Another (equivalent) way of looking at the Miller indices follows on noting that in going from one lattice point to a point a distance a away we cross 2 of the (23) lines, and that in going to the point b away we cross 3 of the (23) lines. In general, if the Miller indices of a plane are (hkl) we will cross h planes in going a distance a; k planes in going a distance b; l planes in going a distance c.

463

CHAPTER 8

Exercise 8.1

To find the mean energy of an oscillator we must multiply the number of oscillators with a particular energy by that energy, sum these products over all energies, and divide by the total number of oscillators (4). The number of oscillators with a particular energy may be found from the last column of Table 6.2, giving

$$\bar{E} = \frac{1 \cdot 50(0\hbar\omega) + 1 \cdot 07(1\hbar\omega) + 0 \cdot 71(2\hbar\omega) + 0 \cdot 43(3\hbar\omega) + 0 \cdot 22(4\hbar\omega) + 0 \cdot 07(5\hbar\omega)}{4}$$

$$\bar{E} = 1 \cdot 25\hbar\omega$$

Exercise 8.2

You should have obtained the five distinct modes shown in Fig. 8.12.

The vibrational frequencies are of course found from eq. (8.31) with $k_s = 5 \times 10^{-2} \, \text{N m}^{-1}$, $m = 0 \cdot 2$ kg, and $r_0 = 0 \cdot 3$ m (that is, $1 \cdot 8$ m/6). Equation (8.31) therefore becomes $\omega_q = \sin(0 \cdot 15q) \, \text{rad s}^{-1}$. Once you have calculated the various values of ω_q, using $q = 2\pi/\lambda$ with λ derived from the standing wave patterns, you may find it helpful to plot a graph of ω_q against q. Draw in the values of ω_q as vertical lines and merely indicate the curve joining the top of these lines as in Fig. 8.14. This will remind you that only *discrete* values of q are permitted.

CHAPTER 9

Exercise 9.1

In exercise 2.4 you showed that the Mie potential could be written as (eq. (2.24))

$$\mathscr{V}(r) = \frac{A}{r_0^m}\left[-\left(\frac{r_0}{r}\right)^m + \frac{m}{n}\left(\frac{r_0}{r}\right)^n\right]$$

where r_0 is the equilibrium separation of an isolated pair of atoms. In section 2·7 we argued that $A = e^2/4\pi\varepsilon_0$, $m = 1$, and $n = 9$ in an Na^+–Cl^- ion pair where e is the magnitude of the electronic charge. Therefore

$$\mathscr{V}(r) = \frac{e^2}{4\pi\varepsilon_0 r_0}\left(-\frac{r_0}{r} + \frac{r_0^9}{9r^9}\right)$$

and so

$$\left(\frac{d^2\mathscr{V}(r)}{dr^2}\right)_{r=r_0} = \frac{8e^2}{4\pi\varepsilon_0 r_0^3}$$

Taking $U = N\mathscr{V}(r)$, rather than as assumed in eq. (9.6), gives eq. (9.9) the form

$$K_T = \frac{1}{9r_0}\left(\frac{d^2\mathscr{V}(r)}{dr^2}\right)_{r=r_0}$$

so

$$K_T = \frac{8e^2}{36\pi\varepsilon_0 r_0^4}$$

Substituting $e = 1\cdot6 \times 10^{-19}$ C, $1/4\pi\varepsilon_0 = 8\cdot99 \times 10^9$ N m^2 C^{-2}, and $r_0 = 2\cdot8 \times 10^{-10}$ m gives $K_T = 3\cdot3 \times 10^{10}$ Pa.

Exercise 9.2
Being, by definition, the force per unit displacement of an atom, $k_s = (Fr_0^2/A)/\delta r$. This may be rewritten as $k_s = r_0(F/A)/(\delta r/r_0) = r_0 E$. Since in copper $r_0 = 2\cdot6 \times 10^{-10}$ m and $E = 13\cdot0 \times 10^{10}$ Pa it follows that $k_s = 33\cdot8$ N m^{-1}. Substituting this value of k_s along with $M = (63\cdot5/6\cdot02 \times 10^{26})$ kg into the relation $(2k_s/M)^{1/2}$ gives the Einstein frequency as $2\cdot5 \times 10^{13}$ rad s^{-1}. This predicts an Einstein temperature $\theta_E = \hbar\omega/k = 190$ K, in good agreement with the value of $\theta_E = 240$ K which must be assumed for optimum fit of the experimental values of $C_{V,m}$ with eq. (8.26) (see Fig. 8.6(b)).

Exercise 9.3
We saw in exercise 9.1 that the potential energy of an Na$^+$–Cl$^-$ ion pair may be written as

$$\mathscr{V}(r) = \frac{e^2}{4\pi\varepsilon_0}\left(-\frac{1}{r} + \frac{r_0^8}{9r^9}\right)$$

The interatomic force is therefore

$$F(r) = -\frac{d\mathscr{V}(r)}{dr} = \frac{e^2}{4\pi\varepsilon_0}\left(-\frac{1}{r^2} + \frac{r_0^8}{r^{10}}\right)$$

The maximum restoring force F_m (see Fig. 9.9(b)) occurs at $r = r_m$ where $dF(r)/dr = -d^2\mathscr{V}(r)/dr^2 = 0$. Applying this condition gives

$$\frac{e^2}{4\pi\varepsilon_0}\left(\frac{2}{r_m^3} - \frac{10r_0^8}{r_m^{11}}\right) = 0$$

or

$$r_m = 5^{1/8}r_0 = 1\cdot22r_0$$

The theoretical strain at which breaking should occur is therefore

$(r_m - r_0)/r_0 = 0.22$. Using the expression for $F(r)$ at $r = r_m$ gives

$$F_m = \frac{e^2}{4\pi\varepsilon_0}\left(-\frac{1}{5^{1/4}r_0^2} + \frac{r_0^8}{5^{5/4}r_0^{10}}\right)$$

$$F_m = -\frac{e^2}{4\pi\varepsilon_0 r_0^2}\cdot\frac{4}{5^{5/4}}$$

The theoretical tensile breaking stress $= -F_m/r_0^2$ is therefore $4e^2/5^{5/4}4\pi\varepsilon_0 r_0^4$ which works out at 2.0×10^{10} Pa. The actual breaking stress of sodium chloride as "taken off the shelf" is 0.01×10^{10} Pa.

CHAPTER 10

Exercise 10.1

The gradient of the graph gives $(E_v + E_d)/k$ as 2.3×10^4 K. So the *fraction* of attempts at jumping into a vacant site which will prove successful at 1300 K is $\exp(-2.3 \times 10^4/1300) = e^{-17.7} = 2.0 \times 10^{-8}$. At 300 K the fraction is $\exp(-2.3 \times 10^4/300) = e^{-76.7} = 5.0 \times 10^{-34}$. The number of attempts at escape is $\omega_E/2\pi = k\theta_E/2\pi h = 5.0 \times 10^{12}$ s^{-1}. Therefore the number of successful hops per second is 10^5 at 1300 K but only 2.5×10^{-21} at 300 K.

Exercise 10.2

The maximum in the κ versus T plot for a non-metal occurs when the phonon mean free path is of the order of magnitude of the specimen's diameter. The maximum κ is about 10^4 W m^{-1} K^{-1} and this occurs at $T \approx 80$ K where $C_{V,m} = 234\, R\, (80/2000)^3 = 0.12$ J mol^{-1} K^{-1}. Dividing the mass of 1 mol of diamond $(A_r(C) = 12)$, namely 12×10^{-3} kg, by its density gives the molar volume as 3.4×10^{-6} m^3 mol^{-1}. Thus the heat capacity per unit volume is $C = 0.12/(3.4 \times 10^{-6})$ J m^{-3} K$^{-1} = 3.5 \times 10^4$ J m^{-3} K^{-1}. Substituting for κ, C, and v into eq. (10.32) gives $\lambda = 1.7 \times 10^{-4}$ m. So the specimen probably had a diameter of order of magnitude 1 mm.

Exercise 10.3

We know from the density and relative atomic mass of copper that there are $N_A = 6 \times 10^{23}$ atoms in $(63.5 \times 10^{-3}/8.9 \times 10^3)$ m$^3 = 7.1 \times 10^{-6}$ m^3 of copper. Therefore each copper atom occupies a volume of roughly $(7.1 \times 10^{-6}/6 \times 10^{23})$ m$^3 = 12 \times 10^{-30}$ m^3, and so has a diameter of about $(12 \times 10^{-30})^{1/3}$ m $= 2.3 \times 10^{-10}$ m. We also deduce that there are $6 \times 10^{23}/7.1 \times 10^{-6} = 8.5 \times 10^{28}$ atoms m^{-3}. We are to assume that the number of free electrons per unit volume is the same as the number of copper atoms per unit volume. So $n = 8.5 \times 10^{28}$ m^{-3}. Substituting for n, e, m, σ, and u_F into eq. (10.51) gives an electronic mean free path of 8×10^{-8} m at 295 K and one of 8×10^{-3} m at 4 K.

We found in problem 5.2 that the classical mean free path of a particle of effectively zero size as it moves through an array of hard spheres, each of radius r, is $\lambda = 1/\pi r^2 n$, where n is the number density of the spheres. It follows therefore that the classical mean free path of a free electron in copper is $[\pi \times (1{\cdot}15 \times 10^{-10})^2 \times 8{\cdot}5 \times 10^{28}]^{-1}$ m $= 2{\cdot}8 \times 10^{-10}$ m. In other words the classical mean free path is of the same order as the lattice spacing.

CHAPTER 11

Exercise 11.1

To check the relation $\frac{3}{2}kT \approx \Delta E$ we can see whether $(\Delta E/k)/T \approx 1{\cdot}5$ anywhere in the range $T = T_{tr}$ to $T = T_c$. Table E11.1 records the values of the ratio $(\Delta E/k)/T$ computed at $T = T_{tr}$ and $T = T_c$. We see that the ratio is indeed constant as expected and that it most nearly has a value of $1{\cdot}5$ at the triple point temperature. This conclusion also holds true for other substances. For example $\Delta E/kT_{tr} = 1{\cdot}5$ for liquid nitrogen and $1{\cdot}2$ for liquid sodium. It follows

TABLE E11.1

Substance	$(\Delta E/k)/T_{tr}$	$(\Delta E/k)/T_c$
Ne	1·45	0·80
Ar	1·43	0·80
Kr	1·48	0·82
Xe	1·38	0·76

therefore that the picture of the atoms of a liquid being neither wholly bound nor wholly free cannot be far from the truth.

Exercise 11.2

The Clausius virial theorem (eq. (11.27)) may be written as

$$pV_m = RT - \frac{4\pi \rho_0 N_A}{6} \int_0^\infty \frac{d\mathscr{V}(r)}{dr} \frac{\rho(r)}{\rho_0} r^3 \, dr \qquad (11.27)$$

The (intellectually) least demanding way to evaluate the integral is to "count squares". The integral is, of course, the area under the plot of $d\mathscr{V}(r)/dr[\rho(r)/\rho_0]r^3$ against r between $r = 0$ and $r = \infty$. When this area is measured in Fig. 11.10(b) it comes out at $3{\cdot}55 \times 10^{-50}$ N m^4. (To find the net area under the curve one must subtract the area under the abscissa from that above the abscissa.)

The mean number density ρ_0 follows on dividing the mass density of $0{\cdot}98 \times 10^3$ kg m^{-3} by the mass of an argon atom. Since $A_r(\text{Ar}) = 40$ it follows that 40×10^{-3} kg contain N_A atoms, giving the mass of an atom of argon as $40 \times 10^{-3}/6{\cdot}02 \times 10^{23}$ kg $= 6{\cdot}64 \times 10^{-26}$ kg. Therefore $\rho_0 = 1{\cdot}48 \times 10^{28}$ m^{-3}.

The integral in eq. (11.27) is multiplied by $4\pi\rho_0 N_A/6 = 1.87 \times 10^{52}$ m^{-3} mol^{-1}. Since the integral has a value of 3.55×10^{-50} N m^4 the second term on the right-hand side of eq. (11.27) has a value of 664 J mol^{-1}. As $RT = 8.31 \times 143$ J mol^{-1} = 1188 J mol^{-1} at 143 K, the right-hand side of eq. (11.27) has a net value of 524 J mol^{-1}. To find the molar volume V_m (and hence p) we follow the now familiar path (with $A_r(\text{Ar}) = 40$ and the density as 0.98×10^3 kg m^{-3}). This gives

$$V_m = \frac{40 \times 10^{-3}}{0.98 \times 10^3} \text{ m}^3 \text{ mol}^{-1} = 4.08 \times 10^{-5} \text{ m}^3 \text{ mol}^{-1}$$

Therefore

$$p = \frac{524}{4.08 \times 10^{-5}} \frac{\text{J mol}^{-1}}{\text{m}^3 \text{ mol}^{-1}} = 1.28 \times 10^7 \text{ Pa}$$

The experimental value of p is 6.7×10^6 Pa. To "force" the theoretical and the experimental values of p to agree we would have to assign the area under the graph in Fig. 11.10(b) a value of 4.9×10^{-50} N m^4. This only requires a slight change in the value of either the positive or negative area under the curve of Fig. 11.10(b). A slight change in the form of $\rho(r)/\rho_0$, particularly at low r, can have a profound change in the form of this curve. When the experimental errors inherent in the X-ray results are considered a net area of 4.9×10^{-50} N m^4 is quite on the cards!

Exercise 11.3

The total molar internal energy (eq. (11.31)) may be written as

$$U_m = \tfrac{3}{2}RT + 2\pi\rho_0 N_A \int_0^\infty V(r) \frac{\rho(r)}{\rho_0} r^2 \, dr \qquad (11.31)$$

Evaluating the integral by direct measurement of the area under the plot of $\mathcal{V}(r)[\rho(r)/\rho_0]r^2$ against r (Fig. 11.11(b)) gives a value of -6.53×10^{-50} J m^3. Following the same arguments as in exercise 11.2 gives $2\pi\rho_0 N_A = 5.6 \times 10^{52}$ m^{-3} mol^{-1}, so the second term on the right-hand side of eq. (11.31) has a value of -3655 J mol^{-1}. At 143 K the value of $\tfrac{3}{2}RT$ is 1782 J mol^{-1}. Therefore $U_m = -1.9 \times 10^3$ J mol^{-1}. Bearing in mind the uncertainty in the precise form of $\rho(r)/\rho_0$ this is in satisfactory agreement with the experimental value of -1.7×10^3 J mol^{-1}.

CHAPTER 12

Exercise 12.1

Working out the interatomic separation from the density in a, by now, familiar fashion gives a value of 3.6×10^{-10} m. To calculate the activation energy E_d we must consider the problems facing i as it attempts to escape from its cell—namely the fact that it must escape the backward pull of neighbours like r, s, and t (Fig. 12.2(a)) and that atoms p and q must be separated sufficiently to allow i through. The energy required to separate p and q from about $r_1 = 3\cdot6 \times 10^{-10}$ m to about $r_2 = 7\cdot2 \times 10^{-10}$ m is, since $\mathscr{V}(r) = -4\varepsilon(\sigma/r)^6$, given by $4\varepsilon(\sigma/r_1)^6 - 4\varepsilon(\sigma/r_2)^6 = 4\cdot75 \times 10^{-21}$ J. In three dimensions there will be (approximately) two more atoms to be separated; one out of the plane, and one behind the plane, of the paper in Fig. 12.2(a). The total energy required to "open up the hole" is therefore about 9×10^{-21} J. We may take it that the energy for i to move away from atoms like s is also about 5×10^{-21} J. There are in all six such atoms (the coordination number in liquid argon is about ten at the triple point but we have already accounted for the effect of four of these) making the total value of E_d about $6(5 \times 10^{-21}$ J$) + 9 \times 10^{-21}$ J $\approx 4 \times 10^{-20}$ J. So the activation energy is of order-of-magnitude 10^{-20} J. Do not worry if your estimate differs by anything up to a factor of 10; because $\mathscr{V}(r) \propto -r^{-6}$, small changes in the values adopted for r will have a large effect on E_d.

The mean thermal energy of an atom in liquid argon at $T = 84$ K is $(3/2)kT = (3/2)(1\cdot38 \times 10^{-23})84$ J $= 1\cdot7 \times 10^{-21}$ J, which is roughly one-tenth of E_d.

Exercise 12.2

The viscosity of a *perfect* gas is independent of pressure (at a fixed temperature). If the pressure is, say, doubled, the mean free path will be halved, so that atoms arriving at the top plate will have diffused there through a distance which is half the former value, from a region of greater drift velocity. The change in momentum of an atom on striking the top plate is therefore halved. But, because the density is doubled, there are twice the number of atoms colliding with the top plate than previously. The overall effect of these two opposing effects is to leave the viscosity unchanged. This argument only applies in a perfect gas where the atoms have zero size.

In a liquid an atom jumps through a distance a—the cell size. However, unlike in a perfect gas—where the atoms are unhindered as they jump through a distance λ, and where every jump is successful—in a liquid only a fraction $\exp(-E_d/kT)$ of the attempts succeed. Close to the triple point this fraction is typically 10^{-2} so the mechanism responsible for viscous flow in a perfect gas would, if it were the only mechanism, predict viscosity values for liquids several orders of magnitude *less* than the value for a perfect gas at the same temperature and density. So we can neglect the effect of atoms hopping from one layer to another in considering viscous flow.

Exercise 12.3

The activation energy required by an ion of charge q to hop into a vacant site will be lowered from E_d to $E_d - (Eq)(a/2)$ when the ion hops in the field direction, and will be increased to $E_d + (Eq)(a/2)$ when the ion hops in the opposite direction. This follows since the force on the ion is Eq and the hop distance is a—the maximum potential energy occurs at $a/2$ (see Fig. 10.3(a)). Applying eq. (10.1) we see that the current J flowing per unit cross-sectional area of liquid is

$$J = nqv_d = \frac{nqa\omega_E}{2\pi} e^{-E_v/kT} \left[e^{-(E_d - \frac{1}{2}Eqa)/kT} - e^{-(E_d + \frac{1}{2}Eqa)/kT} \right]$$

where n is the number density of the positive ions. The expression in brackets represents the number with energies between $E_d - \frac{1}{2}Eqa$ and $E_d + \frac{1}{2}Eqa$. (The first exponential gives the fraction of the ions with energies between $E_d - \frac{1}{2}Eqa$ and infinity; the second exponential gives the fraction with energies between $E_d + \frac{1}{2}Eqa$ and infinity.) Since $\frac{1}{2}Eqa \ll kT$ the exponentials can be expanded to give

$$J = \frac{nqa\omega_E}{2\pi} e^{-E_v/kT} e^{-E_d/kT} \left(1 + \frac{1}{2}\frac{Eqa}{kT} - 1 + \frac{1}{2}\frac{Eqa}{kT} \right)$$

$$J = \frac{nq^2 E}{kT} \frac{a^2 \omega_E}{2\pi} e^{-(E_v + E_d)/kT}$$

or $J = \sigma E$, where σ the electrical conductivity is given by

$$\sigma = \frac{nq^2}{kT} \frac{a^2 \omega_E}{2\pi} e^{-(E_v + E_d)/kT}$$

This therefore predicts that $\ln \sigma \propto -T^{-1}$. It is worth noting that a graph of $\ln D$ plotted against T^{-1} (see eq. (10.3)) should have the same gradient as one of $\ln \sigma$ plotted against T^{-1}. This is so, at least at high temperatures, in solid sodium chloride.

Exercise 12.4

It is perfectly true that the net force acting down on the column is $\pi r^2 \rho g h$; the volume is close to $\pi r^2 h$, the mass is $\pi r^2 \rho h$, and multiplying by g gives the weight. The fatal flaw is in assuming that the upward force is $2\pi r \gamma$. A tension within the *surface* cannot be responsible for lifting up the column of liquid. (A clothes line is in a state of tension, but it will not raise itself!)

Answers to selected Problems

CHAPTER 1

1.2 It may have *looked* the same as the p–V projection before you put in the isobars. Do not be deceived by the similarity!

1.4 The mass fraction of liquid present is $(V_g - V)/(V_g - V_l)$. The mass fraction of gas present is $(V - V_l)/(V_g - V_l)$.

1.5 (a) gas phase, (b) 12.7×10^{-7} m^3, (f) p_{tr} is greater than 1.0×10^5 Pa.

1.8 (a) 6 J, (b) 11 J, (c) 5 J, (d) 5 J, (e) if there is 5×10^{-2} mol present $V_a = 2 \times 10^{-5}$ m^3 and $V_b = 0.5 \times 10^{-5}$ m^3. The pressures are unaltered. The heat fed in and removed is also unaltered, (f) any two of solid, liquid, and gas.

CHAPTER 2

2.1 (a) 10^{29}, (b) 10^{30}, (c) 10^{12} N(!)
Your answers may well differ by a factor of 10 from those given here. (You might, for example, have decided that the average human has a volume of 1 m^3 rather than 0.1 m^3, as was assumed here!)

2.3 6.6×10^{-5} s

2.4 3.4×10^{-10} m

2.6 4.7×10^{-11} m, 1.3×10^{-2} V

2.7 (c) 5×10^{-18} J

2.10 9.2×10^{-19} J

2.11 3.7×10^{-9} N, 5.9×10^4 N

2.13 6.0×10^{-52} J. (Some 10^{33} times less than the actual dissociation energy.)

CHAPTER 3

3.3 Because you are given a lot of data you do not necessarily need to use any—or all—of it!

3.5 $u = d(g/2h)^{1/2}$ where g is the local acceleration under gravity.

3.7 1.41

3.9 Assuming that at fusion $\Delta E = \frac{1}{2}m\overline{u^2}(=\frac{3}{2}kT_f)$ gives $T_f = 44,500$ K. As the experimental value is 1075 K the two-particle model of fusion is evidently only roughly correct with NaCl.

3.10 2.5×10^{-10} m

3.13 9.3×10^3 J

CHAPTER 4

4.1 (a) 1200 kg m s^{-1}, (c) 1200 N s, (e) 240 N

4.2 Many answers are possible! Give several possibilities.

4.3 $\overline{F} = m\overline{u^2}/l$, where l is the distance between the piston face and the end of the cylinder.

4.6 2.9×10^{28}

4.8 7.5×10^{-8} kg m^{-3}

4.11 10^8 m^2 s^{-2}, 10^4 m s^{-1}
4.12 3.9×10^{-8} N
4.13 $T_r = 15/16$

CHAPTER 5

5.1   0·18 m, 0·19
5.2 $4/\pi d^2 n$
5.5 2.27×10^{-2} Pa
5.9 2.5×10^{-11} m. So what do you conclude?
5.10   2·1 Pa
5.13 $(GM/R)^{1/2}$, where G is the gravitational constant, M is the mass of the earth, and R is the radius of the earth.
5.14 6.24×10^{11}

CHAPTER 6

6.1   You should have measured the velocity of a puck involved in a collision either before *or* after the collision has occurred—not both. The precise shape of the histogram will depend on what size energy intervals you chose but it should show more pucks with a low than with a high energy.

6.2

E	$N(E)$	$\overline{N(E)} = N(E)/15$
4	3	0·2
3	6	0·4
2	9	0·6
1	12	0·8
0	15	1·0

6.5   22%
6.6 2.5×10^{-19} J

CHAPTER 7

7.3 $11°, 35°$
7.5   Zn atoms at $000; 0\frac{1}{2}\frac{1}{2}; \frac{1}{2}0\frac{1}{2}; \frac{1}{2}\frac{1}{2}0$. S atoms at $\frac{1}{4}\frac{1}{4}\frac{1}{4}; \frac{1}{4}\frac{3}{4}\frac{3}{4}; \frac{3}{4}\frac{1}{4}\frac{3}{4}; \frac{3}{4}\frac{3}{4}\frac{1}{4}$.
7.6   1·633
7.8   (a) 0·52, (b) 0·74, (c) 0·68

CHAPTER 8

8.1   1·99 s, 3·16 rad s^{-1} (No, the answers are not wrong)
8.3   118 N m^{-2}, 1.13×10^{-13} s
8.4   2·76 R
8.5   2·5%
8.8   5000 m s^{-1}
8.11 1.1×10^{-18} J, 1.6×10^6 m s^{-1}, 5.3×10^4 K
8.12 5.3×10^{-10} m
8.14   340 K

CHAPTER 9

9.1 p^{-1}

9.2 $U_m = -N_A \alpha e^2 / 4\pi\varepsilon_0 r$

9.3 $\alpha = 6 \cdot 00 - 8 \cdot 485 + 4 \cdot 620 - 3 \cdot 000 + \cdots$. This series slowly converges to $1 \cdot 747565$.

9.6 0

9.10 critical shear strain = $0 \cdot 11$

CHAPTER 10

10.2 $12 \cdot 5$ hours

10.5 25 K

10.6 $1 \cdot 6 \times 10^{-8}$ m (This is some thirty times the lattice spacing in NaCl.)

10.7 2

10.8 $3 \cdot 2$ m s^{-1}, $3 \cdot 2 \times 10^{-2}$ m

CHAPTER 11

11.2 $x = 2\Delta C_{V,m}/3R$

11.5 The total number of atoms present minus one (the reference atom).

11.8 7, $5 \cdot 5$.

11.11 Sort of reasonable!

CHAPTER 12

12.1 6×10^{11} s^{-1}, $e^{-4 \cdot 3} \approx 1/75$

12.5 2×10^{-12} s (approximately)

12.7 $2 \cdot 2 \times 10^{-4}$ m (roughly 10^6 atomic diameters)

12.9 $2 \cdot 6 \times 10^{-1}$ W m^{-1} K^{-1}

Index

Index

Accommodation coefficient:
  for energy, 157, 342
  for momentum, 145–9, 157
  (*see also* Sticking fraction)
Activation energy:
  for chemical reactions in gaseous phase,
    214
  for creep, 329–30
  for diffusion:
    in liquids, 407
    in solids, 324
    on surfaces, 439
  for ionic conduction:
    in liquids, 422
    in solids, 469–70
  for vacancy formation in solids, 284
  for viscous flow in liquids, 416, 419–20
Adiabatic wall, 16
Adsorption, heat of, 439
Air:
  composition of, 83
  thermal conductivity of, 158
  viscosity of, 145
Alkali halides:
  diffusion in, 322
  interatomic forces in, 48
  ionic conduction in, 423
  (*see also* Lithium fluoride; Potassium
    chloride; Sodium chloride)
Alkali metals:
  crystal structure of, 234
  isothermal compressibility of, 296
Aluminium, sticking coefficient of gases on,
  147
Amorphous solids, 220
Amplitude of vibration, 241
Angle of contact, 442*n*

Angular frequency (*see* Circular frequency)
Anode, 159
Apparent thermal conductivity, 155
  (*see also* Thermal conduction)
Apparent viscosity, 144
  (*see also* Viscous flow)
Argon:
  atomic diameter, 32
  constants in Lennard-Jones 6–12 poten-
    tial, 382
  critical point data, 10, 121
  gas:
    diffusion in, 136–9
    sticking coefficient at liquid surface,
      438
    thermal conductivity of, 156–7
    viscosity of, 148
  isotherms of, 16
  liquid:
    coordination number of, 373
    diffusion in, 411–12
    equation of state of, 382–4, 394, 467–
      468
    internal energy of, 385, 468
    ionic mobility in, 421–3
    radial density of, 373, 383, 389
    saturated vapour pressure of, 437–8
    tensile strength of, 369
    thermal conductivity of, 424
    viscosity of, 418–19
  solid:
    bulk modulus of, 300
    number of neighbours in, 371
    structure of, 232
    thermal conductivity of, 340
    vacancy concentration in, 285
  triple point data, 10

477

Printed in Great Britain by J. W. Arrowsmith Ltd., Bristol